A Science of Generic Design

SECOND EDITION

A Science of Generic Design

Managing Complexity Through Systems Design

SECOND EDITION

by

John N. Warfield

IOWA STATE UNIVERSITY PRESS / AMES

John N. Warfield is University Professor and Director of the Institute for Advanced Study in the Integrative Sciences at George Mason University, Fairfax, Virginia. He received the A. B. and B. S. and M. S. degrees in electrical engineering from the University of Missouri, Columbia, and the Ph. D. from Purdue University, West Lafayette, Indiana, where his major was electrical engineering with a specialty in communications engineering.

He has about 36 years of university faculty service, mostly in departments of electrical engineering, and served as Chairman of the Department of Electrical Engineering at the University of Virginia from 1975 to 1979. He has about 10 years of industrial experience with the Wilcox Electric Company; the Battelle Memorial Institute, where he was Senior Research Leader; and the Burroughs Corporation.

He has been elected President of the Systems, Man, and Cybernetics Society of the Institute of Electrical and Electronics Engineers, and of the International Society for Systems Sciences (formerly the Society for General Systems Research). He served as Editor of the IEEE Transactions on Systems, Man, and Cybernetics from 1968 to 1971 and as founding Editor-in-Chief of the journal Systems Research from 1981-1990. He is a Life Fellow of the Institute of Electrical and Electronics Engineers and holds that organization's Centennial Medal. He is also a member of the Association for Integrative Studies.

Authorization to photocopy items for internal or personal use, or the internal or personal use of specific clients, is granted by Iowa State University Press, provided that the base fee of $.10 per copy is paid directly to the Copyright Clearance Center, 27 Congress Street, Salem, MA 01970. For those organizations that have been granted a photocopy license by CCC, a separate system of payments has been arranged. The fee code for users of the Transactional Reporting Service is 0-8138-2247-5/94 $.10.

⊗ Printed on acid-free paper in the United States of America

First edition, 1990

Second edition, 1994

Library of Congress Cataloging-in-Publication Data

Warfield, John N.
    A science of generic design: managing complexity through systems design/by John N. Warfield.—2nd ed.
        p.   cm.
    Includes bibliographical references and index.
    ISBN 0-8138-2247-5 (acid-free paper)
    1. Systems design. I. Title.
TA168.W337   1994
003'.71—dc20   94-31802

CONTENTS

CHAPTER 3: A DOMAIN OF SCIENCE MODEL:
The Discipline for the Science   109

CHAPTER 4: MANAGING COMPLEXITY THROUGH
SYSTEM DESIGN:
The Use of the Science   131

CHAPTER 8: ENVIRONMENT AND ROLES OF THE SCIENCE 259

PART III: APPLICATIONS 279

CHAPTER 9: PRODUCTS FROM THE PRACTICE OF GENERIC DESIGN 281

APPENDIX 2: A GRAPHICALLY-INTEGRATED LANGUAGE SYSTEM (GRAILS)   439

APPENDIX 3: CONSENSUS METHODOLOGIES   447

List of Figures

List of Tables

PREFACE

"We are left with the sobering realization that our generation is the first whose decisions
will determine whether the earth will remain habitable."
--Lester R. Brown and Edward C. Wolf, *State of the World,* 1988.

Survival of the world as we know it is not possible. The world will have to be transformed and evolve
for continued survival. This is the necessity and the imperative of our time and will continue to be
so long into the future until this transformation has been achieved, or until there is no longer
any hope that it may be possible.
--Jonas Salk, *Anatomy of Reality: Merging of Intuition and Reason.*

"I'm not advocating the abolition of democracy. What I am advocating is its salvation.
And the only way to save American democracy is to change the fundamental
decision-making process, at the federal level, so that it can come to grips with
the enormous and complex issues that face this nation."
--John Kemeny, *"Saving American Democracy: The Lessons of Three-Mile Island".*

The purpose of this book is to present a thorough discussion of the management of complexity through system design. Hopefully such a discussion may stimulate change in our educational system and our organizational practices and, through such changes, improve substantially the quality of design of large systems.

For better or worse, our society has accepted the idea of large and complex systems. If we are going to have them, it behooves us to learn how to manage them. An excellent route to doing so is to learn how to design them.

Because many professional or technical people act as though they know how to design them, claims of competence have outdistanced performance. The miserable performance of many of our present-day systems seems to have been insufficient to demonstrate the point that the designers of them have much more to learn. It seems that only the emergence of a science of design may be adequate to make the point.

This book reflects over twenty-five years of research on how people can work effectively with complex matters. The second decade of this period has been dedicated to developing and testing a science of generic design. One of the primary motivations comes from recognizing that society today involves large sociotechnical systems whose performance is far from ideal. It is clear that many of these large systems have taken their present forms primarily through evolutionary change that did not involve any systematic overview design, but may have involved some systematic design of parts. Other systems are said to have been designed, but still fail in ways that produce disasters.

Sociotechnical Systems

This book is <u>not</u> mainly about systems involving twentieth-century engineering, technology, and invention; the so-called technological systems. Rather it is intended to apply to a very large class of systems called <u>sociotechnical systems</u>. The identification and organization of knowledge that is critically relevant to this class has largely been ignored by technology-oriented designers. Still it may be appropriate to begin a discussion of system design by talking first about the technological systems. They are highly visible, so things that are said about them can give us a basis for introducing the larger class that is the focus of our concern. The technological systems can be partitioned into three classes which, for purposes of easy reference, can be called Class A, Class B, and Class C.

The Class A component of this partition consists of members that are clearly founded in physical science. Among the examples of these are radio, television, laser and maser technology, semiconductor chips, electrical motors and generators, transmission lines, telephones, airplane wings and control systems, automated chemical plants, and internal combustion engines.

The Class B component of this partition consists of members that are sometimes referred to as "intellectual technology" or products of "artificial intelligence". Examples of this Class include computer software, textbooks about computer software, computer languages, and that portion of the physical layout of human living and working environments that has been designed on the basis of some postulated image of human behavior in that environment.

The Class C component of this partition is comprised of a mix of members from Classes A and B, whose satisfactory performance depends on appropriate integration of these two classes into synergistic units.

Included in this class are information systems, management support systems, decision support systems, expert computer systems, space missions, hospitals, nuclear power plants, and banks.

While the performance of Class A systems can normally be described and even predicted because of the existence of eternal referents that are known to physical scientists and engineers as "primary standards", the Class B and C systems lack such referents. Consequently the merit attached to the use of the primary standards as a basis for world-wide commonality of reference is lost when the Class A components become submerged in Class C systems, much as a small impurity radically changes the behavior of a pure semiconductor. The quality of the design of Class B and Class C systems has to be founded in sources other than the eternal referents that are applied in quality assessment of Class A systems. Part of what this book is about is an approach to determining what substitutes might be available to assess quality of systems for which primary standards are unavailable, and how designer thinking may have to be enlarged in order properly to conceptualize such systems.

A fourth class of system goes well beyond the three considered so far. This is a class referred to as "sociotechnical systems". These systems involve a mix of technology and people, and depend on a synergistic interaction of these two different kinds of entity for their satisfactory performance. Any human settlement is an example of this kind of system.

Although the design of such systems is seldom approached comprehensively, all of the problems mentioned for Class C systems (which are often said to have been comprehensively designed) are found in these more comprehensive systems, and are found in greater severity. For this reason, the book does not focus on discussion of the Class C systems. Instead the focus of this book is what are called "large-scale systems". These systems might be Class C systems, but will generally be envisaged as members of the class of sociotechnical systems.

<u>Designers of technological systems will find that attempts to correlate what is said in this book directly with what they are familiar with, or with what they are accustomed to doing, will not be very helpful unless they approach this study with the view of subsuming what they do within a larger framework.</u>

Divisions of the Book

This book has four principal Divisions. Each of them has been given a one-word title in order to emphasize the principal purpose associated with each part. The full intent behind the assignment of these one-word titles cannot be initially clear to the reader but, hopefully, will become much clearer upon reading the book. Thereafter, hopefully, these one-word titles will comprise useful nomenclature.

Part I, Justification, comprising Chapters 1-4 inclusive, explains the division of design science into three major categories: <u>general</u> design science, <u>generic</u> design science, and <u>specific</u> design sciences. The terms "general" and "generic" are sometimes construed to mean the same thing. We are forced either to take the language as we find it, which often means to use a language that does not contain terms that make needed distinctions; or to adapt it to the need to make distinctions of the type assigned to these words in this book. When a person commented that the distinctions made in Chapter 1 for these two terms might better be expressed through some language other than English, Professor Hasan Ozbekhan, with tongue in cheek, proposed to use the French terms "générale" and "générique".

The main goal of Part I is to present the justification for the Science of Generic Design that is to follow.

The Justification involves first a review, in Chapter 1, of what has been going on in society that makes the need for a science of generic design so pressing. Then there is given in Chapters 2 and 3 a model of what constitutes a science, and what standards must be met by a body of knowledge before it earns the use of the name "science". Criteria for science in general precede a discussion of specific criteria to be met by a science of generic design. Then there is given, in Chapter 4, a view of what constitutes complexity and how a science of generic design assists in the management of the complexity that arises when considering large-scale systems.

Part II, Presentation, comprising Chapters 5-8 inclusive, is the presentation of the Generic Design Science. In this part are given the Foundations, Theory, and Methodology that comprise it; and a discussion of the environment for its application. This Part also discusses key roles in the application of this Science.

Part III, Applications, comprising Chapters 9 and 10, identifies and illustrates some of the primary products, both tangible and intangible, to be expected from applying the Science of Generic Design. Also presented are case descriptions of applications that add insight to the preceding material. A referee of the manuscript suggested, appropriately, that many readers may find the best approach to this book is to read Part III first, as this may be the fastest way to get initial insight into the nature of this work.

Part IV, Amplifications, comprising appendices, a postscript, and a bibliography; amplifies the preceding material in various ways: some mathematical background, some proposed bases for improving the language and documentation of design, some data from applications that provide an empirical basis for some of the Science, a discussion of experience in teaching students about the Generic Design Science, guidance for choosing triggering questions and generic questions, and expanded interpretations of certain ideas.

Features

An attempt has been made to introduce some features to the writing that hopefully will add to the utility of the book. Among these features are the following:

- Presentation in Sets. Ideas often benefit from consideration as interrelated sets. Wherever possible, ideas that require collective consideration in some context will be dealt with formally as a collective by introducing them as a set of ideas.

- Division of a Concept. Frequently a key concept is divided into several subsidiary concepts. Formal acknowledgment of this is presented by including an Index to Divisions which makes explicit the decisions about what is incorporated in a concept. This will facilitate amendments that might later be required as the science evolves.

- Gradation of a Concept. Just as a crystal may grow from a beginning with a small "seed", and the growth may involve outward expansion around the core, so ideas may be graded-- beginning with a core idea. Expanding around that idea in stages enables production of a gradation of progressively more comprehensive conceptualizations. This model is useful in developing the staged evolution of an idea to its fullest expression.

- Integration of Concepts. Division of a concept is viewed as a downward subdivision, traveling to deeper and deeper breakouts. Integration is viewed as the reverse process; taking several ideas and operating on them to produce more comprehensive and fewer ideas, until a single idea that incorporates all the separate ideas is attained. The synthesis lattice is introduced as a means of documenting such integrations.

- Criterion-Response Style. There is a limit to how far one can go in justifying a decision. A minimum expectation is that at least a set of criteria may be given, to which a decision is designed to respond. By stating the criterion or criteria, and presenting design outcomes as responses to the criteria, the logic of choices is exhibited.

The organization of the book reflects a belief that acceptance of the Generic Design Science given in Part II can only be won by developing the subject all the way from foundations through applications in sufficient detail and with sufficient continuity and interrelationship of the components that, in the end, little is left to the imagination.

Processes

The processes that are described in this book inherently invoke at least a modest redistribution of power in the social group within which they are applied. The direction of this redistribution is toward more participative formulation of designs. A modification of oversight and steering roles in organizations, in the direction of facilitation of the integration of knowledge, which inevitability amounts to at least a modest redesign of the role system, accompanies the use of these processes.

The processes incorporate a requirement that those who oversee, steer, and carry out design must change their approach and learn new roles. For some, the stylistic changes required to support participative work may be incompatible with their personalities. The *Washington Post* reported, in its January 1, 1989, business section, that the trend in management of large organizations is away from highly autocratic top management to participative top management. The processes given in this book can strongly support this kind of trend.

The general well-being of society requires changes in the approaches and methods for carrying out certain kinds of large system designs. And certainly the changes will not be made unless the rationale behind the Science of Generic Design appears so compelling that powerful people who are not disposed to change will be moved out of their roles by others who understand this rationale.

Actors and Locations

The early parts of this book will probably seem highly academic. Yet every sentence in this book has been assessed in the light of 20 years of experience in studying how to apply systems thinking in group settings. A few highlights that are excerpted from this experience may be worth mentioning in order to make clear that this book draws heavily on empirical observations of groups of people engaged in serious efforts to succeed in working with complex issues.

When the author presented the process of Interpretive Structural Modeling (ISM) in 1973, as a way for people to formulate relationships among component ideas, Brother Raymond Fitz, currently President of the University of Dayton, took the lead in its early application. The first computer-assisted session using ISM was carried out under Brother Fitz's facilitation at the Kettering Foundation in Dayton, Ohio, involving a problem in planning for the metropolitan area of Dayton.

Shortly thereafter, Koichi Haruna and his colleagues at Hitachi Systems Research Laboratories studied this method and developed approaches that used ISM and related methods in their internal planning, and reported some of this work in 1976 when the IEEE Systems, Man, and Cybernetics Society met in Tokyo. Developments in Japan and elsewhere were aided by Dr. Kazuhiko Kawamura of Vanderbilt University. More recently, Dr. Ohuchi of the University of Hokkaido has offered improved ISM computer algorithms.

Dr. Robert Waller, Professor of Management and former Dean of the School of Business at the University of Northern Iowa, took a strong leadership role in developing applications, and also contributed to the methodology. He applied it to the conduct of his role as Dean, and it helped him build an outstanding program. Also he introduced it to a group of women with interests in developing their capacity to provide leadership in higher education and, together with others, to planning for economic development in Iowa.

Ralph R. Widner provided early financial support through his association with the Battelle Memorial Institute in Columbus, where the work reported here got a strong initial impetus which I reported in my 1976 book. Through his support, Dr. Carl Moore of Kent State University, along with his late associate, Professor James Coke, applied it to prioritization of municipal and county budget line items. Dr. Moore later wrote a book sharing his experience and continues to work toward the improvement of group productivity.

Others who took an interest in this method included Dr. Robert House of Vanderbilt University, who introduced it to a Brazilian Futures Research Group at the University of São Paulo under the leadership of Mr. James T. C. Wright. They applied it to the Brazilian alcohol fuel program, and to develop a soybean marketing concept that empowered farmers to manage their own affairs.

Mr. F. C. Kohli, Director-in-Charge of the Tata Consultancy Services, and Dr. R. W. House of Vanderbilt University helped the author introduce ISM to India in 1978. This approach became part of the methodology base of the Tata Systems Engineering Consultancy in Hyderabad, directed by Dr. P. N. Murthy, who left his professorship to initiate this activity. His colleague, Mr. S. K. Batra, has graciously contributed to Chapter 10. Also active in India were Mr. G. S. Chandy of GeneSys Consultants in Bangalore and Dr. V. Patkar of Bombay, who pioneered in its use in policy formulation.

The hub of activity has been the Center for Interactive Management. This organization was initiated at the University of Virginia and began formal operations in April of 1982 at which time the specially-designed facility was inaugurated. The work done there largely involved applications to forestry, carried out in conjunction with both the National Forest Service (with Mr. Robert McDonald serving as a key individual in this work) and the Virginia Division of Forestry. This was followed by a remarkably-productive meeting held in the ballroom of the Hilton Hotel in St. Louis which involved 160 participants, including the Assistant Secretary of Agriculture, and which formulated a plan for helping assure that privately-owned forest land would contribute to what otherwise was seen as a shortage of wood in the United States. The shortage was destined to appear around 2010. Leadership in this event was provided, as in many other instances, by Dr. Alexander Christakis.

Mr. Ross Janes visited the Center at the University of Virginia as a Fulbright Scholar in the early eighties, and later established the Interactive Management Unit at the City University of London, which has served numerous clients successfully.

Significant applications were carried out at the National Marine Fisheries Service Southwest Fisheries Center in San Diego, California, which produced major benefits to the fishing-related industries involved in Pacific seafood operations near San Diego. Among persons involved from the Southwest Fisheries Center, Dr. Izadore Barrett, Director, and his associate Mr. David Mackett, deserve special mention for their leadership. The Fisheries Center replicated the physical facility developed at the University of Virginia, and applied it thereafter in their operations.

The Center for Interactive Management moved to George Mason University in 1984 and commenced operations in October of that year in the specially-designed facility. The Director of this Center was Dr. Alexander Christakis, and Dr. David Keever was his Associate Director. Under their direction, continued testing of the ideas presented in this book occurred with many groups on many subjects. Some of the subjects involved in this work included the acquisition of large systems by the Department of Defense; the timely procurement of research projects by the Defense Advanced Research Projects Agency (DARPA); and planning for development of several tribes of American Indians, with leadership coming from Chairman Reuben Snake of the Winnebago Tribe and La Donna Harris of the Americans for Indian Opportunity, among others. The emotional experiences of observing how these various groups exposed their difficulties, and of seeing how the processes applied helped them to arrive at consensus on action plans, can hardly be conveyed by ink on paper. But these and other experiences contributed greatly to the motivation and content associated with this book, as well as its organization.

The Science and its Teaching

I am intensely aware that the subject of this book will be approached with a strong evaluatory bent by its readers. At the same time, I am equally aware that just as myopia prevents one from seeing objects that are not close to the eyes, so technomyopia presents one from envisaging concepts that are not already close to the individual's imagination. And just as myopia prevents one from knowing that one has myopia (because inability to see distant objects does not provide the information that the distant objects are there), so technomyopia prevents one from knowing that things not envisaged can, do, or could exist. It is not enough to present a science. Clarification and justification are required in every nook and cranny. Any proposed or extant science can be improved, and improvement is motivated by thorough understanding, carefully communicated.

My belief in the capacity of a properly-applied Generic Design Science to produce productive, concrete results is derived from a very prolonged period of study and testing on real issues with real people. Objections raised have served to stimulate further investigation, driving the studies deeper and deeper into foundational thinking.

The author offered courses in generic design to classes at three universities in the past eight years before deigning to try to communicate it as an integrated body of knowledge through this work.

Cumulative experience with over 100 participant groups working on a large variety of issues, and with five classes offered to students, has strongly affected the organization of this book. This is why Part I occupies so much space before the Science of Generic Design appears in Part II. But in the process of providing new language and foundational justification for such a Science, I firmly believe that the way that science in general may be conceived in the future, at least in terms of how the organization of knowledge is approached, can be favorably influenced. Should this occur, it would largely be a consequence of the insights gained from outstanding philosophers of science who have strongly affected how this book is conceived and how its content is formulated. They are identified at various points in the book.

Some have said that the Domain of Science Model introduced in this book is not novel at all, and that there are other models of science that are just as good or even better. Such a statement misses the point altogether. What is important here is not the novelty of a particular model. What is important is that the means used to evaluate and discipline a science should be both articulated and consistent with what many would believe is a proper way to describe a science. It is not just a matter of articulating a model, but also of using that model as a way to discipline thought and acceptance.

Science as a whole now requires more articulate standards, because in their absence there is nothing to prevent anyone from calling anything "science". In some areas, where the term "science" is embraced in their descriptions, the only apparent standard being used seems to be the existence of exotic languages that help to sustain modern technological monasteries, whose priests can at best communicate only with their closest associates.

For those readers who are engineers, and who may not understand the importance of concepts stemming from what they call "soft sciences", I recommend reading Anthony Downs' book *Inside Bureaucracy.*

For those readers who are social scientists or practitioners involved with human behavior, but who think that the methods of Generic Design Science involve too much reliance on a computer, I suggest that they read George Miller's famous paper on "The Magical Number Seven..." and related research of social scientists (e.g., Herbert Simon) on the same subject (and they might even read my own paper on "The Magical Number Three..."). Then having read Miller's work and perhaps that of Simon on the subject, they might ask themselves whether these works have any significance in the human process of designing large systems.

For those of whatever background who doubt that there is much value in (a) the rather extensive use of formal logic as a way of clarifying complex systems and (b) the related products of philosophers, it may be useful to repeat A. N. Whitehead's statement that "the paradox is now fully established that the utmost abstractions are the true weapons with which to control our thought of concrete fact". It would also be appropriate to review Muriel Rukeyser's *Willard Gibbs* in which there is convincing evidence, both of the value of deductive logic that begins with inspired hypotheses, and of the enormous scope of the applications that can stem from pursuing such a set of hypotheses with discipline, rigor, and indifference to the indifference of others.

The definition of "system" given by Gibbs as "any portion of the material universe which we choose to separate in thought from the rest of the universe for the purpose of considering and discussing the various changes which may occur within it under various conditions" is superior to any that I know of. I would only propose to qualify it by omitting the word "material" from the statement because we cannot be sure what that word includes or excludes.

This book has benefited greatly in its early stages from the work of Charles S. Peirce and I. M. Bochenski, and more recently by the wise writings of Sir Geoffrey Vickers. I hope that the kind of scholarship represented by these individuals will continue to find a place in the world in the future.

While the book concentrates on design, the reader will notice that references to problem-solving in general appear frequently in the text. The connection between design and problem-solving is very strong. Depending on one's point of view, one can argue that either is a part of the other.

One argument that can be made is that if one thoroughly studies a situation and observes certain bad features of it, a design process can then be undertaken to create conceptual resolutions of the bad features. Then one of these resolutions can be the basis for implementation. Seen in this way, design is part of a larger process of problem-solving.

Another argument that can be made is that any human construction constitutes a design, so that the construction of some image of the situation is a design, the identification of dysfunctions in that situation is a design, the creation of approaches to resolution of that situation is a design, and the implementation is also a design process being carried out step by step. In this sense, design is the overriding process, and problems appear as identified dysfunctions in situations.

The matter is important, in my view, because confusion of definitions makes communication difficult. I do not believe that a single rigid point of view is essential, but it is important that collaborators agree to take the same point of view to facilitate action. When a particular point of view is found to detract from group effort, it may be discarded in favor of another that lacks that flaw. Systems scientists talk about "equifinality" in the sense that the same results may accrue by pursuing any of several paths.

The Postscript, "Issues and Responses", identifies key issues pertaining to this book raised by reviewers of the manuscript, and presents my responses to these issues. Because reviewers often reflect potential concerns of other readers, I believe that this semi-dialogue between author and reviewers will add insights that other readers may find both interesting and helpful.

Acknowledgments of Permissions to Publishers and Authors

I want to acknowledge the permissions of various copyright holders to allow me to use material.

From my own previously-published work, I was permitted to use material by the following organizations:

- The Institute of Electrical and Electronics Engineers kindly permitted me to use the following materials:

  From J. N. Warfield, "Crossing Theory and Hierarchy Mapping", **IEEE Transactions on Systems, Man, and Cybernetics, SMC7(7), July, 1977, 505-523,**

  Fig. 33 (part of Fig. A4.1 in this book)

From J. N. Warfield, "Some Principles of Knowledge Organization", **IEEE Transactions on Systems, Man, and Cybernetics,** June, 1979, 317-325,

> Fig. 1 (Fig. A1.9 in this text)
> Figs. 3-8 (combined in Fig. A1.10 in this text)
> Fig. 9 (Fig. A.11 in this text)
> Fig. 10 (Fig. A1.12 in this text)

From J. N. Warfield, "Complementary Relations and Map Reading", **IEEE Transactions on Systems, Man, and Cybernetics, June, 1980, 285-291,**

> Table 1 (Table A1.1 in this text)
> Fig. 1 (Fig. A1.1 in this text)
> Fig. 2 (Fig. A1.2 in this text)
> Fig. 3 (Fig. A1.3 in this text)
> Fig. 4 (Fig. A1.4 in this text)
> Fig. 5 (Fig. A1.5 in this text)
> Fig. 6 (Fig. A1.6 in this text)
> Fig. 7 (Fig. A1.7 in this text)
> Excerpts from the text of the article

From J. N. Warfield, "Principles of Interactive Management", **Proceedings of the International Conference on Cybernetics and Society,** New York: IEEE, January, 1984, 764-750,

> Fig. 1 (Figure 1.1 in this text)
> Fig. 2 (Figure 1.3 in this text)

From J. N. Warfield, "Dimensionality", **Proceedings of the 1986 International Conference on Systems, Man, and Cybernetics,** New York: IEEE, 1986, 1118-1121,

> Fig. 1 (Fig. 2.18 in this text)
> Fig. 2 (Fig. 2.19 in this text)
> Fig. 3 (Fig. 2.20 in this text)
> Fig. 4 (Fig. 2.21 in this text)
> Fig. 5 (Fig. 2.22 in this text)

From J. N. Warfield, "Micromathematics and Macromathematics", **Proceedings of the 1986 International Conference on Systems, Man, and Cybernetics,** New York: IEEE, 1986, 1127-1131,

Fig. 1 (Fig. 2.4 in this text)
Fig. 2 (Fig. 2.3 in this text)
Fig. 3 (Fig. 2.5 in this text)
Fig. 4 (Fig. 1.6 in this text)

- The Society for General Systems Research kindly permitted me to use the following materials:

From J. N. Warfield, "Science and Systems Science: A Technology Perspective", **Proceedings of the Society for General Systems Research**, Jan., 1980, 212-218,

Fig. 3 (Fig. 3.4 in this text)
Fig. 4 (Fig. 3.5 in this text)

From J. N. Warfield, "Organizations and Systems Learning", **General Systems** 27, 1982, 5-74,

Fig. 1 (Fig. 4.1 in this text)
Fig. 2 (Fig. 4.2 in this text)
Drawings from Appendix 1 (Figs. 7.12,
7.13, 7.14, 7.20, 7.22, 7.23 and
all Portfolios appearing in Appendix 3 of
this text, adapted from Appendix 1 of the paper)

From J. N. Warfield, "Education in Generic Design", **Proceedings of the Society for General Systems Research**, Salinas, CA: Intersystems, 1986, H22-H33,

Fig. 3 (Fig. 8.3 in this text)
Table 2 (Table 6.2 in this text)

From J. N. Warfield, "The Domain of Science Model: Evolution and Design", **Proceedings of the Society for General Systems Research**, Salinas, CA: Intersystems, 1986, H46-H59,

Fig. 1 (Fig. 3.2 in this text, adapted)

- The American Society of Mechanical Engineers kindly permitted me to use the following materials:

From J. N. Warfield, "What Disciplines Large-Scale Systems Design?", **Proceedings of the 1987 Conference on Planning and Design in Management of Business and Organizations (P. C. Nutt, Ed.)**, New York: ASME, 1987, 1-8,

Table 1 (Table 1.1 in this text)
Table 2 (Table 1.5 in this text)
Fig. 1 (Fig. 1.7 in this text)
Fig. 3 (Fig. 1.8 in this text)

- Hemisphere Publishers kindly permitted me to use the following material:

From J. N. Warfield, "The Magical Number Three--Plus or Minus Zero", **Cybernetics and Systems** 19, 1988, 339-358,

Table 3 (Table 2.1 in this text)
Table 4 (Table A1.2 in this text)
Fig. 1 (Fig. 2.6 in this text)
Fig. 2 (Fig. 2.7 in this text)
Fig. 3 (Fig. 2.8 in this text)
Fig. 4 (Fig. 2.9 in this text)
Fig. 5 (Fig. 2.10 in this text)
Fig. 6 (Fig. 2.11 in this text)
Fig. 7 (Fig. 2.12 in this text)

- The University of Pittsburgh kindly permitted me to use the following material:

From J. N. Warfield, "Criteria for a Science of Design", **Proceedings of the 19th Annual Pittsburgh Conference on Modeling and Simulation**, Research Triangle Park, NC: Instrument Society of America, 1988, 643-646,

Excerpts, including the criteria for a
science of design, appearing as Table 5.1
in this book

- Kluwer Academic Publishers kindly permitted me to use the following material:

From J. N. Warfield, "On the Design of Language for System Design", **Cybernetics and Systems '88, Proceedings of the 9th European Meeting on Cybernetics and Systems Research** (R. Trappl, Ed.), Dordrecht: Kluwer, 1988, 133-140,

Table 1 (Table 2.5 in this book)
Table 2 (Table 2.2 in this book)
Table 3 (Table 1.4 in this book)
Table 4 (Table 2.3 in this book)
Table 5 (Table 2.4 in this book)
Description of Criteria (Table 2.8 in this book)

- Professor-Dr. Gerard De Zeeuw of the University of Amsterdam kindly permitted me to use the following material:

From J. N. Warfield, "Underconceptualization", originally presented at a conference at the University of Amsterdam and subsequently published in a proceedings: **Systemica** 1-6/8 (1990),

> Table 1 (Table A5.1 in this book)
> Table 2 (Table A5.2 in this book)

Permissions involving other authors and publishers are as follows:

- The International Federation for Systems Research and my co-author Dr. A. N. Christakis, kindly permitted me to use the following material:

From J. N. Warfield and A. N. Christakis, "Dimensionality", **Systems Research** 4(2), 1987, 127-137,

> Fig. 4 (Fig. 6.2 in this text)

- On behalf of co-authors F. R. Janes and R. Jowitt, Plenum Press kindly allowed me to use the following material:

From F. R. Janes and R. Jowitt, "Applications of Interactive Management in Planning for a University Department", in **Systems Prospects (Proceedings of the International Conference of the United Kingdom Systems Society**, R. L. Flood, M. C. Jackson, and P. Keys, Eds.), New York: Plenum, 1989,

> Fig. 1 (Fig. 10.4 in this book)
> Fig. 2 (Fig. 10.5 in this book)

- On behalf of the respective authors, the Institute of Electrical and Electronics Engineers kindly allowed me to use the following material:

From E. Zamierowski, D. Hornbach, and R. Fitz, "Ecological Components of Climax Agriculture: An Example of Structuring Complex Feedback Systems", **Proceedings of the International Conference on Cybernetics and Society**, New York: IEEE, 1976, 667-673,

> Fig. 6 (Fig. 2.16 in this book)

From K. Sugiyama, S. Tagawa, and M. Toda, "Methods for Visual Understanding of Hierarchical Systems", **IEEE Transactions on Systems, Man, and Cybernetics**, SMC-11(2), 1981, 109-125,

> Fig. 6 (Fig. A4.2 in this book)

- On behalf of R. F. Bales, the University of Chicago Press kindly permitted me to use the following material:

  From R. F. Bales, **Interaction Process Analysis**, Cambridge, MA: Addison-Wesley, 1950.

  > Chart 1, Page 9 (Fig. 2.1 of this text)
  > Chart 5, Page 18 (adapted, to be Fig. 2.2
  > of this text)

- The Ford Motor Company and the Southwest Fisheries Science Center of the National Marine Fisheries Service kindly provided photographs for:

  > Figure 8.1 and Figure 8.2, respectively

- The authors who are identified in the next section wrote case studies specifically for this book, and kindly allowed me to include their material in Chapter 10. The authors of the case studies are individually identified at the beginning of the relevant case presentations in Chapter 10.

Acknowledgments to Colleagues and Associates

I acknowledge the advice and help received from various colleagues and associates: including especially Alexander Christakis, Robert Waller, Ross Janes, Bela Banathy, Benjamin Broome, Robert Clark, Brack Brown, Robert McDonald, and David Keever. Harlan Mills introduced me to the concept of Referential Transparency. William J. Reckmeyer convinced me to include a postscript and offered other forms of encouragement. I remember the encouragement extended by the late W. K. Linvill, and hope Bill is watching this work evolve with an approving eye.

I want to acknowledge the freedom that I enjoyed at George Mason University during the administration of Dr. George Johnson, President of George Mason University, and the late Provost, Dr. David King.

I thank the reviewers of drafts of all or parts of this manuscript, including Professors Anita Taylor and Benjamin Broome of George Mason University, P. N. Murthy and S. K. Batra of Tata Consultancy, David Dierolf, Arthur D. Hall III, Scott Staley of Ford Research Laboratory, Robert McDonald of the Florida Division of Forestry and other unknown reviewers commissioned by publishers.

Written contributions to Chapter 10 either came directly from or were based on earlier contributions by Henry Alberts, S. K. Batra, Alexander Christakis, Irene Cromer, Veronica Feeg, Margi Fiore, Ross Janes, David Keever, Steve Landenberger, Harris Sokoloff, and Bill Wood.

Colleen Kearney and Benjamin Broome put the manuscript in form for desktop publishing. Ray Kirrish, Moira Connelly, and Sandra Valderrama produced many of the figures and tables.

Finally I thank my wife Rosamond. She has always provided encouragement and help during the more than forty years that we have spent together, and has made this work possible. She read much of the manuscript and recommended changes that I used to try to improve the readability.

John N. Warfield
Annandale, Virginia, 1990

NOTES ADDED IN THE SECOND EDITION.

Since publication of the First Edition in 1990, new organizations have begun to apply this science through their activities with Interactive Management. The latter topic has been described in a newly-published companion work authored by John N. Warfield and A. Roxana Cárdenas, titled *A Handbook of Interactive Management*. Significant new applications have been made at the main campus and (later) at branch campuses of the Instituto Tecnológico y de Estudios Superiores de Monterrey in Mexico (especially in public-sector strategic planning); at Christakis, Whitehouse and Associaties (especially in the pharmaceutical industries); at the Ford Research Laboratory in Dearborn, Michigan (especially in automobile and software system design) by Dr. Scott M. Staley and his associates; in the United States Department of Defense by Professor Henry Alberts and colleagues at the Defense Systems Management College; at the National Railroad Passenger Service (AMTRAK) by Kenneth McIlvoy and his associates; and by Keith Ellis and his colleagues at the University of Humberside in Hull, United Kingdom. New activity has been announced as being initiated at the International University of Ecuador (Quito), the Center for Interactive Management Leadership in Austin, Texas; and the Center for Interactive Management--India, in New Delhi, but details are not available.

Errors found in the First Edition have been corrected and Study Questions have been incorporated. The original publisher could not comply with contractual terms, which spurred the timely creation of a Second Edition.

The author is a member of the faculty of the Institute of Public Policy (TIPP) at George Mason University. Dr. Kingsley Haynes and Dr. Roger Stough of TIPP have given moral support to this work and to the goals it reflects, which is greatly appreciated.

John N. Warfield
Annandale, Virginia, 1994

QUESTIONS RELATED TO THE PREFACE

1. What is the stated purpose of the book?

2. What three classes of technological systems are discussed?

3. What distinguishes Class A?

4. What distinguishes Class B?

5. What distinguishes Class C?

6. What benefit does Class A have that Classes B and C lack?

7. What is meant by "sociotechnical system"?

8. How is a sociotechnical system distinguished from a technological system?

9. What is needed to develop a good definition of "large-scale system"?

10. What are the four main divisions of the book?

11. What are the three categories of design science?

12. What is the main goal of Part I, "Justification"?

13. What is the thrust of Part II of the book?

14. What are the two main components of Part III of the book?

15. What are the six main ingredients of Part IV of the book?

16. What five features have been introduced to add utility to the book?

17. What are some locations where the ISM process has been used?

18. How is the term "science" defined?

PART I

JUSTIFICATION

"Philosophy is like the mother who gave birth to and endowed all the other sciences. Therefore one should not scorn her in her nakedness and poverty, but should hope, rather, that part of her Don Quixote ideal will live on in her children so that they do not sink into philistinism."

--Albert Einstein

"Modern scholarship and modern science...canalize thought and observation within predetermined limits, based upon inadequate metaphysical assumptions dogmatically assumed."

--A. N. Whitehead

"Science proceeds in two opposite directions from its many technical discoveries. It moves forward with the aid of exact mathematical formulation to new applications, and backward with the aid of careful logical analysis to first principles. The fruit of the first movement is applied science; that of the second, theoretical science. When this movement toward theoretical science is carried through for all branches of science we come to first principles and have philosophy."

--F. S. C. Northrup

CHAPTER 1

A CONTEXT FOR A SCIENCE OF DESIGN: The Need for the Science

"Throughout almost the whole of human history, technology has progressed with an uncanny

ignorance of the scientific principles which were guiding it."

-- Sir Geoffrey Vickers

"When we add complexity and coupling to catastrophe, we have

something that is fairly new in the world"

-- Charles Perrow

Large systems have become prevalent in society. They have a pervasive influence on people everywhere. Their growth can be compared to making a quilt. A variety of components appearing in a variety of forms share an attribute: susceptibility to being linked. As linkages appear, systems grow rapidly in scale.

The impact of a failure of a quilt is normally quite confined, so the comparison of a large system with a quilt stops when we look at the impact of failure. As systems get larger, the impact of failure also grows larger. Not all failures are visible, but many of them become highly-visible. What we learn about those failures that we happen to see or hear about leads us to believe that there are many others that we do <u>not</u> learn about, and still others waiting to happen.

Some of the large system failures that we see or hear about are followed by investigations and assessments. A prominent, almost predictable, conclusion of such investigations is that the failures were caused by human "operators" who made mistakes. The systems themselves are asserted to be sound. Even when the evidence is overwhelming that a system itself is unsound, proposed remedies seem fragile, perhaps infeasible, and not clearly likely to produce permanent relief.

Each system failure tends to be perceived as an isolated event, having little in common with its predecessors. Proposed solutions are expected to be (and are) locally idiosyncratic in time and location. And the cost in human life and economic resources continues to grow.

3

Review of the escalating impact of large system failures indicates very clearly that the system of beliefs that supports thought about the design, installation, operation, and retirement of such systems is grossly underdeveloped, and does not provide the orientation and knowledge required to deal with them.

In order to begin to correct this situation, a name is needed for the prospective system of beliefs that can be brought together to start correcting the oversights and underconceptualizations of the past. The proposed name is "design science".

The major benefit of this title is that it carries very clearly the connotation that the knowledge involved will be high in quality, meeting appropriate scientific criteria; and that this knowledge will be directed to the origins of the systems that we will be involved with.

The major drawback to this title is that it is already effectively dysfunctional because there are numerous clans of practitioners who perceive that they are the bearers of the mace in some particular area of design. It is not the territorial aspect of such perceptions that is fundamentally the problem. On the contrary, it is all of the accompanying baggage that goes along with it. Correcting the underconceptualized base of design thinking is like curing alcoholism. Unless the admission is made that the alcoholic needs treatment, treatment is unlikely even to be started, much less to be effective.While territorialism is very prominent, both in higher education and in those professions that align themselves with academic disciplines, and in the practice of design, the subject of design has been only marginally territorial in higher education. The professional schools and colleges all know that they have some responsibility for design, and some recognize that design is the heart of professional activity. But design is fundamentally different from (though it involves) analysis. Since analysis has been the primary strength of the professional schools and colleges and will remain so, to introduce a strong argument for expanding education in design is not to mount a frontal attack on the disciplines. Design has been one of the few academic areas where entrenched, vested interests were not so powerful or so dominant that there is no hope for change.

Still there is the prospect that those same interests that have kept design largely removed from professional studies will now, in light of the clear need for change, try hard to rename what is already being done with the word "design", and thus give cosmetic treatment where a heart transplant is required.

The most fundamental problem with the title "design science" is that in this primitive form it does not convey critical distinctions that need to be made in order to develop a proper perspective about design science. It is clear that some things are being designed well, which suggests that design science even now is not a total wasteland. It is clear that findings in numerous disciplinary sciences have furnished outstanding knowledge that is useful in design. There are large systems that work pretty well, including telephone systems and water supply systems. People who have contributed in such areas deserve credit and honor. The beliefs that have furnished the design bases in these fields contain gems. Design science has to recognize and incorporate such beliefs.

Still it is clear that the problems with design are not merely surface problems. They are fundamental, and one must go back to fundamentals to create a science. How can it be possible to accommodate to that part of the past of design that is high in quality, while seeking basic constructions?

The answer must lie in finding a way to divide the concept of "design science" into parts, defined by distinctions that make clear where the bulk of the good work has been done in the past and where the severe shortcomings lie that threaten the present and the future.

Such a distinction must be required also to serve four areas of critical need in the development of a system of beliefs about design that will begin to renew our confidence that we can manage the complexity of our large systems instead of being managed by or destroyed by them. These areas of critical need are:

- SCALE. We must be able to make design-relevant distinctions between toothpick and school system, between thumb tack and money-center bank, between check sorter and strategic defense umbrella, i.e., between small components and large-scale systems

- CULTURE IN HIGHER EDUCATION. We must be able to make design-relevant distinctions between ordinary science and large-scale systems science, between humanities and large-scale systems science, between the "two cultures" (humanities and science) of C. P. Snow and a system of higher education to prepare people for large- scale system design work (with substantial contributions to such preparation coming from these "two cultures")

- MEANING. We must be able to make design-relevant distinctions between such concepts as length (made meaningful by the existence of a primary standard of length), time (made meaningful by the existence of a primary standard of time), and purchasing power (made meaningful by the world-wide, long-standing existence of an ounce of gold as a standard of economic value); when compared with such concepts as artificial intelligence, kilolines of software, and social justice. The latter concepts lack reliable and universal meaning. Unlike the former they are open to arbitrary and diverse interpretation that is inadequate to support a system of belief of the kind needed for large-scale system design

• QUALITY. High quality large-scale system designs require attention to SCALE, CULTURE, and MEANING, carefully integrated into a system of beliefs that is commensurate with society's current and projected needs

Even if these factors can be incorporated into our consciousness, philosophically and professionally, it will also be necessary to have bold leadership and management to bring them to reality in our practices, generating much higher quality new system designs, and redesigning our old systems to make them much more valuable to us.

Because underconceptualization is perceived as the principal problem from the past [1], the development of design science should start at the highest level of generality. Starting from such a pinnacle, each division should be clarified and justified, all the way to the level of specific operations. Discipline is required in the development of the science as well as in its application.

Since design has been taking place for some time without a clearly-identified science of design, it seems necessary to show that now a science is needed. But in the process it also seems necessary to say what a science is, because clearly design is not quite like physics or economics. If it becomes possible to demonstrate that a science of design is needed, and to clarify what a science is, two derivative needs appear. It is necessary to discover what realm of knowledge such a science would encompass, and how this realm can be clearly distinguished from scientific knowledge presently being used in design activities. If it can be so distinguished, it is still necessary to say how it relates to other codified knowledge. And it is necessary to consider how or where the learning of such a science of design might be carried out, given the already-crowded educational agenda.

If such efforts succeed, it still remains to say how such a science might be used, what kinds of products might ensue from its use, and what would be involved in providing leadership and management to its usage.

1.1 Motivation for a Science of Design.

Science fills or contributes to the satisfaction of two major social needs: the need to know and the need to know how. A science of design presumably would help assuage the need to know how, but if we already know how, we do not need a science of design. So a beginning toward resolving the question of whether there is a need for a science of design can be made by looking to the world around us to see whether any difficulties can be detected that might possibly respond to an improvement in our know-how.

Insights evolve from simply reading the news with the purpose of finding such difficulties. During the past few years, systematic perusal of newspapers and journals reveals instance after instance of difficulties in society that cry out for better know-how. Areas in which major social difficulties have arisen, typically are characterized by one or more of the following attributes: loss of life, contamination of the environment due to "accidents", mammoth cost overruns on projects costing billions of dollars, significant economic loss accruing to individuals because of criminal behavior in enterprises, transportation accidents, huge loans that cannot be repaid, and erosion of confidence in organizations to accomplish their ostensible purposes.

Areas in which such difficulties have surfaced include the following:

- Software Projects
- Nuclear and Synthetic Energy Projects
- Defense System Design and Acquisition Projects
- Banking, Economics, Finance, and Trade
- Management of Big Corporations
- Government Financial Management
- Transportation Safety
- Food and Shelter
- Health-Care System Design

These areas have some things in common. They all involve systems that are growing progressively larger in scale. The scale may refer to costs, numbers of people involved, extent of influence of the system, extent of complexity of the system, volume of information required to describe what is happening in the system, interaction among system components, the size of the potential for disaster, and the extent of the consequences of failure of the system [2]. The problem areas all involve human planning, oversight, and steering, and thus are dependent upon the quality of human thought. And all of them involve problems that are not aligned with the way knowledge is learned in our institutions of learning. The terms "vertical" and "horizontal" have been used by numerous writers to distinguish knowledge that is organized in frameworks corresponding to the academic disciplines from knowledge that cuts across the academic disciplines. In the disciplines knowledge is organized, so to speak, in "vertical" slices; while in complex problem areas, knowledge is applied, so to speak, "horizontally" across and beyond disciplines [3]. So the problem areas all put a premium on the capacity of human beings to <u>process knowledge on a scale and in a framework that is not encountered in formal learning environments</u>.

Small-scale design experience, as acquired in industrial settings, involves "breadboards" or "pilot plants" or "prototypes" which are built and tested iteratively; allowing discovery of design flaws, remedial research, redesign, retesting, and trial marketing. Many successful design targets will have passed through repeated sequences of this type before being promoted to the general public. Governments may provide rules and regulations governing the development and testing of new pharmaceutical products, delaying their introduction for years until such products have given reasonable proof in trial situations of their probably efficacy. Even with such safeguards, potential disasters such as thalidomides and Dalkon shields sometimes escape timely detection.

Large-scale systems, with huge potential for destruction, do not permit economical testing for years before finding their way into our lives. Nuclear power plants go into service when they are finished. The test arena is our life situation, not a laboratory. Or to put it another way, welcome to your life as a guinea pig [4].

Recognition that problems can be categorized is an initial step toward an ultimate resolution of the difficulties. It is necessary to make distinctions among those areas where knowledge and experience have been proved adequate, and those areas where the converse is true. Such distinctions will help us know how to focus resources toward the necessary change, while preserving those areas that do not require such change; and will also help us know which is which.

Figure 1.1 shows how problems can be categorized by profiles, according to attributes. Profiles of this type typically are arranged by constructing lines that join polar opposites. Each such line provides an opportunity to locate upon it an assessment of where a particular problem stands with respect to the polar opposites at its terminals. Such an assessment may be represented by a single point on the line that conveys an intuitive image of how that particular problem relates to the poles. A problem may be judged to coincide with one or more of the poles and, if it is so judged, the point that describes it on that particular line will coincide with one end of the line. This figure shows the extreme profiles that represent normal and complex problems respectively. Many problems will be represented by a mixed profile, which may involve some but not all of the extremes of the attributes.

Table 1.1 [5] shows data concerning the major losses and catastrophes experienced during the period 1970-1985, as tabulated by a large reinsurance firm. These data show the size of tabulated financial losses and losses of homes during this period. While the data do not distinguish between the so-called "acts of God" and accidents arising from bad design, the distinction may not be that important. The Swedish Red Cross and Earthscan (a branch of the United-Nations-funded International Institute for Environment and Development) published a report indicating

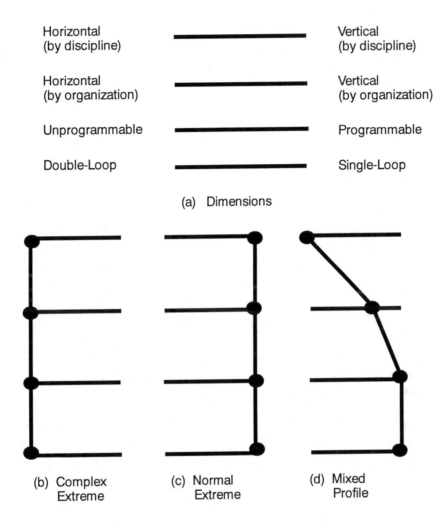

Figure 1.1 Profiles of problem types. Copyright © 1986 IEEE.

that even when disasters have a natural origin or natural component, human factors in the aftermath often determine how severe the effects will be. Bad design of public programs or bad interventions in natural systems based on bad designs may cause the impact of a natural disaster to be magnified. The Sahel region of Africa illustrates such magnified effects [6].

Figure 1.2 shows a graph of the increase over time of the number of disasters reported in the data of Table 1.1. This figure shows a rather alarming rate of increase in such disasters. Other figures compiled by the Swedish Red Cross show that disas-

9

Table 1.1
Major Losses and Catastrophes

Three Year Period	Average Number for the Period	
	Events/Year	Average Insurance Claim Paid
1971-1973	47	$18,000,000
1974-1976	53	$31,200,000
1977-1979	63	$36,000,000
1980-1982	69	$38,700,000
1983-1985	75	$56,000,000
Total Events in Period 1970-1985	2,305	
Resulting Number of Deaths	1.5 million	
Resulting Number of Homeless	50,000,000 people	
Total Financial Loss	$700 billion	
Amount Recovered from Insurance	$36 billion (5.1%)	

ters killed an average of 22,570 people annually during the 1960s, and a much larger annual average of 142,920 during the 1970s. Their preliminary data for the 1980s show further substantial increases in the frequency of such disasters.

It is assumed, for purposes of this work, that society will continue to accept the large-scale systems that are beginning to dominate their lives. Given this assumption, it is reasonable to assume further that such systems are not now being developed in the best possible way. To assume that they are, in the absence of a science of design, is to assume that a science of design could not provide any better way to do things.

An American scientist and philosopher, Charles S. Peirce (1839-1914), has become increasingly recognized for his fundamental thinking about science, knowledge, and meaning. One of his biographers, Karl-Otto Apel, has described him as "America's greatest thinker" [7]. Peirce provided much of the basic thinking that will influence heavily the science of design to be presented in this book. To consult his views on the nature of science is to clarify why a science of design is needed for the continuation of large-scale systems in our society.

1.2 Matters of Scale.

To say that a system is a "large-scale system" is to say something about the limitations of the human mind. Imagine, if you will, that the human mind had direct access to all events occurring everywhere, and the capacity to comprehend and direct a

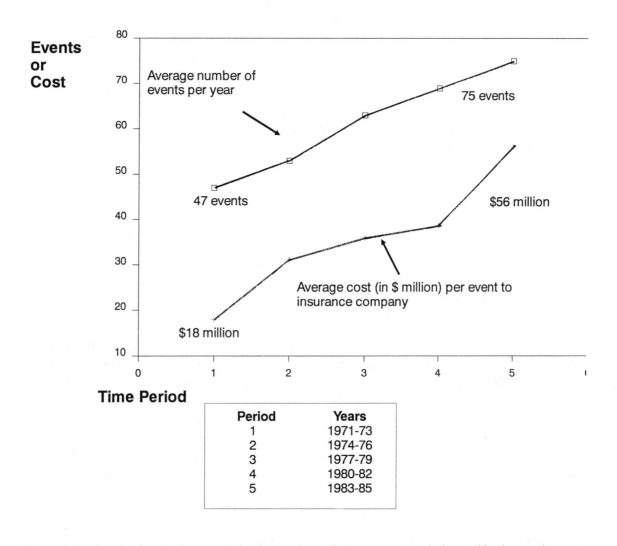

Figure 1.2 Graph of major losses and catastrophes. (Data on events reimbursed by insurer.)

studied response to all of them. Under this assumption, there might be only one large-scale system: the human mind. But our assumption is contrary to reality. Instead, because the human mind is heavily constrained in terms of its ability to gain immediate or even delayed access to all events occurring everywhere; and because it is further constrained by its physical construction and the laws of nature in regard to the volume of information it can operate on in any given interval, and the rate at which it can perform; it is evident that a system becomes a large-scale system in relation to human capacity to observe it, comprehend it, analyze it, steer it, amend it, and tolerate it.

It is for this reason that the greatest single concern in the development of a science of design is to find a way to bring large-scale systems within the purview of the human mind. Clearly this must involve the search for enhancements that supplement what the unaided mind can do. Equally clearly, it must involve a search for ways to minimize detractions for it will not help to provide enhancements, if they are annulled by other factors in the working environment of the designer. But one must also recognize that the design science itself may involve a scale that is potentially troublesome to the mind. So in its development and presentation, it will be advisable to so organize it as to facilitate not only its study, but dialog about it, and amendment of it.

1.3. Cultures in Higher Education.

We need a third culture in higher education: a design culture [8]. The sciences and the humanities are truly well established as two cultures in the universities. The design culture can and must be built on the existing foundation that is provided by the sciences and the humanities. The rationale behind this statement will evolve as Part I of this book unfolds.

One way to view design is that it is the visible manifestation of what we know about the sciences and the humanities, when applied to alter the natural universe. Yet the two cultures are many steps removed from application. They provide vital orientation and valuable information to support design. Yet the very diversity stemming from these cultures may, in the absence of a synergistic culture that is focused on design and supports its presence in the academic halls, be contributory to significant failures to bring salient ideas to bear in design situations. The sciences and humanities provide important raw material and important values to the human mind. They do not bring to it the capacity to integrate in large system design the many attributes that these systems require.

We are challenged, in an Age of Design, to do the following:

- Discover the generic aspects of design, and introduce them in our academic development

- Discover how to distinguish design philosophically and pragmatically from other forms of human endeavor and interest

- Match in magnitude (a) the potential impacts of design on our lives with (b) the amount of energy we put into learning how to do good design

- Translate our discoveries into learning processes

- Institutionalize these processes in higher education

- Improve our designs in all areas, in all conceivable ways, to create superior alternatives for ourselves

We need three cultures in our universities. The humanities and the sciences have demonstrated that they can survive and prosper in the world without significant emphasis in the university on design. But design cannot exist nor can it prosper in the university without significant emphasis on the humanities and science. Nor can it prosper without significant emphasis on itself.

The methods of design are different and the frame of mind is different than in the sciences. The differences reflect the distinction between observation, analysis, and refinement of descriptions for entities already existing in our environment; as contrasted with the process of inventing options, organizing alternatives and, by virtue of human decision-making, expressing our interests and values through creative change of the world that others are observing.

1.4 Methods of Fixing Belief.

One of the fundamental issues raised and answered by C. S. Peirce was the question: what are the ways by which human beings fix belief? Peirce described four methods for doing so [9]. These four methods, listed in Table 1.2, are: (a) the method of authority, (b) the method of tenacity, (c) the method of metaphysics, and (d) the method of science.

From this set of possibilities, Peirce noted that the method of science stood out because it is the only method that demands evaluation against future experience and, if it is found that future experience does not correspond to what the science has asserted, the method of science requires that the assertions be rejected or modified. All other methods involve less stringent conditions for belief fixation.

The history of design practice often has included the word "apprenticeship". An apprentice may fix belief by the method of authority, and retain it by the method of tenacity. One of the prevailing concepts of our time is that of "expert system", which presumes an authority, and strives to emulate the views of the authority. Thus methods other than the method of science are still applied. But whatever may be done

Table 1.2
The Four Methods of Fixing Belief (C.S. Peirce)

The Method of Authority

The Method of Tenacity

The Method of Metaphysics

The Method of Science

still does not invalidate the fundamental superiority of the method of science, which requires a community of evaluators constantly striving to assess the assertions of science and to revise them in the direction of greater validity.

It is this argument that tells us that, even in a field like design, the fixing of belief through the method of science should be the focus of our aspirations.

Peirce further asserted that the scientist should be viewed as fallible (not as an expert); that knowledge is aggregated through inference; that every human being possesses an "unshakeable cognitive burden", which is the state in which the human being necessarily approaches every problem situation (in contrast to the infeasible Descartian prescription to clear the mind); and that it is this human fallibility that necessitates the community of scholars acting now and forever to evaluate conclusions stemming from scientific inquiry. It is in this spirit that the quest for design science must be pursued.

1.5 Referential Transparency and Universal Priors to Science.

Nothing is more devastating to the credibility of a science than lack of agreement upon (a) what constitutes its fundamentals and (b) the interpretation of them. It has been argued that the most basic criterion for a science is that it should have Referential Transparency. A science with this attribute first of all is to be seen as an organized body of knowledge. And a part of the organizing principle has to do with the inferential structure of the science. Structure means relationship, and inferential structure means inferred relationship. When fragments of information are connected by inference, a normal connotation is that one piece of information is more fundamental than another.

To say that one piece of information A is more fundamental than another B is to say also that B is dependent upon A for its interpretation. And if pieces of information are strung out in a chain of inference, pieces deeper or further back in the chain are critical to the interpretation of their successors. While infinite chains are conceivable intellectually, practical considerations (the finiteness of language, the finiteness of human observational capacity) tell us that finite chains are the focus of our interpretations, and will be the basis for representation of our beliefs. Thus there will always be a deepest set of concepts upon which all that are connected to it will be dependent for interpretation. But more than this, there will be a shallowest one whose interpretation depends upon all of its predecessors including, but not limited to the deepest set. The capacity to trace the reasoning in both directions through the structure is a key aspect of Referential Transparency. Yet the structure of science remains invisible or implicit for all of the sciences!

If a deepest set of ideas is found for a science, it will have to enjoy the special property that it has been subjected over time to the most careful consideration, and has been found acceptable to the vast majority of the relevant community, in order for the science itself to enjoy scientific consensus. In the absence of such a demarcated set, other bases for decision-making will find openings.

To illustrate the point consider "nuclear science". A U. S. Congressman (Morris Udall) stated to a group of technical people that, in striving to determine whether nuclear energy was safe, a Congressional Committee invited two groups of Nobel prize-winning scientists to testify on the subject. One of the groups testified to Congress that nuclear energy is safe. The next day the other group testified that nuclear energy is not safe. As the Congressman pointed out, in issues that involve science, but upon which respected scientists do not agree, the issues cease to be scientific and become political. When the issues become political, the reference point for decision-making is not the fundamentals of the science, but rather the fundamentals of politics and economics -- reelection and business income.

It is even in the interests of some to promote the idea that sciences cannot have foundations. An alternative posture is to suggest that science is a collection of disconnected patterns, with freedom for anyone to choose which pattern will fit which preconceived idea of what is valid. Such thinking does not reflect the existence of Universal Priors to Science, four of which are listed in Table 1.3.

These four are brought together in the following Law of Universal Priors [10].

Table 1.3
Four Universal Priors to All Science

The Human Being

Language

Reasoning Through Relationships

Means of Archival Representation

This Law is offered to counter the posture that sciences do not necessarily have foundations. It will also be applied in developing the foundations of Generic Design Science in Chapter 5.

The Law of Universal Priors asserts the following:

**The human being, language, reasoning through relationships,
and archival representations are universal priors to science.
(I.e., there can be <u>no</u> science without each of them.)**

The validity of this Law can be established using what is called the Doctrine of Necessity. This Doctrine holds that, independent of the particular attributes of B, if A is necessary in order for B to exist, then A is a prior of B. (The word "prior", used as a noun, fills a need that no other word quite satisfies.) The test of the necessity of each of the four factors mentioned is to imagine that they are withdrawn, and then inquire as to whether in their absence a science is possible. Imagine first,that there were no human beings. Accepting the common evidence that human beings are the producers of science, and the only producers of science, then it must be that the human being is a Universal Prior to Science. Imagine next that no language were available. Since all of science consists of language, and nothing other than language, there can be no science without language. But even presupposing the human being and language, suppose now that there is no reasoning through relationships. Since all organization of information is through relationships arrived at by reasoning, there can be no organization of knowledge without it. But science <u>is</u> organized knowledge, hence both language and reasoning through relationships are Universal Priors to Science. The human being, language, and reasoning through relationships all can exist and persist without any archival representation, the organization being in the mind. It might, therefore, be argued that these three are sufficient, and that archival representation is not required in order for organized knowledge and, therefore, science to exist. But science depends upon widespread consensus, and library after library attests to the critical importance of archival representation in gaining the necessary widespread understanding and consensus upon which acceptance as science depends.

Overt recognition of the status of the Universal Priors to Science should bury the modest movement to assert that there are <u>no</u> foundations to (at least some) sciences. On the contrary, what is seen here not only states that there <u>are</u> some, but there are some that are foundations to <u>all</u> science. If one is to distinguish one science from another, it may be through finding unique foundations for a <u>particular</u> science that can and must be integrated with the Universal Priors to establish the decision-making basis for the particular science.

One obvious, but misguided, way to try to provide distinctiveness to the foundations of a science is to lay the Universal Priors on the operating table, and to diminish them to shadows of their identity, while retaining slices of them. Thus the human being may be fractionated into an economic entity, a social entity, or other one-dimensional entity such as political, athletic, biological, etc., or through a role such as observer of nature. Language may be diluted by failure to establish and enforce the definitions of its components; and reasoning through relationships may be diluted both by blurring the definitions of the relationship terms and by disguising patterns of relationship. The latter can occur naturally because of the linear sequential nature of prose which does not lend itself to portraying patterns. Moreover archival representations may themselves be so diluted by the emaciation of the other three Universal Priors as to be helpless to offer any assistance in searching for the Referential Transparency.

1.6. Leadership and Management.

Escalation is a term that can be used to express the progressive enlargement of difficulty through the incorporation of one or more new factors in a problem situation. To provide leadership and management in design has become an escalating challenge. The escalation can be imagined by supposing that there is a gradation involved. Start with the idea that one person takes on an assistant to help make shoes, having developed more business than can be handled. The employer now becomes a manager of one person. The employer may teach this person how to make shoes, and may provide overview and steering to that person's behavior. But then as more employees are taken on, matters other than shoe-making require increased attention, such as finance, fringe benefits, payroll, and the like. Whereupon additional individuals are hired not to make shoes, but rather to handle these business- related matters. But as individuals take on management responsibilities, arguments begin to arise over matters involving shared interests. Thus the definition and settlement of management issues now require attention. Now suppose that a new business component is purchased involving an activity less familiar than making shoes, say designing power plants. If the plants are of an old, familiar, long-used type, it may be possible to hire people who are experienced in their design. But if they are new and novel, one sees right away the potential for great escalation of the decision-making difficulties. If there are no points of scientific reference for decisions they become, as has been seen, political and economic. And if mistakes are made such as at Three-Mile Island and Chernobyl, further escalation occurs into a broader social and public health and security arena.

Social development is greatly and, sometimes, gravely affected by management. Figure 1.3 illustrates a single-loop model of social development, as it can be promoted by management.

This model illustrates the view that means and ends may be well-perceived through structural approaches showing how they are related; and emphasizes that an item may be both a means and an end, especially as perceived through such a structural relation. Thus, for example, one means to achieve an effective society is effective management; while an effective society may itself be a means to the end of effective use of the three major components of problem-solving identified as content, context, and process.

Given the escalation that goes on in many human processes, discussions of management and leadership (e.g., in "management science") can then begin to display a need for foundations -- for points of reference against which decision situations might be explored.

17

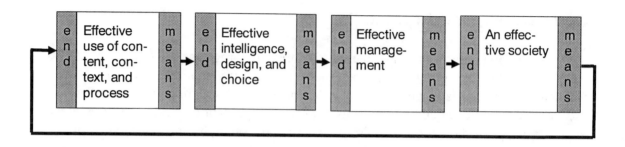

Figure 1.3 Social development through management. Copyright © 1984 IEEE.

We may then be led back to the Universal Priors to Science to determine what aspects of the human being are critical to leadership. In particular, we now may wish to consider the human being in the Leadership Role, and ask what fundamental attributes are required in such a challenging position. Through this approach, we may strive to determine whether or how the human being can exercise initiative in managing the escalation that goes on in problem-solving, and what attributes may be helpful in playing this role. A recent empirical study by Bennis of numerous individuals in many fields who are regarded as leaders in those fields sought to find those attributes which these people might have in common [11]. The study found that they shared the ability to manage four factors:

- **Attention** -- i.e., they could attract people to listen to what they had to say, often by providing a compelling image of an imagined future that might be attained through collective effort

- **Meaning** -- i.e., having gained attention of people, they could articulate and clarify what was being communicated

- **Trust** -- i.e., having gained attention and communicated visions, they could maintain critical positions and meet commitments, and could continue to be perceived as people who remembered their promises, and who took them as seriously as the people to whom the promises had been made. If they were forced by circumstances to make unforeseen changes, they would provide explanations to all those who were affected by such changes, and the explanations would ring true. Moreover, they would not unilaterally usurp the roles that others had assumed as part of a real or implicit social contract.

- **Self** -- i.e., the leader had the capacity to perceive himself or herself as an entity also to be managed, and set personal standards of behavior against which self-behavior would be self-regulated; and these personal standards would be at least as stringent as those that the leader might impose on others.

There is a close connection between these success factors in leadership and the Universal Priors to Science. Because science requires human activity to produce it, and this activity must involve the use of language and reasoning through relationships, the ability to construct portrayals that command attention and convey clear meanings is vital. And the individual ability to present truthful and consistent information of the type that can be broadly accepted by a community of evaluators is closely connected with management of trust and with the self-discipline that is necessary for scientific investigation and reporting.

1.7. Design Science.

Design science must be divided in several ways in order to see how it must advance as a whole.

Design Categories

In this book, design science is divided into three categories [12]: a) <u>Specific Design Sciences</u>, which are found in various disciplinary areas of study, being largely restricted in application to fields closely allied with those disciplinary areas, (b) <u>Generic Design Science</u>, which deals with those matters that are common across the entire spectrum of design activity, and which are distinct from and overlap at most only marginally any of the Specific Design Sciences, and (c) <u>General Design Science</u>, which is an integrating category to absorb and integrate Generic Design Science with the Specific Design Sciences. This last division is dependent for its development upon the development of the Generic Design Science, without which it cannot have any substance. Table 1.4 elaborates.

The structural inclusion relationship among the different components of the Division of design science is represented in Figure 1.4.

Design Activities

Design consists primarily of six fundamental types of intellectual activity: intelligence, analysis, synthesis, choice, communication, and interpretation. The implementation of design is its most concrete phase, but the failure of any one of the six fundamental types will usually assure the failure of the implementation. Intelligence,

Table 1.4
Divisions of Design Science

Specific Design Science. (1) There are many Specific Design Sciences. (2) A Specific Design Science typically is restricted to a single discipline and a well-defined set of applications linked to it; although sometimes more than one (but not <u>many</u> more than one) discipline may be involved. (3) It is not customary to identify these as design sciences, because they are usually presented as tools of analysis; but they also serve in applications as tools of design, because design involves both analysis and synthesis.

Generic Design Science. (1) There can be only one Generic Design Science, but it can evolve through continuing discovery and assessment. (2) It relates to those characteristics, attributes, phenomena, and conditions that (a) are common to all design situations or (b) would be common to them if recognized by designers (except that the intensity of application could vary greatly with the level of design difficulty). (3) It recognizes and incorporates the Universal Priors of all science. (4) It brings its properties to all design applications, but does not substitute for the Specific Design Sciences. (5) Restricted versions of it can be applied to situations that are limited in scope.

General Design Science. General Design Science is the whole of design science. It is comprised of all of the Specific Design Sciences and the Generic Design Science, serving the universe of design activity. At the present time, this concept remains unrealized.

analysis, and synthesis make up conceptualization. Communication and interpretation make up documentation. So another way to view design is that it consists primarily of <u>conceptualization</u>, <u>choice</u>, and <u>documentation</u>.

Synthesis is graded into three stages of difficulty. The first and easiest stage is that of negligible interaction among the components that are synthesized into a whole. The second stage in the gradation is that of non-proionic interaction (i.e., interaction which does not result in the emergence of new components). The third stage in the gradation is that of proionic interaction (i.e., interaction in which new components emerge as the consequence of encounters among old system components).

Referential Transparency

Generic Design Science is required to demonstrate Referential Transparency. By adhering to this requirement in developing and in applying the science, the extensive underconceptualization that is one of the major sources of large system design failure can be avoided. Generic Design Science, by this means, provides a scientific

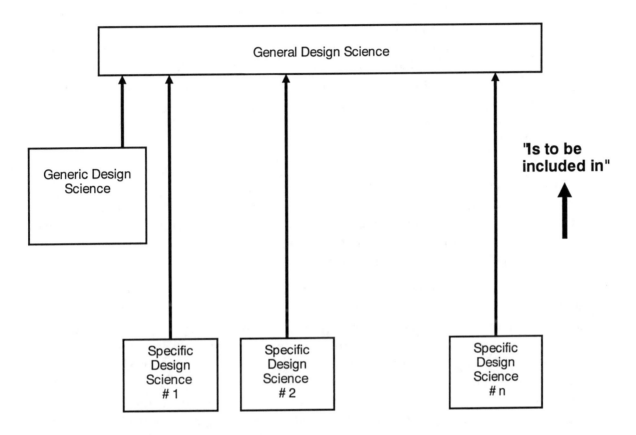

Figure 1.4 Illustrating the divisions of design science.

basis for a practice now called "top-down design", which presently lacks a scientific basis and promotes underconceptualization. The "top" in much current design is the top of some manager's head, while the "top" in Generic Design Science is the Universe itself.

1.8 A Cosmic Partition as a Means of Making Fundamental Distinctions.

Cosmology is the study of the universe viewed as a system. Because Generic Design Science deals primarily with intellectual activity involving the use and transformation of information, the universe is partitioned by what is called a Cosmic Partition, into three blocks: the Library, the Phaneron, and the Residue [13].

The <u>Library</u> is the generic name given to all information that has been recorded in any media form. It is all the world's documentation. The <u>Phaneron</u> (a term applied by C. S. Peirce) is the generic name given to the totality of ideas contained in the minds of all people everywhere. The <u>Residue</u> contains all that remains in the Universe, after the Library and the Phaneron are extracted from it.

The structural relationship among the three components of the partition can be portrayed in what is called by the technical name "lattice" (App. 1). The portrayal appears in Figure 1.5. This particular lattice consists of a lowest level occupied by the "empty set" designated by Φ; a next higher level occupied by the members of a "basis set", comprising the individual components around which the rest of the lattice is constructed; a next higher level containing all possible pairs of components from the basis set; a next higher level containing all possible trios of components from the basis set; and so on, until at the highest level there is a single occupant, this being the set of all members of the basis set.

The Generic Design Science then becomes concerned with interactions among the three blocks of the partition. For the most part, these interactions have been studied for millennia by philosophers, and their thinking forms part of the base of intelligence that is used to construct Generic Design Science. Among the most important interactions are the "information operations" that take place involving these three blocks [14]. They are indicated in Figure 1.6.

The Phaneron, acting through sensory mechanisms, becomes engaged with observations involving both the Residue and the Library. Acting through motor mechanisms, the Phaneron engages with operations collectively designated as "archiving", in which ideas are transformed into components of the Library. Engaged with itself, the Phaneron is involved in inferences using newly-relevant information to restructure information previously held. Among the products of such engagements are hypotheses and, in general, representations. Acting through parts of the Residue, the Phaneron implements design targets that have been conceived as part of the inferential processes.

These information operations appear to be a major part of the potential subject matter of the emerging field called "cognitive science". What is new in our current consideration is the application of over two millennia of thought in carrying out the design of systems, with open respect for the great prior contributions, and a deliberate dedication to incorporating such contributions overtly and without unjustified transformation or distortion into a science of design.

One of the early steps in the creation of a Science of Generic Design must be the manner in which the Universal Priors are dealt with in it. Given that they are critical to conceptualization, choice, and documentation, which are the primary activities involved in carrying out design; and to leadership, which is vital to efficacious oversight and steering; it is not surprising that they will be at the heart of the Science [10].

1.9 Bringing Discipline to the Development of Design Science.

Historical perspective is often useful to help eliminate the technomyopia of the present. Ancient mythology often helps us to see ourselves in new ways.

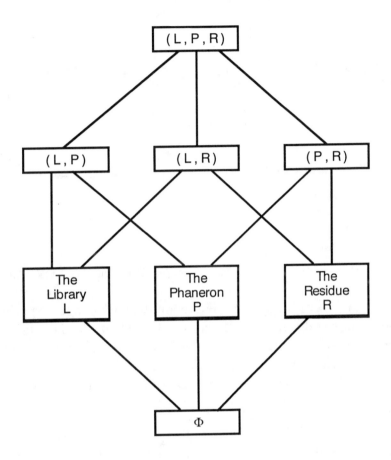

Figure 1.5 A lattice based on a three-block partition (for the cosmic partition).

System design took place in Greek mythology as a service to the gods. The god Hephaestus, the "god that limps", was the forger of implements of war to be placed at the service of gods of higher rank than himself. He was the son of Zeus and Hera. He was thrown out of Olympus by his mother because he was ugly. When he crashed to earth, he was permanently disfigured and thereafter walked with a limp. But his services were indispensable to the gods, so he was brought back to Olympus. Homer publicized his works in the *Iliad*, where the design philosophy and priorities of the time are illustrated.

A strong case can be made that there were only three dimensions influencing system design at that time: (a) the <u>design situation</u>, reflected in aspects of the pre-vailing cultures, both management and technical, and in the motivating circumstances that dictated system requirements; (b) the <u>knowledge about the design</u>

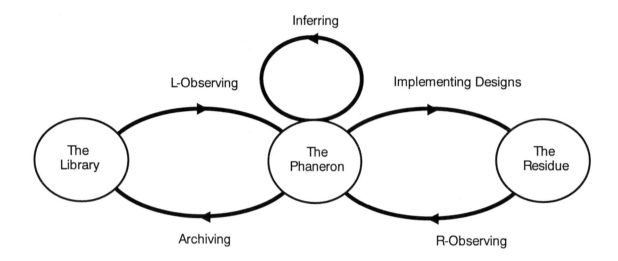

Figure 1.6 Information operations in the cosmic partition. Copyright © 1986 IEEE.

<u>target</u>, consisting of a mix of intuitive belief, technical knowledge, experiential knowledge, and a supposedly very small amount of scientific knowledge; and (c) the <u>processes of design</u>, involving the work breakdown structures, schedules (always running late by the standards of the gods), check lists for good practice, and the systematic application of any available laws of design (none being noted in the literature of the times).

Figure 1.7 shows the presumed hierarchical structure of the priorities that prevailed to discipline design activity in mythology. The Design Situation dominated the Knowledge About the Design Target, and both dominated the Design Process. Once the gods had stated their requirements and put them in the hands of someone having knowledge about the Design Target, the Process of Design was of no consequence to them. The gods viewed their management responsibilities to be limited to expressing their needs, selecting the professional who would fulfill them, and punishing the professional who failed. (Mr. S. K. Batra has suggested that Hindu gods would probably act differently.)

In today's world, the dimensions involved as possible ways to discipline design activity are more numerous. Table 1.5 lists a number of these. The six major headings there are called "dimensions of the disciplinary field" and the entries under each dimension are called "options in the dimension". Three dimensions appear in Table 1.5 that were not present in mythology, while three others are the same as those shown in Fig. 1.7. The new dimensions involve Standards, History, and Insight into Human Limitations; these being much more readily available than in mythological times.

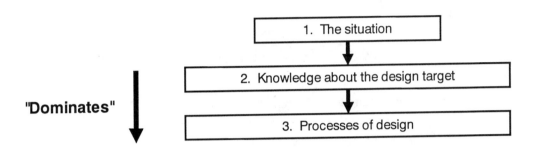

Figure 1.7 Design priority structure in mythology. Copyright © 1987 ASME.

Let us strive to give a brief description of each of these three new dimensions that might discipline large-scale system design, with an eye to their relevance and their potential applicability.

Standards of Behavior

Designers of large-scale systems invariably report to managers or administrators in large organizations. A variety of loyalties may be involved. The designer has personal aspirations that may involve retaining a job, and such aspirations may also relate closely to family security. The designer also is faced with providing loyalty to the manager. The manager's requirements may or may not be coincident with those of the organization. The interests represented by the organization may not coincide with those that are of greatest potential social value.

Some designers have clearly placed the interests of society above those of lesser assemblies. For example, Mr. Gerald W. Gordon, Chairman of the United States Activities Board of the Institute of Electrical and Electronics Engineers Ethics Committee, described the actions of some engineers as follows:

"The TVA engineers eventually went public with their complaints and have been victims of intimidation and harassment ever since. TVA had hired a consulting organization to investigate complaints but phased it out when it became evident that a large proportion of the charges were valid. The Department of Labor fined TVA $150,000 for their treatment of the so-called 'whistle blowers'. TVA has since acknowledged some major deficiencies and has shut down all five of its nuclear reactors, at a considerable economic cost and loss of public credibility."

Table 1.5
Possible Dimensions in Disciplining Large-Scale Systems Design

A. THE SITUATION
- The prevailing engineering culture
- The prevailing culture of the management of engineering
- The motivating circumstances for the systems design

B. KNOWLEDGE ABOUT THE DESIGN TARGET
- Scientific knowledge
- Experiental knowledge
- Technological knowledge
- Intuitive belief

C. STANDARDS OF BEHAVIOR
- Of Ethics in general
- Of professional integration
- Of knowledge utilization
- Of independent review and oversight
- Of quality orientation

D. HISTORY OF CRITICAL INCIDENTS
- Mass media accounts
- Case study manuals
- Commission reports

E. INSIGHT INTO HUMAN LIMITATIONS AFFECTING DESIGNER ABILITY
- Span of immediate recall
- Span of absolute judgment
- Span of memory fixation
- Satisficing behavior
- Organizational constraints
- Implications of the foregoing for a design process

F. PROCESS OF DESIGN (METHODOLOGY)
- Work breakdown structure
- Schedule charts
- Check lists
- Systems engineering practice
- Systematic application of laws of generic design
- Integrated working environments, influenced by Generic Design Science

History of Critical Incidents

There is a tendency to view each new Critical Incident as a totally unique event, without correlation with prior events. The systematic study of mass media accounts and other reports, along with case study materials, is a way to develop invariant features of past Critical Incidents. Invariance in society translates into the goods of science. When such features can be shown to represent whole classes of disasters, rather than to be merely isolated properties of individual events, one begins to see a basis for disciplining future design activity: the application of processes that do not tolerate these features. But the processes must themselves be <u>designed</u> so that they do not tolerate the features. Features that are almost always present, when normal processes are allowed to take place, may be "designed out" of processes developed from scientific foundations.

A reading of the report of the Kemeny Commission on the Three-Mile Island nuclear event, as portrayed by Kemeny [15], will reveal substantial detailed support for what has just been said, as will other reports on disasters. But only when a size-able set of reports covering a variety of cases is studied does the full scope of the situation emerge, and then the necessary corrective measures can be seen as generic and subject to correction through the application of Generic Design Science.

Insight into Human Limitations Affecting Designer Ability

The twentieth-century development of the social sciences has produced insights into human limitations that were not evident in detail to the gods in mythology, or even to designers in prior centuries. These insights reveal the limited capacity of the human mind to process information reaching it from short-term memory. A whole array of limitations exists which threatens the quality and viability of designs [16], most of which are ignored in intuitive design practice of the type that represents an extrapolation of small-unit design to large-scale system design.

A U. S. Secretary of Defense illustrated very well the prevalent failure to recognize differences in scale when he compared criticism of expenditures on the 1980's U. S. Strategic Defense Initiative to early criticism of funds being spent to develop helicopters. Inability to understand the substantial differences between systems of human scale and systems that vastly exceed human scale is a hallmark of current deficiency in design philosophy and practice. The exercise of decision-making power that is hostage to such lack of understanding preempts the necessary corrective measures.

The Design Situation

The Design Situation today is not like that in mythology. In those times, the single god Hephaestus could be responsible for all details of a design, ranging from the conceptual to the implementation. Today vast sums are spent on design targets, and in many instances no one is truly in charge, as huge teams work on disparate aspects of the design of targets that lie beyond human scale. Moreover the variety of interests involved or at least related to large system designs is much greater than in the days when the gods made all the decisions.

The Ethical Dilemma of the Engineer

Engineers are frequently involved in large-scale system design. They may encounter severe ethical problems in this practice. The ethical dilemma of the engineer has been well-explored by Broome [17]. He noted, as have others such as Conant [18] and Vickers [19] that technology has always outdistanced science in its early stages, leaving judgments to be made by intuition that can have major effects on public safety. Broome suggests that "engineers and their industrial employers have already seized the reins of American history", and that a conceivable outcome would be that "these elites could wield such power as to invite unprecedented visitations of technological horror upon the public. With the public out of the way, engineering elites would have license to make their own rules -- empowering them to decide the acceptability of SDI, nuclear power and weaponry, etc., [and] as this sort of practice became the norm, violations of the morality of informed consent...would become the everyday deeds of ordinary engineers. And this license would be cancerous to the moral traditions and values that Americans would hand down to their future generations."

This description may seem out of place in many nations, but as the financial stakes grow high, worldwide movement is in this direction.

Priorities for Generic Design Science

Some who look at the many Critical Incidents from the past are viewing them from the perspective of science enunciated by Whitehead [20]: "to see what is general in what is particular and what is permanent in what is transitory is the aim of scientific thought". Or they may be looking to the perspective of J. Willard Gibbs who stated that "the principal purpose of theoretical research ... is to find the point of view from which the subject appears in its greatest simplicity", and who observed that "the whole is simpler than the sum of its parts". Unfortunately, such views have largely been foreign to the arena of large-scale system design. They are both hard to achieve, and much more support will be required to bring them into public view than has been spent to date.

What **is** general is human behavior that is self-centered, inwardly directed, looking for artifacts as both the source and the cure of difficulties. What has been permanent so far is an unwillingness or lack of diligence in taking the measures necessary to get corrections understood and put in place in a lasting way. In the past, the History of Critical Incidents has been viewed as of lower priority than Processes of Design, because the history of disasters had not yet come into full perspective. Formal recognition of Human Limitations Affecting Designer Ability has yet to make much inroad into the design of large-scale systems. For these and other reasons, a new priority structure is indicated for the design environments of the future. This new structure, shown in Figure 1.8 places Standards of Behavior first, at the top of the priority scale. Definition of the standards, implementation of them in contractual matters, and enforcement of them in environments that traditionally have been immune to them will have to emerge. Very likely the concept of "due design process", like the concept of "due process" in other aspects of life, will become the legal basis for establishing responsibility and irresponsibility.

Second priority is given in the new structure to the History of Critical Incidents. Standards of Behavior will require that such Critical Incidents be studied as a group, and that what is learned from them (not just on the technical side, but especially on the behavioral side, and through the joint consideration of the technical and behavioral) will become part of the science background from which the "due design process" description will emerge.

The third priority is Insight into Human Limitations Affecting Designer Ability. Success in using or carrying out the processes that incorporate knowledge of the Situation and of the Design Target will rely upon appropriate treatment of these limitations in the underlying science.

The fourth priority is Knowledge About the Design Target. This priority should inform the selection of processes for design, and should help assess the likelihood of being successful in designing a target to meet the situation. The analysis of the alternatives of conducting more research, or of stopping wasteful development practices, will be particularly sensitive to the use of such knowledge, and will help eliminate political design of infeasible sociotechnical systems.

The Processes of Design, being informed by all preceding priorities in Figure 1.3, and being informed as well by the Science of Generic Design, will dominate the Design Situation, which will have the lowest priority of all. Even assigning a low priority to the Situation (in contrast to its highest priority in mythology) does not mean that the Situation will not get a great deal of attention; but it does mean that at the point of tradeoffs where resources must be allocated among many competing candidate target systems, the tradeoffs may be wise instead of foolish.

An early step in the development of a Science of Generic Design will involve the consideration of how Universal Priors to Science will enter into it.

29

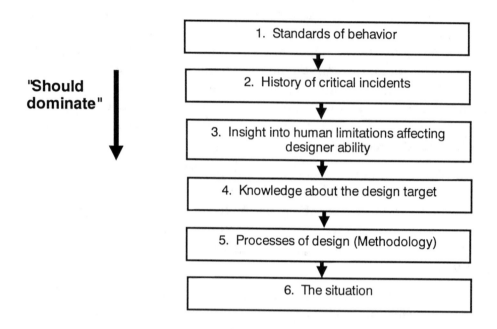

Figure 1.8 Indicated priority structure for tomorrow's design environment.
Copyright © 1987 ASME.

SUMMARY

Our society is witnessing the development, whether deliberate or evolutionary, of very large systems on a scale never before seen. This book is written under the assumption that the trend toward very large systems will continue. The further assumption is that, if it is going to continue, the quality of what is being done can be enhanced considerably, through the availability of a Science of Generic Design.

Given the assumption of continued large-scale system development, such a Science is required for three primary reasons. First, large systems with interdependent parts cannot be built repeatedly in socially-isolated and non-damaging experimental forms and test-operated in failure modes to acquire experience. Second, society is experiencing an unacceptably high and growing level of social disasters from our existing large systems, indicating a need for redesign of many of these systems. And third, the best basis for belief is scientific knowledge, which may permit us to transcend undisciplined practices.

A science of design must not only provide the avenue to structure and realize our large systems in ways that are not presently being achieved, but it must also be exemplary in its own realization of the same ideals and standards that it is intended to represent when it is applied.

The possibility of learning design in higher education through the development of a new (third) culture in higher education is recommended. The established science and humanities cultures are challenged to provide the underpinning for this culture. Without such underpinning the design culture cannot provide the necessary education.

Prior science and philosophy of science influence the development of the Generic Design Science in many ways. Peirce's ideas on how belief can be fixed nominate science as the only reliable approach to fixing belief in the long run. Also they associate responsibility with a community of scholars who must consistently and persistently evaluate and upgrade the science. A premium is attached to courageous assumption of this responsibility in an era where such behavior is more likely to be recommended than supported.

The idea that there exist certain Universal Priors to all science is set forth. Four of them are asserted to be: the human being, language, reasoning through relationships, and archival representations. Withdrawal of any of these is sufficient to prevent the existence of science. Every science must account for these factors in its development and organization. Consequently they play a significant role in developing the foundations of a Science of Generic Design. Moreover, these Universal Priors are underrepresented and underconceptualized in most of the more-established sciences from which a Science of Generic Design must draw.

While design can be founded in science, the design of large systems also requires oversight and steering. Because design is primarily an activity of the mind, the Universal Priors must play a major role in the oversight and steering as well. Teachers and managers of design must correct major educational deficiencies relating to these Universal Priors.

Design science is divided into three categories:

a) Specific Design Sciences, which are found in various disciplinary areas of study, being largely restricted in application to fields closely allied with those disciplinary areas, (b) Generic Design Science, which deals with those matters that are common across the entire spectrum of design activity, and which are distinct from and overlap at most only marginally any of the Specific Design Sciences, and (c) General Design Science, which is an integrating category to absorb and integrate Generic Design Science with the Specific Design Sciences. This division is dependent for its development upon the development of the Generic Design Science, without which it cannot have any substance.

Design consists primarily of three types of intellectual activity: conceptualization, choice, and documentation. The implementation of design is its most concrete phase, but the failure of any one of these three prior types will usually assure the failure of the implementation. Intelligence, analysis, and synthesis make up conceptualization. Communication and interpretation make up documentation.

Generic Design Science is required to demonstrate Referential Transparency. By adhering to this requirement in developing and in applying the Science, the extensive underconceptualization that is one of the major sources of large system design failure can be avoided.

Cosmology is the study of the universe viewed as a system. Because Generic Design Science deals primarily with intellectual activity involving the use and transformation of information, the universe is partitioned by what is called a Cosmic Partition, into three blocks: the Library, the Phaneron, and the Residue.

The Library is the generic name given to all information that has been recorded in any media form. The Phaneron (a term applied by C. S. Peirce) is the generic name given to the totality of ideas contained in the minds of all people everywhere. The Residue contains all that remains in the Universe, after the Library and the Phaneron are extracted from it. The Generic Design Science then becomes concerned with interactions among the three blocks of the partition.

One of the early steps in the creation of a science of Generic Design must be the manner in which Universal Priors are dealt with in it. Given that they are critical to conceptualization, choice, and documentation; which are the primary activities involved in carrying out design; it is not surprising that they will be at the heart of the Science.

REFERENCES

1. J. N. Warfield, "Underconceptualization", *Proceedings of the Conference on Support, Society, and Culture: Mutual Uses of Cybernetics and Science*, Univ. of Amsterdam, March, 1989, 15-39.

2. J. N. Warfield, "Implications of Scale for Systems Design", *Proc. Society for General Systems Research International Conference*, Budapest, 1987, 1205-1211.

3. J. N. Warfield, "Principles of Interactive Management", *Proc. International Conference on Cybernetics & Society*, New York: IEEE, January, 1984, 746-750.

4. Charles Perrow, *Normal Accidents: Living with High-Risk Technologies*, New York: Basic Books, 1984.

5. J. N. Warfield, "What Disciplines Large-Scale System Design?", *Proceedings of the 1987 Conference on Planning and Design in Management of Business and Organizations* (P. C. Nutt, Editor), New York: American Society of Mechanical Engineers, 1-8.

6. J. N. Warfield, "Interpretive Structural Modeling", Chapter 5 in *Group Planning and Problem Solving Methods in Engineering*, S. A. Olsen (Ed.), New York: Wiley, 1982, 155-201.

7. Karl-Otto Apel, *Charles S. Peirce: From Pragmatism to Pragmaticism*, Amherst: Univ. of Massachusetts Press, 1981.

8. J. N. Warfield, "Developing a Design Culture in Higher Education", *General Systems,* Vol. XXX, 1987, 63- 67.

9. T. A. Goudge, *The Thought of C. S. Peirce*, New York: Dover, 1969.

10. J. N. Warfield, "Implicit Aspects of Much Systems Thinking", *Systems Research,* 5(4), 1988, 333-342.

11. Warren Bennis, "The Four Competencies of Leadership", *Training and Development Journal* 38(8), Aug. 1984, 15-19.

12. J. N. Warfield, "On the Design of Language for System Design", in *Cybernetics and Systems '88, Proc. 9th European Meeting on Cybernetics and Systems Research* (R. Trappl, Ed.), Dordrecht: Kluwer Academic, 1988, 133-140.

13. J. N. Warfield, "The Domain of Science Model: Evolution and Design", *Proc. Society for General Systems Research*, Salinas: Intersystems, 1986, H46-H59.

14. J. N. Warfield, "Micromathematics and Macromathematics", *Proc. International Conference on Systems, Man, and Cybernetics*, New York: IEEE, Vol. II, 1986, 1127-1131.

15. J. G. Kemeny, "Saving American Democracy: The Lessons of Three-Mile Island", *Technology Review*, June/July, 1980, 65-75.

16. J. N. Warfield, "Organizations and Systems Learning", *General Systems*, Vol. 27, 1982, 5-74.

17. Taft H. Broome, Jr., "The Slippery Ethics of Engineering", *The Washington Post* (Outposts Section), December 28, 1986.

18. J. B. Conant, *Two Modes of Thought*, New York: Trident, 1964.

19. Geoffrey Vickers, *Responsibility--Its Sources and Limits*, Seaside, CA: Intersystems, 1980.

20. A. N. Whitehead, *An Introduction to Mathematics*, New York: Oxford University Press, 1958 (first published, 1911).

QUESTIONS RELATED TO CHAPTER 1

1. What system of beliefs is proposed as a way to start correcting past oversights and underconceptualizations?

2. What are the areas of critical need to which a design science should be responsive?

3. What is the principal problem from the past that a design science should strive to resolve?

4. What types of needs does science fill?

5. What is meant by the "vertical organization of knowledge?"

6. What is meant by the "horizontal organization of knowledge?"

7. List four paired-opposite attributes that can be used to construct profiles of problem types.

8. What is happening worldwide to the frequency and the cost of disasters?

9. What is the greatest single concern in the development of a science of design?

10. What cultures comprise higher education, and how should this situation be changed?

11. What are the four Peircian methods of fixing belief?

12. Distinguish each of the four Peircian methods of fixing belief.

13. Should scientists be regarded as experts or learners or both?

14. What are four universal priors to all science?

15. What is meant by "universal prior"?

16. What is the "Doctrine of Necessity"?

17. What is meant by "referential transparency"?

18. What is meant by "escalation" in a situation"?

19. What are the four Bennis Leadership Factors?

20. How were the Bennis Leadership Factors discovered?

21. Discuss a well-publicized case involving a system failure, and analyze any discrepancies that attention to the Bennis Leadership Factors might have prevented.

22. What are the three categories of design science?

23. How are the three categories of design science distinguished?

24. What are the six fundamental types of intellectual activity involved in design?

25. Into what three categories can the six fundamental types of intellectual activity involved in design be subsumed?

26. What are the three stages of difficulty in synthesis?

27. What are the three components of the Cosmic Partition?

28. Explain the meaning of "the Library" in the Cosmic Partition.

29. Explain the meaning of "the Phaneron" in the Cosmic Partition.

30. How is "the Residue" in the Cosmic Partition defined?

31. Why is Generic Design Science concerned with the interaction among the three components of the Cosmic Partition?

32. What were the three dimensions of system design in Greek Mythology?

33. What three new dimensions appear to be needed in system design today and in the future?

34. Are there any currently publicized cases of system performance that seem to validate Taft Broome's suggestion concerning the performance of engineers?

35. What priority structure is suggested to guide and discipline large-scale system design?

36. Can the suggested priority structure for large-scale system design be reason ably amended for small system design?

CHAPTER 2

UNIVERSAL PRIORS TO SCIENCE:
The Basis for the Science

ON THE HUMAN BEING: "The clear message of systems thinking is that human scope is limited

and that we cannot use even what scope we have except in a situation in which we are sensitively

and intimately engaged. We have been offered both this insight and the temptation to ignore it,

and vested interests powerfully favour the second."

--Sir Geoffrey Vickers

ON LANGUAGE: "We cannot improve the language of any science without at the same time improving

the science itself; neither can we, on the other hand, improve a science without improving the language

or nomenclature which belongs to it."

--Antoine Lavoisier

ON REASONING THROUGH RELATIONSHIPS: "All or nearly all the propositions that we are accustomed

to express in ordinary discourse turn out upon analysis to be much more complex than we are at first sight

inclined to suppose them to be."

--C. I. Lewis and C. H. Langford

It has been asserted that there are (at least) four Universal Priors to any science. These are the human being, language, reasoning through relationships, and archival representation. This Chapter explores these four Priors in detail, to uncover those aspects of them that must be incorporated in a Science of Generic Design.

The inquiry will follow the pattern of developing multiple characterizations from which associations will be demonstrated and choices will be made.

The characterizations of the human being will be taken largely from research in social and behavioral science, interpreted in the light of philosophical writings. The characterization of language will largely be taken from mathematical and philosophical bases, but with the special requirements for a language of design as one of the goals of the inquiry. The characterization of reasoning through relationships will be drawn largely from analytical philosophy, that branch of philosophy which involves symbolic logic; and will be informed by the outstanding scholarship of Bochenski [1] and Charles S. Peirce [2]. The characterization of archival representation is only lightly treated, because the implications from the study of the other three Priors seem sufficient to point clearly toward the requirements for archival representation.

2.1. Multiple Characterizations of the Human Being.

The human being can be characterized in several ways that are important in Generic Design Science:

- Through imagined roles: among these are the developer, the evaluator, the user, and the beneficiary (or victim) of the use of a science.

- Through imagined attributes: among these are competencies, limitations, cognitive burden, and motivation.

- Through profiles of individual behavior: the Bales categories [3] in Figure 2.1 of individual behavior in non-disciplined groups allow the assignment of individual acts to the broad categories of (a) task-oriented behavior and (b) emotional behavior. Data based on observations of such behavior can be profiled as in Figure 2.2 and compared with the kind of behavior that is likely to be required to do good design work. Process designs will be exhibited in Chapter 7 that go far toward obviating any need to exhibit behavior that is not contributory to progress.

- Through broad categories of group behavior: the Tuckman categories [4] assign a sequential description to the behavior of groups, when operating without significant discipline drawn from overt knowledge of results of research on groups. These categories are: forming, storming, norming, and performing. They reveal how much group activity is spent on what might be called "social overhead costs" that are (at best) indirectly related to task achievement. The sequential flow of activity that is illustrated by the Tuckman categories must be augmented by a consideration of the well-documented phenomenon of "groupthink". As set forth by Janis [5], it refers to a situation that arises in groups where frequently key decisions are reached that superficially appear to have been accepted by the group. Also in such a situation, it may occur that all the members seem in firm agreement, even though most or even all of the members lack a substantive foundation for the agreement.

Janis has characterized groupthink in terms of "eight symptoms [which] are: (1) an illusion of invulnerability, shared by most or all of the members, (2) collective efforts to rationalize in order to discount warnings, (3) an unquestioned belief in the group's inherent morality, (4) stereotyped views of rivals and enemies, (5) direct pressure on any member who expresses strong arguments against any of the group's stereotypes, illusions, or commitments, (6) self-censorship of deviations, (7) a shared illusion of unanimity...augmented by the false assumption that silence means consent, and (8) the emergence of self-appointed mindguards"[5].

There may be no greater opportunity for groupthink to produce despicable outcomes than in the large-system-design situation. Combined with pressure to meet schedules or to conserve financial or human resources, the most unbelieveable deci-

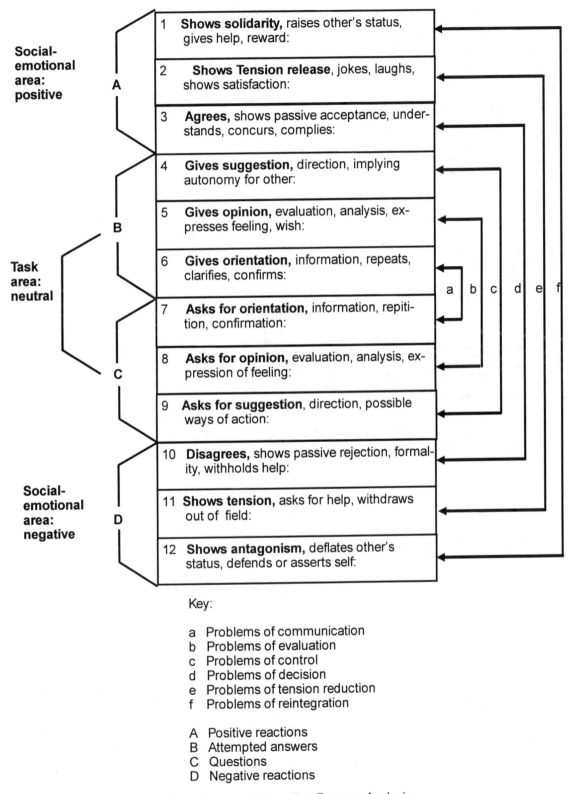

Social-emotional area: positive

A

1 **Shows solidarity,** raises other's status, gives help, reward:

2 **Shows Tension release**, jokes, laughs, shows satisfaction:

3 **Agrees,** shows passive acceptance, understands, concurs, complies:

Task area: neutral

B

4 **Gives suggestion,** direction, implying autonomy for other:

5 **Gives opinion,** evaluation, analysis, expresses feeling, wish:

6 **Gives orientation,** information, repeats, clarifies, confirms:

C

7 **Asks for orientation,** information, repitition, confirmation:

8 **Asks for opinion,** evaluation, analysis, expression of feeling:

9 **Asks for suggestion**, direction, possible ways of action:

Social-emotional area: negative

D

10 **Disagrees,** shows passive rejection, formality, withholds help:

11 **Shows tension,** asks for help, withdraws out of field:

12 **Shows antagonism,** deflates other's status, defends or asserts self:

a b c d e f

Key:

a Problems of communication
b Problems of evaluation
c Problems of control
d Problems of decision
e Problems of tension reduction
f Problems of reintegration

A Positive reactions
B Attempted answers
C Questions
D Negative reactions

Figure 2.1 Bales categories. Source: *Interaction Process Analysis.*

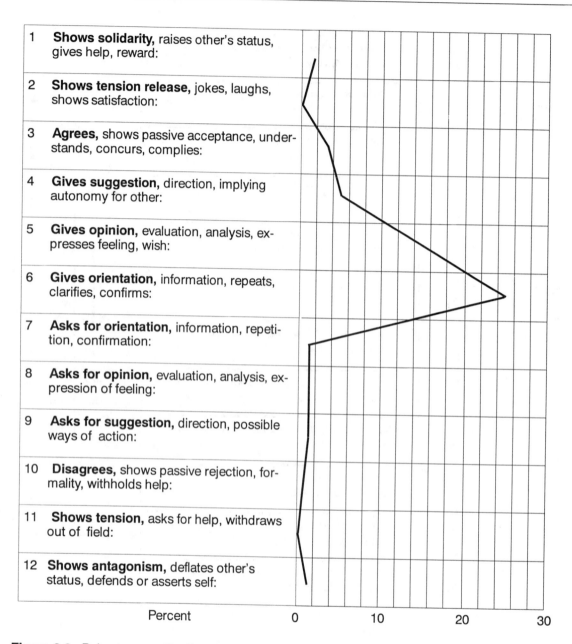

| | Percent | 0 | 10 | 20 | 30 |

1 **Shows solidarity,** raises other's status, gives help, reward:

2 **Shows tension release,** jokes, laughs, shows satisfaction:

3 **Agrees,** shows passive acceptance, understands, concurs, complies:

4 **Gives suggestion,** direction, implying autonomy for other:

5 **Gives opinion,** evaluation, analysis, expresses feeling, wish:

6 **Gives orientation,** information, repeats, clarifies, confirms:

7 **Asks for orientation,** information, repetition, confirmation:

8 **Asks for opinion,** evaluation, analysis, expression of feeling:

9 **Asks for suggestion,** direction, possible ways of action:

10 **Disagrees,** shows passive rejection, formality, withholds help:

11 **Shows tension,** asks for help, withdraws out of field:

12 **Shows antagonism,** deflates other's status, defends or asserts self:

Figure 2.2 Bales type profile. Source: *Interaction Process Analysis.*
Adapted with permission. Copyright © 1976 University of Chicago Press

sions may be made. An example is the case of the missing microchip tester. In this case, one sees the Project Trilogy decision to move ahead with the expenditure of close to a quarter of a billion dollars to design and make the world's largest semiconductor chip, overlooking (incredibly) the seemingly evident requirement to have a tester much larger than any in existence in order to determine whether the chip would perform [6]. But the more cases are examined, the more it becomes apparent that **the unbelievable is normal, the bizarre is the social norm, and what would reasonably be expected in a society that adhered to reasonable behavior is abnormal whenever large systems are involved.**

- Through <u>constraints</u> that limit human achievement: these include species constraints, situational constraints, methodological constraints, and personal constraints [7]. By focusing specifically on means to weaken or eliminate aspects of these constraints, the opportunity for human achievement can be enhanced, often substantially.

All of the foregoing characterizations can be encompassed by noting that each human being is characterized by a unique Virtual World (VW). This is the aggregate of ideas organized into whatever patterns of information and experience may be present in the individual. The VW is only partly overtly accessible (even to its possessor) and, when accessed, gives up information at a very slow rate. To this concept must be added one of its consequences, as described by C. S. Peirce: an "unshakeable cognitive burden" brought to any life experience by the individual.

Manifestly it is not practical to try to incorporate every aspect of every individual in a science of design, or in its practice. But what must be anticipated is that in the VW of every individual there may lie components of value to any Design Situation that may involve that person in some way; and likewise that every individual contains in that same VW components that may be harmful to that Design Situation. There will be differences from individual to individual in the relative extent of the valuable and the harmful, but it will not be possible to determine in advance how this mix will play itself out. For this reason, it is folly to suppose that any one individual will ever represent faithfully any significant group of people insofar as this implies an accurate surrogate for the group. Such representation is what it is: a concession to what is possible in a world of many people who cannot devote themselves always and individually to every situation in which they have an interest. Then in striving to comprehend a situation that involves group knowledge or wisdom, one expects to encounter the challenge of identifying members of a group who can represent adequately the full spectrum of knowledge and interests. Fortunately, it seems eminently feasible to detect individuals whose VWs are quite different and are, therefore, complementary.

What is clear from the Bales studies is that when people work in groups, individuals engage in behavior that is not task-oriented, but rather is emotional. Much of this behavior is a direct response to the low-quality of group dialog and the frequent misunderstanding of ideas expressed by others. It is common to see individuals arguing in ordinary group activity who believe they are on opposite sides of a question, while observers who are not caught up in the heat of the discussion find that the pair engaged in dialogue are in agreement but just aren't hearing each other. One observer developed the habit of saying "you two are in violent agreement!" to try to get the protagonists interested in hearing what each was saying to the other.

In this connection, Bales' designation of behavior as "emotional" should be taken to mean "driven by feelings stimulated by the situation", as opposed to a considered and thoughtful response to ideas relevant to the task. Also one should remember that the context in which Bales' ideas are being considered is one of trying to deal with complex problems that require contributions from a variety of sources. The integration of such contributions is not likely to take place in a setting that is punctuated by emotionally driven outbursts that work against careful integration of knowledge.

However valuable such behavior is to the individual, its contribution to reasoning through relationships is dubious, and if it contributes to poor outcomes it must be regarded as a type of behavior that might better be tolerated in another setting, where it might be less costly.

Another way to view this topic is to say that efforts to solve problems through group activity must somehow be made palatable to all participants. Even the participants, if given a spelled out alternative, will usually prefer to dispense with their own emotional behavior in deference to progress on a complex task in which they have both knowledge and a stake in the outcome.

The historical and widely-based struggle for individual freedom is eloquent testimony that people do not want other people to carry out certain kinds of actions on their behalf, such as preventing them from exercising various freedoms. But the same struggle also testifies that there are individuals whose behavior is antithetical to such views. It is not unduly strange to say that these people who choose to stifle and suppress others are "designers", because their actions often create intolerable conditions. Therefore it can be said that every human being who desires political and religious freedom has an interest in the creation of a science of design that offers the possibility of replacing what might be called evil designs with a widely-understood and supported design process that is less antagonistic to open reasoning and open choice; and which takes into account views of the many, as expressed through representation, even though it may be imperfect.

Still another aspect of the human being, as it relates to design science, is the human being as the developer of science. In the high-speed world of today, where "sciences" may spring up literally overnight, one must look strongly at the creation of evaluative systems that discipline both the development of science, and decisions to apply it under conditions of less-than-credible connections to the Universal Priors.

Weak Capability to Form Deep Logic Patterns

Perhaps the most significant characterization of all for the human being is that of weak capability, when acting without enhancement of intellectual powers, to formulate deep logic; brought about, in part, by the small Span of Immediate Recall (SIR). As Miller [8] and Simon [9] and others have demonstrated, the human being can only bring to mind from short term memory about seven items at a time. (The prominence of the number seven in a variety of measures of human performance led to its designation by Miller as the "magical number"). Table 2.1 shows some typical measures for the SIR [10].

Unlike many results from social science, the results obtained by Miller and Simon and others can be tested directly by any individual using the methods that they have described, working with the individual's own mind. In this way the individual can gain an appreciation for the matters being discussed through direct experience, as opposed merely to reading about it.

While there may be rare exceptions, most people do well to manage seven-digit telephone numbers and have trouble with sixteen-digit credit card numbers. The fact that people with "photographic memory" may depart substantially from the norm is not evidence that the norm is not accurate; only that not every single individual conforms to the norm. The two-headed calf in the carnival also represents an anomaly, but does not prove that all calves are two-headed.

But while the Miller-Simon studies showed that seven seems to be about the maximum in terms of immediate recall of ideas, they did not state explicitly what

Table 2.1
Some Measures of the Span of Immediate Recall

Stimulus Set	Variable	Limit
Single Words	Number of Syllables per Word	Five to Seven
Phrases	Number of Words per Phrase	Two to Four
Digits	Number of Digits	Eight
Digits	Age of Subject	Two to Eight, increasing with age*

* Can be increased with "persistent practice".

seems to be the most significant consequence: that people cannot reason simultaneously about the interactions of more than a small, limited number of factors. Nor did they extend this thought to express its implications for the design of systems that may have many parts, many of which interact, sometimes destructively.

High-Risk Technology, Combinatorics, and the 'Magical Number"

Perrow [11], in his study of high-risk technologies, concluded that the proper nomenclature for describing bad designs is precisely "high-risk technology, as represented in nuclear power plants, chemical plants, aircraft and air traffic control, ships, dams, nuclear weapons, space missions, and genetic engineering". He concluded that some of the disasters that arise in these areas are normal, and that they arise from "interactive complexity" and "tight coupling". Multiple failures arise that were not anticipated, and have unexpected effects. During the period of failure, what is happening may be incomprehensible. It may be discovered after the fact, through the work of a commission or other investigating body.

According to Perrow, "operator error" is high on the list of factors said to be causal, accounting for 60% to 80% of the accidents. Perrow argues that such a designation masks the underlying causes, and that the primary cause is unanticipated system behavior arising from multiple failures.

Combinatorial mathematics tells us something about how many different combinations may be formed from a given set of elements. It is possible to count the number of interactions. It is possible to count the number of combinations, and the number of ways in which a system having a given number of parts may be conceptually partitioned into subsystems. Some have said that it is combinatorial complexity that is at the root of many problems. But suppose now that the resources and time were available to explore all the combinations, and that some combinations involved hundreds of elements. Is it reasonable to suppose that the mind of a human being could simultaneously and systematically run through an analysis of these hundreds, when it can only bring seven ideas into its sphere at a time?

Because of human mental limitations, the idea of modularization of systems in ways that are compatible with the limitations of the mind will have to be a critical part of any science of design. Equally clearly it is necessary to quantify this limitation, in order both to avoid the potential human performance penalty of underestimating it and the potentially more severe catastrophic system failures that would stem from underestimating it.

It is well known in mathematics that if one is dealing with a set of items, having cardinality N (cardinality representing the total count of the items, i.e., their number), then there is automatically and inevitably another collection of items that becomes attached, this being the combinations of the individual members of the initial set. If S_1 is the original set, there is another set S_2 called the power set of S_1. And if S_1 has cardinality N, then S_2 has cardinality 2 to the power N. So, for example, if the cardinality of S_1 is 3, the cardinality of S_2 is 8. But the power set always contains the empty set, which need not be considered. Consequently if S_1 contains 3 members, the effective number of members in the power set S_2 is 7, or precisely the so-called "magical number" of Miller [8].

The implication of this is that if one is presented with or recalls three concepts, and if these concepts interact in all combinations, the individual is implicitly dealing with seven concepts, and may even need to have help to always recall these combinations along with the original three members, whenever the individual is striving to analyze interdependence among members. This is why Warfield suggested that perhaps it is the number three, rather than the number seven, that is the fundamental "magical number" [10].

It becomes critical to recognize that no matter what finite number of elements is involved, it is always possible, if one systematically structures them, to work with groups of no more than three elements, through the effort of so organizing the ideas and so arranging them that three and only three are presented for any small period of consideration.

Triadic Compatibility

The Law of Triadic Compatibility quantifies the limitations of short-term memory as they relate to human decision making:

> **The human mind is compatible with the demand to explore interactions among a set of three elements, because it can recall and operate with seven concepts, these being the three elements and their four combinations; but capacity cannot be presumed for a set that both has four members and for which those members interact.**

A Corollary to this Law is the Principle of Division by Threes. This Principle asserts that:

> **Iterative division of a concept as a means of analysis is mind compatible if each division produces at most three components, thereby creating a tree with one element at the top, at most three elements at the second level, at most nine at the third level, and so on.**

The incapacity of the mind to work with more than a limited number of concepts at a time will hereafter be designated as a component of the idea of "bounded rationality". And the idea of finding ways to rationalize human problem-solving processes and thought processes with this limitation will be one of the primary factors in the development of the Science of Generic Design. The connection between the recognition of this limitation and self-imposed humility in human behavior that involves the welfare of other human beings should not be overlooked. This behavioral feature may well determine whether the earth survives or is destroyed.

2.2. Multiple Characterizations of Language.

Language, the second Universal Prior to all science, can be characterized in several ways, for purposes of considering its role in a science of design. Among these are its characterization in terms of Basic Types, Composites formed from the Basic Types, natural language or designed language, object language or metalanguage, and types of terms that become part of the language of design. Through these varied characterizations, one strives to arrive at a set of criteria for a language of design, against which proposed languages may be evaluated.

Language and Philosophy

Language has been at the heart of philosophical studies for over two millennia. In the first two millennia of philosophical studies, natural language was taken as a given, and the philosopher was expected to do rather precise qualitative work with imprecise natural language. Leibniz recognized the need for a specially-designed language to serve as a way to upgrade the quality of scientific communication [1]. Boole, De Morgan, Frege, Peirce, and others developed and extended a language of logic, characterized by the capacity to work explicitly with relationships within a logic framework called the Theory of Relations. This made possible the design of languages that can be shared by people and machines in synergistic ways.

Lavoisier provided credibility to the idea that the wise use of language is critical to science, when he attributed his success in chemistry to his desire to improve the language of that science. Willard Gibbs said "mathematics is a language."

David Hilbert added to philosophical thought the dyad of object language and metalanguage. His thought was that while one can design an object language, e.g., for a branch of science, it is still necessary to have another language to talk about the object language. The concept of metalanguage for this purpose was accepted as an important insight for communication.

Whitehead and Russell undertook to show that formal logic could be used to provide the basis for mathematics. Lewis and Langford [12] indicated that this goal was achieved, and that its achievement would be recognized as a magnificent event in the history of thought.

Gödel showed that formal languages did not contain the necessary attributes to allow that the set of possible theorems formulatable in such languages could likewise be proved in such languages. Each formal language was thereby declared to be deficient in terms of establishing its own sufficiency. This established the idea of a sequence of languages, each being designed to overcome some but not all of the deficiencies of its predecessors in the sequence. This, in turn, led to the point of view that (impossibly) an infinite sequence of designed languages would be necessary, in some sense, to fulfill all the possible language requirements. On the other hand, the attributes of natural language differ from those of formal languages. Thus it can presently be conjectured and ultimately can be demonstrated that careful design of an object language can be augmented, with natural language serving as a metalanguage, to produce a very powerful means of achieving high-quality communication and documentation.

Basic and Composite Language Types

Written language can be described as consisting of certain types. The types have to do with distinctions among the types of notation or characters that are used to formulate the communications. The types also have to do with distinctions among the means of human reception of them. Written language is serial in nature, and is received sequentially by the eyes, and in the same way the prose that is used in speaking is received sequentially by the ear. Sequential reception, by itself, recognizes only sequential structure; i.e., one element following upon another element. The very manner of presenting the information forces whatever structure might ultimately be imposed to forego the use of vision (for written prose) and hearing (for oral prose).

By condensing concepts through the use of mathematical symbols, one is able to present more per symbol than is normally associated with prose. A given string of symbols may say much more mathematically in a given space than a prose string of the same length. Still the presentation is sequential. It is only the graphical or landscape type of presentation that inherently incorporates the capability of the eye to see the contained structural relationships that help the brain to comprehend organization.

Because of the kinds of distinctions just discussed, it seems appropriate to designate Prose, Mathematics, and Graphics as Basic Language Types. (In the following, Structural Graphics will be emphasized). But then it is also appropriate to consider the four possible combinations of these as the Composite Language Types. Table 2.2 lists the Basic and Composite Types and the functions of each Type.

By examining the attributes of the Basic and Composite Language Types, it becomes clear that language design for complex systems description and design requires the use of Composite Types. Especially it requires the Composite formed from a mix of structural graphics and prose. More specifically, what is required is a Graphically-Integrated Language System (GRAILS) [See Appendix 2 for some details of such a system.]. The attributes of the latter correlate greatly with requirements to interpret chains of formal logic. Correlating the limitations of the human being with requirements for language design sheds further insight upon the design of languages, allowing the development of a Criterion Set for Language Design

Table 2.2
Language Types and Their Functions [13]

Type Number	Type	Functions of the Type
1	Prose	To give incremental meaning to statements
2	Mathematics	To facilitate transformation, manipulation, and compactness in representation
3	Structural Graphics	To document knowledge organization, and to assess the compatibility of knowledge organization; and to provide metrics for decision-making
4	Prose & Mathematics	To give incremental meaning to statements, while providing more flexibility and economy in the use of space for documentation
5	Prose & Structural Graphics	To provide overview, meaning, perspective and integration, while making complex relationships highly visible, drawing on the Theory of Relations
6	Mathematics & Structural Graphics	To provide overview, meaning, and integration, when prose is not needed
7	Prose, Mathematics, & Structural Graphics	To provide maximum flexibility in communication, allowing for possible optimization of mix, under the assumption that the user is a master of all three basic language types

(Sec. 2.5). It can be applied to design and assess a language for use in articulating and applying a science of generic design. The criterion set, naturally, is not harmonious with current ad hoc graphical languages [14], nor with their properties of being hopelessly insensitive to human cognitive burden.

Language for Design

Especially notable in the world of design practice is the virtual absence of recognition of the central role of the human mind, of its limitations in processing information, and of the possibilities for major improvements when the design language and design practice take these matters into account. But only structural language of Type 5 in Table 2.2 can provide all the essential ingredients while not requiring user expertise in mathematics. Table 2.3 spells out requisites for language for Generic Design Science.

Table 2.4 identifies language requisites for mind-compatibility. This table anticipates attributes that will be more fully elaborated in the development of the Generic Design Science in Part II of this book. The concepts of cycle and deep/long logic will be further illuminated in the numerous examples of applications in Chapter 10.

Table 2.3
Requisites for Language for Generic Design Science [13]

Mind-Compatibility with the Unaided Mind

Mind-Compatibility with the Enhanced Mind

Compatibility with Referential Transparency at all Points in the Design Process

Translatability Among All Language Types

Table 2.4
Requisites for Mind-Compatibility [13]

Restricted Size of Relevant Sets in the Language

Restricted Size of Cycles in the Language Syntax

Visibility of Deep/Long Logic

Special Language for Cycles that Identifies Particular Cycle Contexts

Language that is Both Computer-Compatible (to within a transformation) and Mind-Compatible, in Relation to the Bounded Rationality of the Human

With the aid of the foregoing concepts of language, it is possible now to turn to the next Universal Prior: Reasoning Through Relationships.

2.3. Reasoning Through Relationships.

Reasoning through relationships is the third Universal Prior to all science. Any discussion of reasoning through relationships will benefit by awareness of Bochenski's remarkable history [1] of the evolution of formal logic. Highlights of this history have been introduced in Sec. 2.2, and now are brought together in Table 2.5.

Table 2.5
Highlights of Research on Reasoning

Time Period	Highlights
The Early Greek Period beginning around 400 B.C.	Recognition of most of the basic ideas surrounding human reasoning, including definition of terms, inference, and the distinction between true and false
Two thousand years of study and elaboration based in natural language, and ending in the 17th century	Continuing evolution and development that left fundamental questions still being debated with much rediscovery of prior results and a general feeling of milling about, looking for a creative direction
Late 17th century	The recognition by Leibniz that an object language was required to advance science and to provide for adequate communication among scientists, with the first documented use of graphics to assist in logical analysis [1]
Early 19th century	The development of two languages of reasoning and simultaneous publication in 1847, one by Boole, one by De Morgan
Late 19th century	The remarkable work of C. S. Peirce in clarifying the meaning of fixing belief, identifying the different modes of inference, introducing logical quantifiers, and extending De Morgan's Theory of Relations while emphasizing the criticality of language in reasoning, with emphasis on semiotics
	The recognition by David Hilbert of the distinction between object language and metalanguage
Early 20th century	Whitehead and Russell's work relating logic to mathematics, leading to a temporary belief in closed language systems; followed by the Gödel work showing that axiomatically-based languages lead to propositions that cannot be validated in those languages, requiring the unending invention of new object languages in pursuit of completeness

The highlights shown in Table 2.5 are part of the larger history of the development of Western logic, illustrated in Table 2.6 and broken out into four major periods and subperiods, following the classifications by Bochenski.

Table 2.6 *Development of Western Logic*

Subperiods	Years	Contributions	Areas Of Focus Building On The Past	Areas Of New Focus	Notes
Ancient Greek (500 B.C. to 500 A.D.)					
Preparatory Period	500 B.C. to 350 B.C.	Socrates, Plato, Euclid of Megara	None	Modal logic, implication, syllogism, semantic paradoxes, intension	Plato introduced what today is called "top-down analysis". Aristotle introduced inference.
Creative Period	350 B.C. to 200 B.C.	Aristotle, Theophrastus, Philo, Chrysippus			
Commentators Period					
Scholastic (500 A.D. to 1500 A.D.)					
Transition Period	500 A.D. to 1080 A.D.	None	Modal logic, implication, syllogism, semantic paradoxes, intension	Metalogic, formalism, semiotics, semantics, syntax, term logic, antinomies	
Creative Period	1080 A.D. to 1300 A.D.	Abelard, Albert the Great			
Elaboration Period	1300 A.D. to 1500 A.D.	Buridan, Paul of Venice, William of Ockham			
Classical (1500 A.D. to 1716 A.D.)					
Transition Period	1500 A.D. to 1670 A.D.	None	Modal logic, implication, syllogism, semantic paradoxes, semantics, intension	Comprehension, extension, graphical analysis	
Creative Period	1670 A.D. to 1716 A.D.	Leibniz			Leibniz enunciated the reasons for developing a graphical language.
Mathematical Logic (1716 A.D. to present)					
Prehistory Period	1716 A.D. to 1847 A.D.	Euler, Bentham	Modal logic, implication, syllogism, semantic paradoxes, semantics, graphical analysis, intension, extension	Propositional logic, Logic of terms, Logic of classes, Logic of relations, Theory of types, Methods of proof, Metalogic, Formal representations	
Formalism Period	1847 A.D. to 1879 A.D.	Boole, De Morgan, Hamilton			De Morgan introduced and Peirce elaborated the theory of relations, and Peirce reiterated the need for a graphical language.
Proof Period	1879 A.D. to 1913 A.D.	Frege, Peirce, Whitehead, Russell, Hilbert, Venn, Schröder, Peano			
Metalogic Period	1913 A.D to 1930 A.D.	Lukasiewicz, Tarski, Carnap, Gödel			
Recent Period	1930 A.D. to present				Harary brought together the theory of relations, the theory of binary matrices, and the theory of directed graphs, and showed their relation to problem structuring.

The four major periods shown in the Table are the Ancient Greek, the Scholastic, the Classical, and the period of Mathematical Logic in which we now find ourselves. This latter period is also sometimes called the period of Analytic Philosophy. To extend this sequence of development in the directions needed for design science is the task before us.

The central topics to be dealt with are: the types of inference, as outlined by C. S. Peirce, and their respective roles in reasoning; the types of logic patterns; the propagation of relationship which is central in the development of deep and long logic; and some structural metrics and their significance in interpretation.

The discussion of these matters will lay the basis for Sec. 2.4 in which types of representation will be discussed; and following that, it will be possible to bring together the criteria that should be satisfied by a language of design science, to expand on Table 2.3.

Types of Inference

C. S. Peirce identified four types of inference [2]. These are identified in Figure 2.3, which also indicates the precedence relationship among these four types.

The leftmost type, perceptual judgment, is a form of instant inference describing the mental transformation that takes place whenever sensory perception is at work. Light or sound signals reaching sensory organs are converted into mental images and these, in turn, are converted into interpretations which constitute perceptual judgment. This most basic form of inference is least susceptible to analysis, given the present state of knowledge of internal operations with information by human beings. However it is the most fundamental because the cumulative consequences of its application comprise the information foundation for all other forms of inference.

The accumulation of innumerable perceptual judgments, comprising the bulk of the Virtual World of the individual, plays a principal role in the second form of inference, abduction. Abduction is a mental process whereby theories, conjectures, scientific hypotheses, and explanations are produced involving situations where the outcome has not yet been established as a belief by either induction or deduction. It is distinguished by being much less formal in its operations than induction or deduction. Each of the latter can be characterized in terms of priors in the form of hypotheses and experimental data (for induction) and axioms or postulates (for deduction); but abduction operates from more primitive, not necessarily articulated, priors. Of the four types, only abduction "supplies new ideas [and is] the only kind which is, in this sense, synthetic...All the ideas of science come to it by way of Abduction", according to Peirce [2].

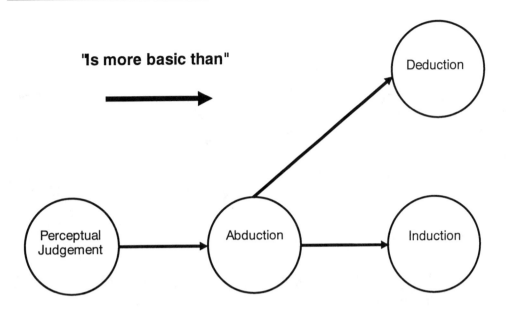

Figure 2.3 Types of inference. Copyright © 1986 IEEE.

Induction corresponds to the inference of a conclusion(s) as a consequence of making observations or conducting experiments that provide data concerning an articulated scientific hypothesis; whereby the hypothesis is validated, invalidated, or (at minimum) displaced on the scale of belief (Fig. 2.4) [15] from its original place.

Deduction, also called "necessary inference" is that kind of inference where a set of assumptions taken as given (but not necessarily true) becomes the starting point for a process of formal reasoning, founded in mathematical logic (analytical philosophy), to produce a conclusion.

Further classification of types of inference, as presented by Peirce, appears in Figure 2.5. This structure of inference enlarges the scope slightly and shows how subtypes are contained within larger categories.

The role of inference in modifying human belief can be elaborated with reference to the scale of belief (Fig. 2.4). Inference is the vehicle for moving human belief along this scale. At the left end of this scale there appears the state of disbelief, taken as the most extreme position against an idea or issue. To the right of this appears doubt, a tendency toward disbelief and, according to Peirce, a source of stimulus to inquiry. Next to the right on this scale is neutrality, which is a position that offers no basis for decision-making. Next to the right is an inclination toward belief which is, in effect, the positive side of doubt concerning an idea or issue. And finally

53

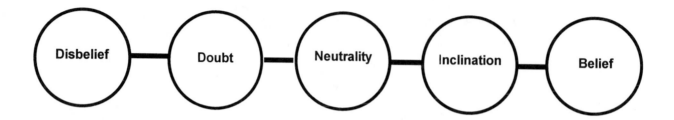

Figure 2.4 A scale of belief. Copyright © 1986 IEEE.

at the extreme right lies <u>belief</u> which, according to Peirce, is the predecessor of habit. Inference works through the structure of belief to bring about the internalization of cues to habitual behavior.

Logic Patterns

While there has historically been difficulty in providing extremely sharp distinctions among the types of inference, and even more difficulty in relating them to human information processes, no such infirmity must be sustained in relation to logic patterns. The formal definition of structure makes possible a kind of logical precision that is not too different from that gained with numbers. For that reason, as the concept of structure is critical in design science, one must keep in mind always the fallacy of attribution that will be described in Sec. 2.6 in relation to numbers, whereby the precision of numbers is erroneously transferred to anything that is quantified. Similarly, one must not erroneously attribute logical precision to structured information <u>solely</u> because it appears in structured form. Nevertheless structure is essential and will be served, hopefully with sound operations.

This will be facilitated if it is understood that structure can exist <u>without content</u> just as numbers can exist without reference to any particular enumeration; and that <u>by regarding organized knowledge as the organic integration of contentless structure with structureless content</u>, a firm foundation is laid for working with complex issues. To move forward with this idea is to become thoroughly aware of the purely structural concepts. (The eight levels of the GRAILS system illustrated in Appendix 2 shows gradation in language from a beginning with the purely structural aspects.)

A full appreciation of the power of structural thinking involves recognition of the types of relationship that the natural language provides, and an assessment of the extent to which relationships and structure can be brought into correspondence. It is

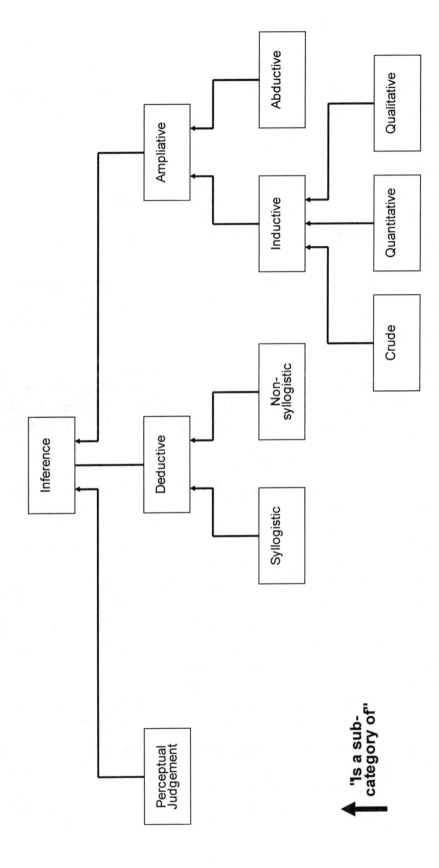

Figure 2.5 The structure of inference. Copyright © 1986 IEEE.

remarkable that the possibilities were clearly seen as early as 1847 by Augustus De Morgan, the founder of the Theory of Relations, as will be corroborated near the end of this Section.

Modes of Definition

Language relies upon modes of definition for its substance. Four common modes of definition have an impact upon the quality of language. These are Definition by Naming, Definition by Extension, Definition by Intension, and Definition by Relationship.

First of all, though not honored by any justification, but rather deriving its identity from common practice, there is the concept of **Definition by Naming**. In this, the weakest mode of definition, a Concept is given a unique name and that is all that is overtly available to give it an identity.

Second, one may consider **Definition by Extension**. In this mode, well established historically, one deals with a Class Name. The Class is defined by presenting a set of names of exemplars of the Class. This approach may often serve for initial introduction to a Concept. It does not provide the depth of insight to allow one always to answer such a critical question as to whether a concept X, not yet accepted as a member of the Class, can or should belong to the Class.

Thirdly, one may consider **Definition by Intension.** In this mode, one deals with a Concept (which can be a Class), and defines the Concept by citing that set of Attributes that is perceived to be integral to the Concept. Oddly, this approach may involve both a Division and an Integration. The Integration brings together a set of Attributes said to belong to the Concept, while at the same time necessarily invoking a Division of the Concept into the set of Attributes; introducing thereby the question of completeness. Once again, a set is encountered.

(Since the notion of set is repeatedly encountered, the idea of a set may itself be regarded as one of the implicit aspects of much systems thinking. A simple way to test this is to examine systematically a number of articles about systems, looking for those key sets of ideas which properly belong together for interpretation, but which are dispersed in the articles without being specifically identified as sets. In the same operation, one may look for justification of the choice of these implicit sets.)

A fourth type of definition is **Definition by Relationship**. This type of definition seems to be in a process of gaining recognition. Churchland [16], for example, in her review of philosophy identifies modern philosophical thought stemming from individuals such as Quine and Duhem, wherein not only is this mode given high significance, but the extent of Relationship is a matter of considerable importance.

Gradation of Belief

The forms of definition just mentioned allow us to introduce a notion which can be called Gradation of Belief. With this notion, we imagine a set of beliefs which we label B_A, B_B, B_C, etc., up to some final member which we label B_N. We specify that no two members of this set are identical.

In comprehending the Gradation of Belief, we find that notions of right and wrong for comparing the different beliefs involved are initially counterproductive. Instead the initial comparison is based on whether (a) one belief is compatible with another, and (b) one belief is more comprehensive than another. If two beliefs B_A and B_B are such that B_A is incorporated in B_B, but B_B includes one or more components not found in B_A, then we would say that the two beliefs are part of a Gradation of Belief, in which B_A is of lower grade than B_B.

[This approach is without prejudice to the concept of a search for Truth, and does not represent acceptance of more recent ideas of relativism. On the contrary, this approach reflects that part of Peircian philosophy that views scientific endeavors as producing an asymptotic approach to Truth, moving toward it in stages, rather than achieving it in one burst of genius. A concept of staged advance toward higher grades is also consistent with the idea of avoiding premature closure that tends to preempt further advance; being also consistent with the idea of acting at any time on the basis of the best available knowledge, while recognizing that such knowledge might at some future time be upgraded through further scientific advance.]

More generally, we can speak of an ordering of the beliefs (or, technically, what may be called in mathematics a partial ordering), beginning with the lowest grade belief and extending to the highest grade belief. The purpose of such an approach is to place the set of beliefs in perspective and show a kind of temporal evolution toward a more comprehensive point of view that lends itself to making things explicit that formerly may have been implicit.

Let us use the four modes of definition considered previously to illustrate the Gradation of Belief.

Let N, E, I, and R represent these four modes, N representing Definition by Naming, E representing Definition by Extension, I representing Definition by Intension, and R representing Definition by Relationship.

Now we can readily see that N is the lowest-grade mode in this set of four, because (a) the belief that a name should be assigned is compatible with the other three and (b) all of the other three modes require that a name be assigned, but also require other attributes to be present.

When we look at E and I, we note that it is not reasonable to say that either is lower grade than the other. Nor is it possible to say that they are of equal grade. We have no concept of what it means to have a set whose members are all unique, while yet two of the members have equal grade; in view of the way we have chosen to go about grading them. E is not lower grade than I because it incorporates exemplars that will not normally be found in I; and I is not lower grade than E because it incorporates explicit attributes not formally identified in E.

Definition by Relationship

Definition by Relationship, is the highest grade of the four modes discussed, and gets special recognition for that status. Both E and I are special cases of lower grade than R. For E, every exemplar given as part of E is related to the Concept C by a relationship of inclusion; i.e., if c is one of the exemplars, $c \in E$, where we have used the set membership notation $\in$ to represent the relationship. For I, every attribute given as part of I is related to the Concept C by a relationship of possession; i.e., if c is one of the attributes, IPc, where we have used the notation P to represent the relationship "contains".

But now we must observe that we have introduced into the discussion elements from the Theory of Relations [1,7,10,12,17]. The Theory of Relations is a higher grade version of the Theory of Sets. Everything in Set Theory is incorporated in the Theory of Relations. However the Theory of Relations allows the use of any kind of relationship in its formal operations, while the Theory of Sets only formalizes two types of relationships: implication and inclusion (or immediate variations of these, such as exclusion)[16].

De Morgan himself (the originator of the Theory of Relations) made the distinction just mentioned, in this language [1]: "The copula performs certain functions; it is competent to those functions...because it has certain properties which validate its use....Every transitive and convertible relation is as fit to validate the syllogism as the copula 'is', and by the same proof in every case." In his essay, "The Critic of Argument", Peirce amplified this view, noting that "the one mood of universal affirmative syllogism ...depends...upon the fact that the relation expressed by the copula is transitive".

(Given the availability of the Theory of Relations, and given the instrumentation of it in the theory of Interpretive Structural Modeling [7] to be discussed later (the latter providing a vehicle to facilitate carrying out Definition by Relationship), the meaning of such Definition can be asserted compactly. To define a concept through relationship, one identifies those factors or ideas or objects or entities that are perceived to be involved with the concept to be defined; then one identifies the types of relationship in which the concept to be defined is engaged; and finally one structures these various relationships using, if necessary, a means such as Interpretive Structural Modeling. Following this, careful review of the structures so produced, with appropriate amendments if required, culminates in a documented Definition by Relationship, giving a comprehensive context in which a concept is perceived and understood. The documentation can be called a Map of Relationship or Relationship Map, and it may consist of several distinct parts. The product of such an approach is consistent with Kaplan's view of how elements and relationships are involved in their mutual definitions [18].)

2.4 Types of Relationship.

The term "relationship" is used to represent an <u>interpretive</u> concept from everyday language that expresses how two or more entities are related. The term "relation", on the other hand, is reserved for a particular <u>formal</u> concept from mathematics.

It is so commonplace in the application of mathematics to make associations of concepts from the world of phenomena with concepts from mathematics (i.e., with concepts from the world of noumena), that it has become common to take the act of association for granted. Neither the association nor its basis in logic is made explicit. Then once associations have been made, the subsequent assignment of specifics also is likely to be dealt with implicitly. And yet both the act of association and the act of assignment are pivotal. They set in motion possibly long strings of analysis or synthesis, whose foundations have been cursorily presumed by acts of association and assignment left unjustified by anything other than normal practice.

The normal practice of implicit association and assignment should, at best, be applied only to normal Situations; and should not covertly and insensitively be applied in abnormal Situations. Thus even in the teaching of mathematics the acts of association and assignment must be highlighted.

By using distinctive terms for the two concepts, we are able to speak of how <u>relationships</u> and <u>relations</u> can be <u>associated</u> in general representational forms, and how specific types can be <u>assigned</u> within these general forms. For example, we can associate with the general algebraic form $x = y/z$ the symbols $I = E/R$, whereupon we have a form of Ohm's Law, one of the most basic concepts from electricity. And if we then assign the values of 5 amperes to I, the current, and 10 volts to E, the voltage, we are able to infer by calculation that the value of 2 ohms should be assigned to R, the resistance.

The principal categories of interpretive relationships will now be identified and examples of each set forth. Then in the next subsection the mathematical relations will be described, and the various types will be discussed; with some indications given as to (a) how the interpretive relationships and the mathematical relations can be associated and (b) the benefits of doing so.

Interpretive Relationships

Table 2.7 shows the six major categories of relationship that are found in English. Numerous examples of each type appear in Table 2.7.

Let us begin with A and B given and illustrate, for each type of relationship, the nature of the relationship.

A <u>definitive</u> relationship is typically used to show that A is a constituent or component of B, where A and B could be either physical or purely conceptual in nature. Alternatively, a definitive relationship may be used to express the thought that B is implied by the knowledge of A. The definitive relationship tends, then, to be a relation of a part to a whole, or of an idea to one implied from it. Still another example of the usage of this type is the expression that A and B are in the same class or category, or that A is arbitrarily assigned to B, or that it is possible to reach A from B.

A <u>comparative</u> relationship is one in which A and B are assessed on the basis of some attribute or descriptor that is inherent to both A and B, or which may be assigned for the purpose of distinguishing them from each other. While arbitrariness is possible for both definitive and comparative relationships, the definitive relationships are expressions that are intended to be permanent in nature and independent of local circumstances, or at least very long-lasting; while the comparative relationships tend to be temporary in nature and can be subject to change as local conditions change.

An <u>influence</u> relationship typically describes how B is affected by A. Relationships of this type are those most commonly studied in experimental science. In physics, influence relationships are often described as causal. However influence relationships also appear frequently in the social sciences and are of great importance in economics, for example.

A <u>temporal</u> relationship typically indicates that A has occurred at an earlier time than B, or that A and B occur at least partially during the same period of time. The necessary aspect of such a relationship is the involvement of time, which means that temporal relationships are heavily involved in historical studies, as well as in studies of human performance. They are also commonly found in system planning and design studies, where conceptual sequences are created to help project future activities or events, as one might wish or expect that they would unfold in the future.

A <u>spatial</u> relationship typically indicates relative position saying e.g., that A lies to the east of B, or A lies above B.

A <u>mathematical</u> relationship is one that expresses, in mathematical symbolism, either a logical condition involving A and B, or a condition of calculation involving A and B, such as A is the square of B.

Table 2.7 Illustrating the six types of contextual relationships, examples

Types of Relationships and Examples of Each

Definitive	Comparative	Influence	Temporal	Spatial	Mathematical
- Includes	- Is greater than	- Causes	- Must precede	- Lies east of	- Is a function of
- Is included in	- Is heavier than	- Affects	- Must follow	- Lies west of	- Affects the likelihood of
- Implies	- Is preferred to	- Aggravates	- Precedes or coincides with	- Lies to the right of	- Can be computed by
- Is implied by	- Is of higher priority than	- Enhances	- Requires more time than	- Lies to the left of	- Is computable from
- Is a member of	- Is of equal or higher priority than	- Supports	- Overlaps in time with	- Lies above	- Is disjoint with
- Covers	- Is more useful than	- Confirms	- Is disjoint in time with	- Lies below	- Has a non-zero intersection with
- Is a partition of	- Is more important than	- Weakens		- Has a component that lies to the left of	- Equals
- Is necessary for	- Is more critical than	- Strengthens		- Crosses in a plane	- Is greater than
- Is sufficient for	- Requires more space than	- Is independent of			- Is less than
- Is in the same category as					
- Is assigned to					
- Is reachable from					
- Is isomorphic with					

The numerous examples given in Table 2.7 are intended to help clarify further the distinctions among the types of relationships.

A given relationship, such as "is greater than" may be found in more than one category, as Table 2.7 illustrates. This illustrates the point that, in general, the titles A and B of the elements being related and some particular relationship used to express some kind of connection between A and B quite frequently will help clarify each other: elements help us understand the meaning of relationships, and relationships help us understand the meaning of elements. Kaplan [18] has seized on this mutuality to help distinguish two types of theory: field theory and monadic theory. In the latter the elements are known and, by observing their behavior, we are able better to understand the meaning of the relationships among them; while in the former the relationships are assumed to be known and, by observing instances of such relationships, we are better able to understand the elements that are being related.

While no reliable estimate is available, one can readily imagine that there are billions of distinct elements in the universe that may be involved in relationships with other elements. Fortunately, by contrast, the number of types of relationships is small. Because of this, we are able to judge in most situations the type or types of relationship which, if investigated, will shed most light on the situations. Again, while no reliable studies are known to bear on the matter, it seems that in most systems studies and designs, the intuition is most powerful in terms of focusing upon the kinds of relationships that are important, while it is less capable of determining the full set of elements that may be relevant to an analysis or design. The number of types of relationship is comparable to the "magical number seven". The number of types of elements greatly exceeds this number.

In later parts of this book, examples will appear to show how the different types of relationships have been applied in a variety of applications. These examples will give concreteness to the foregoing comments.

Propagating Relationships

Relationships that propagate are among the most important concepts in human knowledge. To illustrate this idea, imagine the discovery that a great many elements are involved in some situation; e.g., the world economic situation. Imagine that some event takes place involving A and B. Suppose that A occurs before B and has a considerable influence on B. Now suppose that B, in turn, has a considerable influence on another element C. And suppose that C in turn has a considerable influence on another element D, and so on. Suppose instead of A merely influencing B that A influences a whole set of B's; and instead of each of the B's merely influencing one C, each influences a whole set of C's and so on. We may describe this situation as one involving the propagation of the influence relationship through a system.

A much more familiar situation will illustrate this idea. Imagine the hours on the clock. Each hour precedes one that follows it, which precedes one that follows it, and so on.

Can you imagine a situation where the relationship between 8am and 9am was fundamentally very different from the relationship between 9am and 10am? Or suppose the relationship between 8am and 9am on Wednesday was substantially different from the relationship between the same two times on Thursday. The propagation of relationship is responsible for regularities without which everyday life would be impossibly complex.

The matter of establishing means of generalizing about relations has occupied philosophers for thousands of years, as was illustrated in Table 2.6. But let us look at the thoughts of one particular philosopher, Peter Abelard (1079-1142).

Abelard also dealt with two elements A and B, but he referred to one of them as the <u>antecedent</u> and the other as the <u>consequent</u>[1]. The particular relationship with which he was concerned was the relationship "implies", one of the definitive relationships. The use of the terms antecedent and consequent illustrates the notion that <u>relationship embodies a direction</u>. It is one thing to say that A implies B, and a different thing to say that B implies A. In the statement "A implies B", A is the antecedent and B is the consequent. But in the statement "B implies A", B is the antecedent and A is the consequent. If we chose to shorten the statement that A implies B by simply writing (A,B), it would be understood that the direction of the relation is from A to B, whereupon (B,A) would by the convention indicate that B implies A.

Abelard set forth these two rules:

- Whatever follows from the consequent follows also from the antecedent

- Whatever implies the antecedent implies also the consequent

Let us try to phrase these statements symbolically. For the first statement, suppose that C follows from the consequent B. Then, according to Abelard, C also follows from the antecedent A. Or stated another way, if <u>A implies B and B implies C, then also A implies C</u>. For the second statement, suppose D implies the antecedent A. Then, according to Abelard, D also implies the consequent B. Or stated another way, <u>if D implies A and A implies B, then also D implies B</u>.

It is relatively easy to see that the two preceding emphasized statements are merely two ways of saying the same thing. The idea expressed by either of them now has the name "transitivity". It is truly notable to realize that one can assign to the symbols A, B, or C any idea whatsoever, and the statements made by Abelard still hold true. Here is an example of a generic concept of the kind that helps make possible a Science of Generic Design. On the other hand, one should note especially the use of the single relationship "implies". A question that is of considerable importance in the Theory of Relations and its applications to human reasoning is whether the substitution of a different relationship as a replacement for "implies" gives a valid statement; or whether the validity depends on a property unique to the relationship "implies".

One of the most critical events in the history of human thought was the recognition that transitivity can be a property of a relationship. While in the above expression the relationship is "implies", the same property also adheres to the relationship "precedes": a temporal relationship. Thus if 1pm precedes 2pm, and 2pm precedes 3pm, we infer that 1pm precedes 3pm. Furthermore the same property adheres to the relationship "is heavier than", a comparative relationship. Thus if Harry is heavier than Sam, and Sam is heavier than Marie, we infer that Harry is heavier than Marie. The reader will be able to see as well that the property of transitivity applies to the spatial relationship "is west of", as long as the distances involved are not so large as to render the usual interpretation of "west" meaningless in a round world.

The property of transitivity is one that illustrates the propagation of relationship mentioned earlier.

On the other hand, not every relationship is transitive. Consider, for example, the relationship "loves". It is possible, for example, that Harry loves Alicia, and Alicia loves Walter but, notwithstanding, Harry does not love Walter but, rather, dislikes him immensely. Emotional relationships, in general, are not necessarily transitive. Thus Millie may dislike Jezebel, and Jezebel may dislike Martha, while Millie and Martha may be the closest of friends. There is no assurance at all that relationships such as those just presented will be transitive, and one observes that they do not, therefore, propagate, in general.

Relationships that do not propagate are called "strictly local" relationships. While they may be very important locally, they compare to the propagating relationships much like a drip from a faucet compares to the Mississippi River. The propagating ones are the ones that require the most extensive analysis, may include large numbers of elements, and may be the most comprehensive in considering design issues.

(Propagation of a relationship is a logical phenomenon, not necessarily a temporal or spatial or influence type of phenomenon. It is the logical propagation that is critical. Relationships that do not propagate in a logical sense may still propagate in terms of influence or impact.)

The high-incidence of propagating relationships, that involve numerous elements being related, makes demands on the language that go well beyond those involving strictly local relationships. For this reason, we turn to the mathematical relations in a quest for ways to enable us to formalize complex relationships that will allow us to consider the use of the powerful computer to help us interpret them.

2.5 <u>Mathematical Relations</u>.

In considering the relationship between human intuition and reason, Jonas Salk [19] observed:

> "If a respectful intellect becomes conscious of intuition and reflects upon what it observes, a self-correcting, self-modifying, and self-improving process is established."

In the same reference, he noted that:

> "The remedy for the human predicament, for the malfunctions in the human condition, lies in the reconciliation of the intuitive and the reasoning powers of human beings."

It was observed in Sec. 2.2 that David Hilbert had introduced the dyad of object language and metalanguage, and it was indicated that the combination of a specially-designed object language together with the use of natural language as a metalanguage could prove to be a very powerful combination.

In the present context, the word "relationship" is part of the natural language. The word "relation", on the other hand, is part of an object language, a designed language, a part of mathematics.

Intuition operates through natural language to expose its products. Reasoning, in its most open display, operates through the object language of the Theory of Relations; and without such an object language suffers all the difficulties that philosophy experienced in its study of logic in the period before the appearance of formal logic in 1847 [Table 2.6].

Salk commented further that:

> "I suspect that if appropriately cultivated, the two [intuition and reasoning] would work best together if the intuition were liberated from bondage and constraints, and put in charge of a respectful intellect."

Connecting the foregoing ideas, in today's world of computers and information processing, the industry has not learned, for example, that creative work rarely is induced by requiring it to be constrained by thinking in narrow object languages, but instead benefits from the most liberal environment, and use of the natural language. Moreover it should not be constrained to use technology in unnatural ways merely to promote the sale of equipment. On the contrary, in those situations where intuition and reason must be brought together, the division of labor between human and machine should be designed in such a way that the machine operates behind the scenes to bring the power of portrayal of reason to supplement the power of human intuition. Precisely how this can be done will await the later treatment in Part II of this book. But for the present, the complementarity of natural language and object language is to be exploited through its parallels with desired complementarity between liberated intuition and disciplined expression of reason.

In order for this complementarity to be achieved in practice, it must be possible to make associations and assignments between intuitively-generated relationships expressed through natural language and formal statements of these expressed in terms of the object language. Movement in this direction will motivate the next section.

Some Types of Relation

Some types of relation, e.g., the ideas of antecedent and consequent, terms from the object language, have already been introduced in a way that shows how they may be assigned to expressions from natural language. Terms from the object language will inevitably appear in expressions involving the metalanguage (the natural language), in all contexts where the latter is being used to explain the former. What distinguishes the terms as belonging to the object language is that they are subject to certain requirements that terms from the metalanguage do not have to satisfy; e.g., terms from the object language cannot have multiple definitions.

A first consideration in opening the discussion of the mathematical relations is the notion of a set S of elements. This is a natural opening because the very idea of relationship implies the existence in a single context of at least two elements which would be the subjects of the relationships. It is true, of course, that set theory admits the idea of a set containing no members, i.e., the empty set, usually designated as Φ. And it is also true that a set can consist of a single member. But such sets as these are the limiting cases, and the normal expectation is that a set will consist of some finite number of members, and will have a cardinality (the count of the number of members) of at least 2. On the other hand, sets having an infinite number of members occur only in mathematics, where they are important in number theory.

Certain kinds of mathematical relations can be introduced with sets having only two members, while other kinds require three or more members for their introduction. Those kinds that can be introduced with sets having only two members are not restricted to such sets, but are appropriate for sets having any finite cardinality.

Suppose that a set exists whose two members are A and B. What kinds of mathematical relations can be discussed with this set? Let us first write the set in the common form $S = \{A,B\}$ where the brackets identify the set. Immediately, we can write a second set that is called the Power Set of the set S. This set will be designated as $P(S)$. It can be expressed as follows: $P(S) = \{A, B, (A,B), \Phi\}$. Note that the members of the power set include: (a) the members of S, (b) all possible combinations of the members of S, and (c) the empty set Φ.

A third set that is formed from S is called the <u>Cartesian Product</u> of S with itself. This set C can be written as

$$C = S \times S = \{(A,A),(A,B),(B,A),(B,B)\}.$$

The cross in the above product identifies the product as the Cartesian Product, and the bracketed terms represent the definition of the Cartesian Product of two sets. It contains <u>all ordered pairs</u> that can be formed from the set S.

Now to simplify our notation, let $(A,A) = x_1$, $(A,B) = x_2$, $(B,A) = x_3$ and $(B,B) = x_4$. Then we can write:

$$C = \{x_1,x_2,x_3,x_4\}$$

Now the set C also has a power set which we can write as

$$P(C) = \{x_1,x_2,x_3,x_4,(x_1,x_2),(x_1,x_3),(x_1,x_4),(x_2,x_3),(x_2,x_4), (x_3,x_4),$$
$$(x_1,x_2,x_3),(x_1,x_2,x_4),(x_1,x_3,x_4),(x_2,x_3,x_4), (x_1,x_2,x_3,x_4), \Phi$$

As before, it contains (a) the members of C, (b) all possible combinations of members of C, and (c) the empty set Φ.

We call this set P(C) <u>the relation set for S</u>. We can now formally define the meaning of the phrase: <u>a relation involving the set S</u>. It means exactly one member of the relation set for S. In words, if we have a set S, a relation involving the set S will be one and only one member of the relation set for S. And the relation set for S is the power set of the Cartesian product of the set S. The requirement that exactly one member of the relation set shall constitute the relation means that, in a given circumstance, one and only one member is valid. When it is said that a member is valid, it means that it incorporates all of the instances of relation involving the set S. If, for example, the member that is valid is (x_1,x_4), this means that A is related to A and B is related to B. It is unacceptable to say that the condition that A is related to A is "the relation involving the set S". It would be proper, however, to say that the condition that A is related to A is a "subrelation involving the set S", and likewise the condition that B is related to B is a "subrelation involving the set S". The strictness of this terminology has to do with the importance of a comprehensive expression of a relation, and the desirability of identifying less comprehensive expressions as what they are through the use of the prefix "sub".

This definition of relation and its accompanying definition of subrelation is very general, and it allows us to develop a number of specifics applicable to special types of relation. We will now identify certain special categories for the members of the set P(C).

Empty Relation (Null Relation). The term Φ corresponding to the empty set is called the empty relation. If the empty relation is valid, it means that no member of the set S is related to any member, including itself.

Universal Relation. If the term (x_1, x_2, x_3, x_4) is valid, it means that A is related to A, A is related to B, B is related to A, and B is related to B. In other words, all possible ordered pairs from the set S are related. It was indicated earlier in this section that relation is directional. The notation (A,A),(A,B),(B,A),(B,B) indicates the four directions that are involved, and shows that each member of the set is involved in the universal relation, twice in the role of antecedent and twice in the role of consequent.

Reflexive Relation. The term "reflexive" as used here is a strictly defined term taken from the object language known as the Theory of Relations. If the term (x_1, x_4) is valid, the relation is described as reflexive. Writing out this term in its more detailed form it becomes {(A,A),(B,B)}. It is seen that for a relation to be reflexive, the components of the relation must consist entirely of terms where each member of the set S appears in the relation as its own antecedent and its own consequent, and does not otherwise appear in the relation. Given the reflexive relation as stated, then (A,A) is a reflexive subrelation.

Symmetric Relation. Several possibly valid symmetric relations can be found in the relation set for S. They are: x_1; x_4; (x_1,x_4); (x_2,x_3); (x_1,x_2,x_3); (x_2,x_3,x_4); (x_1,x_2,x_3,x_4). For this total of seven possibilities, only one can be valid at a time. If, for example, the universal relation is valid, then all the other six are subrelations of S. But if, for example, x_1 is valid, then none of the other six possibilities is a subrelation of S. It can be seen, by looking at the details of the seven possibilities, that a relation can be symmetric if and only if the presence of any term of the form (a,b) is always accompanied by the term of the form (b,a). This means that if a is related to b, necessarily b is also related to a when the relation is symmetric.

Asymmetric Relation. Two possibly valid asymmetric relations are contained in the relation set for S. They are: x_2; x_3. A valid relation is asymmetric if the <u>presence</u> of any term of the form (a,b) coincides with the <u>absence</u> of the term of the form (b,a).

Hybrid Relation. A relation is described as a hybrid relation if it is <u>not</u> symmetric, but it does have at least one subrelation that <u>is</u> symmetric.

If a relation is a hybrid relation, removal of its symmetric subrelation(s) leaves an asymmetric relation as the remainder.

The mathematical relation types that have been discussed all could be treated by working only with a set having two members. Now a set {A,B,C} with three members will be considered.

Transitive Relation. The concept of a transitive relation has already been introduced. Let us now expand on the ideas presented so far in relation to transitivity.

When a human being makes a judgment or, more specifically, an inference, inevitably some form of information resource is being used. Whether it be immediate perception, the accumulated experience of a lifetime, a set of postulates, a set of experimental data, or some combination of these, a rule of inference is at work. The rule of inference represented by transitivity stands out as the major means of reasoning. The general statement of this rule is as follows: <u>If A is related to B and B is related to C, then A is related to C; provided that the relationship that is involved is transitive.</u> While this defines a process for making the inference, it leaves open the basis for making the judgment that the relationship is transitive.

The issue just raised has been the subject of considerable philosophical speculation. However it is often mistakenly replaced by a different issue. The literature of decision-making has often <u>referred to the behavior of people as intransitive</u> in certain respects. This idea transfers the notion of transitivity from a relationship among elements to a behavioral property of a human being. Because of the widespread incidence of this line of thought, it seems essential to clarify here precisely its nature, for otherwise the confusion will persist.

There are two alternative explanations involved. The first explanation is that what is really meant by the statement that a human being or human behavior is intransitive is that the individual makes judgments that do not correspond to a transitive relationship. A commonly-cited example of this has to do with personal preference. A person may say that I prefer a dress having a yellow color (A) to a dress having blue color (B). I prefer a dress having a blue color (B) to a dress having a crimson color (C). And I prefer a dress having a crimson color (C) to a dress having yellow color (A).

Stated in shorter form, A is preferred to B, B is preferred to C, and C is preferred to A. If the behavior were transitive, it is argued, necessarily A would be preferred to C. Proponents of the concept of behavioral intransitivity then argue that the human being is not transitive, showing that transitivity is not an appropriate rule for human decision-making, unless one wants to override the views of the people involved in the intransitive behavior.

Whatever merit this argument may have, it has the severe flaw that it represents the absence of an overview of the situation; instead it deals only with a limited aspect of the situation involving human preference. The more general way to view this situation will be discussed thoroughly herein. However we will postpone this discussion until a later section, because we want to make the argument in the most efficient way, and this requires that we extend the language being used to discuss mathematical relations.

The foregoing discussion of mathematical relations has been given in a Composite Language of Type 4, Table 2.2 (page 2.14), prose and mathematics. We have already indicated that the Composite Language of Type 5, Table 2.2 is much to be preferred. To see why the Type 5 language is preferred, it is helpful to experience the presentation of material first in Type 4 and then in Type 5. While these two types have unique advantages, for general purposes Type 5 is much better. Before the full benefits of Type 5 can be experienced, preliminaries that lay the basis for it will be studied. Once these preliminaries have been completed in the next Section, they will be followed by the transition from the language of the present Section into the Type 5 language. The foregoing Section has provided a basis for making the transition.

2.6 Types of Representation.

There exist, as a consequence of the studies of mathematicians, formal ways to represent structured information. The most primitive and also the most useful concept for doing so is the digraph (directed graph), which is both a very simple and a very profound concept.

A digraph consists of two primitive parts, known by various names. Here they will be called <u>vertices</u> and <u>edges</u> (shown in Figure 2.6). In using digraphs to develop information structures, one engages in associating concepts with the vertices and edges, in order to use these parts of the digraph to show relationships that permit graphical assimilation and interpretation. Elements are associated with the vertices and relations are associated with the edges. Specific concepts are assigned as elements, and specific relationships are assigned to relations.

Figure 2.6 shows a simple digraph consisting of two vertices (represented as circles) and one edge (represented by the arrow joining the two vertices). Let us develop the utility of this representation in a step-by-step way, giving increasingly sophisticated figures.

Now, visualizing the digraph in Figure 2.6 as a container into which information can be placed, let the number 1 be assigned to the left-most vertex and let the number 2 be assigned to the other vertex. Knowing that 1 is less than 2, it is natural to assign the relationship "is less than" to the arrow from 1 to 2. With these three assignments made, as indicated in Figure 2.7, it is easy to see that this Figure now

Figure 2.6 Elementary digraph. Copyright © 1988 Hemisphere Publishing Corporation.

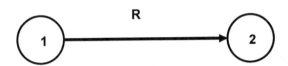

Figure 2.7 Elementary digraph with associations.
Copyright © 1988 Hemisphere Publishing Corporation.

represents the prose statement "one is less than two". But it is also possible to represent the same prose statement by the algebraic expression 1R2, where the symbol R represents the relationship "is less than".

The versatility of this form of representation is seen by noting that any other two elements could have been chosen, and any other relationship could have been chosen, so that Fig. 2.6 <u>is sufficiently general to represent any relationship whatsoever between any two elements.</u>

To take a slightly larger example, let the digraph in Figure 2.8 represent five people named A, B, C, D, and E respectively. Let the relationship represented by the edges be "is heavier than".

It is now easy to see that Fig. 2.8 represents, by its edges, the following four statements:

A is heavier than B (edge A,B)

B is heavier than C (edge B,C)

C is heavier than D (edge C,D)

D is heavier than E (edge D,E)

But we now note that the relationship "is heavier than" is a propagating relationship. Let us call any sequence of edges that follows the arrows a "walk" on the digraph. Then not only does each edge represent a statement, but also <u>each walk represents a statement.</u> Besides the edges, there are six additional walks on the digraph in Fig. 2.8, which correspond to the statements:

A is heavier than C (walk A,C)

A is heavier than D (walk A,D)

A is heavier than E (walk A,E)

B is heavier than D (walk B,D)

B is heavier than E (walk B,E)

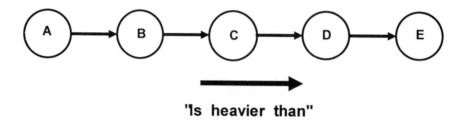

'Is heavier than"

Figure 2.8 Digraph with five vertices. Copyright © 1988 Hemisphere Publishing Corporation.

C is heavier than E (walk C,E)

Note that the number of statements represented by a structure goes up more rapidly than the number of edges. Figure 2.7 with a single edge represented just one statement, but Figure 2.8 with four edges has ten walks, and represents ten statements. But Figure 2.8 still consists only of the two basic components, edges and vertices.

A structure that has all its walks in a single directed line is called a "linear structure", and the thinking represented by such a line is called "linear thinking" to correspond with the idea that linearity is a structural concept.

More generally, digraphs incorporate two fundamental structural component types: hierarchies and cycles. A linear structure is a special case of a hierarchy.

Hierarchies correspond to asymmetric relations. Cycles correspond to symmetric relations. Hybrid structures contain both cycles and hierarchies as substructures, and correspond to hybrid relations.

Cycles are very significant structures. They will be discussed and illustrated later. For the present, one particular kind of hierarchy called a lattice will be examined.

The Analysis Lattice (The Lattice of all Partitions of a Set S)

The lattice shown in Figure 2.9 illustrates all of the partitions of a set S consisting of 3 elements. The set that is represented here is the set of three integers {1,2,3}.

A partition Π of a set S consists of components called blocks. Every member of the set S is contained in exactly one block, so that the union of all the blocks consists of the set S. The two extreme partitions are Π_0, consisting of three blocks, one mem-

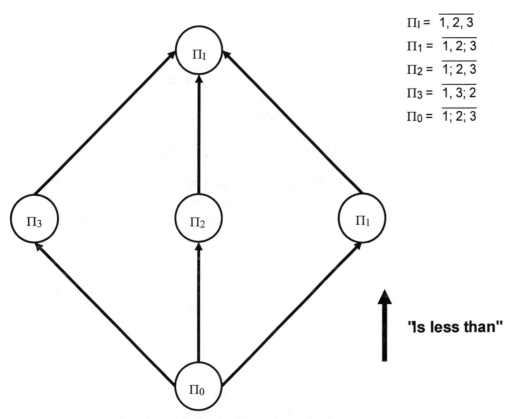

$$\Pi_I = \overline{1, 2, 3}$$
$$\Pi_1 = \overline{1, 2; 3}$$
$$\Pi_2 = \overline{1; 2, 3}$$
$$\Pi_3 = \overline{1, 3; 2}$$
$$\Pi_0 = \overline{1; 2; 3}$$

"Is less than"

Figure 2.9 Lattice of partitions of a three-element set.
Copyright © 1988 Hemisphere Publishing Corporation.

ber of S being in each of the three blocks; and Π_I, consisting of a single block that contains all three members of S. The intermediate three partitions each contain two blocks, and the element contained in a block by itself differs from one partition to the next.

Given two partitions, they may take part in a relationship such that one and only one of the following holds: (a) one is greater than the other, (b) one is less than the other, (c) the two are equal, or (d) none of the foregoing is true. A partition is less than or equal to another if each and every block of the first one is contained in some block of the second one. This definition can be tested against Figure 2.9 to see that this digraph does show the relationship "is less than" among the five partitions shown in the Figure. An arrow joining two of them means that one is less than the other; while the absence of such an arrow between two of them means that neither is less than the other.

This particular lattice is called the "analysis lattice" for the set S. The reason for this name is that the lattice is the fundamental structural equivalent of the Aristotelian idea of division of a concept into its essences, which is the heart of analysis.

Theorem 8 in Appendix 1 shows that it is possible to use combinatorial mathematics to find the number of elements in the analysis lattice corresponding to a set of known cardinality.

The Synthesis Lattice (the Lattice of All Subsets of a Set S)

Figure 2.10 shows another lattice. This time, however, the lattice portrays the structural equivalent of synthesis. Beginning with individual elements, labeled 1, 2, and 3, the elements are combined into pairs and then into a triple. The relationship portrayed by this lattice is "is contained in", with the lower members being contained in the upper level ones to which they connect. This lattice is called the "synthesis lattice".

What is the relationship between the analysis lattice and the synthesis lattice? At first, one might be inclined to think (mistakenly) that they are simply two ways of portraying the same thing. But this is clearly not true as one readily sees by compar-

$P_0 = \Phi$
$P_1 = 1$
$P_2 = 2$
$P_3 = 3$
$P_4 = \{1,2\}$
$P_5 = \{1,3\}$
$P_6 = \{2,3\}$
$P_7 = \{1,2,3\} = S$

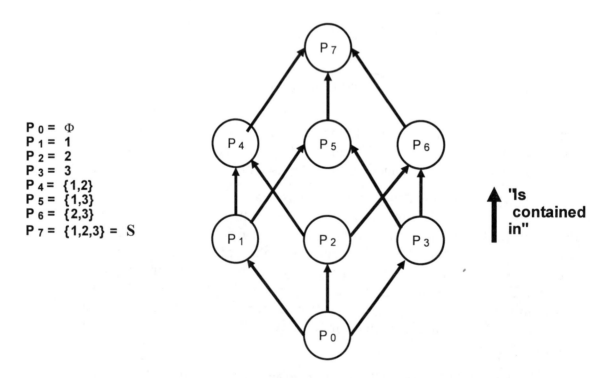

Figure 2.10 Lattice of subsets of a three-element set.

ing the two structures. They do not have the same number of elements in total, nor do they have the same number of elements in the several levels of the hierarchical lattice structure, in general.

One of the basic attributes of both lattices is that they represent an organization of information: something that is fundamental to science. Each lattice suggests a basic approach to the description of systems. One represents what happens when a system is divided into subsystems, represented by the partitions; and the other represents what happens when elements are combined into larger wholes.

Both lattices represent what are called <u>non-proionic</u> situations, in that identity is preserved among the various levels, without emerging elements. Proionic situations on the other hand involve the loss of identity and the emergence of new elements: situations that are not discussed in the mathematics of set theory.

The synthesis lattice represents structurally what was discussed previously. It shows for a given set all the members of the power set. Thus the synthesis lattice always contains a number of components equal to 2^N, where N is the number of elements in the level of the lattice lying just above the null set. This structure then shows graphically what the mind must encompass in assessing a system comprised of 3 elements; or, for larger sized sets, what the mind must encompass in dealing with such larger sets.

Levels

For convenience, the components of any lattice can be aggregated into what are called "levels". By definition, a level is itself a set, comprised of those components that lie in the same relative position in the lattice, as indicated in Figure 2.11 for the synthesis lattice of Figure 2.10. This designation into levels is of great assistance when discussing the relationships in a hierarchy, using the hierarchy itself as a visual aid to the discussion. The benefits of this will be quite evident when working, for example, with hierarchies that involve many elements and numerous levels.

Figure 2.12 shows a lattice of communication alternatives. Here the three fundamental kinds of language are shown, and their combinations as well, in the form of a synthesis lattice. This lattice is the structural basis for Table 2.2, Language Types and Their Functions.

Tautologies

According to C. S. Peirce, all reasoning is done through inference (Sec. 2.3). The form of inference known as deduction, or as "necessary inference", is particularly powerful when it is possible to construct a tautology that represents some situation. Two types of tautology will be considered: a "pure" tautology and a "contaminated" tautology.

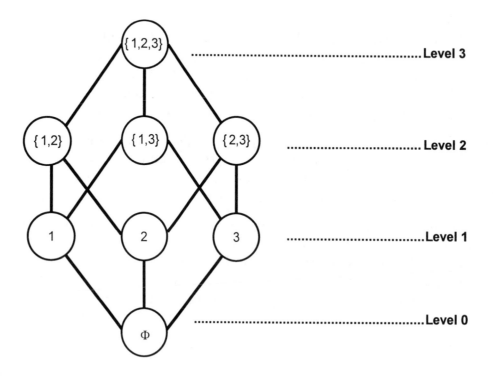

Figure 2.11 Levels in the lattice of subsets.
Copyright © 1988 Hemisphere Publishing Corporation.

A pure tautology is <u>defined</u> here as a set of mutually exclusive and exhaustive members that represent the possible alternatives in some decision situation. In light of the foregoing discussion of divisions, a pure tautology consists of those members of the bottom level of an analysis partition, where the first level consists of the name of the concept that is being partitioned. An example of such a tautology has been given in Table 1.2, "Methods of Fixing Belief". The four methods given there are mutually exclusive and, according to Peirce, are exhaustive.

If a pure tautology can be found that is suitably constructed for purposes of making a relative assessment of the members of the set, it is often possible to determine the one member of the set which is distinguished by a uniquely valuable attribute. In the four-member tautology developed by Peirce to explain how belief is fixed, the Method of Science was asserted by Peirce to be the superior method of the four, because it possessed unique attributes mentioned earlier which relate to the criterion of "truth-seeking" in a way that the other three members cannot satisfy.

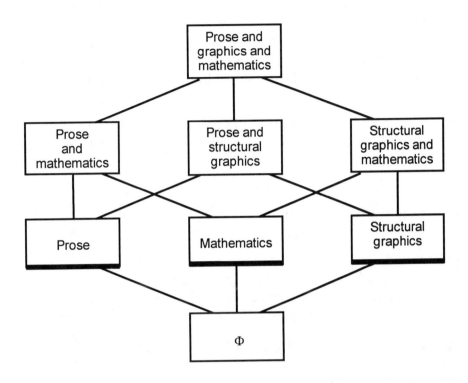

Figure 2.12 Lattice of communication alternatives.

Pure tautologies, as instruments of analysis, have several important benefits: (1) They provide a comprehensive framework for analysis that stimulates thorough appraisal of a decision, (2) They lay bare the total scope of consideration and, thereby, offer the possibility to anyone to have the opportunity to detect any prevailing fallibility in the set, and to correct any that may be discovered by increasing the cardinality of the tautology, (3) In the absence of any such proposed amendment to a tautology, and especially if the tautology has been available for scrutiny for a prolonged period of time, a certain special credibility is attached to an argument that is founded in the tautology, and (4) Anyone who chooses to attack deductions founded in a tautologically-based argument has, on the one hand, a well-articulated base from which to construct an attack, but has on the other hand the responsibility of proposing some new construction that is equally vulnerable. This is a very important point in regard to the development of consensus on critically-needed action.

A "contaminated" tautology also is asserted to be mutually exhaustive in respect to a certain situation, but differs from the pure tautology in that the members of the set are not mutually exclusive. This kind of tautology is described mathematically as a "cover" for the situation. While a partition is also a cover, a contaminated tautology is <u>not</u> a partition. Awareness of these two commonly used types of division of a concept, partition and cover, helps add clarity to a division by stimulating the classification of a proposed tautology. The classification sharpens thought by distinguishing between overlapping and non-overlapping concepts. This in turn enhances the quality of any analysis lattice or synthesis lattice that may be invoked in a Design Situation.

(Readers who wish to examine a method for formal construction of pure tautologies are advised that one is available, which involves the use of set theory [20].)

Breakout

Any decision is always based upon some set of alternatives, even if that set consists only of retaining the status quo.

A distinction can be made, in decision-making, which involves the concept of tautology in a double way. Consider the tautology that consists of the mutually exclusive and exhaustive set: tautology, and non-tautology. If decisions are based on a non- tautological set of alternatives, some alternatives are inherently omitted from consideration.

The term "breakout" can be applied to describe a division of some concept or situation into components. Just as every partition is a cover, but not every cover is a partition, so every cover is a breakout, but not every breakout is a cover. In constructing a language to describe different kinds of division, it is believed that it is more beneficial to apply an inclusion hierarchy of the type just described. Then some breakouts will not be tautologies, while some will. If a breakout is a tautology, then it can be further clarified by identifying it as either a cover or a partition; while if it is definitely not a tautology, or if it is not yet established whether it is or not, the term "breakout" may be used.

Cycles

Cycles in structures are quite different from hierarchies. Figure 2.13 shows the simplest possible cycle, namely a cycle that is called a "self-loop". Keeping in mind that the arrow represents a relationship, this kind of cycle means that an element is related to itself in some way. An example of a relationship of this type is the mathematical relationship $A = A$.

A slightly more complex cycle contains three mutually-related elements. Figure 2.14 illustrates such a cycle. An example of a mutual relationship is one involving three sisters. The sisters Mary, Ellen, and Julia are related as follows:

- Mary is a sister of Ellen
- Ellen is a sister of Mary
- Mary is a sister of Julia

Figure 2.13 A one-element cycle (a self-loop).

- Julia is a sister of Mary
- Ellen is a sister of Julia
- Julia is a sister of Ellen

A relationship of this type is symmetric, as described earlier.

As the number of elements in a cycle grows, it becomes quite evident that the form of representation shown in Figure 2.14 is not very satisfactory for analysis. As cycles grow larger, the form of representation that shows vertices and edges becomes counterproductive. Instead of this representation, an alternate form has been chosen whose readability is independent of the number of elements in the cycle. The name of this form is the "box-bullet" form. The box-bullet equivalent of Figure 2.14 is shown in Figure 2.15.

It is understood that, with the box- bullet representation,(a) every distinct element in the cycle is preceded with a bullet, for ready identification, and easy counting of the cardinality (number of members) in the cycle set; and (b) every element identified in the box is a member of the cycle, and thus is in a symmetric relationship with every other member of the cycle.

Inner and Outer Cycles

To facilitate the analysis of cycles, the representation of cycles is divided into two parts: <u>inner</u> cycles and <u>outer</u> cycles. It is not always necessary to distinguish the two. When there is no need for the distinction, the term cycle will always be under-

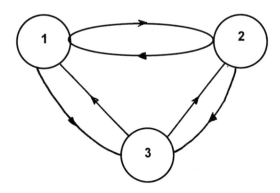

Figure 2.14 A three-element cycle.

stood to represent the outer cycle. The outer cycle is what has just been described, namely the representation that shows the membership of the cycle and represents the condition that every member is symmetrically related to every other member.

The outer cycle may be represented as in Fig. 2.14, but generally the box-bullet representation illustrated in Fig. 2.15 is preferred. The inner cycle, on the other hand, uses the vertex-edge form, and it does not contain a directed edge from every member to every other member. Instead it reflects a more detailed analysis of the situation represented by the cycle, and it represents a different relationship than does the outer cycle. It <u>may</u> contain a box-bullet sub-form, under appropriate conditions.

The distinction is readily made by considering the days of the week. Every day in the week precedes every other day in the week, in the sense that whatever day you pick, you will be able to say that any other day occurred previously. Thus Sunday precedes Tuesday, but Tuesday also precedes Sunday. Clearly we are not talking here about specific days which occur only once in history; but rather we are talking about the days as a child might learn them. In this sense the seven days are in a cycle of relationship based on the relationship "precedes" (or also based on the relationship "succeeds"). But by mak-

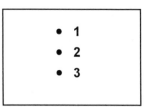

Figure 2.15 The "box-bullet" equivalent to Figure 2.14.

ing a slight change in the relationship, choosing the strictly local relationship "immediately precedes", we cannot say that Sunday immediately precedes Tuesday, because Monday intervenes. Nevertheless as we continue to develop this relationship we again encounter the cyclic nature. But this type of relationship involves many fewer edges than the cycle that shows all the symmetry. The structure of the outer cycle relationship contains 42 edges, while the structure of the inner cycle contains only 7 edges. The relative ease of interpretation of the inner cycle should be clear.

The number of instances where cycles occur in design is very high. To take just one example, one version of the well-known computer language Pascal contains four cycles in its syntax having, respectively, 19, 12, 12, and 5 elements. Theoretically, to master the syntax, one would have to master each of these cycles, where the definition of each term depends on the definition of all of the other terms in the cycle.

The outer cycle representation for the cycle with 19 members would have 342 edges. Detailed examination of the syntax in one of its specifications shows that there exists an inner cycle for this same cycle that has only 27 edges [10]. While either representation poses major cognitive issues related to learning the syntax, the advantage of dealing with only 27 edges as contrasted with 342 should be clear.

In the study of ways to redesign the desert environment of the Sahel region of Africa, Zamierowski and his colleagues [21] discovered numerous cycles, some quite large, that are operative in a desert environment. The possibility of intervening in the cyclic relationships is the basis for hope that the desert can be restored to the condition in which it existed before deep wells were dug there, ostensibly to help the nomads by furnishing water for their animals. But this deep-well intervention was really a redesign of the desert environment. Unfortunately it was a redesign done without considering the cycles that were operational there. Consequently the potential beneficiaries of the redesign, the nomads, lost all their animals to starvation. The nomads were victims of a badly underconceptualized design.

Figure 2.16 illustrates one of the small subcycles found to be relevant to that region: the Soil Stabilization Subsystem. This subsystem, shown in the form of an inner cycle in the Figure, represents an approach to increasing the stability of the soil in the region, to try to make it more suitable for sustaining life.

Although all members are in a cycle, the use of the inner cycle gives a greatly simplified picture. The relationship illustrated in the inner cycle is "contributes directly to", while the relationship represented by the outer cycle is "contributes to". Note that the relationship for the outer cycle is transitive (see page 65 to review the concept of transitivity), while the relationship for the inner cycle is not.

Note also that while the relationship "contributes directly to" is not a propagating relationship, the relation "contributes to" is a propagating relationship. In interpreting Figure 2.16, which is strictly constructed in terms of the non-propagating

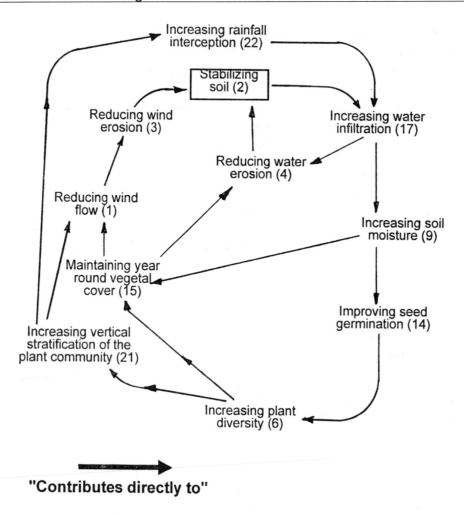

Figure 2.16 Soil stabilization subsystem. Copyright © 1976 IEEE.

relationship, it is still quite appropriate to apply the propagating relationship to the interpretation. In effect, the non-transitive relationship engenders the transitive relationship. This is why the inner cycle often is much easier to interpret than the outer cycle, without loss of rigor or significance.

The importance of the distinctions not only lies in the relative ease of "reading" and interpreting the cycle, but also resides in the empirically-determined fact that it is much easier to construct initially the outer cycle relationship because of its transitivity; and that once the outer cycle is available, it furnishes a ready entree into the possible determination of the inner cycle. Only rarely is it easier initially to develop the inner cycle. Frequently even the presence of a cycle may not be detected, unless a process is used that is sufficiently powerful to establish the presence of the outer cycle.

The study of classes is the study of cycles, wherein each member of a class is related to each other member in the class through the relationship "is in the same class as". Classification thus depends heavily on a sense of structural symmetry. In design, the symmetric relationship "is an alternative to" is frequently encountered.

Structural Types

The pure structural types are cycles, as just discussed, and hierarchies (which contain no cycles). Structures encountered in complex situations typically are comprised of hierarchical and cyclic components. Such structures are called hybrids or mixed structures.

Among the attributes that the computer possesses are the ability to compute structures, lay out structures, manipulate structures, and even control the drawing of structures. This is why it is so important to have the computer as an aid in those cognitive matters that involve complex structures.

Translatability of Structural Types

It is clear by now that to every walk on a digraph, whether it be cyclic, hierarchical, or hybrid, there will correspond a prose statement. This statement will involve the concepts assigned to the two vertexes, and the transitive relationship that applies to the structure.

Clearly it is possible to "translate" the graphical structure into its prose equivalent, even for the computer, by simply writing out the prose equivalent of each statement. Yet it must also be clear that while the set of prose statements contains all the information that is present in the structure, something has nonetheless been lost in making this transition from the structure to the prose. What has been lost is that elusive ability that the mind has to internalize and interpret the relationships that is greatly aided by seeing the well-laid-out structural form. When the material is only in prose form, the mind has a potentially major job of sorting out and mentally arranging the ideas, which may prove to be impossible in the absence of the structural model.

Supposedly one of the longest, if not the longest, structural models ever created was the model of the steps required to fabricate a Boeing 747 aircraft. Reputedly, this structure was over 2 miles long and was displayed in a long tunnel connecting two large buildings. The advantages of displaying this structure permanently where it could serve as a reference and also allow for any necessary modifications over time, as opposed to merely showing a collection of printouts of all the relationships in prose form, may be clear: there are no pages to turn, there is not a great deal to remember at a time, and the convenience of amendment is dramatically greater than if the information had been limited to a prose representation.

Multiply-Structured Sets

In applications, representations that involve multiply-structured sets, or involve structuring that leads to the augmentation of the initial set or sets with new elements, are often very useful. Some examples of multiple structuring will show some of the possibilities.

Consider first the concept of multiple-structuring by the union of two relationships involving the same set. Figure 2.17 shows the five-element set that appeared previously in Figure 2.8 where the elements represented people having different weight, and was structured by the relationship "is heavier than".

In part (a) of the Figure, the weight relationship is repeated. In part (b) of the Figure, the same set is structured using the relationship "is younger than". Notice that in both instances the relationship yields a linear structure. These two relationships may be united, using the concept of set union, to yield the structure shown in part (c) of the Figure. The compound relationship represented there is "is younger AND heavier than". This Figure illustrates that the union of the two linear structures is not a linear structure or, more generally, that preservation of structure under the operation of union of relationships is not to be anticipated. The implications of this for operations of the human mind in trying to combine mentally a set of linear relationships are unknown, but may be significant.

Experience in working with managers of complex organizations has shown that many of them have internalized the belief or the habit of taking for granted that linear sequences of action are always what is to be sought; while experience in studying their complex issues uniformly shows the need for parallel action on several fronts, often with several different, cooperating organizational components [22]. This may mean that managers succeed in working with linear sequences, and believe that all action sequences are inherently linear: a concept that would correlate well with Argyris' double-loop problem concept to be described in Chapter 4.

In the foregoing example, the sequence of structuring was irrelevant, in that either the weight or the age relationship could be done first, and the union is independent of the sequencing. However it is quite possible for structuring to be sequence-dependent, especially when it produces new elements.

Consider the following abstract situation that will be encountered frequently in design (as will be seen in Part II). Suppose there is some concept T that is to be described by a set of attributes that it contains. Then a set, say Θ, may be generated, and every member of this set will be "included in T", as the two-level inclusion structure of Figure 2.18 shows.

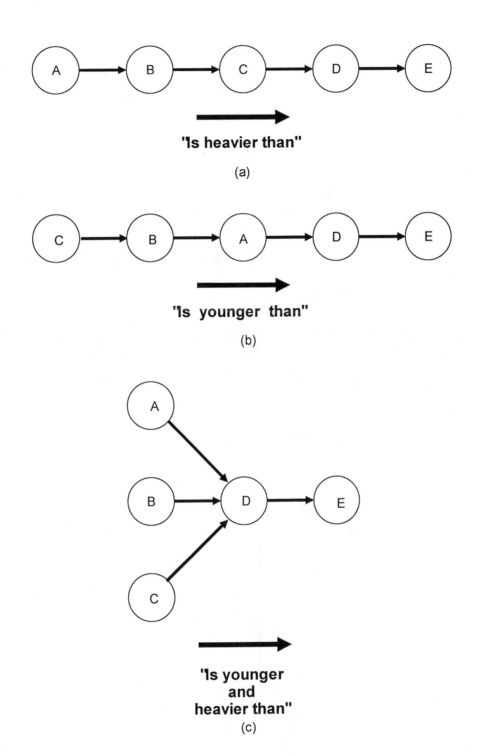

Figure 2.17 Illustrating double-structuring by union of relations.

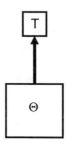

Figure 2.18 Symbolizing a two-level inclusion hierarchy. Copyright © 1986 IEEE.

Now in the event that the set Θ has high cardinality, it may be desirable to partition this set into a set D_s of subsets of Θ such that each member of Θ "is included in" a member of D_s and each member of D_s "is included in" T. Figure 2.19 illustrates the ensuing structure. However this second structuring is a little more subtle than simply would be represented by inclusion. There must be some criterion for choosing how the members of Θ break out into the subsets. The basis for this might be, for example, a relationship like "is in a similarity class with", in which some interpretation of similarity would be defined. With this arrangement, although the inclusion relation applies, it is based on this more subtle relationship.

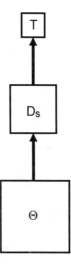

Figure 2.19 Symbolizing a three-level inclusion hierarchy. Copyright © 1986 IEEE

Level Width

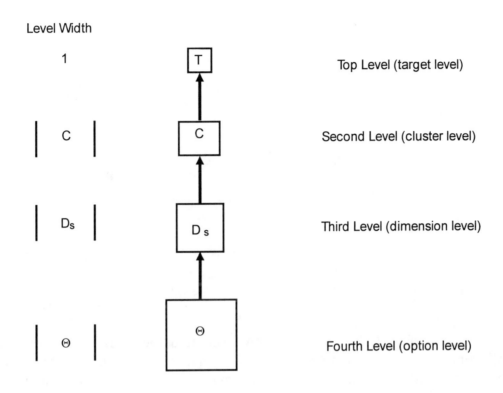

Figure 2.20 Symbolizing a four-level inclusion hierarchy (Quad). Copyright © 1986 IEEE.

Now suppose that still another relationship is invoked, perhaps "is interdepend-ent with", and this is applied to the members of the set D_s. The consequence of this may be to produce a new set, say C, whose members would be sets formed from members of D_s. A structure formed in this manner is represented in Figure 2.20. An-ticipating the later elaboration of this for purposes of design, the names "Options", "Dimensions", and "Clusters" appear in Figure 2.20 to represent the members of the sets at the various levels.

The (somewhat premature) use of these names allows us to talk about the vari-ous levels freely. One possible interpretation of these levels that is important in de-sign applications is that the top-level element T represents the target (desired outcome) of the design; that the bottom-level set represents the options available to the designers; that the set D_s represents the dimensions of the design, each consist-ing of a set of similar options; and that the set C represents those clusters of dimen-sions that are mutually dependent [23,24].

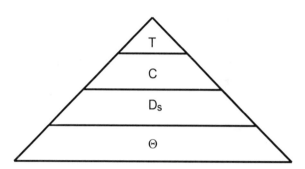

Figure 2.21 Another quad symbol. Copyright © 1986 IEEE.

Because of the way in which the sets were created, the cardinality of the levels usually diminishes and certainly never increases in moving from the bottom to the top in Figure 2.20, so the representation shown in Figure 2.21 is a reasonable alternative way to suggest the pyramidal character of the size of the sets.

The object in Figure 2.21 is called a "quad" to reflect its four-levels, arrived at by multiple structuring. But it is possible now to visualize a continuation of the pattern just described. Suppose that one member of the set Θ now takes on the role originally assigned to T. It is then possible to initiate the same sequence of activity to produce a new quad where the selected member of Θ is partitioned into a set of members and, continuing, to produce a new quad topped by that member. This new quad may then be "knitted" onto the first quad to produce an arrangement shown in Figure 2.22.

Having done this quad generation by multiple-structuring twice, it is easy enough to envisage that it might be done many times with repeated knitting, to produce a structure of quads that may be called a tapestry. Throughout this tapestry inclusion relationships appear, but they are conditioned by other relationships through which the elements generated by the structuring were created. This offers a very powerful way of producing organized knowledge in a form that is readily interpreted and used. Illustrations of quads associated with applications can be found in Chapters 6, 7, and 10, and in Appendix 6.

The Occasional Necessity for Equivocal Relationships

Occasionally it is necessary to use relationships that may be called equivocal. Such relationships typically take the form "R_1 or R_2". An example of a common relationship of this type is "less than or equal to". Equivocal relationships are to be used

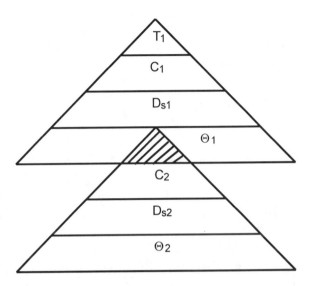

Figure 2.22 Two quads knit together to form a two-quad tapestry. Copyright © 1986 IEEE.

in those situations where (a) logic dictates that multiple relationship possibilities are present and (b) failure to use an equivocal relationship will preempt arriving at a proper outcome.

The most common example of this situation involves the preference relationship discussed earlier. If someone is asked whether A is preferred to B, this preempts the possibility that the two are of equal preference; i.e., it ignores the possibility of indifference [25]. This preemption has actually caused misleading conclusions to be drawn in interpreting structures ostensibly showing preferences among possible expenditures [26]. Perhaps one of the reasons that people make this mistake is that they do not appreciate that logical structures can and usually do include cycles as well as hierarchical components.

A good form of a relationship to be used in structuring preference is "is preferred to OR is of equal preference to". When this relationship is used, and the total set of elements is structured, the equivocation inherent in the relationship disappears at the end. Those preferences that are one-way appear in the form of hierarchical relationships, and those that are equal appear in the form of cycles. This presumes that a transitivity-enforcing process is used to arrive at the structure (such as Interpretive Structural Modeling, Appendix 3).

In structuring preference, if transitivity of preference is enforced, and if the most general relationship is used, nothing is done that invalidates the possibility of restoring intransitivity. Structuring of sets should always be reviewed when the full structure becomes available. It is easy to change a structure, once it is in view. But what is difficult and can have serious consequences is to deal with preference preemptively by assuming that there are no cycles, or by avoiding a systematic structuring altogether on the grounds that human preference is intransitive.

Transitive Closure and the Preference Relationship

Any relationship that is not transitive has a transitive closure. The determination of the transitive closure of a given relationship is straightforward [7]. If a relationship that is thought to be not transitive forms an inner cycle, the transitive closure will always be the outer cycle including all members of the inner cycle. If the relation is a preference relation, the transitive closure in effect says that there is no basis for choosing any one member over any other. This is precisely the conclusion that has to be reached when all items are equally preferred, but it is also the conclusion that has to be reached when preference is intransitive. This is another reason why it is appropriate to enforce transitivity in structuring preference. The conclusion reached from treating it as transitive is the same as the one reached from presuming it to be intransitive. Structuring preference under an assumption of transitivity greatly simplifies its structuring and subsequent correction, if necessary -- while structuring preference under the assumption of intransitivity (and, especially, using the preemptive relationship that does not allow for the possibility of equal preference) leads only to potentially troublesome outcomes [25].

Some Metrics for Structures

Metrics are numbers chosen to represent aspects of an object that help to facilitate interpretation. Structural metrics represent aspects of representations in ways that help to facilitate their interpretation for both specific and general conditions.

One of the most useful metrics is simply the length of the longest walk on a hierarchy. Recalling that a walk is just a sequence of edges along which the arrows point in the same direction, we can compute the length of a walk simply by counting the number of edges on it. By doing so, we are able to describe the nature of the logic in the structure by sorting it into the following three categories: (a) local logic, represented by a walk of length 1, i.e., by an edge, (b) intermediate logic, represented by a walk of length 2 or 3, and (c) deep logic, represented by a walk of length 4 or greater.

Local logic is easy to generate in the mind, if the needed information can be found. Intermediate logic is more difficult, but certainly can be produced in the mind. Deep logic is frequently very difficult to produce in the mind, simply because the mind cannot manage to recall and work with simultaneously the necessary volume of information, and even if it could there would be substantial difficulty in envisaging or describing the structure when relying entirely on the memory.

It has been demonstrated repeatedly, as the data in Appendix 5 show, that deep logic structures are discovered in studying complex issues or producing complex designs, when the supporting environment makes such discoveries feasible. This is why it is so important to incorporate in the study or design of complex issues or objects a process that enables the production and representation of the deep logic.

While deep logic occurs in hierarchies, it is also found in cycles, where it is even more troublesome. A cycle with 4 or more members always has a walk of length 4 or greater. Thus it always has deep logic. But the deep logic in a cycle is compounded because it does not involve just one such walk, but has many. For this reason, theories and processes have been developed for the specific purpose of facilitating the study of this deep logic, by using the computer to provide additional, related structures that are easier to examine and interpret. These processes take advantage of any inner cycles that may be produced to simplify the analysis, and also offer a way to sequence the study of the deep logic of a cycle by working with a lattice-like structure, proceeding from the simplest subrelationships to the most complex systematically, in a learning sequence [7].

Another structural metric offers the possibility of computing the "structural complexity" of a given structure. This metric has been applied to compare the relative structural complexities of several high-level computer languages [27]. It is discussed further in Appendix 1, Section 4.

Structural metrics is an area that requires research for its full development. Among other things, this area should provide metrics that are very valuable in the oversight and steering of complex design projects.

Carefully documented data from repeated studies of complex designs will reveal common aspects that allow anticipation of process attributes, permitting responsive process design.

2.7 Language, Structure, and Gradation.

Natural language, such as English, provides a ready opportunity (in its written attributes) to uncover examples of the concepts of gradation and structure, and to show their ubiquity and application.

91

Beginning with the alphabet, there is seen an arbitrarily structured linear hierarchy, having length 25 (from a to z), with the structure serving to allow "alphabetical order" in such works as dictionaries, telephone directories, and schedules of classes.

Individual written words may likewise incorporate a linear hierarchy, whose length is one less than the number of letters contained in the word. But even in words additional symbols like the apostrophe may be introduced to expand the number of elements available for word construction. This introduces the first gradation, for with the alphabet there is a set of 26 symbols, but in going to the next grade the number of symbols expands to provide the raw material for word construction.

The next two stages in gradation comprise the phrase and the sentence. The sentence includes phrases and the phrase includes words, and all of them incorporate symbols chosen from progressively larger sets of symbols. The sentence can contain a period and all of the punctuation marks that might be incorporated in a phrase. Both a sentence and a phrase can be viewed as a linear hierarchy that is comprised of sub-hierarchies which are linear. In view of this, one can see that human beings frequently construct linear hierarchies as part of ordinary written communication. They do so by using as components smaller linear hierarchies that are part of the given written language.

In learning to write sentences, the concept of "syntax" is introduced. This illustrates a choice of terminology that tends to preempt the general. In describing a paragraph, for example, one seldom or never hears the word "syntax" applied as a descriptor of a paragraph, unless the paragraph is also just a sentence. Yet when viewed solely in structural terms, there is no way to determine from examining the structure of a sentence, in comparison with the structure of a paragraph, which structure represents a paragraph and which represents a sentence. Structure is structure no matter what name is given to it. Thus if the word "syntax", as narrowly used, were eliminated from the language, the phrase "sentence structure" could replace it entirely.

In moving from sentences to paragraphs, the use of space and indentation provides additional symbols for making structural distinctions. Gradation is, thereby, represented by additions to the set of elements from which choices can be made.

In moving from paragraphs to sections to chapters to parts to volumes to multi-volume sets to collections to libraries, one sees still more and more arbitrary additions to the underlying sets, along with arbitrary collections of symbols used to make clear which stage in the gradation is being discussed. Included in this mix is the Dewey Decimal System used to bring order to libraries.

The teaching of writing focuses on structure only idiosyncratically, and with special attention to the sentence structure. Sentence diagramming is sometimes used, but never with the idea that it could be done in a way that serves the larger purposes of perceiving structure as underlying all forms of communication. Rather it is done in the specific context of designing a sentence, with the intent of serving only local purposes related to that task. The opportunities both to gain generality in what is taught and (possibly) to take advantage of the student's perception of that generality even as a way of seeing better how to apply syntax in the specific instance of the sentence, are lost. Yet here is the way the teaching of English as it relates to prose construction can find an entree into the more global concept of language types, and begin to emphasize the structural possibilities.

In writing the mystery story, large components can be restructured. The "flashback" technique permits permutation of normal time sequence, allowing the structure of the story to be non-congruent with the passage of time. Structural features like this augment the possibilities for variety in composition.

What about cycles in language? The swing went up and down, up and down, up and down, and slowly came to rest, after the child had leaped from it to the ground below. Here we see repetition of phrases in a sentence that is very much like the repetition that goes on in a computer when it is iterating within a computing cycle. The point is not so much that there might be some benefit to introducing the concept of cycles in sentences for some particular reason -- but rather that by not even mentioning them a sense of incompleteness or lack of concern with full exploration of language emerges. And once again one sees the preemptive nature of a kind of teaching or learning that misses opportunities to be holistic in approach and anticipatory in character.

Structural metrics can be applied directly to language, as illustrated by the use of length to describe a linear hierarchy and, consequently, most words, phrases, sentences, paragraphs, etc. The application of such metrics might serve many purposes. For example one might look at the mean length of sentences employed by the Immortal Bard, which would provide structural information that could be compared to similar measures for Dashiell Hammett or Ernest Hemingway. Would such studies be significant for purposes of design of literary works? In the absence of sensitivity to structure or comprehension of its metrics, we will never know.

Language in use also offers the opportunity to make distinctions among types of logic. In this manuscript, we talk about deep logic, long logic, local logic, and protracted logic. There are subtleties here that remain to be explored. If a book is perceived as a linear hierarchy structured from a set of symbols consisting of all those in e.g., the A.S.C.I.I. character set, we then have a very, very long hierarchy. Yet the length of this hierarchy, like the length of the hierarchy that portrays the construction sequence for the Boeing 747, is not necessarily vexing or troublesome.

On the other hand, the construction of a hierarchy having only seven levels may be extremely difficult when the elements being related are sub-problems, and what is being examined is the influence one has upon another.

Striving to construct an inclusion hierarchy that tells whether each member in the set is or is not included in each other member can often be quite difficult. Or it may become more so if the hierarchy is intended merely to show overlap among the members of a set.

The term "length", as applied to measure a structure, is indifferent to content, and we may speak of long logic as purely a structural concept. Deep logic, on the other hand, is intended to convey more than length. It is intended to convey the difficulty of "mining" the language to construct and interpret relationships among concepts where the composite impact of the local relationships that form the deep logic has proved difficult to uncover. Protracted logic will be long logic, but it may also be deep logic. There are great differences between the relative ease of constructing and interpreting protracted logic that do not stem merely from the length, but which involve the depth of comprehension. These are fundamental concerns in all human thought that goes beyond the superficial.

A technologist who has become adept at constructing long logic to represent, e.g., steps in a manufacturing sequence, may mistakenly assume that this skill applies as well, and just as intuitively, in arriving at the design of a manufacturing system which could benefit greatly from appropriate deep logic, to which the technologist may be insensitive.

2.8 Criteria for Object Language Design.

Criteria are needed to steer the design of an object language, as well as to design the interactions between an object language and any metalanguage associated with it, such as natural language (as used herein). Four kinds of criteria have been examined. These are: (a) priorities among the Language Types shown in Table 2.2 (page 2-17), (b) properties of symbols allowed in the language, (c) general structural concerns, and (d) connections to other sciences. The thirteen criteria that have been identified are shown in Table 2.8.

2.9 Validity in Science.

Historically, validation in science has corresponded with substantial agreement within a scientific community. Such agreement is said to be based upon replicability of discovery that is independent of investigators, time, and place. The history of science also makes clear that substantial agreement does not always mean correctness, as Galileo's life illustrates; but, as Peirce has indicated, convergence to agreement in the long run is a hallmark of science. Consensus is, therefore, a hallmark of validation.

Yet validation by virtue of replication of discovery clearly may rely on implicit aspects. Among these is agreement upon the meanings of the terms used in designing the experiments and in presenting the outcomes of scientific study. Such outcomes often go

Table 2.8
Thirteen Criteria for Object Language Design

PRIORITIES

1. The priority among Language Types should be as follows: first, Type 5, a combination of prose and structural graphics; second, Type 6, a combination of mathematics and structural graphics; and third, Type 7, the most general combination.

SYMBOLS

2. No symbol is allowed whose meaning is not defined, and each symbol that is used must be justified with respect to its impact on human capacity to absorb complex information arrays.

3. Terms admitted to the language shall have only one meaning, not multiple meanings as in natural language; hence a dictionary or glossary is required that is specific to the language.

4. Terms shall be compatible with the corpus of knowledge wherever possible, as opposed to being idiosyncratic to any particular design application.

5. Outer cycles (the graphical representation of symmetric relations) should always use the box-bullet form in which edges are suppressed, because cycles with edges become unreadable as the cardinality grows; while the box-bullet form continues to be readable as the cardinality grows.

6. Inner cycles should always use a form based on Type 5 that is isomorphic to a digraph, but any subcycles within the inner cycle that are also outer cycles should be represented using Criterion 5.

7. When sets are used, they should be identified as such and not dealt with implicitly by identifying the separate members in prose, because the use of sets with many members may not be mind-compatible, yet this may be overlooked when only prose is used.

GENERAL STRUCTURAL CONCERNS

8. The Quad Format based on Language Type 5 should be used uniformly to show inclusion relationships of a situation or system.

9. When concepts are partitioned, effort should be devoted to create successive three-block partitions, because a partition whose block-cardinality is less than three is inefficient, while one whose cardinality is greater than three tends to produce mind-incompatibility.

CONNECTION TO OTHER SCIENCES

10. Generic design language should be distinct from specific design language.

11. Structural graphics should always be translatable into collections of mathematical relations, with clear identification of the relationships that are used.

12. The language should be as close as possible to that developed at primitive levels of accepted science, and should not be corrupted by unnecessary language permutations or superfluous layers of terminology that lie between the concepts and the primitive levels.

13. Both the design and the evaluation of a language for a Science of Generic Design should apply the Domain of Science Model (see Chap. 3) as a steering mechanism.

beyond the data to interpretations which are crucially dependent upon language. The language itself is one of the implicit aspects of systems thinking and of science in general.

The matter of implicit usage has been discussed several times in this Chapter. Perhaps it is appropriate to use the language "arrogance of the implicit" to pin a label on the particular behavioral trait of failing to make explicit the most fundamental assumptions that underlie choices being made by some for others, without involving those others.

The highest grade of definition among those modes considered is Definition by Relationship. Development of this kind of definition is a highly-effective antidote to the arrogance of the implicit. Agreement upon meaning rightfully should take this highest grade as a constraint upon reaching conclusions, for until this highest grade is attained, and until it is made explicit, one can always foresee a frontier for improvement. Moreover this frontier is not off in the distance, but is immediately before us, waiting for the will and the action required to attain it.

A Law of Validation

A Law of Validation may now be asserted, as follows:

> **The validity of any science depends upon substantial agreement within the scientific community of meaning at its highest grade, i.e., meaning attained through Definition by Relationship.**

It may be observed that the Law of Validation just asserted is a necessary condition, but not in general a sufficient condition for scientific validity. But likewise it may be observed that its heretofore implicit character has colored greatly philosophical thinking such as that summarized, e.g., in Churchland [16].

Further, a First Corollary to the Law of Validation can be asserted as follows:

> **The validity of any science depends upon the capacity of the scientific community to construct definitions through Definition by Relationship for the full complex of relevant concepts involved in the science.**

Through the Law and its First Corollary we again perceive the criticality of the Theory of Relations to all of science; a perception previously established by Whitehead and Russell [12] for mathematics.

Since the Law given above is only a necessary condition, clearly additional laws of validation would be required to establish sufficiency. In this respect, in view of the heavy modern emphasis upon quantitative thinking as distinct from logical thinking, or rather as a lower grade of logical thinking, it is appropriate to turn to the special role of quantitative methods.

Quantitative Validation

Since the Law of Validation discussed previously does not even mention the quantitative, it can be anticipated that there will be some Gradation of Belief in establishing scientific validity. In this respect, certain special attributes that adhere to numbers and counting deserve attention. The numbers are ordered such that there is no question or ambiguity about the ordering relationship. And since the numbers are developed independently of animals, vegetables, or minerals, there is no compounding of interpretation involved in thinking about them. It is only when we assign a number to be associated with any particular physical entity, for example, that the interpretation of the result is compounded by the need for knowledge of how to distinguish a unit of that entity. It is only when such a unit is itself clearly distinguished that the cool clarity associated with numbers can be transferred to the entity or multiple manifestations of it.

Perceived as a set, there is total clarity about that part of the Definition by Relationship as it pertains to the relative magnitude of numbers. Agreement and validity in this instance amount to perfect consensus: a rarity in science. And taken a term at a time, any one number takes precisely the same meaning to anyone who has learned to count, when numeration applies only to counting.

Because there are few, if any, concepts in science that have the degree of validity, acceptance, and perfect consensus that the numbers enjoy; there may be a tendency in science, or at least in its applications, to endow whatever is being discussed with the same kinds of acceptance in any context where numbers appear, whether they are being used only for counting or not.

Implicit transfer of validity in this way appears to be one of the greatest abuses of science in applications.

In a spirit of unbridled enthusiasm, it is possible to attach to a quantification of any type those properties that the numbers possess; even though the determining factors in validation and agreement are totally obscured by lack of any high-grade agreement upon the meanings of the concepts to which the numbers are assigned.

No doubt it is this kind of attachment that has induced those who are frustrated by it to embrace the colloquial expression "bean counting", to describe the most flagrant use of numerical measures to make judgments about situations in which the quantification carries meaning in terms of the quantity, but not in terms of the situation to which the quantification has been attached. It is appropriate, though not necessarily more descriptive than "bean counting", to refer to this misuse of quantification as the "fallacy of attribution". An example of bean counting would be the arrest by a policeman of a person driving a fire truck for going 36 miles per hour in a 35-mile per hour zone, when the fire truck is trying to extinguish a fire next door to a dynamite factory.

Exploring the Deep Logic of High-Utility Science

Validity in science is attained through Referential Transparency, and the latter implies deep logic. However there is no reason to suppose that all kinds of science have to rely on precisely the same factors for validity in applications. It is very helpful in considering the utility of science, as well as the distinctions among the sciences to recognize that some sciences can be distinguished from others through exploration of their deep logic. The critical distinguishing factor is whether the scientists are able to build in between the Universal Priors and the Applications a system of standards that effectively buffers the user from those impacts of the Universal Priors that are negative. To elaborate on this issue, a deep-logic view of the physical sciences is considered next.

Figure 2.23 displays a deep-logic view of physical sciences. As we look into the structure of physical sciences via this Figure, we observe that the validity is dependent on the buffering gained through the use of physical standards. Reading up from the bottom level in this Figure, we note that the human being is necessary for language and literacy, and for mathematical relations as well. The latter are necessary in order for arithmetic to exist and hence for numeracy and integers. All of the foregoing are needed for representation systems which are necessary for controllability, replicability, and security of the environment for instruments, as these systems provide the documentation around which the environment for instruments is constructed and maintained. The ordering of integers contributes to the gradation of units and that, together with materials knowledge, makes possible the so-called "primary standards" for length and other physical parameters, including time standards. The primary standards which often remain fixed in location are used to calibrate secondary standards that may be much more widely dispersed. The latter, in turn, provide for calibration of tertiary units which serve industrial and university laboratories. Out of all this grows a measurement system that is standardized throughout the world and now begins to be present in outer space as well. The availability of such a system provides essential discipline to the language, and makes possible equivalent interpretations of physical concepts everywhere. Because of this, products can be made in one place and sold in another with very little ado. The measurement system buffers the applications from the Universal Priors.

No such degree of standardization is available in the social sciences, where even the currency standards are variable from country to country and where purchasing power of currency fluctuates, sometimes wildly.

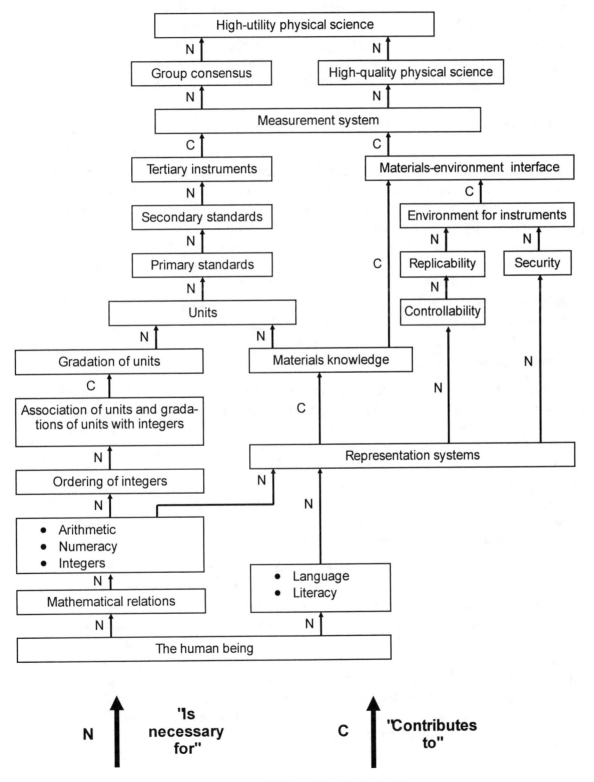

Figure 2.23 Exploring the deep logic of high-utility physical science.

Until the social sciences are able to find standards of measurement that are pervasive and universally recognized, these fields must rely on disciplined management of the Universal Priors for validity. Among the implications are that the language has to carry the burden that is automatically enforced by physical standards. In view of the vagaries of language, it seems very clear that creative representations with very careful delineation of relationships is absolutely necessary for validity.

Implicit Deep Logic and its Impostors

No doubt it frequently occurs in complex situations that people believe they should put faith in the views of others whose demeanor suggests that they may be working from a scenario founded in deep logic. Yet the only real evidence that people are working from such a scenario is that they are able to display it. If the deep logic seems to be implicit, a sensible rule is to assume that if the actors are not _displaying_ it in detail, one must suppose that they are not _using_ it either. Even if there are occasional exceptions to the rule, it does no harm to follow the rule. Deep logic may be present but implicit, but more often it may be absent, even though individual demeanor may sometimes be like an impostor trying to appear endowed with the deep logic.

Recent Empirical Results

Since this Chapter was initially written in 1988, many Interactive Management workshops have been held that have yielded significant amounts of data concerning human beliefs about complex issues. These data were not obtained by consciously setting out to collect data on human beliefs or human performance in group activity. On the contrary, the data were taken directly from products developed by highly-motivated groups who were striving to find a way to resolve complex issues, and thus reflect precisely what one would seek in trying to understand how groups of people, when working together on issues of great significance to them, represent their beliefs and understandings about the complex issue with which they grapple together.

Individuals who have tried to work with others in groups are well aware of the frustration that is very frequently encountered in trying to reach some form of agreement relating to complex issues. However until the data from the various workshops extending over approximately a ten-year period were examined in totality to see what, if anything, could be found that was characteristic of such human activity, it was not known that groups share something very dramatic in common. The name given to this shared characteristic is "Spreadthink". It reflects the fact that the views of group members working together on a complex issue are spread "all over the map". That is, individual views of any given group member are quite different from those of any other group member. That this finding has been found to be true no matter what the complex issue, and no matter who the members are, shows that validity is virtually meaningless in the products of such groups, as long as the group members do not engage in a kind of activity that has been demonstrated to act as an antidote and correction mechanism to the Spreadthink phenomenon.

What has been learned, as is discussed in more detail in Appendix 5, is that such groups can arrive at majority viewpoints on many matters, provided these groups engage in the process of Interpretive Structural Modeling, to be discussed in Chapter 7, which causes the group to pass through an extended sequence of responding to questions, each of which asks that the group discuss the presence or absence of a particular kind of relationship among two small components of the issue being examined. Through this extended sequence of activity, individuals learn from one another, and modify their viewpoints accordingly. As a result, time after time, groups are able to reach a majority or even consensus point of view propelled into being by their in-depth consideration of many micro-relationships involved in that complex issue. Perhaps there are other ways that such results can be achieved, but none has been shown to be effective to date other than the one mentioned here.

It is important to recognize that these findings extend into many arenas, including the arena of scientific validity itself. Wherever investigations are carried out that do not reflect an adequate overview or a comprehensive exploration, one can expect that disparate views will regularly emerge, and that no firm platforms for action can be anticipated. It is only when systematic, careful, comprehensive exploration is carried out that one can expect to use the shared views of highly-knowledgeable persons as valid in the sense that scientific results can be valid.

Why a Model of Science is Needed

Conflicts between science and technology; possible abuse of science; the impact of missing the Referential Transparency; invisibility of the deep logic of science in the Library, and in its applications in public policy and other matters germane to the general welfare; the possible propagation of the impact of bad decisions and incorrect relationships; no evidence that construction of deep logic by the unaided mind is a widely-enjoyed human trait; and lack of ability to communicate deep logic by ordinary means all foster low quality communications and prevent the development of focused and unified action. The society is more sensitive to the invisibility or lack of credibility of decision-making-bases than ever before, because of the frequent propagation of effects of bad decisions.

Attention to the Universal Priors, while necessary to produce an explicit, well-founded science, is not sufficient. Still more steering is required to gain and sustain control of quality in science. Therefore, in the next Chapter, we turn to the explicit definition of science through the Domain of Science Model and its extensions.

SUMMARY

In-depth consideration of the Universal Priors to all science is essential to the proper development of a science.

The human being can be characterized in several ways that are important in Generic Design Science: through imagined roles, imagined attributes, types of behavior seen in group settings, broad categories of group behavior, constraints that limit achievement, and priorities of individual behavior.

The millennia of studies related to language has produced concepts that now enable us to attack overtly the weaknesses of language, while taking advantages of these concepts. The Basic Language Types, prose, structural graphics, and mathematics, can be consciously adapted in combinations to the need for effective means of representing complex situations and design ideas.

Classification of types of relationships allows us to work, as well, with this small number of types, to select consciously those relationships or sequences of relationships that are critical to the exposition of complex issues or designs. Design of language for mind compatibility promises to lend still more value to a Science of Generic Design.

Normal problems involve local logic or occasionally intermediate logic, but complex problems involve deep logic. Since deep logic is generally absent from representations, or if present is often masked by being embedded in thicket-like prose, a consequence often is underconceptualization and underdocumentation, as well as poor communication.

Relationships that propagate are of critical concern in developing and interpreting deep logic. The propagation of the relationships is paralleled in society by the propagation of consequences of bad decisions.

A thorough awareness of the Universal Priors and the relationships among them will be essential in developing a Generic Design Science. Like the social sciences, a Science of Generic Design will not always be able to enjoy the buffering from the negative impacts of the Universal Priors that are enjoyed by the measurement systems found in the physical sciences.

To help in incorporating the Universal Priors into any science, it is useful to have a Domain of Science Model as a steering mechanism. Such a model will help overcome numerous other defects presently at work in society wherever it is related in some way to science. Use of this Model will not only make easier the integration of the Universal Priors in the Generic Design Science, but will also promote Referential Transparency in the Science itself.

REFERENCES

1. I. M. Bochenski, *A History of Formal Logic*, New York: Chelsea, 1970.

2. T. A. Goudge, *The Thought of C. S. Peirce*, New York: Dover, 1969.

3. R. F. Bales, *Interaction Process Analysis*, Addison-Wesley, Cambridge, 1950.

4. B. W. Tuckman, "Developmental Sequences in Small Groups", *Psychol. Bull.*, 63(6), 1965, 384-399.

5. I. L. Janis, *Stress, Attitudes, and Decisions*, New York: Praeger, 1982.

6. W. L. Alpert, "A $230 Million Turkey: The Sad Saga of Trilogy", *Barrons*, New York: Dow-Jones, 1984, Aug. 27.

7. J. N. Warfield, *Societal Systems: Planning, Policy, and Complexity*, New York: Wiley, 1976 (reprinted, Salinas, CA: Intersystems, 1989).

8. G. Miller, "The Magical Number Seven, Plus or Minus Two: Some Limits on Our Capacity for Processing Information", *Psychol. Rev.*, 63(2), 81-97.

9. H. A. Simon, "How Big is a Chunk?", *Science* 183, February 8, 1974, 482-488.

10. J. N. Warfield, "The Magical Number Three -- Plus or Minus Zero", *Cybernetics and Systems* 19, 1988, 339-358. (First presented at the annual conference of the International Society for General Systems Research, Budapest, 1987.)

11. Charles Perrow, *Normal Accidents: Living With High-Risk Technologies*, New York: Basic Books, 1984.

12. C. I. Lewis and C. H. Langford, *Symbolic Logic*, New York: Dover, 1959.

13. J. N. Warfield, "On the Design of Language for System Design", in *Cybernetics and Systems '88, Proc. 9th European Meeting on Cybernetics and Systems Research* (R. Trappl, Ed.), Dordrecht: Kluwer Academic, 1988, 133-140.

14. James Martin and Carma McClure, *Diagramming Techniques for Analysts and Programmers*, Englewood Cliffs: Prentice-Hall, 1985.

15. J. N. Warfield, "Micromathematics and Macromathematics", *Proc. International Conference on Systems, Man, and Cybernetics*, New York: IEEE, Vol. II, 1986, 1127-1121.

16. P. S. Churchland, *Neurophilosophy: Toward a Unified Science of the Mind-Brain*, Cambridge: MIT Press, 1986.

17. P. Suppes, *Axiomatic Set Theory*, New York: Dover, 1960.

18. A. Kaplan, *The Conduct of Inquiry*, San Francisco: Chandler, 1964.

19. Jonas Salk, *Anatomy of Reality: Merging of Intuition and Reason*, New York: Praeger, 1985.

20. J. N. Warfield, "Some Principles of Knowledge Organization", *IEEE Trans. Syst., Man, and Cybern.*, June, 1979, 317-325.

21. E. Zamierowski, D. Hornbach, and R. Fitz, "Ecological Components of Climax Agriculture: An Example of Structuring Complex Feedback Systems", *Proc. International Conference on Cybernetics and Society*, New York: IEEE, 1976, 667-673.

22. G. R. Bushe and A. B. Shani, "Parallel Learning Structure Interventions in Bureaucratic Organizations", R. W. Woodman and W. A. Passmore (Eds.), *Research in Organizational Change and Development*, Vol. 4, Greenwich, CT: JAI Press, 1990.

23. J. N. Warfield, "Dimensionality", *Proc. International Conference on Systems, Man, and Cybernetics*, New York: IEEE, Vol. II, 1986, 1118- 1121.

24. J. N. Warfield and A. N. Christakis, "Dimensionality", *Systems Research* 4(2), June, 1987, 127-137.

25. J. N. Warfield, "Priority Structures", *IEEE Trans. Syst., Man, and Cybern.*, SMC-10(10), Oct., 1980, 642-645.

26. Carl M. Moore, *Group Techniques for Idea Building*, Newbury Park: Sage, 1987.

27. John N. Warfield, "A Complexity Metric for High-Level Software Languages", *Proc. International Conference On Systems, Man, and Cybernetics*, New York: IEEE, 1987, 438-442.

QUESTIONS RELATED TO CHAPTER 2

1. What four Universal Priors are asserted to be essential in any science?

2. What are the sources of information re the human being as a Universal Prior?

3. What are the sources of information concerning language as a Universal Prior?

4. What are the sources of information concerning reasoning through relationships as a Universal Prior?

5. What five ways are used to characterize the human being?

6. What does a Bales-type profile show?

7. What are the Tuckman categories?

8. What do the Tuckman categories show?

9. What is "groupthink"?

10. What are the eight Janis symptoms of groupthink?

11. What types of constraint limit human achievement?

12. What is a "Virtual World"?

13. What is meant by "the magical number seven," studied by Miller and later by Simon?

14. If a set S_1 has 5 members, how many members are there in the set S_2, which is the power set of S_1?

15. What is the meaning of "cardinality of a set"?

16. To what does the Law of Triadic Compatibility relate?

17. For how long was natural language used exclusively as a basis for study in philosophy and logic?

18. What are the main basic types of written language?

19. What features apply to the combination of prose and structural graphics that distinguish it from all other language types shown in Table 2.2?

20. What language requisites apply to a language for generic design science?

21. What are language requisites for mind compatibility?

22. What are the four principal periods in the development of Western logic?

23. What individual is credited with initiating the Period of Mathematical Logic (also called Analytic Philosophy)?

24. How are the four types of inference distinguished?

25. What is the connection between inference and habitual behavior?

26. What are the four common types of methods of definition?

27. How is gradation illustrated by the four common types of methods of definition?

28. What is the highest-grade method of definition?

29. Who originated the Theory of Relations?

30. How and why are "relation" and "relationship" distinguished?

31. What is meant by "association?"

32. What is meant by "assignment?"

33. Give an example of an association and an assignment.

34. What six types of relationship have been identified?

35. What distinguishes a propagating relationship?

36. What aspects of ordinary life illustrate that transitivity is a critical property of a relationship?

37. What is Jonas Salk's prescription for remedying "the human predicament?"

38. What distinguishes: a) object language from natural language? b) a set from its power set? c) a set from its Cartesian Product? d) a Cartesian Product from its power set?

39. List and define six categories of relations, all of which can be found in the power set of a Cartesian Product.

40. Construct the <u>analysis</u> lattice for the set S = {1,2,3,4}.

41. Construct the <u>synthesis</u> lattice for the set S = {1,2,3,4}.

42. List metrics for the synthesis lattice for the set {1,2,3,4} (e.g., how many levels?).

43. What are the benefits of pure tautologies?

44. How does a contaminated tautology differ from a pure one?

45. Construct an inclusion hierarchy for the set {partition,cover, breakout}.

46. Represent a cycle of four elements {1,2,3,4}: a) in a vertex-edge configuration b) in a box-bullet form.

47. How many edges are there in the <u>outer</u> cycle representation of the cycle shown in Figure 2.16?

48. How many edges are there in the <u>inner</u> cycle representation of the cycle shown in Figure 2.16?

49. What are the pure structural types?

50. What structural type typically is encountered in complex situations?

51. What corresponds to every walk on a digraph?

52. What is involved in translating a graphical structure into its prose equivalent?

53. Construct an example to illustrate the answer to Quest. 52.

54. What is meant by a "multiply-structured set"?

55. Explain the four levels in Fig. 2.20.

56. What is meant by "transitive closure"?

57. Analyze Fig. 2.23 to determine structural metrics of the type mentioned on pages 90 and 91.

58. What is the difference between "syntax" and "structure"?

59. Distinguish "deep logic" from "long logic".

60. What value lies in applying criteria to object language design?

61. What is meant in science by "validation"?

62. Is "validation" congruent with "truth"?

63. Does the Law of Validation provide: a) necessary conditions for truth, b) sufficient conditions for truth, c) necessary and sufficient conditions for truth or d) none of the above?

64. What is meant by "transfer of validity"?

65. How does "transfer of validity" relate to "bean counting"?

66. How is physical science buffered from the impact of the Universal Priors?

67. What is meant by "implicit deep logic"?

68. What purposes are served by developing and using a model of science?

CHAPTER 3

A DOMAIN OF SCIENCE MODEL:
The Discipline for the Science

"To see what is general in what is particular and what is permanent in what is transitory is the aim of scientific thought."

--A. N. Whitehead

"...it is a sense of cognitive unity...which imparts meaning to the world and from which our values unfold. We cannot go backward to look for this unity; but perhaps it lies before us if only we can cleanse the gates of our perception."

--Frederick Turner

Decision-making in the construction of a science requires the discipline that can be furnished by a set of core beliefs. Some of these beliefs will themselves be a part of a science, including beliefs about the Universal Priors described in Chap. 2. Others of them will be belief about science itself. The former govern what will be admitted to a science both in terms of the subject matter of the science, and the way in which the relationships are described and justified. The latter determines the standards by which the science will be judged as science, rather than in terms only as a body of knowledge. Part of the basis for judging must include standards pertaining to the way in which the knowledge is organized.

Science has usually been perceived as apolitical, having only to do with the objective description of the universe. There are two things wrong with this perception.

First, this perception automatically sheds responsibility for how science is used, for surely simply describing something does not make the describer responsible for how the description is used or misused. Yet we know that things can be described in many ways. Some descriptions are accessible to many people, while others are restricted to those that share a specialized language. The very choice of language and the organization of descriptions both assume a political character when seen in this light.

Secondly, this perception is at odds with the common perception that science is the key to social advance in terms of producing such benefits as better food, better transportation, and better health. The choices of how science is presented, of what is studied and of what is emphasized have clear political implications. While such views seem to be formally recognized in such matters as the award of academic tenure, their lack of recognition in the community of scientists is becoming more and more critical as science assumes a larger and larger role in the systems of our societies.

The decisions that are made about using science, how its use is to be paid for, and which sciences will be given priority over which other sciences are important to everyone. It is not possible to make a credible claim that government is democratic when those who are governed are not in a position to assess for themselves the quality of the decisions that are made about science. This is not the same as saying that everyone must know everything, or even know most of science. Rather it is saying that the science must be reasonably accessible upon demand.

This means, as mentioned in earlier chapters, that a science must have Referential Transparency. And it falls upon scientists to determine how this must be made possible. Moreover, a science must be clearly distinguished from matters that are proximate to it, so that it is not confused with technology or popularized metaphysics. Otherwise the subtlety of decisions that involve science will not be penetrated by those who have a right to be involved in understanding and promoting certain choices.

It is necessary to be able to describe what a science consists of, how its information must be organized in order to fulfill reasonable standards, and in what way a science must relate to applications. Without this basic information, scientists and science will be too aloof from the rest of civilization.

A Domain of Science Model (DOSM) [1] furnishes a way to describe what should make up a science, and how its information should be organized for Referential Transparency. Such a model will provide not only useful knowledge for general awareness, but also will provide a needed discipline to the development of the science itself. Moreover it can highlight the foundations of the science, that part of it which can propagate from fundamentals throughout a science into its applications. And by following its standards, it will be possible to judge whether an area of study that takes the name "science" actually merits it.

Figure 3.1 is intended to highlight some of the communication challenges associated with a science. For this purpose, there is postulated a hierarchy of communication relevant to science. The first two levels, behavioral and logical, correspond to the Universal Priors discussed in Chapter 2. The behavioral level corresponds to the human being who is engaged in developing and presenting results of scientific investigation. The logical level corresponds to the way in which the developer of science elects to present the results of the inquiry. Underlying the presentation of results is something very close to a formal logic, and something covertly resembling a designed language.

A typical applier of the science is operating at the technical level, using very specific language and quantitative enhancement of prior reasoning coming from the science. There is a communication interface between the scientist operating at levels 1 and 2 and the applier of science operating at level 3. This interface, labeled "interface # 1" is, in one sense, the easiest of the three interfaces to bridge; but in another sense it is difficult. The image of the scientist as a "natural philosopher", inherited from the nineteenth century, is not one that merges well with the reality of today's technologist.

Level	Name of Level	Components of Level	Relevant Disciplines	Domain Part
5	General public	• Natural language • Informal reasoning	All	**A**
Interface # 3				**R**
4	Managerial and administrative	• Natural language • Informal reasoning	• Public administration • Political science • Business administration	**E** **N** **A**
Interface # 2				
3	Technical	• Specific language • Quantitative enhancement of prior reasoning	• Professional studies • Micro-mathematics • Natural sciences	
Interface # 1				**C**
2	Logical	• Designed language • Formal reasoning	• Philosophy • Behavioral sciences • Linguistics • Macro-mathematics • Some natural sciences	**O** **R** **P**
1	Behavioral	• Human being		**U** **S**

Figure 3.1 Referential transparency: Three interfaces to cross.

Interface #2 involves communications from the technical level to the managerial and administrative level. Where system design is concerned, this communication interface is very difficult. The individual educated in administration and political science, for example, is ill-equipped to converse with a highly-specialized technologist, or even with a "software hacker", for example, in regard to managing technical work that deals with large system design. There is only a modest overlap in the respective languages that are in use in levels 3 and 4, and when there is much more to be said than there is language to say it, the result is the emergence of a jargon that sometimes appears to communicate slightly at a global level of discussion, while conveying almost nothing at the working level.

Interface #3 between managerial and administrative people and the general public is almost moribund. The kinds of communication that go on between these levels convey only the barest amount of information, and are often incoherent. Each of the three interfaces presents issues of fidelity of communication that are only marginally being dealt with. This is why a language of design must be available that minimizes the difficulties of crossing these interfaces, and this is why a Science of Generic Design must concentrate on Referential Transparency.

3.1 Divisions of a Domain of Science.

The Domain of Science Model is initially divided to reflect four components or blocks. These are: Foundations, Theory, Methodology, and Applications. The first three of these make up the Science. The Model represents a relationship of steering in that the Foundations steer the Theory, the Theory steers the Methodology, the Methodology steers the Applications, and the Applications steer the Foundations (and through the Foundations the other blocks of the Science).

Foundations

The Foundations in the model have the specific function of providing the decision-making basis for the Science. Whenever issues arise in the Theory or the Methodology, it must be possible to refer them to the Foundations for resolution. If it is not possible to resolve an issue in this way, one must assume that the Foundations are, in some way, lacking and must be upgraded.

In order to fulfill its function, the Foundations must incorporate the Universal Priors (the human being, language, reasoning through relationships, and archival representations) in a way that is directly relevant to the particular science being constructed. The Foundations also must incorporate those particular concepts (the Essences) that are required to distinguish the particular science from other sciences. To the extent possible, the Foundations must integrate the Universal Priors with the Essences.

In order for the Foundations to steer the Theory, it is clear that the Foundations must be prior to the Theory, i.e., they must contain concepts and propositions that do not depend on still deeper ideas foreign to the science and they must not depend on the Theory. The dependence must be from the Foundations to the Theory. A certain parsimony must prevail in the Foundations. Matters must be included that are clearly established as necessary; but matters must be excluded that are not so established. To fulfill the function of being a fount of resolution for issues arising in the Science, the Foundations must not be equivocal and overstuffed. Postulates will always be necessary, but they must not be too great in number. To the extent possible, ideas should move out of the Foundations toward the Theory and out of the Theory toward the Methodology, where greater volumes of information can be tolerated.

Theory

Theory also has a specific role in the Science. Its role is to explain the concepts and relationships so that the integrity of the Science as a body of coherent knowledge becomes plausible. This means that Theory is largely descriptive, but not necessarily entirely descriptive. Theory may also be prescriptive in the large. It may contain Laws and Principles that are consistent with the Laws, and both the Laws and the Principles may relate to behavior in the large.

Just as the Foundations provide priors to the Theory, laying the basis for the Laws and Principles, as well as the explanations, so the Theory must provide priors to the Methodology. It is particularly critical that the Theory should provide screening criteria for the acceptability of Methodology, as well as an identification of the roles and environments that are needed to be consistent with the Laws and Principles. If this function is not responsibly met in the Theory, the door is left open for anyone to invent and espouse any methodology used in any manner by anyone for any purpose at any time and at any place. This is precisely what has been happening in large-system planning and design. If science cannot provide an intellectual discipline for human activity, it is no better than mysticism.

Methodology

Methodology also has a unique function in the Science. That function is to provide the situational guidance appropriate to Applications. This means that Methodology is almost entirely prescriptive, its descriptive components being only those necessary to communicate adequately the kinds of actions to be carried out and the circumstances in which they are to be carried out. The kinds of actions will vary substantially from one science to another. If, for example, the science is a conceptual science, the actions may pertain to acts of conceptualization; while if the science is a science of geology, the actions may pertain to how to carry out underground seismic tests, or how to construct geological maps.

113

Applications

The Applications block of the Domain of Science Model is restricted only by the content of the Science that supports the application. But this may be a very severe restriction indeed, in the sense that many existing sciences are inadequate to support by themselves a very significant class of applications. It is more often the case that a science may be contributory toward an application, but not nearly adequate to encompass the knowledge needs of the application. This is certainly the situation with regard to the design of large systems.

Because a complex application may relate to a number of sciences, and may find that its knowledge requirements are not totally encompassed by all sciences put together, it becomes exceedingly difficult to maintain lines of communication from Applications back to the Foundations of the various sciences that may be relevant to particular applications. Our society has not recognized this vital function in the area of large-scale systems, where it may be needed the most. This is an organizational problem that is only made worse by the low visibility of the blocks of the various sciences. If the various sciences were clearly organized in terms of the three blocks of the Domain of Science Model, people who have to work across the sciences would find the task of drawing upon them much easier. And this would permit the integration of parts of the recognized scientific disciplines into newer integrative sciences. But so far the scientists who are allied with the recognized disciplines have not seen as a major responsibility the organization of their sciences in forms that lend themselves readily to integration into broader, integrative sciences. This is a major deficiency in terms of applying the recognized sciences.

3.2 Alternative Divisions of a Domain of Science.

Figure 3.2 shows the Domain of Science Model. The four blocks identified previously appear in their steering relationship. It is readily seen from the Figure that the Model is divided in other ways than previously described.

Corpus and Arena

The two blocks consisting of the Foundations and Theory of the science make up the Corpus of the Science. The two blocks consisting of the Methodology and the Applications make up what is called the Arena.

The Arena is, of course, where the action is. This part of the Domain is often identified with "action research": a kind of research based in the view that there is no substitute for becoming thoroughly familiar with a problem as it occurs in a particular situation. By immersing oneself in the problem environment, it is believed that feasible solutions may be discovered that are acceptable within that environ-

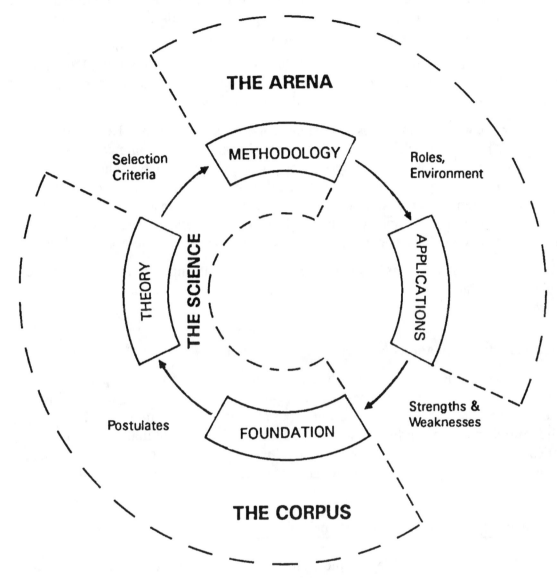

Figure 3.2 The domain of science model. Copyright © 1986 SGSR.

ment. There is abundant reason to believe that this logic is sound. But it is also insufficient from the point of view of creating science. In the absence of any articulated steering Corpus, action research lends itself much better to problems of modest scale than to problems that are large in scale.

The Corpus refers to a body of knowledge but not to application-specific knowledge. Nonetheless there are people whose interests lie only with the Corpus, or whose presence in association with the Arena is lacking. Striving to construct a Corpus of a science is a most laudable goal that is largely ignored by the action researchers.

Unfortunately when the effort is made to construct a Corpus independently of the Arena, which the action researchers quite properly would disdain, the discipline of correlating what is done with events in the world is lost.

It is possible to imagine that we live in a world where, in effect, the Domain of Science Model has been split into two parts: a Corpus which exists independent of the Arena, and an Arena which exists independent of any Corpus.

Had the world assumed this posture throughout history, we would have no viable science. The Domain of Science Model depends for its validity upon continual movement around the cycle, which requires steering from block to block in a never-ending sequence. To the extent that high-level decision makers are unaware of this the Science suffers greatly, the Arena suffers as well, and the consequences of human and economic investment in unsupported technology are not likely to be very favorable. Those who apply science but do not provide feedback concerning outcomes are strip miners of the science.

Corpus and Arena, as described here, are meant to supplant the terms "basic science" and "applied science", for these terms lack meaning when used apart from a comprehensive model.

Science and Applications

It was mentioned previously that three blocks of the Model comprised the Science. When appropriate, the Model can be discussed with only two blocks in its division: the Science and the Applications of the Science. But again it is critical to keep the mutual steering conditions in mind. Moreover it is critical that the term "science" not be viewed as a synonym for any of its components, but rather as the consequence of their aggregation in a recognizable and mutually consistent body of knowledge.

3.3 Linkages Among Divisions of a Domain of Science [2]

The four primary divisions of the Domain of Science Model are connected by four linkages, which will be examined in turn.

The Foundations-Theory (FT) Linkage

The FT Linkage represents a steering relationship, i.e., "Foundations steer Theory". This means that the Theory will represent an elaboration of the Foundations that is consistent with the Foundations. Whatever definitions, explanations, laws, and principles appear in the Theory must be consistent with and draw upon the Foundations. This is not the same as saying that the Foundations must necessarily be discovered first. Rather the distinction between Theory and Foundations is made after enough vision has been achieved to develop a proper ordering that reflects the more basic nature of the Foundations. Generally speaking the Foundations will contain ideas that are not necessarily proved, but which have been distilled from observation, experiment, experience, and prolonged thought and discussion. The Theory, on the other hand, will generally follow from the Foundations through logical inference, while at the same time helping to add to the understanding of the Foundations themselves.

The Theory-Methodology (TM) Linkage

The Theory-Methodology (TM) Linkage also reflects a steering relationship. To understand what this relationship must be like, one may note that it is very easy to propose one methodology after another. As long as no Theory is available to which the Methodology must conform, the choice of Methodology takes place without adequate criteria, and is therefore unduly open to abuse and irresponsibility. The Theory must, therefore, incorporate an adequate treatment of the kinds of situations to which Methodology must apply; as well as an adequate treatment of the kinds of roles that are required in those situations.

Use of methodology frequently cannot be carried out independently of roles, nor with indifference to the situations in which it is applied. Methodology itself is a prescription for behavior, not an explanation of the Situation or its attributes. But Methodology need not simply conform to a descriptive Theory. On the contrary, the best Theory will not only provide descriptions of the Situations, but also it will provide explanations of what can be brought to those Situations to enhance them. There is every reason for people to recognize situational constraints or detractions, but no reason to enshrine them by assuming they are unassailable.

But in order for Theory to prescribe for the environment of the situation and for the roles in that environment, the Theory must not only offer explanations of the Situation and distinctions among the roles; but also it must provide whenever possible the laws and principles that govern the choices that will be made not only in selecting Methodology, but in designing Methodology specifically for those situations, and articulating roles that reflect the content of the Theory.

In this respect, it is helpful to recognize a hierarchical structure offered by Russell Ackoff in a talk given at the 1988 Annual Meeting of the International Society for General Systems Research. According to Ackoff, there is a five-level structure relating to conceptualization. At the lowest, most elementary, level one finds <u>data</u>. At the next higher level, one finds <u>information</u>. Then at the next higher level, one finds <u>knowledge</u>. One level higher, one finds <u>understanding</u>. And finally, at the highest level, one finds <u>wisdom</u>. Also, according to Ackoff, in the total realm represented by this tautology, there is much more data than information, much more information than knowledge, much more knowledge than understanding, and much more understanding than wisdom. And the percentages of the total decrease rapidly as this hierarchy is ascended.

Science has not yet distinguished sharply among these five components, but there is a clear gradation involved, and it is important to assess what is being dealt with in a given context. Generally speaking, the most important attribute of Theory will be wisdom and the next most important will be understanding. Data, information, and knowledge may all contribute to this understanding and wisdom, but are not substitutes for it.

The Methodology-Applications (MA) Linkage

The Methodology-Applications (MA) Linkage, like the other linkages, is a steering relationship. What is steered is the practice associated with serving Applications. To the extent that prescribed Methodology is faithfully followed, it becomes possible to gather, accumulate, analyze, and interpret repeated uses of the Methodology, and thereby to assess its strengths and weaknesses in Applications. When such assessments are carried out, any weaknesses in Methodology, as uncovered by difficulties in Applications, can be referred back to the relevant part of the Theory and, thereafter, to the Foundations themselves. Accordingly, it seems most appropriate to characterize the remaining linkage not as merely an Applications-Foundations Linkage, but rather as an Applications-Science Linkage.

The Applications-Science (AS) Linkage

The consequences of the use of Methodology in Applications must steer the Science. But this can only be done if the Methodology is scrupulously followed in Applications; otherwise it will not be possible to endow the Science with the Referential Transparency that it requires. To say it more crudely, the use of methodology that is only a shadow of what the Science proposes, or that is an ad hoc variation therefrom, only serves to make much more difficult the creation of a Science. It is for this reason that those practitioners who construct or apply methodology without regard to Foundations or Theory cannot be said to be performing consistently with the long-term aims of science. This does not mean that they may not be performing a valuable service; but one should not confuse this service with scientific progress. It is a short-term oriented practice; not a long-term oriented contribution.

3.4 Uses of a Domain of Science Model.

The Domain of Science Model described in the foregoing has multiple uses [2]. Six of these uses will be discussed now.

Claims Mediation

Suppose it is claimed by someone or some group that contributions are being made by them to a science, while others deny this claim. It is self-evident that unless agreement can be reached on what constitutes a science, no resolution of the claim is possible. Yet the existence of a science rests upon widespread consensus upon its content. Thus the question of existence of a science itself depends upon the ability to say what a science is and to reach agreement upon whether some content matches the description.

It seems that it should be easier to make this determination if one does not merely speak about science as an undivided concept, but rather if one identifies certain attributes or divisions that a science should possess. Still one would expect that the reduction of a science into components would not be adequate; whatever set of components might be found, it would be necessary to say how they are related.

The Domain of Science Model permits discussion at the more detailed level, as well as discussion of how the components are related, and thereby can serve as a mediating factor in moving toward agreement on the content of a science as well as agreement that a science exists.

In applying this Model as a mediating factor, one holds constantly in view the concept that Science is intended to be an increasingly better approximation to truth, and that the quest involved is often a very long-term one. Thus the use of the Model as a mediator is not in an absolute sense as one would attempt if the view were held that the Final Truth had been achieved. On the other hand, it does make some minimum demands which might very well not be met by some areas of higher education that now are described as science.

The Model may, therefore, serve not only as a "yes or no" mediator concerning the existence of a science; but also it may serve to highlight those areas where further work is needed in order to demonstrate the science; and this may stimulate the better organization of already-existing knowledge that has not yet been structured well enough to say where it falls in the Model.

Linkage Promotion

If an assessment of some particular content area reveals that further organizational work needs to be done in order to establish that the area meets the minimum requirements of the Model, the linkage descriptions given in the preceding section may stimulate or promote the better development or articulation of those linkages.

Transparency Enhancement

It has been stressed earlier that Referential Transparency is a requirement for a Science. The combined impact of the use of the Model for Claims Mediation and Linkage Promotion will surely be to enhance the Referential Transparency of the Science.

Organizational Clarification

The clarification of the organization of the Science is not only important for Referential Transparency, but it is also important for the development of the Science itself. Given the various functions assigned to the three components of the Science, one needs to be able to identify which parts of the Science truly are fundamental; for without this determination, the Science can hardly be internally consistent. The Model offers guidance concerning the approach to clarifying the organization of the Science, and thereby serves to enhance the development of the Science.

Investment Guidance

Potential Applications of a Science may arise in the development of other Sciences that depend upon it. But many Applications arise in Situations that lack a scientific orientation. People who suffer in such Situations may face a decision about whether to invest in the application of a Science, or take the alternative which is to rely upon other forms of Belief Fixation, of the type described in Section 1.4.

If a Science is sufficiently well organized that its Methodology can be presented in the light of the existing Foundations, it may well be that those Foundations themselves can serve to enlighten the potential consumer of Science and help that consumer make the decision as to whether or not to invest in applying that particular Science in the Application of interest.

Constructing Supersciences

It is becoming progressively more important to society to find ways to construct "supersciences". Perhaps the best way to see what this term connotes is to imagine that any particular Science will be adequate to provide the Methodology for only a small collection of Applications. If Science W and Science X serve, respectively, Applications Y and Z, perhaps it will be true that the integration of Sciences W and X to form a new and larger science will serve not only Applications Y and Z, but also additional applications.

Another way to look at this is to start with some area of Application and inquire into what the scientific requirements would be to support that Application fully. This kind of question may well suggest the need for a superscience. For example, one might desire to have a "life science" that would support the Application of maintaining human health; and this science, when constructed, might draw on several lesser sciences.

It seems very clear that if each of the lesser sciences were organized according to the Domain of Science Model, the task of integrating these sciences into a superscience would be significantly easier than if one had to face these subsciences in their present state of organization.

3.5 Extensions of a Domain of Science Model.

The Domain of Science Model, as presented in Figure 3.2, can be extended as shown in Figure 3.3. This extension consists of showing more detail concerning what is a normal expectation for inclusion in relation to the components of the Domain of Science Model. Incorporated in the Figure are the Universal Priors along with definitions and postulates that form an integral part of the Foundations; laws, principles, and steering doctrine that form an integral part of the Theory; as well as ingredients of the Methodology and Applications.

3.6 Restrictions of a Domain of Science Model.

If one or more parts is omitted from the Domain of Science Model, what remains is called a "restriction of the Model". While such omissions are not recommended, it is appropriate to identify several restrictions of the Model that appear to be representative of what is happening in various situations.

A Two-Component Version

One restriction of the Model that enjoys considerable allegiance in some quarters, and furnishes a basis for activity in them, is the version that deletes Theory and Foundations, leaving a circular Model that contains only Methodology and Applications. This restriction is perilously close to what animates much "action research". Action research quite properly embodies recognition of the importance of immersion of the professional in a Situation in order to gain a realistic knowledge of it. But then the professionals often go further and elide from explicit consideration any existing theory or foundations, or any intent to contribute to them, as though methodology alone provides a proper basis for professional activity in problem situations.

121

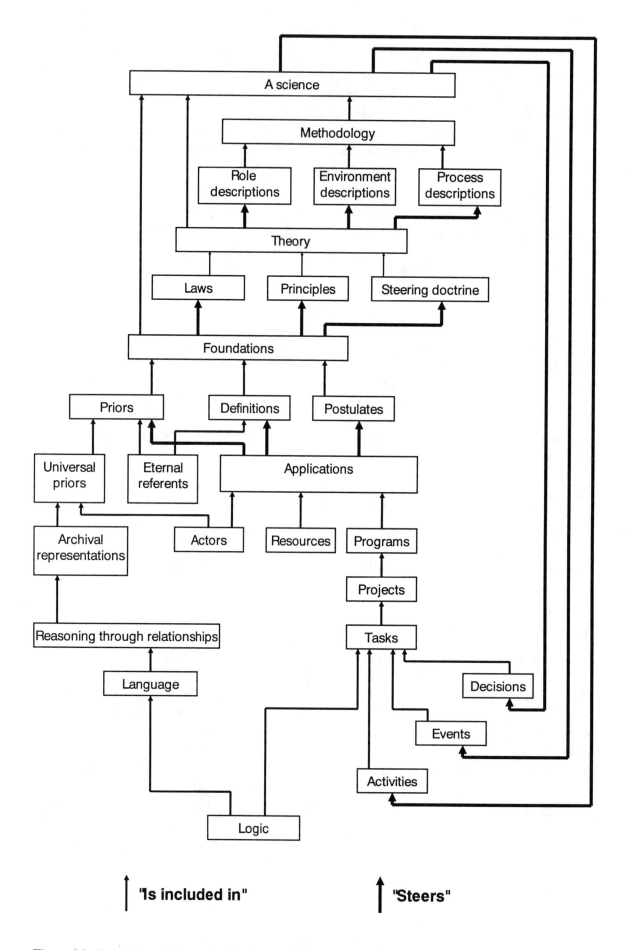

Figure 3.3. Extending the Domain of Science Model

A Two-Part Version

Still another restriction of the Model involves opening the linkage from the Theory to the Methodology and the linkage from the Applications to the Science. These openings of linkages convert the Domain of Science Model into two separate parts. In one part, the Corpus stands alone, separated from the Arena. In the other part, the Arena stands alone, separated from the Corpus. This separation describes a world in which academic thinking is isolated from practice, and vice versa.

This restriction of the Domain of Science Model differs from the Two-Component Version. In that Version, only the Arena is acknowledged. In the Two-Part Version, both the Corpus and the Arena are acknowledged, but neither is linked to the other.

A Three-Component Version

In a particular three-component version, the Foundations are deleted leaving the remaining parts of the Model. In effect, this restriction substitutes the Theory for the Corpus, and denies the possibility of partitioning the Corpus into one part that is more basic than another part.

3.7 Tentative Classification of the Sciences [3].

That part of the scientific agenda which relates to the integration of sciences presently viewed as distinct or only marginally overlapping remains open. Traditionally, philosophers have sought to classify the sciences, in order to help build a more comprehensive overview of science as a whole, rather than science as a collection of sciences.

Such classifications have generally been met with indifference or with alternative classifications. Perhaps it is because the act of classifying has been regarded merely as a philosophical exercise. Such a view is hostile to the pressing need to integrate sciences into larger sciences, in such a way that the larger sciences are sufficiently well-organized and sufficiently substantive that they can become the basis for working with applications that lie beyond the scope of existing sciences. With this motivation in mind, two particular areas of science that presently need to be more highly developed, and which need to draw on more specialized areas will be discussed: systems science and conceptual science.

Figure 3.4 suggests a tentative classification of recognized sciences into six major categories: physical sciences, social sciences, life sciences, conceptual sciences, applied sciences, and systems science.

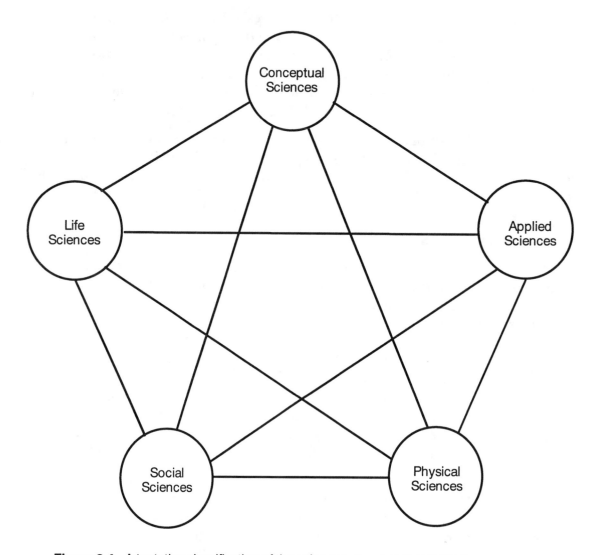

Figure 3.4 A tentative classification of the sciences. Copyright © 1980 SGSR.

The three classifications involving physical sciences, social sciences, and life sciences are already reasonable well accepted. Applied sciences are commonly recognized though seldom subjected to the kind of scrutiny suggested in the Domain of Science Model. Conceptual sciences are those that relate to and heavily involve generation by the human mind as a matter of great emphasis. Systems science, it is argued, must be involved in defining the linkages among the other five. Thus, for example, when some situation involves the interaction or overlap of physical sciences and life sciences, systems science should come into play as the integrating mechanism. This view is supported by

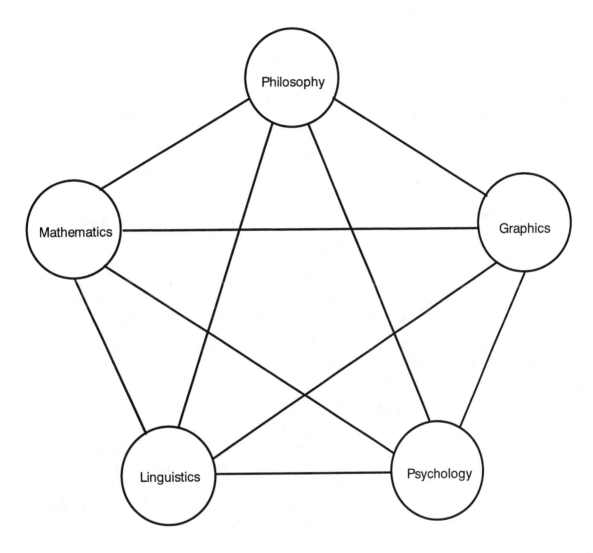

Figure 3.5 A tentative classification of the conceptual sciences. Copyright © 1980 SGSR.

the membership in the broad-scope systems societies of representatives from the several types of sciences shown in Figure 3.4, or in the content of broad-based systems science journals such as *Systems Research*.

Figure 3.5 suggests a tentative classification of the Conceptual Sciences. Portrayed here are linguistics, graphics, and mathematics representing the language components; psychology, representing the uniquely human component; and philosophy perceived both in its Greek interpretation as "love of wisdom" and in its archival

125

interpretation as the writings of philosophers. Again, a systems science may provide the kind of integrative activity needed to construct a unified science from the components shown in Figure 3.5, thus systems science is represented here by the linkages.

Both Figures 3.4 and 3.5, and the remarks about systems science and conceptual science are to be viewed as speculative, and not as claims that these or other sciences exist. In the framework of this discussion, such claims would invariably be referred to the Domain of Science Model for resolution or, alternatively, to some successor to that Model that would achieve wide consensus as representative of what constitutes a science.

In the present context, the Model serves the primary purpose of providing discipline to and a framework for discussion of the Science of Generic Design.

SUMMARY

To provide adequate Referential Transparency in a science of generic design, at least three communication interfaces are critical. One is the interface between the producers of basic science and the users of methodology in problem- solving and design. A second is the interface between the technical people engaged in design and the managerial and administrative people who provide oversight and steering. A third is the interface between the managerial/administrative people and the general public.

Division of a science into recognizable parts helps in this regard. Tracing logic through a network often involves deep logic. Categorization within the science can facilitate the search.

The Model can be presented in several ways. In one statement of the Model there appear only the Science and its Applications. Each steers the development of the other. In another statement of the Model, there appear only the Corpus of the Science and the Arena where the Science is being applied. In the most basic statement of the Model, there are four blocks. Three of these form the Science: the Foundations, Theory, and Methodology. The fourth block is Applications. The linkages in the Model are critical, and in today's societies they frequently are ignored. Ignoring them has very bad implications both for the Science and the Applications.

Extensions of the Domain of Science Model shed light on its interfaces with other forms of knowledge. Restrictions of the Model consist of submodels that lack the generality of the whole. A Restriction that currently enjoys unwarranted favor is one that omits from the Domain of Science Model the Foundations and Theory, and includes only the Methodology and Applications. In this restriction, Science is cavalierly taken as synonymous with Methodology; or, alternately, one may say that the Arena is floating free of any scientific Corpus. The restoration of the connections between Corpus and Arena in both directions is critical to the health of science and to the health of applications, and is especially so in design.

REFERENCES

1. J. N. Warfield, "The Domain of Science Model: Evolution and Design", *Proc. Society for General Systems Research*, Salinas: Intersystems, 1986, H46-H59.

2. J. N. Warfield, "Simple System Models Based on Sophisticated Assumptions", AAAS Meeting, Boston, 1988.

3. J. N. Warfield, "Science and Systems Science: A Technology Perspective", *Proc. Society for General Systems Research Annual Meeting*, January, 1980, 212-218.

QUESTIONS RELATED TO CHAPTER 3

1. What is required to serve decision-making in the construction of a science?

2. What governs what is admitted to a science?

3. What governs the standards by which a science is judged as a science?

4. Is science value-free, as some have argued?

5. To whom are decisions about science important?

6. If an organized body of knowledge lacks Referential Transparency, what are the political implications concerning the potential application of this body of knowledge?

7. Who should be responsible for Referential Transparency in a science?

8. What are some distinguishing characteristics of the Domain of Science Model, when contrasted with other descriptions of science?

9. Identify and describe three critical communications interfaces that affect the relationship between science and the public.

10. To what does the <u>behavioral</u> level refer in the 5-level description of communication about science?

11. To what does the <u>logical</u> level refer in the 5-level description of communication about science?

12. To what does the <u>technical</u> level refer in the 5-level description of communication about science?

13. To what does the <u>managerial and administrative</u> level refer in the 5-level description of communication about science?

14. How was the term "natural philosopher" applied in the nineteenth century? Is it a useful term today?

15. What are the four divisions of the Domain of Science Model?

16. What are the purposes of the three major divisions of a science?

17. Select ten major public issues of the times and discuss whether any one of them constitutes an application of any one field of science by itself; then repeat the exercise allowing combinations of different sciences as required to support the study and design related to the ten issues.

18. What is the Corpus of a science?

19. What is the Arena?

20. How do the Arena and Corpus overlap in (a) the Domain of Science Model, (b) society?

21. How does the common term "basic research" relate to the Domain of Science Model?

22. How does the term "applied science" relate to the Domain of Science Model?

23. Discuss the linkages in the Domain of Science Model in terms of the kinds of relationships that are represented by the linkages.

24. What are some of the uses of the Domain of Science Model?

25. What is meant by "extensions" of a Domain of Science Model?

26. What is meant by "restrictions" of the Model?

27. Is there any potential benefit to be obtained by classifying sciences?

28. The term "cognitive science" has gained considerable attention, and is prominent in research involving information. The term "conceptual science" is proposed in Chapter 3. Discuss the relative merits of these two names, and how the terms might be similar or different in their implications.

CHAPTER 4

MANAGING COMPLEXITY THROUGH SYSTEM DESIGN:
The Use of the Science

> The principal purpose of theoretical research...is to find the point of view
> from which the subject appears in its greatest simplicity.
>
> **--J. Willard Gibbs**

The principal utility of a Science of Generic Design is its contribution to the management of complexity through system design. Complexity will either be managed or it will overwhelm the individual and the society. To illuminate the possibilities, it is appropriate to begin by posing a definition of complexity, and to discuss its dynamics, i.e., how it escalates or contracts. Necessary conditions for its management will be offered. These include the control of situational escalation, the reduction of personal cognitive burden, the elimination of situational detractors, and the provision of personal enhancers.

Machines are not seen as the saviors of the human being; rather they are seen as potential assistants to the human being to enhance human capability. This means, in general, that human beings taking the roles of system designer or manager of complexity will not interact directly with the levers, knobs, or keys of machinery. The route to enhancement of human capacity to deal with complexity does not lie in requiring the human to exercise motor skills. Rather it lies in providing the human being with assistance in organizing information and in creating those information displays that the human needs, in a form designed to serve the purposes of the tasks at hand.

The principal avenues to the management of complexity are designed processes; designed working environments; and specialized roles filled by actors educated specifically for the management of complexity, leadership, and quality control of the foregoing. A Science of Generic Design must illuminate all of these in order to enable the management of complexity through design.

131

4.1 Two Meanings of Complexity.

There is a difference between the definition of a term and its meaning. The definition is a formal statement of the kind that appears in dictionaries. The meaning is a personal concept, having to do with how an individual relates to the term in the Virtual World of the individual. Congruence between definition and meaning is, nonetheless, a goal to be sought with fervor whenever people need to agree on something in order to make progress. In striving to develop an appropriate definition of complexity.that can become congruent with meaning, one must go well beyond a simple statement to develop a discussion that aims at establishing such congruence. And one may, perhaps, be forgiven for using the term "meaning" instead of the more proper term "definition" as a way of keeping constantly in front of the reader the importance of congruence between definition and meaning. The meaning of complexity may be clarified through an analogy that not only illustrates features of complexity, but also illustrates its escalation.

Consider the often-discussed question about whether sound is present if a tree falls in the forest and no one is there to hear it. When the tree falls, its movement through the air and its collision with other trees or with the earth produces vibrations in both the air and the earth, which travel outward from the site of the disturbance. The outward flow is omnidirectional, not limited to any particular direction. The ears of an observer who is in the path of the vibrations as they move outward will intercept a very small amount of the total disturbance, which will produce sensations in the ear mechanisms that are interpreted by the mind as sound. If no observers are present, there will be no interception, no sensations, and no detected sound.

The issue of whether sound is there clearly depends on how the word "sound" is interpreted. If it is viewed as the disturbance produced in the media of air and earth by the motion and impact of the tree, then one infers that sound is present because in all observed instances such disturbances arose; and even when human observers are absent, disturbances can be detected by mechanical and electronic sensing equipment, just as earthquakes are detected. If, on the other hand, sound is interpreted as the sensation experienced by the mind when the ear intercepts a small amount of the energy carried in the media, then sound is only present when the human is there.

One may now observe that the most encompassing view of the situation is that sound generally is a system attribute, gaining its identity from the set consisting of the producer of the disturbance, the medium through which energy is propagated away from the source of the disturbance, the interceptors of fractions of that energy, and the human sensation produced in the mind by the impact of that fractional energy. The term "sound" can then be modified by various adjectives to spell out any particular part of its existence. The generated sound is produced by the falling tree as it encounters other matter, the propagated sound is carried by the air and the earth, the intercepted sound is that extracted by the ear from the media, and the interpreted sound is that impression in the mind of the human being.

Parallels can be drawn with complexity. In the ancient philosophical thinking, phenomena corresponded to the falling tree, the disturbance being propagated, and the impact of the intercepted energy on the human hearing mechanism; while noumena corresponded to the interpretation of the sound by the human minds of those observers in the path of the sound.

Similarly one may speak of situational complexity as those aspects of phenomena that are open to being "intercepted" by the mind, and cognitive complexity as those aspects of noumena that make interpretation difficult. Just as the media essentially mediated between the generated sound and the interpreted sound, so do representations mediate between the situational complexity and the cognitive complexity. But while the air and earth offer only modest ways to affect the transmitted disturbance (which is affected by the temperature and humidity in the air, for example), the quality of representations can be extremely influential in the interpretation of the situational complexity by the mind.

The situation involving the falling tree can be analyzed reasonably well by the use of the sciences of mechanics and acoustics. But in many forests the situation is not as simple as has been portrayed so far. Not only may sound arise from the tree falling; but there may be airplanes overhead, traffic on nearby roads, other trees falling, tractors plowing nearby fields, and other sources of sound. These other aspects of the situation can be viewed as escalations of it that make it less readily analyzed. Similarly, while some situations are often idealized for purposes of analysis, real situations are often considerably more encompassing than these analyses suggest. This is why it is well to perceive complexity as a system attribute that may have components of the type described here as situational complexity and cognitive complexity. By convention, the term "Situation" refers to that which is under study by a human being. The Situation may include human beings, but the particular human being(s) who are studying the Situation are, by definition, not part of it. This does not mean, however, that they do not have an impact upon it merely by being there. Our language must enable us to divide our sphere of concern into those parts that require both distinctive treatment and treatment as a collective.

The most common interpretation of complexity, as seen in the literature of design, would be that complexity is the same as what has been called situational complexity; but without allowing the human being to be part of that situation at all, either as observer or as actor. This interpretation shuts out the cognitive complexity. But clearly this is inappropriate.

To return to the falling tree, suppose now that the human being, instead of being a relatively small resident of the forest and receiving only a small amount of the sound energy produced by the tree, suddenly took on the shape of a giant human doughnut, totally surrounding the tree, with giant ears all around its circumference, and all of the energy being received by all of the ears were fed directly to a giant brain. This new kind of human might be large enough, in principle, to intercept all of the sound energy. If the mind of this new human behaved proportionately to the mind of the ordinary human, one can imagine that it would believe that a huge explosion had occurred, rather than simply that a tree had fallen.

By comparison, suppose that the human being who formerly thought a situation to be quite complex now gained a new organic information system enabling the human to see everything going on all around the world just as it occurred, to hear everything that is being said, and to process and interpret all the received information with the speed of light. This human being would be very different from most of us. To this human being, there is no situational complexity and no cognitive complexity. Hence any definition of complexity must recognize the sensitivity of the concept to how the human being is viewed. If the human being has only a limited sphere of perception, and a limited information-processing capability, both in terms of amount of information and rate of processing of it, then clearly what is or is not complex in a situation must be assessed in the light of these limits.

One may ask which type of complexity is the most important, situational or cognitive. Again the answer depends on the definition of "important", i.e., the criteria for assigning saliency to an idea. Perhaps the most important type is the type most susceptible to management by system design. This suggests that a key attribute of an investigation of complexity would be to uncover what can be done to manage both situational and cognitive complexity. Such an investigation may help to determine where attention should be focused.

4.2 How Complexity Escalates.

Having said that there exists both situational and cognitive complexity, let us use the term "complexity", without a modifier, to represent their (interacting) combination. Now consider how, beginning with a certain state of complexity, complexity may escalate.

Until the mind begins to focus upon a problem or issue, cognitive complexity does not come into play. But when the mind does become oriented toward a complex situation, it is very likely that complexity will escalate.

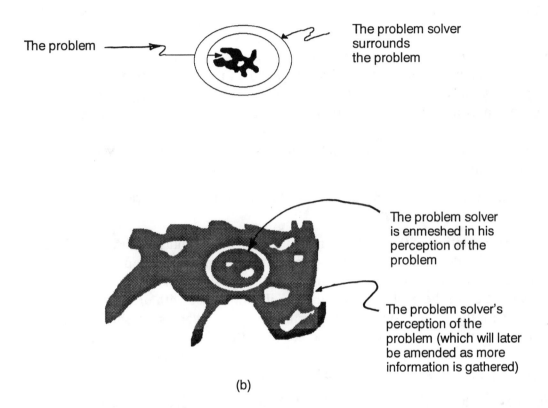

The problem ⟶

The problem solver
surrounds
the problem

The problem solver
is enmeshed in his
perception of the
problem

The problem solver's
perception of the
problem (which will later
be amended as more
information is gathered)

(b)

Figure 4.1 Illustrating two problem situations. Copyright © 1982 SGSR.

Escalation may occur because of linkages that take place, in which case it may be called "linkage escalation". To see how this can happen, a beginning can be made with two problem situations illustrated in Figure 4.1. In part (a) of this Figure the problem solver, represented by the ring, surrounds the problem and solves it. Normal problems admit this paradigm.

In part (b) the individual problem solver, again represented by the ring, is enmeshed in a certain perception of the problem. This perception is represented by the "ink blot". In perceiving an inability to surround the problem, a perfectly reasonable step is taken: to seek out others who will be part of a (formal or informal) problem-solving team.

A double escalation now begins. Linked to the original perception of the problem are new components of it introduced by those who join the problem-solving team. This is the first type of linkage escalation. A second type occurs by virtue of linking to the enlarged set of problem perceptions all of the process-related difficulties that go along with the attempt to get a group of people to work together to solve a problem.

While the group members may each possess significant content knowledge germane to the problem, they may not be knowledgeable in how to make a group effective as a problem-solving team. Even if they have academic knowledge of group behavior, they may not be able to use this knowledge effectively. Dual roles in groups are always difficult. If one is contributing knowledge to a solution, while trying to steer the group's activity, a conflict of interest is likely to be perceived by other group members.

But even if the group does begin to become functional in the escalated context, further escalation may lie ahead.

The next escalation of the problem may occur through linkages with the values, policies, practices, identities, or self-interests of the organization(s) represented by the members of the group. If contributions toward a possible resolution or solution or even dissolution of the problem appear to be incompatible with organizational factors, e.g., with the value system of the organization(s), progress may be halted. Now a solution must be seen as one that solves the escalated problem: harnessing the capacity of the group to perform effectively in working on the original problem, in the light of constraints imposed by the organizational culture.

One way in which this organizational influence can be represented is through Argyris' concept of a double-loop problem [1]. Figure 4.2 offers an illustration of this concept [2].

To interpret Figure 4.2, suppose that, in the initial stage of activity, the first loop is entered with a set of actions in mind. These actions are those that are normally taken in problem-solving activity. The actions are taken and the consequences are observed. If there is a match between the desired and actual consequences, the problem is deemed to have been solved. If there is a mismatch between them, the actions are repeated with minor variations, possibly with other actors being involved. Continued unsuccessful iterative treks around this loop mark the inability of those who are steering the operations to recognize the need to move to the second loop.

In the second (larger) loop, the failure to succeed by traversing the first loop leads to the conclusion that the governing variables in the process are at fault, and that it is necessary to rethink those assumptions and values that promoted or tolerated the actions taken in the first loop. In working on the revision of the governing variables, a problem is being addressed that is different from

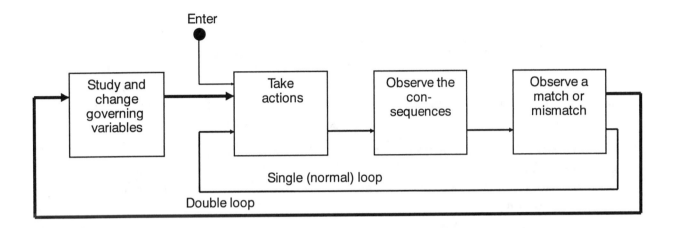

Figure 4.2 Illustrating Argyris's concept of double-loop problem. Copyright © 1982 SGSR.

the one that was first addressed, and whose only connection to the first one may be that failure in working on the first one motivated the effort to rethink the governing variables. Unfortunately it is frequently true in organizations, as Argyris has succinctly described the situation, that:

> "people who want to double-loop learn
>
> (1) do not know how to do so,
> (2) do not know that they do not know,
> (3) do not know that they have designs in their heads
>   to ensure (1) and (2) [above], and
> (4) do not know that they cannot learn to do so by using their
>   present skills"

The implications of this disability for organizations are severe, and may be compared to the plight of the alcoholic who traditionally is unprepared to acknowledge that plight, and for whom no remedial action to cure the situation is possible in the absence of such an acknowledgment.

Now even if those linkage escalations can be surmounted, more appear. An attempt to implement a proposed solution to the original problem may fail simply because the capacity to communicate the solution adequately to implementers may not be present. It may even occur that the solution demands new roles for which the society is not staffed; or for which actors cannot be found. The design of a training program now offers an additional linkage escalation.

137

While all the escalation is taking place, the nature of the problem may change, or the problem itself may overwhelm the organization to make problem-solving virtually impossible.

In spite of the extensive, highly-visible, and repeated incidence of linkage escalations as described, our educational institutions behave as though such escalations do not exist. Traditionally these institutions teach students small processes for problem-solving that will not be functional in the escalating situations just described. Repetition of such experiences prepares learners to fail later if they become associated with practitioner organizations that regularly involve complexity.

By overlooking or ignoring linkage escalation, educators promote the undiscussability of some aspects of problem-solving in organizations. In view of this, it is not surprising that Argyris [1] found that in many organizations people deal with complex problems by:

> "using games whose primary features are that they are known by all players, they are undiscussable, and their undiscussability is undiscussable."

When problem-solving encounters incompatible organizational values, more reasons for undiscussability may emerge. Churchman [3] noted that there has developed in this century a practice of ignoring the ethical factors that ought to be considered at the beginning of potential immersion in a problem-solving effort. As Churchman described it, matters quickly are placed in a context of "bounded systems thinking" in which ethical concerns are suppressed. While this avoids still another linkage escalation, it also leaves the problem-solving effort unattached to any fundamental value base, opening the effort to the rule of expediency. A common practice that supports this approach, according to Churchman (and one that is completely consistent with the double-loop problem concept of Argyris) is to try first to define the problem in terms of potential actions that can be taken, and one of the consequences of this is

> "that such a step provides feasible boundaries to the ethical issues...which stops the conversation."

Linkage escalation, besieged with incapacity, inability to move to the second loop, and lack of process for handling its several features; and constrained by organizational interests and other factors, is a primary reason why complex problems can continue to plague a society indefinitely. A science of design must offer ways to prevent such escalation or, if prevention is impossible, to offer means of coping with it. As unchecked escalation threatens to add to the complexity, purposeful contraction must be called on to diminish it.

4.3 Necessary Conditions for Managing Complexity.

Is it possible to identify necessary conditions for managing complexity? Even if it is possible to do so, the discovery of such conditions does not assure that the conditions will be sufficient. What is required is to learn the conditions that are both necessary and sufficient. Yet to demonstrate sufficiency is a philosophical impossibility at present. It is necessary to understand complexity in order to manage it; and because it intrinsically involves substantial elements of the unknown in any given situation, one cannot know what would be sufficient to deal with those unknown elements. Inability to assure the management of complexity is not a flaw in a science or in components of a science, but rather is simply a fact of life. Still data can be taken on problem-solving efforts based in science, and conclusions can be drawn therefrom that offer reasons to be optimistic (Appendix 5).

Let us consider four approaches to managing complexity: namely the control of situational escalation, the reduction of personal cognitive burden for those engaged in problem-solving or design, the elimination of situational detractors that may negatively affect problem-solving or design, and the provision of personal enhancers to help individuals be more effective in problem-solving and design.

Controlling Situational Escalation

Situational Escalation occurs because of the following factors, among others: (a) varying perceptions among members of a problem-solving team, (b) difficulty in managing group problem-solving efforts, (c) the presence of organizational or cultural constraints that suppress useful contributions to problem-solving, (d) difficulty of communicating solutions to implementers, (e) change in the problem situation with time, (f) lack of actors to fill new, needed roles, and (g) the difficulty of dealing coherently with some or all of the foregoing when they appear in combination. It is reasonable to be optimistic about overcoming these factors, but only if they are dealt with as a set, because resolutions to one factor are not necessarily resolutions of others, and may even escalate them.

Reducing Personal Cognitive Burden

If one is in the position of trying to be part of an activity that solves a problem or designs a system, and if the situation is one represented by Figure 4.1(b), the cognitive burden on the individual is significant. The individual may be thrown into a position requiring that the individual provide opinions and decisions for which the individual is not cognitively prepared. The common incidence of this situation, and the expectations of performance even though appropriate bases for performance have never been developed in the individual, are part of the evidence of mismanagement of complexity.

It is reasonable to expect that a Science of Generic Design would incorporate specific provisions for reducing the cognitive burden that would otherwise be impressed on the individual by the culture in which the individual exists.

Eliminating the Situational Detraction Set

Aside from the factors that enter into complexity through escalation, there are many other situational factors that are frequently <u>present</u> which detract from problem-solving or design activity. And also there are other factors that are <u>absent</u> in the situation which, if present, would enhance problem-solving or design activity. Figure 4.3 offers an interpretation of these factors according to their frequent presence or frequent absence.

Of those that are frequently present, some are intrinsic to a Design Situation, others are cultural, and still others are extrinsic, i.e., they are brought to the Situation independently of what is intrinsic to it or independently of an existing culture. ("Technical chauvinism" refers to the belief that anything can and should be achieved with technology, whether it makes sense from humanistic considerations or not.)

The organization of the factors in Figure 4.3 reflects the view that any factor that is listed in a certain column will propagate to the right, thus those factors that are individual-specific also affect the professional, the organization, and the society at large. Here the individual is taken to be anyone having any interest in the problem at hand other than the professional, who is viewed as someone with a highly-developed interest in the problem. Since almost all complex problems inherently involve organizations, the organization will be the environment for many of the individuals and professionals.

Because of the pervasiveness of the factors listed in Figure 4.3, it is reasonable to insist that a Science of Generic Design provide, to the extent possible, an approach for managing them.

Providing the Personal Enhancement Set

The last of the necessary components for managing complexity to be discussed here is the provision of a Personal Enhancement Set. This means to make available suitable conditions or objects or entities or other means or mechanisms for enhancing the capacity of the individual to be effective in a problem-solving situation.

The four necessary components clearly are not independent of one another. Nevertheless it is easy enough to overlook the needs of the individual for enhancement, which warrants specifically identifying them. Table 4.1 lists several potential enhancements that can be provided, which have the potential to assist the individual.

Origins of	In the	In the	In the	In the Society at
A. Intrinsic	• Bounded rationality • Imbalanced perception of problem factors • Spurious saliency			
B. Cultural	• Parochialism and myopic vision	• Preemptive language	• Groupthink • Indifference • Cultural canals	
C. Extrinsic	• Consuming egotism • Arrogant abuse of power • Knowledge disavowal	• Invention of or acceptance of "floating methodology" • Extrapolation of experience and process beyond the scale of relevance	• Bad incentive systems • Territorial imperative, elitism • Substitution of authority in place of design • "Technical chauvinism"	

Identification	For the	For the	For the	For the Society at
	• Discipline of behavior • Design experience at scale	• Knowledge of design science	• Leadership and discipline • Means for knowledge integration • Designed environment for design	• Science of design • Formal design education • Evaluation criteria • Access to pervasive decision sources • Units to quantify performance comprehensively • Instruments to give direct performance measures

Figure 4.3 Features relevant to effective system design.

Table 4.1
Potential Enhancements

- Effective Group Process
- Computer Assistance to the Individual Mind
- Computer Assistance to the Group
- Display of Unstructured Information
- Display of Structured Information
- Storage of Unstructured Information for Recall
- Storage of Structured Information for Recall
- Capacity to Structure Information Effectively
- Organized Dialog

As with the other factors, it is reasonable to expect that a Science of Generic Design will make the appropriate provisions for these enhancements. Many of the enhancements will be effective in overcoming detractors to effective performance. Table 4.2 compares the potential for improvement that may be brought about by three possible interventions: authority, science, and working environment. Science historically has not been able to deal comprehensively with hostile or indifferent authority, which competes with science for influence upon human belief; but science can deal with the working environment, if authority will allow it.

Inspection of Table 4.2 indicates that science and the working environment can be beneficial in dealing with many of these detractors, while authority can be beneficial in dealing with some that science and the environment cannot; but also authority can be beneficial indirectly by providing conditions where science and environment are allowed to exercise their influence on effectiveness.

4.4 Designed Processes.

Processes can be designed that can deal with formulations of a situation in the form of sets, limit situational escalation, reduce personal cognitive burden, eliminate most situational detractors, and provide many personal enhancements.

One of the primary keys to designing processes that can deal with all of these matters is to choose as the basis for the design of such processes something that is common to all of them: namely operations carried out with ideas, such operations not being dependent upon any particular specific kind of idea, nor upon any particular narrow field of study, but simply with ideas themselves.

Table 4.2 *Impacts on Detractors from Authority, Science, and Designed Environment*

Detractor	Notes on Authority	Notes on Science	Notes on Working Environment
• The limit to the human span of immediate recall (1) • Imbalance among situational factors (5)	Not very useful re these detractors	Can explain these and tell how to correct them	Can incorporate means to enhance the design process by controlling information flow rate, and assist in getting the necessary situational balance
• Defects in the working environment (2)	Can authorize funds to construct proper environment	Can explain what the environment should be like	Can eliminate the defects and enhance human performance substantially
• Extrapolation of design processes beyond scale (3) • Lack of discipline (8) • Substitutes for design (9) • Lack of design knowledge (18) • Lack of formal education in design (21) • Organizations (28)	Can bring influence to bear to stop bad practices, and authorize appropriate ones	Can show how to correct bad practices, how to compensate for things that are lacking, and how to redesign disfunctional units	Can provide an environment that uses the results from science efficiently to create discipline, eliminate inappropriate processes, and replace them with appropriate processes, tested against the foundations of the design science. Can also provide for substantial learning during the design activity, with suitable documentation
• Floating methodology (4) • Lack of leadership discipline (19) • Bad incentive systems	Can set higher standards that incorporate scientific knowledge, and that reflect new incentives	Can explain why and how to correct these detractions, and show how to replace them with enhancements	Generally not needed, but might be useful to design new incentive system
• Institutional indifference (6)	Use influence to change priorities		
• Egotistical designer (7)	Require behavioral flexibility		Accommodates this role as a member of a facilitated team
• Lack of sound reference criteria (10) • Lack of instruments and units (11)		Can furnish such criteria, and can develop appropriate instruments and units	
• Knowledge disavowal (12) • Groupthink (13) • Spurious saliency (14) • Lack of knowledge		Can clarify these detractions and provide methodology and facilitation system to correct them and to enhance appropriate replacements	Presents an environment and processes that make such detractors inoperable, while replacing them with constructive activity, and means, as needed

(Continued on next page)

Table 4.2 *Impacts on Detractors from Authority, Science, and Designed Environment (Concluded)*

Detractor	Notes on Authority	Notes on Science	Notes on Working Environment
• Arrogant abuse of power (15) • U.S. technical chauvinism (17)	Can enhance sensitivity to these matters and bring influence to bear against them and in support of alternatives	Can provide means that make such attitudes obsolete	Presents an environment that allows for effective movement and results that are based in science rather than personality or culture
• Lack of relevant design experience (20) • Territorial imperatives and elitism (23)		Can clarify what is needed to allow the experience to be gained and to be valuable, and can show clearly how to replace territories with collaborative effort	Presents an environment designed and equipped to eliminate these detractors
• Parochialism (24) • Cultural canals (25) • Hardening of the Categories (26) • Preemptive language (27)		Corrects and replaces these detractors by providing satisfying alternatives	Corrects and replaces these detractors by providing neutral turf and facilitation and methodologies that eliminate the possibilities of sustaining such detractions
• Myopic individual behavior (29)		Explains what is needed to self-correct	

Another key to this is to use as an underlying language for the design a branch of mathematics that has been called one of the three major achievements of mathematics in its entire history: set theory, and its extension to the Theory of Relations.

Still another key is to use, as a basis for specifying the roles and the working environment, the applicable research on human behavior in groups, together with a vision of the kind of products needed to work with complex issues.

The variety of fundamental operations that can be carried out with ideas is quite limited. Almost everything that needs to be done can be conceived as (a) generating ideas, (b) clarifying ideas, (c) structuring ideas, (d) interpreting structures of ideas, and (e) amending ideas. While some might like to see human values and valuing made explicit in this list, they are omitted here for two reasons. First of all, everything that a human being does, singly or in groups, involves a human value basis, hence they are implicitly included. Secondly, the direct analysis of values is possible only under very restrictive conditions, which are not found in most complex situations.

The limited number of "idea actions" means that the variety of processes needed can also be quite limited. One need only to get processes for generating ideas, processes for clarifying ideas, processes for structuring ideas, and processes for interpreting the structures produced.

Idea-generating methods can be used to produce sets of ideas that share a common context, simply by focusing idea generation on a particular situation through a "triggering question". Once a set of ideas is available, the ideas can be structured by first determining what relationship is to be the basis for a structuring stage, and then applying the knowledge available in the Theory of Relations and its constructive embodiment in methodology to develop a structure that includes all members of the set. A given set can be poly-structured, i.e., structured by applying several different relationships to the set, either independently or in a desired sequence. Clarification of ideas can take place using normal facilitated discourse in which the facilitator's task can be limited primarily to managing the dialog according to ordinary rules of courtesy and sequence. Interpretation of structured information can be done intuitively by many, but a very modest amount of formal education in "reading" structures will be very beneficial. All of these ideas will be made more concrete in the development of the Science of Generic Design and in the discussion of its Applications.

Processes can limit Situational Escalation very effectively. The processes are designed in such a way that the persons who possess the content knowledge about the issue or design target are role-limited, their role being only to offer their content knowledge. At the same time, specialist roles are identified for process management, so that persons who are not heavily involved with issue content specialize in the process roles. Normally those process roles will be professional roles that specifically involve management of the process. But those roles do not extend to design of the processes, for that is an outcome from the Science.

145

Processes reduce personal cognitive burden primarily through the way in which information is sequenced. If members of groups are given rein to choose the topic of their discussion at random, and if several speak at once, sensible discussion that leads to some organized product is hard to obtain. But if the process is designed so that the subject is broken down into a series of carefully-designed questions which are presented under computer control for group discussion and resolution, the dialog becomes focused and the products of the dialog can be aggregated and organized with ease. Such a design will meet with group approval, provided the group is assured that important subjects will not thereby be excluded, and that their contributions will ultimately be incorporated on all matters perceived by group members to be relevant.

Persons who are not familiar with such designed processes typically expect all of the familiar difficulties to surface with groups when such processes are used; but intuition does not serve well here. Experience with many faulty, poorly-designed processes leads observers to think that group behavior itself is pathological. Group behavior is a response to whatever process the group must face. Only experience with well-designed processes can be used to predict future experience with well-designed processes. Experience with non-designed processes is highly misleading when used to predict what will happen with a group that benefits from well-designed processes.

Well-designed processes will eliminate most situational detractors. This is fairly easy to do, because many of them are present simply because no one bothered (a) to identify them and (b) to prevent them from being present through design of an appropriate working environment. But those that are not subject to elimination by appropriate design of the environment often are a response to cognitive overload which, as has already been indicated, can be essentially eliminated by proper process design. Consequently those detractors that are generated in response to poorly- designed processes very seldom surface with well-designed processes.

Personal enhancements can also be provided by well-designed processes. For example, by simply using a round-robin approach to the presentation of ideas, the opportunity to be heard is made available. This greatly enhances the morale of the individual, and encourages the expenditure of thought and contributions to the task. The opportunity to engage in open, courteous dialog on each component issue also is a form of enhancement, because such dialog sharpens ideas and helps to reward thoughtful contributions.

4.5 Designed Environments.

Designed environments can also provide benefits like those provided by well-designed processes. The integrated design of processes and environments is mutually-reinforcing.

When the idea-generating or structuring processes produce content that is vital to problem-solving or design, a well-designed environment will provide ready visual displays to keep that information before the group. Sets of ideas can be presented on large wall displays. Such displays reduce personal cognitive burden substantially.

By designing the space and furnishings to emphasize the importance of visual access to information, personal comfort, maneuverability to align the viewing angle with location of information displayed, continuous updating and documentation, and other requirements for working with complex information, situational detractors are eliminated, and enhancement of personal capacity to contribute is achieved.

4.6 Role Specialization.

The benefits of role specialization have already been mentioned. When a topic is complex, it is important that the individuals who possess knowledge relevant to a solution or resolution should enjoy the benefits of a respectful, thoughtful, situation in which to act. Inventory of things that can be envisaged which would detract from individual capacity to be effective will show that it is critical to provide a variety of supporting roles.

Certainly a facilitator is needed to manage the process. But the facilitator role must be conceived in the light of an inventory of the essential role requirements. The role of the facilitator should be limited to holding a prior understanding of the details of the processes to be managed and of the skills needed to oversee the group dialog. Tasks that need not be attached to the facilitator role include: remembering the group products, organizing the group information in an ad hoc way, and documenting group contributions. Support can be provided to carry out those functions.

Persons in supporting roles can carry out specialized tasks. Moreover, in those tasks where numerous operations on information are needed, the computer must be called into play. Some facilitators will take special pride in being able to do many different operations. They want to manage the group dialog, reinterpret group contributions from their own perspective, keep track of group output, and introduce their own substantive contributions in considering the issue. But this requires that they distribute their focus. They may be developing what they perceive as substantive contributions when they should be applying their skill to regulate the dialog. And when processes are such that individual mistakes in dealing with information organization can invalidate contributions by the group, why should not the computer be used to hold the information?

Contributors to the solution should not be expected simultaneously to exercise motor skills at a terminal. The objective of group activity in problem-solving and design is not to use computers. It is to solve the problem or create the design. A specialist can operate the one or two terminals that need to be involved. Such specialists

147

do not need to become involved directly in the dialog aimed at solving the problem or creating the design. Computer manufacturers would like to have every human being connected to computer terminals for all time. Their group research studies tend to begin with the assumption that everyone in the group is sitting at a terminal.

4.7 Leadership.

While a variety of roles is appropriate, leadership is required of all roles, though not with equal intensity and not at all times. Leadership will be especially critical in managing complexity through design. It is once again appropriate to discuss the constituents of this attribute. In Section 1.6 there were identified what we call the four Bennis Leadership Factors, or just the Bennis Factors. These were found to be attributes of all those people who were acknowledged to be excellent leaders. The four factors that all of them were able to manage were: Attention, Meaning, Trust, and Self.

When we reflect upon the nature of change of direction in positions of great power (which is not necessarily synonymous with great leadership), such as the change in Germany under Adolf Hitler, the change in China under Mao-Tse Tung, and the change in the U. S. S. R. under Mikhail Gorbachev, we observe that persons who exercise great power will have influence upon the lives of millions or even billions of people. Even those with lesser positions may have great influence on the lives of others. Does it not seem reasonable, then, that a simple set of standards might be applied both to assess and to provide leadership? And does it not seem reasonable that a set of four factors identified as being held in common by great leaders might be applied to this end?

And does it not seem reasonable that whenever complexity is involved the need for leadership is especially strong? And does it not seem reasonable, therefore, that those who come into a position where they are able to oversee and steer approaches to the resolution of complexity should be assessed against the four Bennis Factors? And does it not seem reasonable to ask such people to accept them as a means both for striving to improve their own behavior, and to help them consciously assess their own decision-making activity?

If the Peirce tautology of four ways in which belief is fixed is seen in conjunction with the four Bennis Factors, is it not reasonable to ask that leadership strive consciously to make use of scientific results whenever it is possible to do so, and to make a significant effort to determine whether such scientific results exist even if this requires going beyond the normal practice in seeking knowledge? And given the several communication interfaces identified in Figure 3.1 as being critical to understanding, does it not seem reasonable that in complex situations one might consciously strive to assemble a team of individuals with special skills to translate across these interfaces as a part of the task of providing leadership?

But even in those lesser positions of responsibility, is it not appropriate to begin to use the Bennis Factors as a set of criteria both for educating for leadership and for selecting individuals to fill leadership roles? Is it not true that if people develop the habit of working to these standards in lesser positions, they will be quite likely to work to them as they advance into positions where they are responsible for managing complexity?

4.8 Quality Control.

Responsibility is the foundation of quality control, and criteria are the bases for it. In establishing criteria for quality control, responsible individuals are armed to exercise it. Language is the "lubricant" of quality control. While physical standards serve in specific areas, we have seen that in many other areas that involve complexity, physical standards are not available, and the stress must then be placed on the language. High-level attention to the language therefore becomes critical to quality control. Oversight and steering are the means of carrying out the leadership that is required to manage complexity. And to the extent that such oversight and steering can be informed by science, higher quality can be anticipated in all phases of human activity.

Because systems for controlling quality based upon the Bennis Leadership Factors are seldom visible, we may suppose that wherever an urge to have such a system arises there will be a concurrent task to design such a system. This task may itself benefit from referring to a Science of Generic Design for suitable methodology founded in appropriate foundations and theory.

Then in anticipation of the later presentation of such a science and applications of it, one must expect that criteria and provisions for quality control will have to occupy a prominent position in whatever is developed.

4.9 The Cultural Environment.

In the preceding discussions of the impact of environment upon high-quality work, the emphasis was upon the immediate, local, working environment.

Environment is best perceived as a graded concept. Begin with the local working environment, which may involve a single room. Then consider the specific institutional component under which the work is directly managed as the second stage in gradation. Then consider higher level encompassing components up to the total organization itself. And then go beyond this to the national cultural environment. And then consider the world itself as an environment, continuing to the envisaged limits of the universe.

In all stages of this gradation, particular influences coming from particular stages will have some impact upon the quality of design or other work activity.

Yet some of these stages are much more susceptible to design than others. The local working environment can be designed on the basis of what must be accomplished and what is known about the necessities to accomplish it. But even this local working environment is subject to approval at the highest level of the organization.

The general principle for designing environments is that there must be a recognizable authority able to give approval to the design and to ensure that it is implemented. With this principle, the most likely candidate for design other than the local working environment is the organizational environment, because it meets the conditions mentioned.

If the organization as it exists were properly designed, no design would be needed, so it is reasonable to begin discussion of organizational design with the assumptions that (a) the existing design is unsatisfactory, (b) a strategy for redesigning the organization is needed, and (c) the strategy will be informed by a Science of Generic Design (if one is available). Let us then propose a strategy and suggest how such a strategy might evolve naturally in an organizational environment over a prolonged period of time.

An Institutional Change Strategy

The compact description of a proposed institutional change strategy is, in the language of Argyris [1], "framebreaking and remodeling". Whatever cultural attributes are present, and whatever deeply-embedded assumptions are behind these attributes, there will occur over time, as a consequence of frame-breaking and remodeling, replacement of this culture, animated by new vision.

Some of the events that will typically occur en route to the change are as follows:

- External intervention in the organization with the approval of its principal executives

- The installation, in the organization, of new processes that enable the organization to carry out the interactions needed to break the old frames and design the new model [4]

- The construction and use of a new physical environment for participative design, involving newly-recognized roles staffed by actors who have been educated to fill those roles

- Use of those processes to create the new vision of the organization and elaborate its meaning, and to construct improved program criteria and means for assessment in the light of a long-term image of the organization

Some of the expected consequences of such changes would include changes in the attitude and behavior of managers; the acceptance of open problem-solving environments; more global contexts for planning; increased productivity, effectiveness, and harmony; fewer long reports; crisp, understandable design rationales; better designs; salient resource allocations; reduction in internal conflict; higher productivity; more credible programs; less waste; and greater human fulfillment.

But how is such a change likely to evolve in a way that would be consistent with the prior discussions of the deliberate use of science as the primary method for fixing belief?

Figure 4.2 showed a way of visualizing Argyris' double-loop model of problem-solving in organizations. The basic idea behind this model is that repeated failure in problem-solving within the confines of the first loop must give way to action within the second loop; and the action in the second loop must step back from the original problem and look behind it into the problem-solving assumptions, philosophy, and approach with an eye to making changes in these. But manifestly the organization will not reconstruct a new model of itself every time a failure occurs. On the contrary, we must expect that such a reconstruction will be motivated by failure in a class of problems, and that when it occurs it will have broad sweep and implications for the organization.

The Poly-Loop Model

The double-loop model of Argyris (Figure 4.2) can itself be reconstructed to make it compatible with the Domain of Science Model. Figure 4.4 shows an enlarged model called the Poly-Loop Model. One can imagine a staged view of this model of problem- solving in an organization.

Suppose first that problem-solving efforts take place without invoking any loops. Such efforts might be referred to as 0-loop problem-solving. With this approach, one applies some methodology coming from prior experience to the issue or problem, and never compares the results with what was desired.

The cybernetic approach to control involves the use of feedback and comparison. In a single-loop model, the 0-loop model is augmented by feeding back the results of actions and comparing those results with what was desired. Continued divergence of results from what was desired corresponds to the similar phenomenon in the Argyris single loop. As his studies show, it is difficult to get managers to recognize the need to go to the second loop.

In the second loop in Figure 4.4, suppose that in contrast to Argyris' concept of broad revision, only the methodologies are changed. This may perhaps be done without management acceptance of a new and broad philosophy, but as a concession to past failures which suggest that something new should be tried. It is reasonable to suppose that some successes will result from use of the new methodologies. Some of them will, no doubt, fail, as well. If enough failures occur, management may now be encouraged to recognize that the change to new methodologieswasfruitful,butthat it was not well-managed because management was not able to determine just which of the new methodologies were going to be successful and which ones were going to fail.

This suggests that management may be persuaded of the need to go somewhat deeper and look into the theories behind the methodologies, to see whether these theories offer some way to predict which methodologies are needed and under what circumstances. This involves going to loop 3, and rethinking how methodologies are selected.

Hopefully as a consequence of this, managers will find still more success in problem-solving, as they become more skilled in the choice of methodologies. But some failures will still occur, and managers may then be willing to consider which theories hold the greatest promise and, by becoming advised about the relative quality of competing theories, may achieve still greater success. But this involves going to loop 4 where the foundations themselves are examined, and thereby where finally the Argyris' goal of framebreaking may achieve its ultimate result: the replacement of the original organizational frame and the development of a new model to animate the organization.

Should such an evolution take place, it would require some consideration of the various interfaces involved in building an overall, unified meaning among diverse groups of individuals with different backgrounds and interests, as indicated in Figure 3.1. Evidently the kind of framebreaking and remodeling suggested in Figure 4.4 will require a cooperative approach that involves individuals from the various groups. Managers will have to get good advice from staff. And in order to provide the Referential Transparency in the organization that comes from leadership, it will be necessary to use processes that are very similar to those to be presented as part of a Science of Generic Design.

With framebreaking and remodeling as a goal, and with the Poly-Loop Model as an evolutionary image of the possible movement toward that goal, the Generic Design Science will provide Methodology, Theory, and Foundations that will lend insight into the practical aspects of using the Poly-Loop Model as a route to framebreaking and remodeling.

SUMMARY

Cognitive Complexity is the dilemma presented to the human mind when it engages with conceptualizations that are beyond its unaided powers. Situational Complexity represents those aspects of phenomena that are intercepted by the mind which induce Cognitive Complexity. Together the two components produce complexity which, when overcome, yields to a conceptualization that exhibits Referential Transparency.

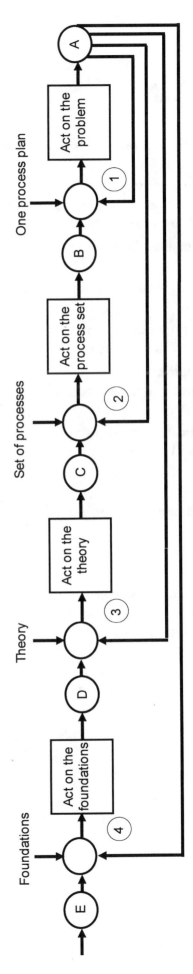

Foundations   Theory   Set of processes   One process plan

0-LOOP   Enter with a process plan. Act on the problem (as perceived via the plan) and achieve result A.

1-LOOP   Enter with a desired outcome at B and A process plans. Act on the problem (as percieved via the plan) and achieve result A. Feed back the results and compare with what is desired. Try the plan a second time, using the new information to provide additional input to the process, and achieve result A. Keep doing this until you decide that the problem is not getting solved.

2-LOOP   Enter with a desired outcome at C and a set of process plans. Act on the set on the set to pick a new plan that promises to outdo the original plan. Now use the new one to act on the problem. Feed back the results to compare with desired outcome C. Repeat with new information supplied to the new plan. Iterate as long as necessary until either the problem is solved or you conclude that the set of processes is not adequate.

3-LOOP   Enter with a desired outcome at D, and a theory. Act on the theory to develop a new process set. Provide this set as entry to the 2-LOOP situation, and keep trying until either the problem is solved or it is decided that the new theory is inadequate. Iterate with a new theory, and try again. If you still cannot solve the problem, go back to point E.

4-LOOP   Enter with a set of foundations to accompany the desired outcome entered at point E. Act on the foundations to produce a new theory. Act on that to produce new processes. Act on the problem and observe the outcomes at point A. Keep trying until you get a set of foundations, a theory, and a methodology that works. Then declare that you have a science that is relevant to the problem.

Figure 4.4   Poly-loop model.

Complexity will either be managed, or it will overwhelm the individual and the society.

The management of complexity refers to an overt, integrated mode of operation that:

- Identifies detractors to human mental activity that diminish conceptual power. Emphasis is placed on those detractors that arise from the Universal Priors and the working environment.

- Recognizes the classes of detraction, and eliminates those that can be eliminated.

- Recognizes possible enhancements to human mental activity.

- Acknowledges process requirements for providing such enhancements, including role requirements and environmental requirements to support the roles and the processes.

- Studies human performance in complex situations, and recognizes bad outcomes from such performance and the sources and commonalities of these outcomes.

- Involves the establishment of a dedicated (maxi-min) environment that maximizes the enhancements and minimizes the detractions through conscious environmental design.

- Recognizes the division of labor among roles, to provide the variety of expertise needed to implement the processes within the maxi-min environment.

- Provides for the education and training needed to fill the entire set of roles.

- Provides the resources based on the rule that even a very small percentage of the potential losses that will accrue in the event of failure can wisely be dedicated to a systematic and thorough attack on complexity itself.

- Derives its intellectual basis from a Science of Generic Design. The latter is disciplined by the Domain of Science Model, and is highly responsive to the impact of the Universal Priors.

- Adopts specific criteria, based on the Generic Design Science, as the primary basis for governing the operation.

- Assigns special importance to quality control.

Necessary conditions for managing complexity include the control of escalation of complexity, the reduction of cognitive burden on the designers, the elimination of the detraction set, and the provision of the enhancement set.

Specially designed processes can deal with information sets, can limit or eliminate escalation, can reduce cognitive burden, can eliminate many detractors, and can provide many enhancements.

An especially designed environment can deal with information sets, help limit escalation, reduce cognitive burden, eliminate many detractors, and provide many enhancements.

Leadership can draw not only on personal charisma and experience, but can also be sensitized to the importance of a set of factors that collectively promote good leadership, which have been found empirically by Bennis.

Within the organization, problem-solving can be greatly enhanced through a strategy of framebreaking and remodeling, informed by the Poly-Loop Model. An approach to instrumenting the latter is to use a Science of Generic Design, organized through the Domain of Science Model.

REFERENCES

1. Chris Argyris, *Reasoning, Learning, and Action: Individual and Organizational*, San Francisco: Jossey-Bass, 1982.

2. J. N. Warfield, "Organizations and Systems Learning", *General Systems*, Vol. 27, 1982, 5-74.

3. C. West Churchman, *Thought and Wisdom*, Seaside, California: Intersystems, 1982.

4. B. L. T. Hedberg, P. C. Nystrom, and W. H. Starbuck, "Camping on Seesaws: Prescriptions for a Self-Designing Organization", *Admin. Sci. Quarterly* 21, March, 1976, 41-65.

QUESTIONS RELATED TO CHAPTER 4

1. According to Willard Gibbs, what is the principal purpose of theoretical research?

2. What is the principal utility of a Science of Generic Design?

3. What are four necessities for managing complexity?

4. One way to discuss the management of complexity is to consider the following:
   a) necessary conditions for managing complexity, b) sufficient conditions for managing complexity, c) necessary and sufficient conditions for managing complexity. Discuss how these three descriptions differ, and which of them is likely to be realistic, given the current state of our ability to manage complexity.

5. What is the role of machines in the management of complexity?

6. What are the principal avenues to the management of complexity?

7. What is the difference between the <u>definition</u> the <u>meaning</u> of a term?

8. If someone says to you "Nytol will help you get your z's", are you hearing definitions, meaning, or neither?

9. Distinguish between situational complexity and cognitive complexity.

10. Is the merging of situational and cognitive complexity adequate to give a definition of complexity, or should other aspects be included?

11. Distinguish between phenomena and noumena.

12. What is meant by a "situation"? Did John Dewey give a clear definition of "problematic situation"?

13. List a variety of ways in which complexity can escalate.

14. What is the most essential concept behind Argyris' double-loop problem idea?

15. Select a major issue discussed in the news. Say whether it is "discussable" in those organizations to which it pertains. In doing so, deal with the past, present, and future.

16. Mention some matters that might fit the description of being undiscussable in some organizations with which you are familiar.

17. Why does situational escalation occur?

18. Distinguish between detractors and enhancers in group work.

19. Consider the ordinary approach to group problem solving, where people are brought together by a boss in a typical conference room, by discussing how each of the detractors and enhancers (Chapter 4) is dealt with in this typical process.

20. List the fundamental operations that can be carried out with ideas. Can you add to this list?

21. List factors in the environment that can be dealt with through design to help people manage complexity.

22. For quality control, what is (a) the foundation, (b) the basis, (c) the "lubricant"?

23. Let A represent a system of quality control based on physical standards. Let B represent a system of quality control that cannot be based on physical standards. Discuss how B can move toward the effectiveness of A.

24. Discuss gradation in the environment for working with complexity.

25. What is meant by "framebreaking and remodeling"?

26. What are some events that may occur in (a) framebreaking?, (b) remodeling?

27. What is meant by (a) "received language"?, (b) "received doctrine"?

28. To what extent are received language and received doctrine interrelated?

PART II

PRESENTATION

"My main thesis is that a social system is kept together by the blind force of instinctive actions, and of instinctive emotions clustered around habits and prejudices. It is therefore not true that any advance in the scale of culture inevitably tends to the preservation of society. On the whole, the contrary is more often the case, and any survey of nature confirms this conclusion. A new element in life renders in many ways the operation of the old instincts unsuitable....There is then opportunity for reason to effect, with comparative speed, what otherwise must be left to the slow operation of the centuries amid ruin and reconstruction. Mankind misses its opportunities, and its failures are a fair target for ironic criticism. But the fact that reason too often fails does not give fair ground for the hysterical conclusion that it never succeeds. Reason can be compared to the force of gravitation, the weakest of all natural forces, but in the end the creator of suns and of stellar systems: -- those great societies of the Universe."

--A. N. Whitehead

"...we will examine the dangers of this new alchemy where body counting replaces social and cultural values and excludes us from participating in decisions about the risks that a few have decided the many cannot do without. The issue is not risk, but power."

--Charles Perrow

CHAPTER 5

FOUNDATIONS OF THE SCIENCE

"God invented and gave us sight to the end that we might behold the courses of intelligence in the heaven, and apply them to the courses of our own intelligence which are akin to them...; and that we, learning them and partaking of the natural truth of reason, might imitate the absolutely unerring courses of God and regulate our own vagaries.

--Plato

"The difficulty in describing the work of [Willard] Gibbs lies precisely in the fact that it is fundamental. It is like a ponderous foundation on which so great a superstructure has been built that no one notices the foundation any more unless it is specially pointed out..."

--F. B. Jewett and Karl K. Darrow

"Uncovering the presuppositions of those who think they have none is one of the principal means by which philosophers find new issues to debate."

--Richard Rorty

Ajustification for a Science of Generic Design was offered in Part I of this book. As part of this justification, there was introduced a Domain of Science Model. According to this Model, a Science can be structured in a natural organization of the form shown in Figure 5.1. In this hierarchical structure, Foundations steer Theory and Theory steers Methodology.

In a certain broad sense, the material in Part I forms part of the foundations for a Science of Generic Design. Nevertheless it is necessary to focus sharply the conceptualization of the Foundations of the Science, in order to meet the practical needs of potential users of the Science. Therefore the material in Part I is now to be

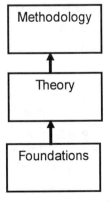

"Steers"

Figure 5.1 Steering structure of a science.

filtered, strained, congealed, and otherwise synthesized into a more highly-organized set of expressions that can be seen as the Foundations for a Science of Generic Design, chosen to satisfy the requirements for Foundations set forth in this Chapter.

Before proceeding to the Foundations, it is appropriate to draw further upon the insights gained in Part I to set forth specific requirements for a Science of Generic Design. Table 5.1 identifies four criteria that the Science must satisfy.

These criteria arise directly from Part I of this book.

Table 5.1
Criteria for a Science of Generic Design

---

1. It must be organized to provide Referential Transparency

2. It must overtly incorporate the Universal Priors

3. Its organization must be disciplined by a model of a science (and here it is so disciplined by the Domain of Science Model)

4. The Representations that it presents must be organized formally to (a) reflect sensitivity to the Universal Priors (b) incorporate self-documentation capabilities, and (c) provide for machine operations that facilitate the application of human Reasoning through Relationships, without imposing additional cognitive burden on already-overburdened human minds

---

Copyright © 1988 University of Pittsburgh

Given these conditions that the Science must satisfy, it is now appropriate to turn to the Foundations themselves. The Foundations of a Science of Generic Design originate from four principal sources: (1) research on the Universal Priors (Chap. 2), including the study of past research on them by others, and the study of ways in which such past research can be integrated, (2) the study of past research on systems by others, (3) the cumulative results of experience in working with groups on complex issues in both specially-designed and ad hoc working environments, and (4) extensive discussions with colleagues.

The purposes associated with the Foundations are of three kinds. The first kind is intrinsic to the nature of foundations, as expressed in the Domain of Science Model (Chap. 3), in which Foundations are declared to be those concepts to which final reference is made in decision-making about the science as a whole. The second kind also relates to the Domain of Science Model, but involves the linkages of the Foundations to the Theory. In regard to linkages, the Foundations must steer the development of Theory, and also must be responsive to what is learned from Applications of the Science, being steered by that learning. This learning will either reinforce what is contained in the Foundations or cast doubt upon some part of that content, thereby stimulating amendment and improvement. The third kind emanates from the general requirement to contribute to the universal scientific goal of Referential Transparency.

In response to these purposes, and as a result of the learning that has come from the identified origins, it has been concluded that contributions to these Foundations can be organized appropriately in six categories. Four of these are the Universal Priors. The other two are the Design Situation and the Design Process. They incorporate considerations of the Target of Design and of the Design Environment, as well as process outcomes.

In the following development, postulates are set forth for these areas and, in the light of these and the foregoing, a suggested way to evaluate the Foundations is given.

5.1 Postulates of the Human Being.

The first set of postulates relates to the human being, with emphasis upon human attributes that are critically important in design.

HB-1. Bounded Rationality. Every Actor in a Design Process has a Bounded Rationality (Sec. 2.1).

HB-2. Error Detection. The Actor's ability to detect errors in the Representations of other Actors is much higher than the ability of the Actor to detect self-made errors.

HB-3. Unshakeable Cognitive Burden. Every Actor who takes part in a Design Process has an Unshakeable Cognitive Burden (Sec. 1.4).

HB-4. Self-Calibration. Every Actor who takes part in a Design Process has limited powers of Self-Calibration.

HB-5. Internal Reasoning. Successful processes of human reasoning are neither sufficiently understood nor sufficiently common to all human beings to be a prominent part of the basis for a Science of Generic Design.

HB-6. Virtual World. At the outset of a Design Process, every Actor involved in it possesses a Virtual World stemming from life experience, which incorporates a view of the Design Situation that is unique to that Actor.

HB-7. Restricted Access. Every Actor in a Design Process has only restricted access to the Design Situation.

5.2 Postulates of Language.

The next set of postulates relates to those features of language that are most critical in making decisions about the content of a Science of Generic Design.

L1. Eternal Referents. The high quality of communication associated with physical science stems from the existence of universal, eternal referents (Sec. 2.6) called primary standards.

L2. Language Surrogate. For any science that incorporates components for which no eternal referents exist in nature, the corresponding quality of communication must be attained in each individual Design Situation, through management of the language and its usage in that Situation (Sec. 2.6).

L3. Structural Inadequacy of Prose. Prose alone is inadequate to present structured information in a science that must both (a) deal systematically with complexity and (b) possess Referential Transparency.

L4. Natural Language. Natural language is insufficient as the means of representing Targets of design (Sec. 2.2).

L5. Object Language. An Object Language of Design, with Natural Language as its describing Metalanguage, is the minimum expectation for a Language of Design (Sec. 2.2).

L6. Object Language and Referential Transparency. Comprehension of the Object Language of Design (Sec. 2.2) is necessary to provide Referential Transparency (Sec. 1.5) in a Science of Generic Design.

5.3 Postulates of Reasoning Through Relationships (Sec. 2.3).

Continuing with postulates related to the Universal Priors, the following deal with Reasoning through Relationships.

RR-1. Protracted Logic (Deep Logic and Long Logic). Protracted Logic (Deep Logic and Long Logic) is integral to complexity and its resolution.

RR-2. Formal Logic Representation. If the Language of Design provides an adequate collection of well-defined, stand-alone terms to describe the Design Situation, then the long-standing methods of presenting formally the results of human reasoning are sufficient to provide a basis for expressing what must be expressed in order to define a Target Design.

5.4 Postulates of Archival Representation (Sec. 2.5).

With regard to the way in which the products of design activity are presented, the next set of postulates refers to Archival Representations.

AR-1. <u>Target Description</u>. The Target of Design must be unambiguously described in the Representations of the Science.

AR-2. <u>Target and Design Situation</u>. The Target of Design must be unambiguously related to the Design Situation in the Representations of the Science.

AR-3. <u>Target of Design</u>. In most design, the Target of the design activity will be a realization in the Residue, following the prescriptions appearing in the Representations.

AR-4. <u>Origins of Formalism</u>. The only formalism presently available that is (a) sufficiently fundamental, (b) sufficiently well-developed, and (c) sufficiently broad to meet the requirements for a Science of Generic Design is the Theory of Relations in its most fully developed form (which is understood to incorporate all of its isomorphic Representations).

AR-5. <u>Origins of Representations</u>. Representations are mappings from the Phaneron to the Library.

AR-6. <u>Ad Hoc Representations</u>. Ad Hoc Representations (i.e., those which cannot be or are not embedded in some formal language from mathematics) invite errors in communication, promote vagueness and misunderstanding, severely inhibit the ability to work with large amounts of relevant information, and lie outside the realm of scientific development.

5.5 Postulates of the Design Situation.

The Design Situation is that Arena into which the Generic Design Science is introduced as an ameliorating agent. But in order for the Science to serve in this capacity, it is important that the Design Situation be captured adequately to permit design to be insightful.

DS-1. <u>Understanding</u>. Understanding of the Design Situation is critical to successful system design.

DS-2. <u>Underconceptualization</u>. Underconceptualization promotes failure.

5.6 Postulates of the Design Process.

The Science of Generic Design must provide processes that serve in Applications. The assumptions made about processes will be pivotal to the quality of the processes.

DP-1. <u>Integration and Disintegration</u>. The participative, mutual testing of Virtual Worlds transforming integration of their strengths and disintegration of their weaknesses into amended Virtual Worlds is a powerful means of upgrading belief.

DP-2. <u>Finite Resources</u>. Every Design Process is limited in extent by the finiteness of resources.

DP-3. <u>Stopping Rule Requirement</u>. Every component of a Design Process requires a termination statement called a "stopping rule".

DP-4. <u>Ad Hoc Stopping</u>. Ad hoc stopping promotes underconceptualization.

DP-5. <u>Appropriate Stopping Rule</u>. Acknowledgment by all actors of their inability to offer relevant additional concepts to the design process is an appropriate stopping rule, both to the process and to its component processes, unless such acknowledgment stems from "groupthink" situations.

DP-6. <u>Environment and Process Outcomes</u>. The outcome of the design process depends significantly upon the Design Environment.

DP-7. <u>Maxi-Min Environment</u>. An Environment that maximizes human effectiveness and minimizes identifiable detractions will strongly support the process of development of effective design outcomes.

DP-8. <u>Failure Condition</u>. Failure of an activity typically can come from inadequacy of a single factor.

DP-9. <u>Success Condition</u>. Success of an activity typically depends on a <u>set</u> of <u>several</u> success factors, as opposed to depending on a <u>single</u> factor which alone could produce success.

The last two Postulates may be amplified as follows. To any design activity there corresponds, in general, a set of AND-BUNDLES, each consisting of a set of factors that are <u>all</u> necessary for success of some component of the activity; and likewise there corresponds a set of OR-BUNDLES, each consisting of a set of factors such that if <u>any one</u> is not present, failure of the component to which it pertains will occur.

Further it is held that to any <u>feasible</u> design activity there corresponds at least one SUCCESS BUNDLE, consisting of sufficient conditions for success. From this, at least one AND-BUNDLE and at least one OR-BUNDLE of the type described above can be extracted. It is further held that in some Situations there will be no known way either to discover or to achieve the requirements of a SUCCESS BUNDLE, in which case the design will be described as <u>unrealizable</u>. A SUCCESS BUNDLE will, in general, originate from connecting the Design Situation with the factors that are developed in the process of transforming the Postulates into Theory and, ultimately, into Methodology for Generic Design Science, in line with knowledge from Applications.

5.7 Evaluation Criteria for the Foundations.

Criteria for judging the Foundations are of three types. These are: (a) the Purpose Served, (b) Responsiveness to Prior Contexts, and (c) Attributes of Utility.

Purpose Served

There are three criteria related to the purpose served. The first is that the Foundations provide a basis for decision-making in developing the Theory and Methodology components of the Domain of Science Model, when it is applied to discipline the development of Generic Design Science. The second is that the Foundations should steer the Theory. The third is that the Foundations shall enhance Referential Transparency in the Science.

Responsiveness to Context

There are four criteria of Responsiveness of the Foundations to Context. These are responsiveness to (a) the definition of Generic Design initiated in Section 1.7, (b) relevant prior science, (c) the Universal Priors, and (d) relevant empirical evidence from previous Applications of the Generic Design Science.

Attributes of Utility

There are four criteria relating to Attributes of Utility of the Foundations. They all have to do with the statements that make up the foundations. These statements should be (a) sharply distinguished, (b) clear, (c) likely to be relatively stable through time, and (d) succinct.

SUMMARY

The evaluation of the proposed set of Foundations is based on Responsiveness Criteria, (b) Criteria of Purpose, and (c) Criteria of Utility.

The Foundations consist of sets of postulates that have been chosen to reflect the requirements imposed upon the Foundations by the criteria to be satisfied by a Science of Generic Design.

The Foundations of Generic Design Science are required to inform the Theory. They are also required to be vulnerable to research on Applications, in which they must either be upheld or must be reexamined and modified. In this way, the Domain of Science Model disciplines the development and application of the Science of Generic Design.

QUESTIONS RELATED TO CHAPTER 5

1. What criteria should be satisfied by a science of generic design?

2. What are three purposes of Foundations of a Science?

3. What are the six "Postulate areas" for the Science of Generic Design?

4. Write a short essay describing the human being as seen in terms of the Postulates of the Human Being.

5. What is meant by "self-calibration"?

6. Discuss the structural inadequacy of prose.

7. Distinguish natural language from object language.

8. What is meant by "protracted logic"?

9. What is meant by "origins of formalism"?

10. What is meant by a "representation"?

11. What is meant by "underconceptualization"?

12. What are some causes of underconceptualization?

13. What is meant by "integration of Virtual Worlds"?

14. What is meant by "stopping rule"?

15. What criteria are used to judge the foundations of a science?

16. Why are the foundations of the Science of Generic Design comprised of sets of postulates?

CHAPTER 6

THEORY OF THE SCIENCE

It is the first step in sociological wisdom to recognize that the major advances in civilization are processes
which all but wreck the societies in which they occur -- like unto an arrow in the hand of a child.
The art of free society consists first in the maintenance of the symbolic code; and secondly in fearlessness of revision,
to secure that the code serves those purposes which satisfy an enlightened reason. Those societies which cannot
combine reverence to their symbols with freedom of revision, must ultimately decay either from anarchy,
or from the slow atrophy of a life stifled by useless shadows.

--A. N. Whitehead

The primary functions of Theory are (a) to explain the key concepts of the Science, and (b) to anticipate the consequences of the Theory for Methodology. The priors to Theory include the Foundations of the Science in which the Universal Priors are incorporated. The Foundations provide the basis for Laws of the Science. Interpretation and elaboration of the Laws take place in Principles of the Science. To the extent that the application of Methodology can benefit from clear Role definitions and from a designed working Environment for Applications, Theory must provide the requisite steering to the definitions of Roles and Environment.

Just as Foundations are steered by (and incorporate) the Universal Priors and by empirical evidence coming from Applications, so the Theory likewise must be steered by these, but normally through the way they are incorporated in the Foundations. The Theory may also be steered by prior science from any source that is of adequate relevance and quality.

Figure 6.1 shows the general framework of this Chapter, as a "implication structure". It is seen that the Postulates imply the remainder of the structure (implication is a propagating relationship, described in Sec. 2.4).

A Theory of Dimensionality, introduced briefly in Sec. 2.5, is first elaborated as a major component of a Theory of Generic Design. Next there is presented a set of Laws of Generic Design, which are primary components of the Theory. Following this is a set of Principles which elaborate the Theory in the direction necessary to arrive at Criteria for Methodology.

An approach to evaluation of the Theory concludes the Chapter.

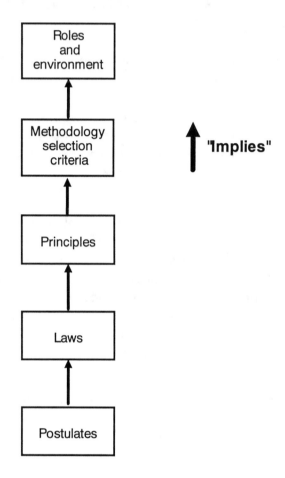

Figure 6.1 Implication structure for generic design science.

6.1 The Theory of Dimensionality.

The structural theory of situations and processes introduces the Options Field and Options Profile as key products of design activity. The former is describable as a Triply-Structured-Quad (TSQ) (Sec. 2.5). It is a Quad because it is a four-level structure, whose levels are named: Target, Cluster, Dimension, and Option, reading from the top down. It is triply-structured because its structure incorporates three distinct relationships.

The <u>first relationship</u> takes a set of options as the elements to be related. The relationship among the options is one of <u>membership in a dimension</u>. When this relationship is clarified, it will be seen that options for attaining the Target fall into a collection of sets, each of which represents one dimension.

The <u>second relationship</u> takes the just-discovered set of dimensions as the elements to be related. The relationship among the dimensions is one of <u>interdependence</u>. If several dimensions are interdependent, they form a cluster, so the second relationship places the dimensions into clusters.

The <u>third relationship</u>, also one among the dimensions, is a <u>time-preference relationship</u>, showing in which time sequence choices should be made from among the dimensions. This relationship is developed after the interdependence (if any) is known, in order that each set of interdependent dimensions may be treated as a cluster, with choices being made among the interdependent dimensions as an integrated decision-making task.

Knitting a Tapestry

For a given TSQ, it may be necessary to knit to it at the lowest (fourth) level another overlapping TSQ, wherein an option from the first TSQ becomes a design Target for a second TSQ. Other instances of this situation may occur, so that the final structural portrait of the Target design may consist of a Tapestry of TSQ's, arrayed hierarchically.

Since sets frequently occur in the TSQ's and elsewhere, it is helpful to keep in mind the impact of Bounded Rationality upon the human mind. In structuring sets, those that have exactly three members enjoy a special quality: even when all three members of the set interact, the cardinality of the power set being considered (i.e., the original set of three together with all the possibly-interacting subsets that can be formed involving more than one member -- excluding the null set) does not exceed the so-called "magical number" seven (Sec. 2.1). With more than three members, there is always the possibility that the mind cannot simultaneously recall or consider the interactions and make good judgments. For this reason, <u>triads</u> (sets with three members) and <u>tetrads</u> (sets with four members, which might have only modest interaction), are to be emphasized wherever possible, as they tend to represent mind-compatible divisions. Sets having eight or more members should generally be divided into subsets, each of which involves triads or tetrads.

When the TSQ or collection of TSQ's forming a Tapestry is completed, it provides the representation from which design choices may be made. Such choices can be represented at any stage of the Design Process by "tying" design options to the "Tie Line" (Sec. 6.2) used to form the Options Profile from the Options Field. Such a Profile represents one Design Alternative.

169

The Necessity for a Space

The Theory of Dimensionality takes as fundamental the requirement for a space in which the dimensions are embedded. That such a space is necessary follows from the concept that complex systems involve knowledge from many disciplines, but not merely as multidisciplinary components. As is well-known in academic circles, the term "multidisciplinary" is more likely to be interpreted as an unintegrated collection of information components than as an integrated body of knowledge that has given up the disciplinary identity of its components.

But how is knowledge to be integrated and thereby positioned for application, unless there is some underlying key to its integration? And must not this necessarily involve a commonality of form and an accepting receptacle that is sensitive to the requirements of integration, rather than sustained distinction? The idea that a "space" furnishes the framework for integration lies just beneath the surface of every branch of mathematics. It is almost impossible to imagine that there can be some totally new concept unlike that of mathematical space that somehow furnishes us with the framework and means of relating, which has totally escaped the attention of mathematical scholars during their twenty-five hundred years of relatively unconstrained search for means to formalize all kinds of thought.

Mathematical space and relation represent two ideas that are absolutely fundamental to systems thinking. One can visualize mathematics itself as a family of spaces elaborated by definitions, theorems, and operations. But of course mathematics is not to be perceived just as a field of scholarship possibly having potential applications; rather it is like a massive mine containing all kinds of valuable ore. And like the mineral deposits of the world that have furnished us iron to build our buildings, aluminum to build our airplanes, copper and silver to carry our electricity, platinum to help eliminate air pollution from auto exhausts, gold to sustain a medium of exchange that is indifferent to political systems or deficits or the passage of time, natural gas and petroleum to heat our homes, and petroleum to power our automobiles and ships; mathematics offers us a host of conceptual frameworks in which to embed our thinking, and in which to operate with our ideas. Thus our task is to find that branch of mathematics that offers the attributes needed to enable the integration of knowledge to be carried out.

While dimensionality has been a backbone concept for physical science, it has only weakly been applied in the social sciences and then often as a metaphor, rather than as a component of the practitioner's art. Yet it is almost unthinkable to believe that some mathematical framework could be discovered that would enable the integration of knowledge as needed from many disciplines, while at the same time not providing the means of representing information dimensionally and thereby shutting out the physical science components from the larger analysis.

Thus it seems natural to conceive of an extension of the concept of dimensionality that (a) accommodates to its interpretation in the physical sciences while (b) generalizing upon that concept as required in order to accommodate knowledge from other disciplines (or even from non-disciplines).

The idea of dimensionality has been highly conditioned (and thereby unduly constrained) by the classical views of our understanding of geographic space and time. Most of our intellectual work typically involves information presented in two-dimensional form, and most of our spatial observations involve perceiving motion in a three-dimensional geographic space, occurring as time (a fourth dimension) unfolds. Motion in space and time is undoubtedly the most vital part of physics, with key discoveries by Galileo, Newton, and Einstein being among the most important and well-known intellectual developments in recorded history.

Along with these common views of dimensionality, one typically assigns to the dimensions, without question, numerical values. Thus time is recorded in terms of numbers, and space is recorded in various quantified units whose meaning is relatively secure as a result of the common understanding of the eternal referents.

Perhaps the most notable invasion of this basic view of dimensionality was made by J. Willard Gibbs and others who developed thermodynamics and statistical mechanics as a discipline. Through this branch of science we are able to envisage, for example, an object moving through time and space while exchanging energy with its environment, so that not only its position changes, but also its temperature changes, the energy that it stores changes, and even its size and weight may change, with at least some of these variables being interpreted as dimensions.

A somewhat more comprehensive view of what constitutes a dimension tends to be supported by this kind of model. Spatial dimensions are of interest because they allow us to make precise the variations in position of an object or particle at different times. Quantified variables tell us properties that may be important in describing and guiding action.

The idea that a dimension is a physical variable subject to quantification is sufficiently broad to allow us to include, as dimensions, not only a particle's position in space and time, but also a measure of its electricity or magnetism, as well as measures of its thermal properties involving energy and mass.

Being somewhat more general than a definition that encompasses only space and time, we can say that the definition just expressed dominates the earlier definition for two reasons:

- It encompasses the earlier definition
- It extends the definition to a larger class of situations

Thus we can begin to perceive the notion of gradation of concepts, as discussed in the Preface, being applied to the concept of dimensionality.

But the definition given must be extended to higher grades, because as stated so far, quantification is a necessary condition for its use. As already indicated, this condition cannot be allowed to stand. When it is required that factors be taken into account that are not defined in terms of a standard, any quantification will be arbitrary and may even be stilted in order to meet an artificially imposed quantification requirement.

Narrow definitions tend to be disabling to progress. They often are restrictive in application, and also may tend to be accepted without question, along with a host of adjunct ideas that are restricted by association, thereby preventing wider exploration and application.

A generic definition of dimensionality has the potential for dominating all other definitions extant and proposed, and could offer the great benefit of being applicable across the board in many fields of science and in many applications.

Among the questions that need to be aired en route to discovery of a generic definition of dimensionality we may include the following:

- What is required of a definition to serve both the purpose of (a) observation and description of a system and (b) design and implementation of a system?

- What is the meaning and significance of the dimensionality of a system?

- Given a system, is its dimensionality a constant over time, or can it change?

- What are the properties of dimensionality?

- Does human intervention in a system affect its dimensionality?

In responding to these questions, we begin with the Doctrine of Necessity (Chap 1). As described earlier, to apply this doctrine we imagine that certain concepts are withdrawn from the realm of possibility and observe the effects on other concepts to examine connections among concepts.

Suppose we agreed to withdraw from our analytical framework elements and relations. We could work with whatever remained, but none of the remaining things could be elements and relations. It seems crystal clear that thought would then be totally disabled. Elements and relations are among the small set of primitive ideas that underlie our thought.

If we tentatively impose the restriction that we will consider only theories that are founded in some kind of mathematical space, we can then assert that any such space will include elements and relations. We can designate the set of all elements by the symbol E and the set of all relations by the symbol R, all with reference to an imagined space that contains them.

172

We may then assert formally that a space is given by

$$S = \{E, R, Z\}$$

where Z, left undefined for the present, consists of all those components of the space S, if any, not included in the sets E and R. If nothing more can be found, Z may be taken as the empty set Φ.

According to the definition of relation given by Wiener [1], a relation is a subspace of a space definable in terms of the set E. But if this definition is accepted for relation, one also accepts automatically the concept that a space is the universal relation. But the universal relation is nothing more than the set of all n-tuples, i.e., expressions of the form $(x_1,x_2,x_3,...,x_n)$, in which the x's are allowed to range over the set of all possible assignments. It has been illustrated by example that this interpretation applies equally well to situations where the x's are quantifiable variables of the type commonly seen in physics, and where the x's are concepts having a qualitative nature [2]. Part of this interpretation is that a dimension is a set of elements of the same type lying in the same space. This definition leaves open the determination, in any given situation, of the criteria for type definition, and for assigning elements to particular types.

One of the principal reasons why generalization of the concept of dimensionality has been so slow in coming is that there has been no satisfactory way to represent high- dimensional phenomena. Fortunately this situation has changed with the introduction of concepts of fields and profiles, as the next section will illustrate.

6.2 Representations.

Every Representation is a structured set. The set may be singly-structured or poly-structured. Or it may be a set of sets, each of which may be singly-structured or poly-structured; and the set of sets may also be singly-structured or poly-structured. Two general types of Representation are an integral part of the Theory of Dimensionality: the field representation and the profile representation.

Figure 6.2 illustrates both the field representation and the profile representation. The field representation is that part of the Figure that would remain if the heavy lines connected to the bullets preceding the elements were removed. What would remain would be the headings, the elements grouped into sets, and the tie line(s). The profile representation is the entire Figure, including the embedding of the lines in the field. The lines correspond to a restriction of the field (which represents the space) to a subset that forms the relation, as defined by Wiener. The Figure illustrates several of the advantages of the field and profile representations, when compared with previous modes of representing the dimensionality of a space:

- The representation accommodates a 10-dimensional space

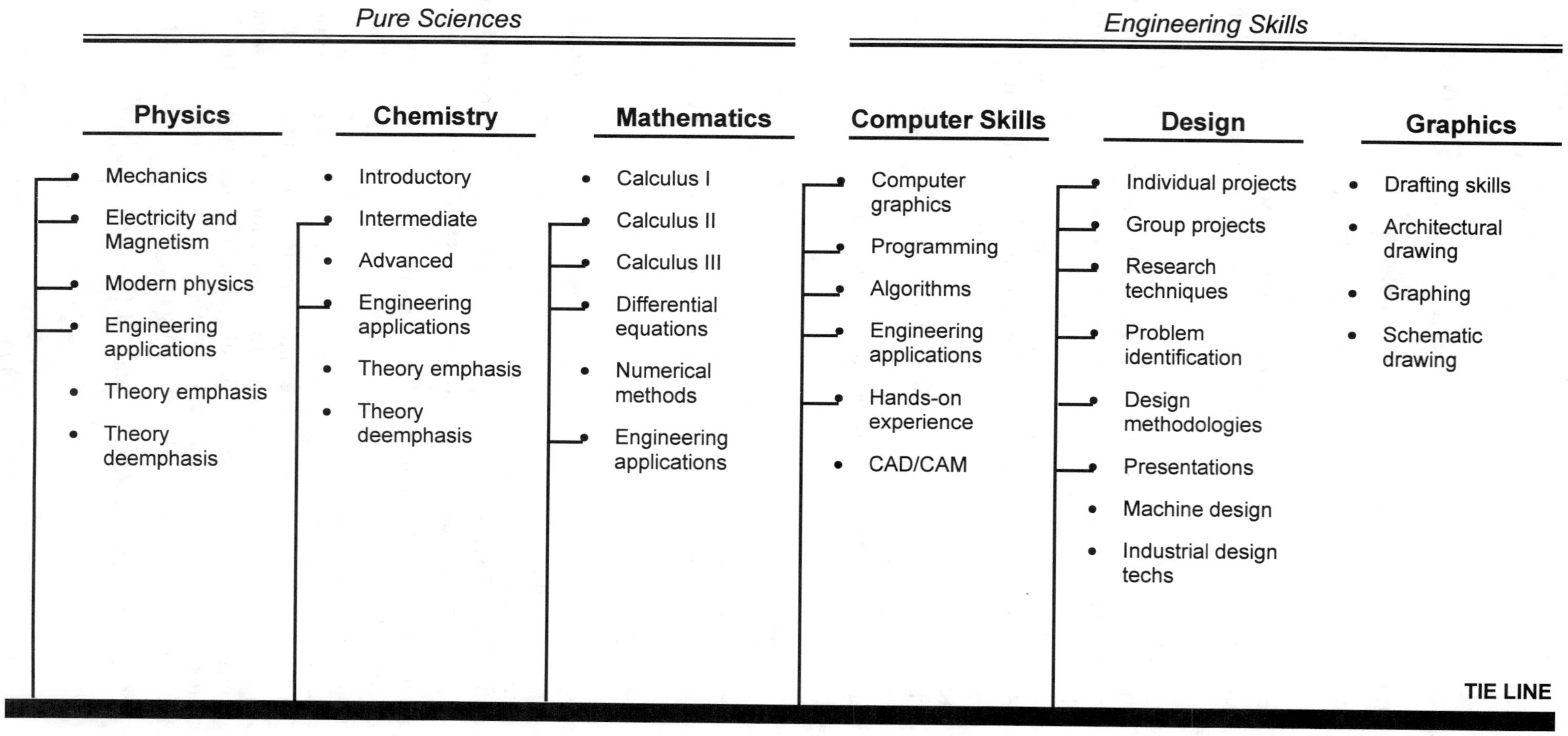

174

Figure 6.2 Representation of an alternative in a ten-dimensional space. (Continued on next page)

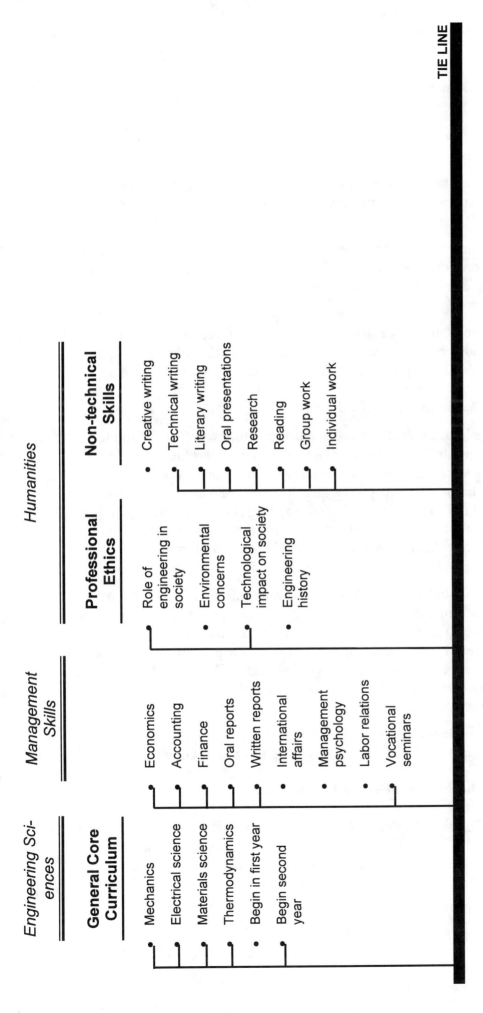

*Engineering Sci-
ences*

*Management
Skills*

Humanities

**General Core
Curriculum**

- Mechanics
- Electrical science
- Materials science
- Thermodynamics
- Begin in first year
- Begin second
  year

**Management
Skills**

- Economics
- Accounting
- Finance
- Oral reports
- Written reports
- International
  affairs
- Management
  psychology
- Labor relations
- Vocational
  seminars

**Professional
Ethics**

- Role of
  engineering in
  society
- Environmental
  concerns
- Technological
  impact on society
- Engineering
  history

**Non-technical
Skills**

- Creative writing
- Technical writing
- Literary writing
- Oral presentations
- Research
- Reading
- Group work
- Individual work

TIE LINE

Figure 6.2 Representation of an alternative in a ten-dimensional space. (Concluded)

175

- The same representation can be extended to spaces of any finite number of dimensions

- The profile on the representation allows portrayal of a particular sub-space, corresponding to some chosen concept of interest, e.g., a design alternative

- Within a dimension, this representation allows for choice or portrayal of a simple option (just one member of the set that makes up a particular dimension) or a composite option (several members of the set that make up that dimension)

Science thrives upon "stopping rules", but such rules are very elusive. They are responses to the question: how can we tell when a theory, methodology, or experiment is complete? In the Theory of Dimensionality, primary questions of this type are: "how can we tell when all the dimensions have been found?" and "how can we tell when we have all the components of a dimension?"

The stopping rule informs us about these matters as follows. First of all the rule states that you cannot tell when all the dimensions have been found, nor can you tell when you have all the components. The reason you cannot tell is that you are a finite being with finite mental capacity, and the world of complete discovery does not cater to such limitations. Secondly, the stopping rule states that "stopping occurs when the relevant actor(s) or expert(s) have exhausted their ideas". This is pragmatic, practical, and realistic. It satisfies philosophical requirements, is consistent with behavioral research results, and gives the practitioner useful guidance.

There is a third point to be relearned from the stopping rule. This is the often stated but not always internalized aspect of science which admits its vulnerability, its incompleteness, its fallibility, and its perpetual need for continuing assessment. But this aspect also is tempered by the philosophy of interim acceptance of the best available knowledge as guidance for action, in recognition that while a higher grade of knowledge may become available tomorrow, it is also possible that it will not be known for hundreds of years, if ever.

Further discussion of dimensionality will be found in Chapter 7, where its specific use in design will be discussed. Our discussion now turns to Laws of Generic Design.

6.3 Classes of Laws of the Science of Generic Design.

The Laws of the Science of Generic Design fall into two classes. The first class is designated "External Laws". These are Laws that arise outside of the Science and are of more general application. In effect they are made available to the Science of Generic Design to become Laws of this Science, without prejudice to their more general character.

The second class is called "Intrinsic Laws". These are Laws whose primary province appears to be the Science of Generic Design.

In Sec. 6.2 there was a discussion of "stopping rules". That discussion is relevant here to the question of when it would be known that the Laws of Generic Design have all been discovered. Consistent with the prior discussion of stopping rules, one may say that there does not appear now, and there may never be, any way to show that all such Laws have been discovered. What can be said now is that six Laws will be offered, partitioned into the two categories. These Laws are sufficiently well-established that their value to a Science of Generic Design can be articulated and, consequently, can be subjected to careful review by any skeptics.

6.4 External Laws of Generic Design Science.

Two External Laws of Generic Design Science are the Law of Limits and the Law of Gradation. Each of them will be discussed in turn.

The Law of Limits

The <u>Law of Limits</u> asserts that <u>to any activity in the universe there exists a corresponding set of Limits upon that activity, which determines the feasible extent of the activity</u>.

The significance of this Law to the Science of Generic Design is that it conveys the importance of discovering (a) what the Limits may be upon design in general and how these Limits may relate to any particular Design Situation and (b) those additional Limits that are at work in a particular Design Situation.

This Law has strong implications for the development of Theory because it imposes upon Theory the requirement that the Theory contain explicit identification of <u>generic</u> Limits and explicit provision for the incorporation of <u>special</u> Limits.

In addition to the illumination provided by the Law itself, several Corollaries add further insight.

The <u>first Corollary</u> to this Law asserts that for any particular situation, the set of Limits can be partitioned into two blocks: an <u>active</u> block and an <u>inactive</u> block. This Corollary is called the Corollary of Active Limits.

The active block is the subset of the set of Limits that is determining at a given time, while the inactive block is not determining at that time.

The active block may often consist of a single, dominating member of the set of Limits. Such a member may be so strong in its power to limit that, in effect, all other Limits are forced into hiding by the dominant one. When this occurs, it has both advantages and disadvantages. An advantage is that the designer who recognizes this situation can focus attention upon the dominant Limit and look for ways to modify its impact. A disadvantage is that the non-active Limits may go unrecognized, only to make their impact felt later upon the design activity that has focused overly on overcoming the dominant Limit.

The second Corollary to this Law asserts that the set of Limits also can be partitioned into these two blocks: movable and fixed. A movable limit is one that can be altered, while a fixed limit is one that is unchanging. Clearly if there is a dominant Limit and it is fixed, the potential exists for wasting substantial amounts of time, effort, and resources if one does not understand that it is fixed. On the other hand, if one mistakenly assumes that a Limit is fixed, when it really is movable, the potential exists for missing opportunities for major improvements. This Corollary is called the Corollary of Movable Limits.

The third Corollary to this Law asserts that the movable subset of Limits can be partitioned into these two blocks: movable through discretionary action by people, and autonomously movable. Limits that are autonomously movable change on their own, and thereby drive the system. Clearly the strategic posture for dealing with such Limits is to maintain cognizance of their status and to have some predetermined alternatives in mind for coping with them when they move into prominence. This Corollary is called the Corollary of Discretionary Action.

Limits that are movable through discretionary action by people are, of course, those that should be clearly recognized by designers, and to which attention should be given in the event that they are not overshadowed by more prominent Limits that effectively nullify the latent impact of those lying in the background.

The fourth Corollary to this Law asserts that the membership of the active blocks and of the inactive blocks of the partitions changes with time. If, for example, discretionary action brings about a change in some moveable Limit that previously was dominant, one or more new Limits will take the place of the previously dominant Limit. This Corollary is called the Corollary of Shifting Limits.

The Law of Limits does not provide any means of identifying the Limits or of partitioning them after they have been identified. This capability must arise from other sources.

The Law of Gradation

The Law of Gradation asserts that any conceptual body of knowledge can be graded in stages, such that there is one simplest stage, one most comprehensive stage (reflecting the total state of relevant knowledge), and intermediate stages whose content lies between the two extremes. The importance of this Law to the Science of Generic Design lies in the guidance that it provides to the designer concerning how to perceive any particular Design Situation with respect to the Science.

In this respect, one notes that design Targets may range from very small, limited-scope Targets to very large, broad-scope Targets.

It is not reasonable to take as a criterion for Generic Design Science that all of its Theory and all of its Methodology should be demonstrably required for all design activity. On the contrary, such a Science would be too brittle for use. The Law of Gradation overtly recognizes that Design Situations and Design Targets are themselves graded according to a variety of descriptions, not all of which can be foreseen. Accordingly, the Science of Generic Design should be applied judiciously, extracting from it one of its stages that is most appropriate for the particular Design Situations and Design Target.

The word "generic" does not mean "always required". What it does mean is "covering the set of gradations of Design Situations and Targets as a whole, without overlapping the applicable Specific Design Science; but subject to judicious restriction commensurate with the grade of the Design Situation or Design Target in any particular instance."

It is not the function of a Science of Generic Design to provide a recipe appropriate to every Design Situation. It is the function of such a Science to actuate the designer's professional responsibility to assess and correlate the gradation in the Situation and Target against the total sweep of the Generic Design Science; and to choose that restricted version of the Science which will be used openly, rather than to accept subliminally a restricted version that leads to underconceptualization of the Design Situation and the Design Target. It is the further function of the Generic Design Science to provide the means of documentation consistent with what the Design Situation requires.

The first Corollary to this Law asserts that the class of situations to which a conceptual body of knowledge may apply, in whole or in part, likewise may be graded according to the demands that individual situations can reasonably make upon the body of knowledge. This is called the Corollary of Congruence, because it relates to the congruence between the Design Situation and Target with a restricted grade of the Generic Design Science that is called into play in the specific case. Clearly the designer is not required to uncover every detail of relevance, no matter what the cost. When in doubt, a conservative posture will call for erring on the side of the higher grade.

The second Corollary to this Law is the existing economic Law of Diminishing Returns, which states that the application of a body of knowledge to a Design Situation should be made through that stage at which the point of diminishing returns to the Situation (as opposed to only the user) is reached. This is called the Corollary of Diminishing Returns, and it highlights a major responsibility of the designer to make judgments about when this point is reached. Once again, a conservative posture will call for erring on the side of the higher grade.

The <u>third Corollary</u> to this Law states that the identification of the stage at which diminishing returns to the situation is reached normally requires the integration of the Virtual Worlds of the affected parties in the situation in relation to the dimensions of the situation. This is called the <u>Corollary of Restricted Virtual Worlds</u>, and it reflects the need for a global point of view in making the kinds of judgments that are required to achieve the appropriate congruence of gradation.

6.5 Intrinsic Laws of Generic Design Science.

Four Intrinsic Laws of Generic Design Science will be discussed. These are: the Law of Success and Failure for Generic Design, the Law of Requisite Variety, the Law of Requisite Parsimony, and the Law of Requisite Saliency. Each of them will be discussed in turn.

The Law of Success and Failure for Generic Design

The <u>Law of Success and Failure</u> for Generic Design asserts that <u>there are seven critical factors in the SUCCESS BUNDLE for the Design Process</u>. It further asserts that <u>inadequacy in any one of these factors may cause failure</u>. The seven factors are: leadership, financial support, component availability, design environment, designer participation, documentation support, and design processes that converge to informed agreement.

This Law indicates that a Science of Generic Design must define these critical factors in sufficient depth to enable (a) the assessment of their adequacy and (b) their application in the Design Situation. Success and failure must also be elaborated and, in this context, success in all stages of work, including the implementation and operation, is required in order to proclaim that the design is successful; while failure in any stage is sufficient to constitute failure of the design.

This Law furnishes the impetus for what is called the Sigma-N Concept to be elaborated in Sec. 6.9. This Concept will also be relevant to the use of the Law of Gradation, as will be seen.

The Law of Requisite Variety

The <u>Law of Requisite Variety</u> indicates the <u>need for a match between the dimensionality of the Design Situation and the Target of the Design Process</u>. This Law was discovered by Ashby [3], the version being presented here having been inspired by his work and informed by the Theory of Dimensionality given in Sec. 6.2.

This Law asserts that <u>a Design Situation embodies a requirement for Requisite Variety in the design specifications</u>. Every Design Situation S implicitly represents an (initially unknown) integer dimensionality K_s such that if the designer defines an integer K_m number of distinct specifications (whether qualitative or quantitative or a mix of these), then:

i) If $K_m < K_s$, the Target is <u>underspecified</u> and the behavior of the Target is outside the control of the designer

ii) If $K_m > K_s$, the Target is <u>overspecified</u>, and the behavior of the Target cannot be compatible with the designer's wishes

iii) If $K_m = K_s$, the design specification exhibits Requisite Variety, provided the designer has correctly identified and specified the dimensions; and the behavior of the design should be that which the Situation can absorb and which the designer can control, subject to the requirement that the dimensionality of the Situation is not modified by the introduction of the Target into the Situation. If the dimensionality is changed thereby, the design process can apply the Law of Requisite Variety iteratively, taking into account the dynamics of the Situation.

The Theory of Dimensionality has been introduced, in part, to make possible this formulation of the Law of Requisite Variety, especially to enhance applicability of it to those situations where some dimensions are naturally quantitative and some are naturally qualitative, requiring that both kinds of dimensions be in a common space and subject to comprehensive interpretation in order to achieve a sound design result.

The question might be raised as to how designers have succeeded in the past in the absence of overt response to this Law. Many, if not most, Targets of design are redesigns that benefit from decades of experience which have permitted the development of intuitive knowledge that substitutes for overt application of this Law. Regrettably, it is this same cumulative experience that mistakenly leads designers and their managers to believe that somehow they can intuitively design systems much larger in scale that have never been designed before.

The Law of Requisite Parsimony

The <u>Law of Requisite Parsimony</u> indicates a need for <u>controlling the rate of presenting information for processing to the human mind</u>, in order to avoid its overload during the Design Process.

This Law has been formulated in the light of the findings of Miller, Simon, and others concerning bounded rationality of the human mind. Its statement has been tailored to be responsive to their findings.

Every individual's short-term brain activity lends itself to dealing simultaneously with approximately seven items (a number that is reached with three basic items and four of their joint interactions). Attempts to go beyond this scope of reasoning are met with physiological and psychological Limits that preclude sound reasoning. For a given designer, there is some number K_d that is characteristic of that designer which typically is chosen from the set {5,6,7,8,9} that represents the Limit of that designer's short-term idea-processing capability. If a design methodology requires a designer to cope intellectually at any one time with some number of concepts K_c, then

i) If $K_c < K_d$, the designer is <u>underburdened</u>, being uninfluenced by the Law of Requisite Parsimony, since the designer is operating in a Situation that exhibits the Requisite Parsimony, through regulation of the rate of flow of information to the designer as the designer engages in the design process

ii) If $K_c = K_d$, the designer is <u>operating at the Limit</u> of reasoning capability

iii) If $K_c > K_d$, the designer is <u>overburdened</u> and no reliance can be placed on the designer's decisions.

It can be confidently predicted that the Target will embody bad outcomes that are beyond the control of the designer, because the design process did not exhibit the Requisite Parsimony, but instead allowed the rate of flow of information to the designer to exceed processing capacity.

It may be questioned why designs have succeeded in the past without overt adherence to this requirement. Again one must consider the Law of Gradation, and note that design Targets vary tremendously in their scope. If this Law is being unknowingly violated, one would expect that the impact would be revealed in the failure of large system designs. This is precisely what is being observed all around the world. Those who doubt this Law must accept the burden of providing other explanations for the failures. The explanation of "operator error" may often, itself, reflect the same fundamental cause to which this Law responds in terms of the design process.

The Law of Requisite Saliency

The <u>Law of Requisite Saliency</u>, supported by empirical evidence showing that wide variability invariably exists among members of task forces in their assessment of relative saliency of factors pertaining to a complex situation or to a complex issue (Appendix 5), insists that <u>the Design Process must incorporate specific provisions for human learning that offer the strong possibility of diminishing significantly the variability in perception of relative saliency of design options</u>. The statement of the Law is as follows.

<u>The situational factors that require consideration in developing a design Target and introducing it in a Design Situation are seldom of equal saliency</u>. Instead there is an underlying logic awaiting discovery in each Design Situation that will reveal the relative saliency of these factors.

Characteristically individuals who become involved in the design process exhibit great diversity in their assessment of relative saliency (App. 5). This diversity, if uninfluenced by thorough exploration of the Design Situation, will support unfocused dialog, unjustified decisions, and arbitrary design outcomes not likely to be understood or even actionable.

The design process must incorporate specific provision for uncovering the relative saliency of the factors in the Design Situation and the factors that characterize the Target, in order to achieve the kind of understanding that is needed to put the design factors in proper perspective.

6.6 Linking Foundations to Theory.

Foundations are linked directly to theory by connecting individual postulates to the Theory of Dimensionality and to the six Laws that have been set forth. Indirect linkages are found by connecting the six Laws to the Principles offered in Sec. 6.7.

The present section links the Foundations to the Theory through Table 6.1 by showing how postulates from each of the six major divisions in Chapter 5 inform the Theory of Dimensionality and the six Laws.

6.7 Principles of Generic Design.

The Principles of Generic Design form a set of concepts stemming from the Laws. The Laws provide broad guidance, but the Principles provide specific direction, and thereby bring the thinking contained in the Laws closer to practical applications.

While each Principle set forth in the following is numbered, the numbers are not intended to convey relative importance; since relative importance will depend upon the specific Design Situation, and the congruency of gradation of the Situation and the Generic Design Science. Rather the numbers are intended to be markers that enable people to point directly to a Principle and share a discussion or critique without incurring undue search time to locate specific statements.

In addition to numbering these Principles for ready reference, there is a parenthetical note following each that indicates which of the several Laws strongly support that Principle. A mnemonic coding is used to key to the Laws:

- LL, the Law of Limits
- LG, the Law of Gradation
- LSF, the Law of Success and Failure for Generic Design Science
- LRV, the Law of Requisite Variety
- LRP, the Law of Requisite Parsimony
- LRS, the Law of Requisite Saliency

Table 6.1
Linking Foundations With Theory

Category	Theory of Dimensionality	Law of Limits	Law of Gradation	Law of Success and Failure	Law of Requisite Variety	Law of Requisite Parsimony	Law of Requisite Variety
Human Beings	1,2,3,4,5,6,7	1,2,3,6,7		1,2,3,4,5,6	6,7	1.3.4	2,3,4,5,7
Language	2,3,4,5,6	3,4		2,3,4,6		6	1,3
Reasoning Through Relationships	1,2		1,2	1,2		1,2	1,2
Archival Representation	1,2,3,5	4,6	4	1,2,6		4,5,6	6
Design Situation	1,2		2	1,2	1,2	1,2	1,2
Design Process	1,3,4-9	2,6,7,8,9		2,6,7,8,9	1,8,9	6,7,8,9	1,8,9

P1. <u>The Principle of Designing by Groups</u>. Design should be carried out participatively by groups, the membership of which is chosen to help ensure that the requisite variety in the Design Situation is articulated (LSF,LL,LRV).

P2. <u>The Principle of Articulated Dimensions</u>. Design groups should sort descriptions of the Design Situation into dimensions, and they should then sort options for the Target description into dimensions, for the purpose of developing congruency between the Design Situation and the description of the Target (LSF,LRV).

P3. <u>The Principle of Computer Support in Defining Dimensions</u>. The computer should play a major role in the work, being used in ways that enhance the capacity of the group to be productive, without introducing new detractions. This includes a computer role in assisting in the development of the dimensions of the Design Situation and the Design Target (LSF,LL,LRP).

[This Principle does <u>not</u> assert that the members of the participant group should spend time operating computers. The operation of the machines is relegated to specialists.]

P4. <u>The Principle of Interdependent Clusters</u>. Those dimensions of the Design Situation and of the Design Target that are interdependent should be grouped into Clusters, and retained both as wholes to be examined collectively and individuals to be specified integratively, in the interests of avoiding system failures due to interactions caused by these interdependencies that otherwise would go unexamined in the design process (LSF,LRV,LRP,LRS).

P5. <u>The Principle of Formal Iteration</u>. The design process must be formally iterative with respect to the development and assessment of all relevant logic structures that bear on the description of the Design Situation and of the Design Target (LRP).

P6. <u>The Principle of Computer Support in Iteration</u>. The computer must provide support to the group in its iterative work having to do with the logic structures that describe the Design Situation and the Design Target. The types of support that are to be provided include support in (a) developing and organizing the initial structures, (b) displaying those structures, (c) testing them for correctness and completeness (when appropriate), and (d) amending them as required (LRP,LRS).

[Again, this does <u>not</u> mean that individual participants should be engaged in operating computers, as this task is left to specialists.]

P7. <u>The Principle of Sequencing the Dimensional Choice-Making</u>. Before developing a design Alternative, the design group should experience a process in which they are asked to consider in depth the sequences in which choices should be made from among the design dimensions, in order to recognize the benefits of grading the choice-making so that the most salient choices are made first and, in following the sequence of gradation, the least salient choice is made last (LRP,LRS).

P8. <u>The Principle of Computer Support in Sequencing</u>. Sequencing of choices in the design dimensions should be computer-assisted (LRP,LRS). [Again, a specialist operates the computer.]

P9. <u>The Principle of Visible Design Status</u>. The preparation and maintenance of large, continually-updated displays of design status is essential to maximize productivity, minimize errors due to faulty human memory, and to provide clear evidence of on-line documentation and design progress (LRV,LRP,LRS).

P10. <u>The Principle of the Special, Dedicated, Design Laboratory Environment</u>. A specially-designed and appropriately equipped design environment should be used to support the work, with the environment being designed in the light of the Generic Design Science (LRV,LRP,LRS).

P11. <u>The Principle of Specialty Role Distinctions</u>. Responsibility for control of three distinct design concerns: (a) content, (b) context, and (c) process, should be assigned to three distinct specialty roles, each role being designed in accordance with the requirements of each of these three specialties (LRV,LRP,LRS,LSF,LL,LG).

P12. <u>The Principle of Actor-Role Congruence</u>. The choice of actors to fill the roles of providing appropriate content, context, and process, should be a formal process of matching actors to role descriptions that have been prepared specifically for a design situation; and may involve assigning multiple actors (groups) to particular roles in order to meet the requirements of those roles (LSF,LRV,LRS).

185

P13. <u>The Principle of Individual Cybernetic Embedding</u>. In the light of the now-recognizable human shortcomings in system design, the individual designer should learn self-reference criteria for self-assessment of the fragility and fallibility of the individual actor in a design process. Designers should then apply these criteria as guidelines to place and sustain themselves in learning networks, being thereby embedded cybernetically in a network of self-corrective feedback loops. They should likewise help create the discipline of being systematically informed by sustained, iterative documentation, and appropriate cognitive assistance in complex endeavors.

The multiple, self-governing, self-reference criteria should be applied by designers to govern their own behavior, in the light of the Bennis leadership factors, namely, the management of attention, meaning, trust, and self (LL,LSF,LG,LRV,LRP,LRS).

P14. <u>The Principle of Criteria-Selected Design Methodologies</u>. A choice of overtly-articulated criteria that lead to criteria-selected design methodologies should be available, founded in relevant science, to enable design groups to achieve worthwhile design outcomes (LL,LG,LSF,LRV,LRP,LRS).

P15. <u>The Principle of Sigma-N</u>. The Principle of Sigma-N asserts that there are N factors that are critical in determining success or failure, and that the assurance that the factor-integration (represented by the Sigma) is adequately supported is the primary function of management in oversight and broad steering roles (LSF).

P16. <u>The Principle of Oversight and Steering</u>. It is the role of the actors who provide oversight and steering to design to learn (rather than to invent) the science that relates to design, and to learn when this science should dominate activity and events; and to test proposed or ongoing activity to determine whether such dominance is being effected; and, if it is not, to take the necessary remedial steps to bring about the needed dominance, in the interests of successful design (LL,LG,LSF,LRV,LRP,LRS).

6.8 Screening Criteria for Generic Design Methodology.

The methodologies admitted to use in carrying out Generic Design should be restricted to those that meet criteria stemming from the Foundations and Theory of Generic Design Science. The methodology-screening criteria reflect the dual-basis concept of Generic Design. The behavioral aspects associated with the human being and the creative and productive performance of the human should provide one part of the basis for the criteria for screening. The logical aspects associated with language and the documentation of reasoning through relationships should form the other part of the basis for the screening criteria. Integrating these two aspects produces a sizeable number of screening criteria for methodology, which most of the hundreds of methodologies suggested by various authors will not meet. Table 6.2 shows screening criteria.

Table 6.2
Screening Criteria for Generic Design Methodology

1. Provide constructive group capabilities for generating and structuring ideas, for designing alternatives, and for doing tradeoff analyses.

2. Possess explicit dual (anthropological and logical) design basis.

3. Provide in the anthropological basis for full role definition, enhancement of facilitator (Pilotos) credibility, and means for group maintenance.

4. Couple to a strong, sound, historical basis.

5. Show openness.

6. Enhance transferability of the product of its use by providing on-line documentation.

7. Promote group design efficiency.

8. In promoting group maintenance, do not demand infeasible behavior from participants; promote full participation; and provide opportunity for focused group dialog in structuring, designing alternatives, and doing tradeoff analyses.

9. Offer special properties (such as some unique benefit when compared to competing methodologies), such as anticipating future automation to increase utility, and being transferable from source organization to client organization without a major training requirement.

10. Do not require those who are content-knowledgeable to dilute their group effort by requiring them to sit at a computer terminal; but delegate computer-terminal operation to an individual who is expected to be very capable in that role, but not to contribute to the substantive discussion of the issue.

6.9 The Sigma-N Concept.

The Law of Success and Failure in System Design, together with Principle P-15 have introduced the Sigma-N Concept. The Sigma represents the idea of integration, and the N represents factors to be integrated in order to achieve success.

The Law of Gradation is relevant to the Sigma-N Concept, because it suggests the possibility that the value to be assigned to N will depend upon the particular Design Situation.

The Law of Success and Failure identifies seven critical factors in the SUCCESS BUNDLE for the design process. If some particular subset of k factors is chosen from this SUCCESS BUNDLE, one could say that the Sigma-k restriction of the general situation is being applied.

To make this clear, suppose that in some particular Design Situation, the context makes clear that financial support and component availability (two of the factors mentioned in the Law of Success and Failure) are readily available, but that in this situation, the critical factors of leadership, design environment, designer participation, documentation support, and design processes have not been integrated. Then we would say that we are dealing with a potential Sigma-5 situation.

It has been found in practice that the Sigma-7 and Sigma-5 concepts are the most significant, with other numerical values such as Sigma-1 and Sigma-2 representing situations that are normally ineffective in dealing with complex issues.

If designer participation can be assured, if a design environment that meets the necessary criteria (see Chapter 8) can be made available, if the design processes (see Chapter 7) can be found that are adequate to the task, if documentation support is available, and if the proper type of facilitative leadership (represented by the term Pilotos, see Chapter 7) can all be integrated to permit sound design to take place, the Sigma-5 Concept then forms the general descriptor of the working context for the design activity. Further discussion of this Concept will appear in Chapter 8, after additional background has been provided.

6.10 Steering Functions of the Theory.

The Theory presented in this Chapter, as stated earlier, must provide steering functions for processes, for design environments, and for roles.

Chapter 7 will present the processes that this Theory steers. Chapter 8 will present a discussion of the design environments, and how the Theory relates to them; as well as a discussion of the roles, and how the Theory relates to them.

6.11 Evaluation Criteria for Theory.

How can Theory be evaluated? The ultimate test must lie in its consequences in Applications. But for this test to be possible, a certain discipline is required in applying the Methodology that is steered by the Theory. Unless the Methodology is faithfully applied, it will not be possible to generate enough valid test information to make an assessment possible. Observation of the way complex design issues have been dealt with in the past indicates that the lack of adherence to disciplined methodology is commonplace. If lack of discipline is an invariant, this lack in itself carries one of the classical properties of a scientific finding. And one might then conclude from the frequent failures that lack of discipline in Methodology is one of the (possibly) several causes of the failure.

Other tests could involve consistency checks that match the logic of Foundations against the logic of Theory, and match the logic of Theory against the logic of Methodology. Such tests only establish consistency or lack of consistency in the Science itself.

Putting the two test concepts together, we arrive at the double requirement that (a) the Science be logically consistent internally (which provides the necessary internal Referential Transparency) and that (b) its faithful use provides success in Applications. These two criteria are tempered by the eternal requirement upon science that findings from Applications be used as appropriate to produce amendments in the relevant science.

SUMMARY

The primary functions of Theory are to explain the key concepts of the Science, and to anticipate the consequences of the Theory for Methodology. The priors to Theory include the Foundations of the Science, as well as the Universal Priors. The Foundations provide the basis for Laws of the Science. Interpretation and elaboration of the Laws take place in Principles of the Science. To the extent that the application of Methodology can benefit from clear Role definitions and from a designed working Environment for Applications, Theory must provide the requisite steering to the definitions of Roles and Environment.

Just as Foundations are steered by the Universal Priors and by empirical evidence coming from Applications, so the Theory likewise must be steered by these, but normally through the way they are incorporated in the Foundations. The Theory may also be steered by prior science from any source that is adequately relevant and of adequate quality.

The Theory of Dimensionality forms an introductory part of the Theory of Generic Design Science. It provides the basis for transforming contexts into mathematical spaces of a certain type, namely a logical type founded in the Theory of Relations.

Six Laws form part of the Theory of the Science. Two of these are general Laws that relate to larger contexts than Generic Design. Four of them are particularized to Generic Design.

The Principles of Generic Design assert that design should be carried out participatively by groups chosen to help ensure that the requisite variety is articulated. Moreover the groups should sort options for the design into dimensions, in the light of a description of the Design Situation also arranged by dimensions.

The computer should play a major role in the work, being used in ways that enhance the capacity of the group to be productive, without introducing new detractions. This includes a computer role in assisting in the development of the dimensions of the Design Situation and the Design Target.

The design process must be formally iterative with respect to the development and assessment of all the major structural logic configurations that may naturally arise. Sequencing of choices in the design dimensions should be computer-assisted, as should the preparation and maintenance of large, continually-updated displays of design status.

A specially-designed and appropriately equipped design environment should be used to support the work, with the environment being designed in the light of the Generic Design Science.

Responsibility for control of content, context, and process should be divided among three role types, one type for each of these three aspects of design concern.

Multiple, self-governing, self-reference criteria should be applied by designers to govern their own behavior, in the light of the Bennis identification of four critical factors in effective leadership; namely, the management of attention, meaning, trust, and self.

The methodologies admitted to use in carrying out generic design should be restricted to those that meet criteria stemming from the Foundations and Theory of Generic Design Science.

The methodology-screening criteria reflect the dual-basis concept of Generic Design. This means that the behavioral aspects associated with the human being and the creative and productive performance of the human should provide one part of the basis for the criteria for screening; while the logical aspects associated with language and the documentation of reasoning through relationships should form the other part of the basis for the screening criteria. Integrating these two aspects produces a sizeable number of screening criteria for methodology, which most methodologies will not meet.

The Methodology, steered by the Theory, requires an integrated assessment against the criteria developed in the Theory. To the structural considerations just mentioned, it is necessary to add further considerations in order to distinguish those methodologies that meet the criteria to be useful in Generic Design. Finally the Sigma-N Concept is an integrating concept that can be used as a guide to oversight and steering of the design process in specific situations.

REFERENCES

1. N. Wiener, "A Simplification of the Logic of Relations", *Proc. Cambridge Philosophical Society*, 17, 1914, 387-390.

2. J. N. Warfield and A. N. Christakis, "Dimensionality", *Systems Research* 4(2), June, 1987, 127-137.

3. Ross Ashby, "Requisite Variety and Its Implications for the Control of Complex Systems", *Cybernetica* 1(2), 1958, 1-17.

QUESTIONS RELATED TO CHAPTER 6

1. Whitehead says that "the major advances in civilization are processes...". What might be the rationale for using the term "processes" in this way? Give some examples that illustrate his statement.

2. What are the primary functions of theory?

3. What are the three main components of the Theory of the Science?

4. What does the term "quad" signify?

5. What is meant by "triply structured"?

6. What is meant by "knitting quads together"?

7. What is meant by "tapestry"?

8. What does a tapestry show?

9. What is the graphical way to show that a certain option has been selected?

10. What is meant by a "mathematical space"?

11. What has produced our common current concept of dimensionality?

12. What is meant by "one definition dominates another"?

13. What is the Doctrine of Necessity?

14. What formal definition is used for a space?

15. What is an n-tuple?

16. Expand on the statement: "every Representation is a structured set".

17. What are the two general types of Representation that are an integral part of the Theory of Dimensionality?

18. What does a stopping rule tell us?

19. What are the two classes of Laws of Generic Design Science?

20. What are the names of two External Laws of Generic Design Science?

21. What does the Law of Limits say?

22. What does the Law of Gradation say?

23. What are the names of four Intrinsic Laws of Generic Design Science?

24. What does the Law of Success and Failure say?

25. What does the Law of Requisite Variety say?

26. What does the Law of Requisite Parsimony say?

27. What does the Law of Requisite Saliency say?

The following six questions pertain to the Laws given in Chapter 6.

28. How many of the six Laws are influenced by the Postulates of the Human Being?

29. How many of the six Laws are influenced by the Postulates of Language?

30. How many of the six Laws are influenced by the Postulates of Reasoning Through Relationships?

31. How many of the six Laws are influenced by the Postulates of Archival Representation?

32. How many of the six Laws are influenced by the Postulates of the Design Situation?

33. How many of the six Laws are influenced by the Postulates of the Design Process?

34. How many of the types of postulates influence the Theory of Dimensionality?

35. Explain the Sigma-N concept. Illustrate with various values of N.

36. What criteria may be used to assess Theory?

37. What is the dual-basis concept of generic design?

CHAPTER 7

METHODOLOGY OF THE SCIENCE

"The concept of systemic relations, though not new, has been developed in the last few decades
to an extent which should be welcome, since it is the key to understanding the situations
in which we intervene when we exercise what initiative we have and especially to the
dialectic nature of human history. It has, however, become so closely associated with man-made systems,
technological design and computer science that the word 'system' is in danger of becoming unusable
in the context of human history and human culture. I seek to contribute something to its rescue
and restoration. For we need it for understanding and for action in human and social contexts
far too complex and imprecise to admit of formal modeling."

--Sir Geoffrey Vickers

M ethodology consists of prescribed process components, singly or in sequence, each of which is dedicated to attaining specific products, both tangible and intangible, related to problem-solving and design. The priors to Methodology are to be found in Theory and Foundations.

Some workers in the Arena have invented methodologies that are tailored to specific Applications needs, but which are presented without noting or emphasizing connections to any prior Scientific Corpus. Such methodologies can be judged initially and temporarily on their immediate consequences in problem-solving or design situations. Nevertheless the lasting benefits come from adherence to the ideals of science in developing, applying, evaluating, and amending Methodology.

Frequently, the focus for the development of methodology is thought to lie in specific applications, involving particular contextual features, thereby tying methodology to some particular subarena, such as banking, electrical engineering, writing legislation, developing computer software, or designing power plants. If all methodology is so perceived, the consequence will be that people working in one area will have little language or experience in common with people in another area, thereby creating instance after instance of difficulty in working across application areas. While it cannot be denied that each of these areas does contain some unique aspects, the uniqueness is much less than might be imagined.

Methodology for Generic Design Science is viewed not in terms of these specific areas, but rather as an area that is common to almost all human beings, no matter what kinds of specific activities occupy their attention. That area is the area of <u>ideas and operations with ideas</u>.

There are just a few operations that are carried out with ideas when doing design. <u>The small number of types of operations is what makes possible and practical the development of Generic Design Science</u>. The primary types are as follows:

- <u>Generation</u> of ideas
- <u>Clarification</u> (interpretation) of ideas
- <u>Structuring</u> of ideas
- <u>Interpreting Structures</u> of Ideas
- <u>Amending</u> of ideas

Reflecting upon these five types of design operations, individuals may elect to test their own activity to see whether these categories do not encompass most of what they do with ideas. The fact that people do these things naturally might induce some to believe that it is superficial to imagine that benefits would be attained by electing to carry out these operations using very highly prescribed methodologies. After all, why use formalities when things come naturally? But such a view is only admissible when confined to those situations where the scope is limited, the consequences of errors in communication are few, the organization of knowledge is neither difficult nor critical to proper interpretation, and the requirement for careful documentation to serve numerous purposes is absent. None of these descriptors applies to the design of large-scale systems where the consequences of errors in communication may be very expensive in resources and life, the organization of knowledge is critical to its proper interpretation and application, and careful documentation is required in order to be responsible to the many who are affected by its absence or by low-quality documentation.

As is often the case, excellent results can be obtained with methods that are localized to a particular type of operation. What is most important in using such localized methods is that the total set of <u>methods</u> is conceived with a global view or holistic view of the total set of <u>requirements</u>, and that the component methods complement each other in relation to this overall perspective.

In Sec. 1.7 it was indicated that the Divisions of Design could be identified as conceptualization, choice, and documentation. The foregoing Divisions of Operations with Ideas clearly contribute to conceptualization and choice. It can be shown that they also contribute to high-quality documentation. This requirement often is ignored or underconceptualized in some very expensive and socially significant areas.

Criteria for choice of Methodology stem from the Laws and Principles in the Theory. These criteria can be applied stringently to individual methods, and relaxed only if necessary to obtain a set of components that satisfies the collective needs for design purposes.

Methodology is also correlated with capacity to help eliminate the detractors identified in Chapter 4. It must also serve to enhance mind function.

It has already been indicated that the Methodology component of a Science of Generic Design must serve the needs of groups of people working collaboratively. As the Law of Gradation implies, nothing about Methodology so conceived implies that it cannot or should not be used at times by individuals acting alone; but it will nevertheless be described in terms of its primary requirement for collaborative activity. The component methodologies selected for this purpose were chosen to meet the criteria set forth in the Theory. And because they embody attributes that support and generally produce consensus or near-consensus, they were designated as "Consensus Methodologies" in the early 1980's. Extensive testing of them since that time in a wide variety of applications has revealed nothing to suggest that this nomenclature is inappropriate.

Seven methodologies were chosen to satisfy the requirements for Generic Design Science. They are: Ideawriting (also called Brainwriting), Nominal Group Technique (NGT), DELPHI, Interpretive Structural Modeling (ISM), the Options Field Methodology (OFM), the Options Profile Methodology (OPM), and the Tradeoff Analysis Methodology (TAM). Each of these methodologies will be discussed in this Chapter. Every one of them is self-documenting in the sense that as these methodologies are used, the information produced through their use becomes the documentation needed to provide an "audit trail" of the design activity. This is a very important feature that distinguishes these methodologies individually from many others. Various sequential combinations of them can be packaged to form self-documenting processes. Included in such aggregate processes are those that correspond to the four types of design operations with ideas mentioned earlier in this chapter. Consequently, the use of these methodologies in the various "packages" permits a very versatile approach to system design, while assuring that high-quality documentation of participant contributions is achieved, consistent with the knowledge held by the participants.

It will be recalled that the Generic Design Science is complementary to the Specific Design Sciences. Nothing in the Methodology of Generic Design Science prevents the supplementary use of any aspect of any of the latter. On the contrary, any appropriate part of any of them can be introduced at any time as an integral part of the activities carried out using the seven Consensus Methodologies.

7.1 The DELTA Chart.

A common type of representation called the DELTA Chart will be used to describe these Consensus Methodologies. The DELTA chart was first introduced in 1971 [1]. In terms of the experience gained with it, and the perspectives since developed, it can be seen as a prototypical structural form specifically designed to show a temporal relationship. Its general applicability is indicated by the explanation of the acronym DELTA. The acronym has the following connotations:

- The D stands for "decision"
- The E stands for "event"
- The L stands for "logic element" (i.e., AND or OR)
- The T stands for "time"
- The A stands for "activity"

The choice of these five as the components of a structure intended to portray temporal relations reflects the belief that these five make up a sufficient set both to describe and to prescribe any process adequately.

The decision D indicates a selection from two or more options, each of which is represented on the chart.

The event E occurs at a particular instant of time that typically corresponds either to the initiation or the conclusion of an activity.

The logic element L either represents a logical "AND" operation or a logical "OR" operation.

The logical "AND" operation represents that two or more immediately preceding components must occur before anything succedent can take place; while the logical "OR" operation represents that anything succedent can take place as long as any one or any combination of priors have occurred. (This "OR" is, therefore, what is called an "inclusive or" in formal logic.)

The element T represents a relationship of time precedence; e.g., the relationship "occurs before" or "should precede". Following the convention described initially in Chapter 2, this element is represented by an arrow showing the sequence being followed by the other components.

The element A represents an activity having a beginning, an end, and a duration. Unlike the Event which is characterized by a single instant of time, the Activity is characterized by three time values corresponding to the beginning, the end, and the duration of the Activity.

Sensitization to Graphics Language

Experience with the DELTA chart has shown that people, in general, either were not sensitive or have been desensitized to the importance of each component symbol used on the chart. Among the things that have not been understood is the notion that poorly-conceived graphical symbols have the power to produce cognitive overload. Those in the information industries tend to use a variety of symbols quite freely, using a variety of shapes to represent different ideas. In our view symbols should be given as much respect and attention as vials of explosive fluid. They should not be tampered with. They should be as simple as possible to draw, while making those distinctions that seem essential. They should not be preemptive and thereby foreclose possibilities.

The language of music illustrates very well the requirement that whatever symbols are used should be readily translatable into prose equivalents. The combined use of graphics and prose (Language Type 5, Table 2.2) is readily observed in sheet music. Such a language thereby attains the degree of communications rigor required to allow its readers to replicate the composer's intent, even though the feature of translatability into prose is seldom or never formally used. It is like the sky, present but not operated with; yet we would not know what to do if it were absent. Though there is no incentive to write out in prose the full information content of the sheet music, it is only the fact that such an activity is made feasible by the design of the language that permits the message to be conveyed through the centuries to diverse cultures which do not share even the same natural language.

Notably also, in sheet music, no writer imagines that by substituting a new kind of symbol for a half note a remarkable feat of creativity will be acknowledged. Instead the view is that the symbols from the language are sacrosanct. What is important is the particular combination and sequence of symbols which the composer's work represents.

Nor is it to be supposed that the language of sheet music was developed without regard to cognitive burden or human limitations. On the contrary, this notation reflects a beautiful synergism between the rate at which the human can read and exercise motor skills and the volume of symbolism to be assimilated per unit of time. It also illustrates an application of the Law of Requisite Parsimony in a situation where the effects of ignoring this law would produce immediate detection. (Regrettably in many non-musical situations detection does not occur until long after the fact.) Imagine the sound of "Eine Kleine Nachtmusik" played by an orchestra whose members are reading the prose version of the sheet music rather than the music as supplied by music publishers. If you can imagine this, you can be sensitive to the critical nature of simple, standardized language, faithfully applied, and tailored to minimize human cognitive burden and maximize human readability.

With this in mind, the specific symbols used to represent the components of the DELTA chart will now be introduced, and in light of the contribution made by music to our understanding of graphical communication needs, we will ultimately illustrate the use of the DELTA chart to show a simplified version of how the process of making reeds for oboes is carried out.

Overview of DELTA Charts

Every methodology is characterized by at least one sequence of activities. The DELTA Chart enables portrayal of sequences that involve a mix of activities, decisions, and events. It is often true that several sequences are possible, depending on which of several intermediate choices is made by the user as a sequence evolves. Also certain events may be expected to occur in the sequence which are worth spelling out to add greater definition. Other flexibilities will become clear as the discussion unfolds. Carrying out the sequences amounts to following the methodology to its logical conclusion. Thus a DELTA Chart can be viewed as a prescription for action. In this sense, it is like a recipe. But unlike a recipe a DELTA Chart may include decision points where different courses of action are followed at the discretion of the user. Some of the advantages that DELTA Charts provide to users are:

- Common Language. Once the user masters the DELTA Chart language and format, the user will be able to read with facility all of the graphical methodology descriptions, and will not have to learn a new (and probably idiosyncratic) format every time another methodology is discussed.

- Compact Description. Once the user learns a methodology, the DELTA Chart can serve as a compact reminder and descriptor of the methodology, which can be hung on a wall or used in a notebook in a flexible way. Also it is a teaching aid.

- Clarity of Sequencing. In contrast to a strictly verbal description of a methodology, wherein long sequences are hard to present and hard to remember (especially when the sequences include options), the DELTA Charts show clearly most or all of the sequencing involved in using the methodologies, thereby providing a clarity that is hard to attain without a graphical language.

- Nesting. Activities, Events, or Decisions can be nested. For example, a single Activity Box can itself be represented by a DELTA Chart that shows a sequence of lesser Activities, Events, and/or Decisions which, collectively, describe the single Activity in much greater detail. By using this principle of nesting, individual Charts can be created that provide broad overview as well as the most minute detail, with an inclusion structure being used to guide the reader to some desired level of scrutiny.

Comparison with English

The DELTA Chart can be thought of as a new language, a graphical language focused upon one of the several types of relationship given in Table 2.7. It can be compared with English as follows. The English language is made up of building blocks such as nouns, verbs, pronouns, adverbs, etc., while the graphical language includes the English expressions together with boxes that identify the prose contained there as a decision, an event, logic, or an activity. Also the graphical language includes directed lines representing time precedence, and includes a special symbol to portray the end of a sequence.

To understand how sentences are put together in English, one learns to distinguish the building blocks and how they are related. Likewise, to understand how sequences are created using the graphical language, one learns to distinguish the various kinds of boxes from one another, how to read sequences represented by graphical paths, and how to interpret the meaning represented by a path.

Fortunately, it doesn't take nearly as long to learn the graphical language as it does to learn English. However it does require some effort and practice. The reader who is willing to take the time to learn the DELTA Chart terminology and use should find that the investment is amply repaid by the convenience of using the DELTA Charts.

Elements, Connectives, and Relationship

The three main ingredients of DELTA charts are elements, connectives and a relationship. The elements are of three types: Decisions, Events, and Activities. There are two connectives: AND and OR. The relationship shows the order in which elements occur in time, and is designated as "time precedence".

Graphics Principles

Three graphics principles are applied to the extent possible in the DELTA Chart concept. They are as follows:

- A different graphic symbol should be assigned to each distinct type of entry on a graphic chart, to help the reader make a visual discrimination among the different entries

- The symbols should be as easy to draw as possible, preferably using only straight lines

- The number of different kinds of symbol should be no more than seven, if possible (see Table 2.1)

All of the DELTA Chart symbols can be drawn with only straight lines, and they are intended to be compatible with simple computer-drawn graphics. Each symbol is distinguished in some way from other types, but simplicity is the goal rather than elaborate means of discrimination.

Portraying an Activity

An Activity is portrayed on a DELTA Chart by a rectangular Activity Box, divided into an upper cell and a lower cell. The form of the Activity Box is shown in Figure 7.1.

The lower cell of the Activity Box will contain a verbal description of the Activity. It will always be written so that an action word appears first. For example, an Activity could appear as follows:

Carry coals to Newcastle

Note that the action word "carry" appears first. The presence of the action word at the beginning identifies the phrase as the description of the Activity.

The upper cell of the Activity Box is sometimes left empty on a DELTA Chart. If it is empty, it is still shown to make sure that the box can be visually identified as an Activity Box. Normally the upper cell contains the name or title of an "actor". An actor may be a person, a group, an organization, a specific kind of social role, a machine, or even a collection of organizations. Whatever designation appears, it is intended that the actor be the one to carry out the Activity.

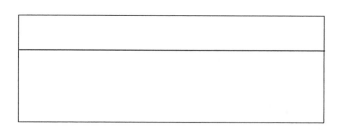

Figure 7.1 Empty activity box.

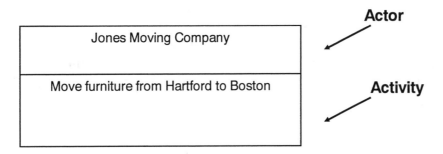

Figure 7.2 Filled-in activity box.

Figure 7.2 shows an example of an Activity Box that is completely filled in. In this example, the actor is the Jones Moving Company, and the Activity is "Move furniture from Hartford to Boston." Note again that the action word "move" appears first in the statement.

In planning for a future Activity, sometimes one does not know who would carry out the Activity. Figure 7.3 shows an Activity Box that does not identify the actor, but does leave space for it in anticipation that a responsible actor can be identified in the future.

If a DELTA Chart has been prepared that shows an actor in terms of some characteristic, e.g., "analyst", it may turn out later on that one can identify a particular person who can serve as an analyst, whereupon one might then put that individual's name in the Chart instead of the more general designation of analyst.

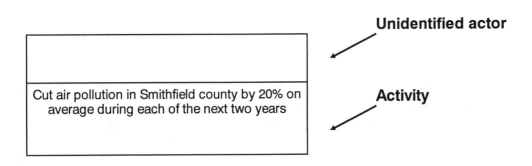

Figure 7.3 Activity box with actor unidentified.

Portraying Time Precedence

Generally on DELTA Charts, it is desired to show sequences, hence one portrays a time precedence relation graphically. The way this is done is simply to draw a straight line and put an arrowhead on the line to show the flow of time. Figure 7.4 shows how the time arrow is used to portray that Activity 1 precedes Activity 2 in time.

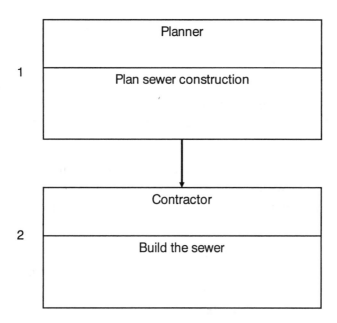

Figure 7.4 Time arrow shows precedence.

Portraying an Event

An Event is an outcome, a result, a consequence, a happening, or in general, something that normally is considered to have occurred or is expected to occur at some particular time. Unlike an Activity which has a beginning, a duration, and an end, the Event is specified at a point in time. To show an Event, an Event Box is used. It is simply a rectangle with a single cell. It is distinguished from an Activity Box which has two cells.

In describing or writing an Event, the action word is intermediate, and the primary object appears first. For example, an Event may be designated thus:

Coals reach Newcastle

or alternatively:

Newcastle receives coal

Notice that the first word in the Event is **not** a verb.

The distinction between Activity and Event by way of phrasing is particularly helpful when one has to deal with a large number of Activities and Events in a common context. The redundancy introduced by having the Event designated both by the graphic attributes and the prose syntax (which also was done in distinguishing an Activity), is very helpful in minimizing cognitive burden. It is intended that the observer be able to recognize the nature of the forest by rapidly scanning the trees instead of spending valuable intellectual effort in reasoning about whether each component element is an Activity, an Event, or something else.

Figure 7.5 shows a DELTA Chart that contains two Activities and one Event. The reader can compare Figure 7.5 with Figure 7.4 to see how Activities can be thought of as generators or producers of Events, and reciprocally, how intended Events can be viewed as the motivators for preceding Activities.

The Event "Sewer is completed" in Figure 7.5 comes about because of the preceding Activities. Thus one may say that the Event is produced by those Activities.

Figure 7.5 illustrates again the time precedence relationship. First the sewer is planned, then it is built, and finally it is completed.

Concluding Event

A special symbol is used when an Event is known to be the last in a sequence of elements. This symbol is the same as the ordinary rectangle, but there is appended to it an additional symbol that is the same as one used for an electrical ground or earth symbol, as shown in Figure 7.6. Such an Event is called a concluding Event.

In view of the possibility that choices can be made during the traversal of a DELTA Chart, it is conceivable that a given Chart may have several concluding Events. In application, it is possible that only one would be realized as a concluding Event, depending upon the choices that were made previously. Alternatively, it is possible that several concluding Events might be realized for different sequences, depending upon the logic of the Chart. The use of the AND and OR Boxes will make this clear.

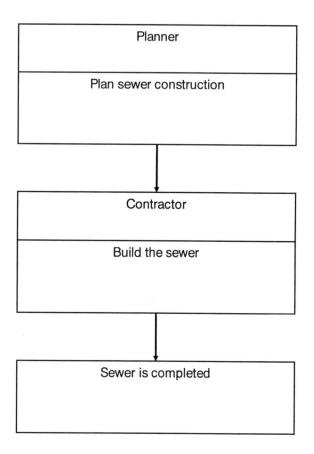

Figure 7.5 DELTA chart with two activities and one event.

A reader may inspect a Chart to determine the different concluding Events and thereby get a measure of the variety of choice that is inherent in any particular Chart. However the most important reason for including the symbol for a concluding Event is to assure that errors in drafting do not suggest misleadingly that an Event is a concluding Event when it is not. Addition of the ground symbol is intended to help assure that concluding Events are properly identified as such.

Initiating Event

Normally a DELTA Chart sequence begins with an initiating Event. No special symbol is used for such an Event. However the Event Box will have no entering lines, and can be distinguished in that way. The initiating Event will always appear

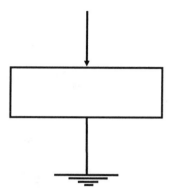

Figure 7.6 Concluding event.

either at the top or at the left of the DELTA Chart. Unlike concluding Event symbols, which may appear in several places on a Chart, the initiating Event is detectable by position on the Chart.

Consequence (Event)

When a decision is made, the possible consequences are always construed to be Events in the DELTA Chart terminology. Hence, for example, if there are three possible options associated with a Decision, each of them would be shown as an Event that may follow the making of the Decision. In addition to the standardization that this arbitrary requirement provides, it also permits rectangular portrayals to qualify for certain automatic computer programs for making highly-readable drawings.

Milestone Event

Frequently, when time sequences are structured for complex projects or programs, special significance will be attached to certain events that represent intermediate levels of achievement. Such events are called "Milestone Events". These events are represented by using the ordinary event box symbol, but in addition the bottom line of the symbol box is given heavy emphasis, in the manner shown in Figure 7.7.

Figure 7.7 Milestone event.

Portraying a Decision

By a Decision is meant a choice of one option from a set of two or more options (or the language "alternative" may be used in place of "option", depending on the context). In some graphical portrayals, a diamond-shaped box is used to represent a Decision. This portrayal has the advantage that it makes Decisions on a Chart stand out rather sharply from other kinds of boxes, which is often helpful in reviewing a Chart to see what key choices have to be made. But a major disadvantage of the diamond-shaped box is that it places artificial restrictions on the number of options that can be conveniently represented.

In the DELTA Chart terminology, a Decision will be represented by a rectangle with an interior vertical line parallel to and adjacent to each outer edge, as well as a cross line perpendicular to these. The cross line separates the Decision Box into an upper and lower portion. The upper portion will show which actor is expected to make the Decision, while the lower portion will contain a question that identifies the Decision to be made. The two side rectangles are shaded for visual emphasis. Following the Decision Box, there will be Event Boxes, each of which will show one possible consequence of the Decision. The possible consequences will be mutually exclusive, by definition, unless otherwise indicated.

Figure 7.8 illustrates these points by showing a Decision Box arrayed for three possible options, as indicated by the three outgoing lines, each of which connects directly to an Event Box. Each Event Box will contain one possible consequence of the Decision. When the Decision is made only one of the consequences will be selected.

Now that the form of the Decision Box has been seen, along with the way in which the options (Events that are possible consequences of a Decision) are shown, it is possible to incorporate this arrangement into the example that was shown in Figure 7.5. Again it is supposed that the City Council plans to build a sewer and that

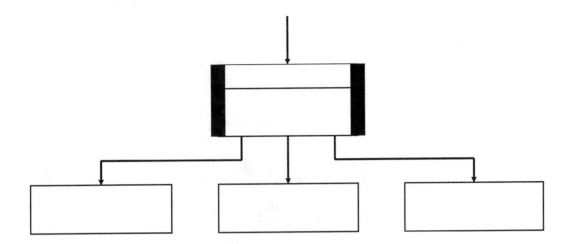

Figure 7.8 Empty decision box with three possible options.

there are three possible contractors. Note that the Decision Box in Figure 7.9 shows who is expected to make the Decision, and that the three options appear in the Event Boxes following the Decision Box.

Walks on a DELTA Chart

A walk on a DELTA Chart is a sequence found by following the arrows. As illustrated in Figure 7.9, every time a Decision Box appears there will be alternative walks leaving the Decision Box. As a result there will often be several walks from the initiating Event to the concluding Event(s).

For example, suppose that in Figure 7.9 the last three Events are concluding Events, just for purpose of illustration (even though the symbol for concluding Event is not shown there). Then using the element numbers shown in Figure 7.9, we can trace 3 walks from the initiating Event to a concluding Event. These are identified as:

$$1\text{-}2\text{-}3\text{-}4\text{-}5\text{-}6$$
$$1\text{-}2\text{-}3\text{-}4\text{-}5\text{-}7$$
$$1\text{-}2\text{-}3\text{-}4\text{-}5\text{-}8$$

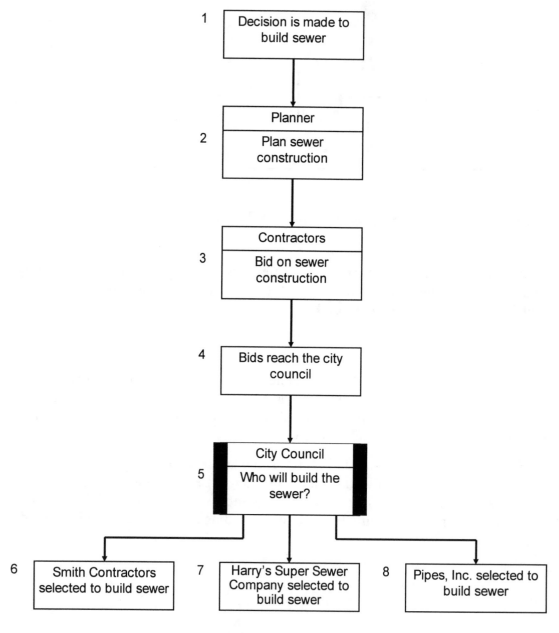

Figure 7.9 Filled-in decision box with three options.

The walks just identified are called the <u>major walks</u> of the DELTA Chart, to reflect the fact that they go from beginning to end. Any other walks on the Chart would be called <u>minor walks</u>. There are usually many walks. Any lesser part of a major walk would be a minor walk. In Figure 7.9 some minor walks would be 1-2-3-4-5, 2-3-4-5-7, 2- 3, 4-5-8, etc.

Realization of a Walk

It is said that a walk on a DELTA Chart has been <u>realized</u> if all the elements of the walk have been carried out or have occurred. With reference to Figure 7.9, suppose that Event 1 has occurred, and that Activities 2 and 3 have been completed, and that Event 4 has occurred, but the Decision 5 has not yet been made. Then one could say that the walk 1-2-3-4 has been realized, while the remaining parts of the effort have not yet been realized. Some may never be realized (e.g., if Pipes, Inc., is selected to build the sewer, then Smith Contractors and Harry's Super Sewer Company would not be selected, barring unforeseen difficulties or changes). This terminology enables precise discussion of intermediate points of an incomplete process with reference to the DELTA Chart that describes the entire process.

When is a Logic Box Used?

The reader will observe that so far no Logic Box has appeared in any of the figures in the Chapter. Also every box on each figure has no more than one input line. Further, the only box with more than one output line was a Decision Box.

Logic Boxes are typically used whenever multiple inputs or outputs are involved. The general rule for the use of Logic Boxes is as follows:

> Logic Boxes are used whenever an Activity Box or Event Box otherwise would have more than one input line or more than one output line, or whenever ~~otherwise~~ a Decision Box would have more than one input line.

With proper use of Logic Boxes, every Event Box, every Activity Box, and every Decision Box will have at most a single input line. Moreover every Event Box and Activity Box will have at most a single output line.

The Logic Boxes to be added will have the following properties:

- Every AND Box will have either more than one input line or more than one output line or both

- Every OR Box will have more than one input line, but will have only one output line

It can be envisaged from these assertions that the Logic Boxes are used to assure that the three elements (Events, Activities, Decisions) are driven from a single input line, and that Events and Activities have only single output lines. This prevents ambiguity on the DELTA Chart by clarifying the logic associated with these elements. To confirm this, examples will now be given showing the use of the Logic Boxes.

The Logic Boxes

The symbols for the Logic Boxes are shown in Figure 7.10. While connectors such as these are often symbolized by using non-alphabetic symbols, it is cognitively beneficial for the user to have the words written out, as shown in Figure 7.10. After all, the main utility of DELTA Charts is to show extended sequences, and it is advisable to reduce cognitive complexity wherever possible to facilitate capacity to examine the whole without spending too much time deciphering parts.

To help explain the use of the Logic Boxes, an example will be offered that shows their use in portraying an iterative process. Iteration is frequently used when the results of some chain of activity cannot be assessed until the chain has been realized, whereupon it is found necessary through an assessment to repeat some or all of the activity chain.

As an example, one may mention part of the process of making reeds for oboes. An oboe player must carve reeds from cane to use in playing the instrument. The reed is less than two inches in length when completed. The player carves the reed from cane for a while, then blows on it to check the tone with a tuning fork. If the right tone is attained, the reed may be set aside for a full scale test with the oboe itself; otherwise, additional carving is done until the proper tone is attained external to the oboe. Thus the process of reed-making is iterative (many trials are normally required). A part of this process may be DELTA- Charted as shown in Figure 7.11. This illustrates iteration and shows how the AND and the OR Logic Boxes are used to help depict the process.

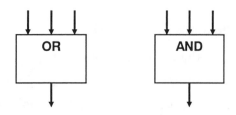

Figure 7.10 Logic boxes.

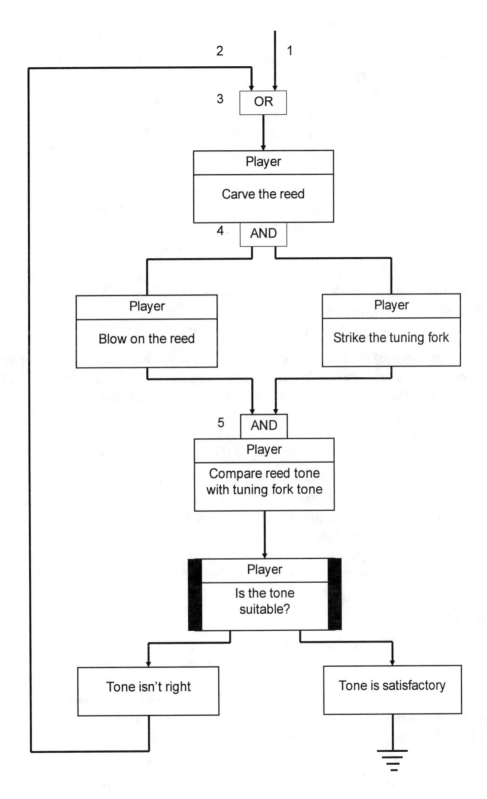

Figure 7.11 DELTA chart for Oboe reed-making.

Observing point 1 in Figure 7.11, there is seen an incoming line from some previous Event, Activity, or Decision. The OR Box labeled 3 can be interpreted as allowing one to move on a walk right through the box without interference, whether the arrival is via line 1 or line 2. Thus the sequence begins with the player carving the reed material. The AND Box labeled 4 is meant to indicate that both of the two following activities need to be carried out, though either could be done first. If one had to be done before the other, there would be no reason to use the AND Box labeled 4. The AND Box labeled 5 means that both of the preceding Activities must be carried out before proceeding to the next Activity. This is clear also from the nature of the Activities, since the player cannot compare the reed tone with the tuning fork tone unless both preceding Activities have been carried out.

The AND Box labeled 5 thus acts to block a continuation of a sequence unless both of the preceding Activities that furnish input arrows to the AND Box have been done. This should be contrasted with the OR Box. The latter allows a sequence to go on as long as any one of the inputs represents the tail end of a realized sequence.

Upon completion of the comparison, the player makes a Decision as to whether the reed tone matches the tuning fork tone. If it does so, and the tone is satisfactory, the DELTA Chart indicates that the sequence is finished. If it does not, i.e., if the tone is not right, the actor will follow the return line or feedback line going back to the OR Box with input labeled 2. This feedback line allows for the anticipated iteration. The whole process may begin again, and may be repeated many times until it is judged that the tone is satisfactory.

Figure 7.11 thus illustrates the use of Logic Boxes as means of establishing walk conditions, illustrates the use of the OR Box to help show an iteration condition, and also shows how one approximates a real situation. Clearly other alternatives could occur beyond those shown. For example, it might be that in carving the reed the player would damage the cane so badly that further carving would require a new piece of cane. This possibility is not shown on the DELTA Chart. However it could be, depending on the extent of detail desired.

Extended Capability

Since the DELTA Chart was first introduced in 1971 [1], other authors have carried out research that lends itself to providing automated assistance to people who wish to formulate, draw, and amend these or other types of structures that show relationships. Examples of such research are found in [2], which deals with how to place the logic elements in the structure systematically; and [3] which presents algorithms for machine construction of digraphs to meet certain conditions of readability.

Having discussed the DELTA Chart in considerable detail, it can now be used to portray the steps in carrying out the several processes that constitute the Consensus Methodologies.

7.2 Ideawriting.

Ideawriting is an efficient method for eliciting many ideas relevant to a stated issue from one or more small groups in a fraction of an hour. It is self-documenting. Its use is generally appropriate for all efforts where collective idea generation is expected to be valuable. It is especially useful for issue formulation, including problem definition, and for identification of objectives and options. Also it provides a quick method for group evaluation of their immediately prior work results.

This method can be used whenever there is a need to collect ideas or elements relevant to some issue and little time available to do so. Other conditions for its use are: the information needed is spread among a variety of people, it is desired to eliminate the potentially inhibiting influence of dominant personalities in collecting the information, and people are available and willing to take part in the generation of ideas.

This method has the potential for spurring the generation of many ideas concerning organizational, behavioral, and other aspects of an issue. It will encourage contributions from those normally noted for reticence and quietness. It has the potential for stimulating greatly enhanced stakeholder input into a planning process.

Outcomes of its use include the spontaneous occurrence of ideas, triggered by other ideas. Typically one may expect to gain a list of 50 to 150 ideas about an issue or question in 20 to 30 minutes. Also one can anticipate increased understanding of an issue as a result of the manner in which the ideas are produced.

To carry out the method, it is required that a specific **triggering question** be formulated. All ideas generated will be in response to this question.

A group leader who has some experience with the process will act as the process facilitator. No more than six people will take part in each instance of the process. However any number of these processes can be carried out simultaneously. Each individual group will need a table, chairs, paper, pencils, and a quiet room in which to work. Groups can share a single room.

The triggering question is displayed to the group throughout its working period, which will seldom exceed 30 minutes. Each participant is asked to carry out the silent generation of ideas in writing, in response to the triggering question. Exchange of sheets of paper is desired, after about each 5 minutes of writing, or at the convenience of the participants. When a participant gets a page from another participant, the page is read and will normally stimulate new ideas which can be written on the page presently in hand. Continued informal exchange takes place until all participants have examined all the written ideas and no further ideas come to mind.

The Ideawriting terminates with the collection of the products of the group activity. Clearly a variety of actions might follow, either immediately or at a later date, but these actions are not part of the Ideawriting process itself.

Figure 7.12 gives a DELTA Chart to describe this process. Appendix 3 contains a summary description sheet of the process that can be distributed to groups to explain its general character.

7.3 Nominal Group Technique (NGT).

The Nominal Group Technique has multiple properties. It is a method for: (1) generating ideas, (2) clarifying ideas, (3) doing a preliminary partitioning of the set of generated and clarified ideas, based on a criterion of relative saliency, and (4) helping to build a spirit of participation and teamwork or group morale. The NGT is self-documenting.

This process is more sophisticated than Ideawriting, and generally achieves considerably more. However Ideawriting has four attributes that will sometimes make it the method of choice for generating ideas. Ideawriting can be more easily learned by facilitators. Also it requires less time, perhaps only about 20% as much time as NGT. Many groups can carry out Ideawriting simultaneously, and it is less demanding on physical facilities and space availability for wall displays.

A very-well written description of the NGT has been published by its inventors [4]. The following descriptions are intended to familiarize the reader with this process and with some results of analysis of its use, but not to substitute for the more encompassing description in the cited reference.

The use of the NGT is generally appropriate whenever collective idea generation is of value, and it is therefore especially useful for issue formulation. It is also useful in business and government planning, and for fostering stakeholder participation in planning. In these situations, controversy and uncertainty are often present concerning the nature of an issue or problem and its possible resolution. Frequently it is important to neutralize the effect of dominant individuals in small group meetings. Also it may be important to get an initial rough prioritization of problem elements in terms of relative importance. The NGT, when managed by a skilled facilitator who is sensitive to the behavioral design of this process, is highly effective in achieving all these ends.

On many occasions the NGT has demonstrated its potential to stimulate the generation of many ideas concerning organizational, behavioral, and other issues; and for encouraging contributions from those normally noted for quietness.

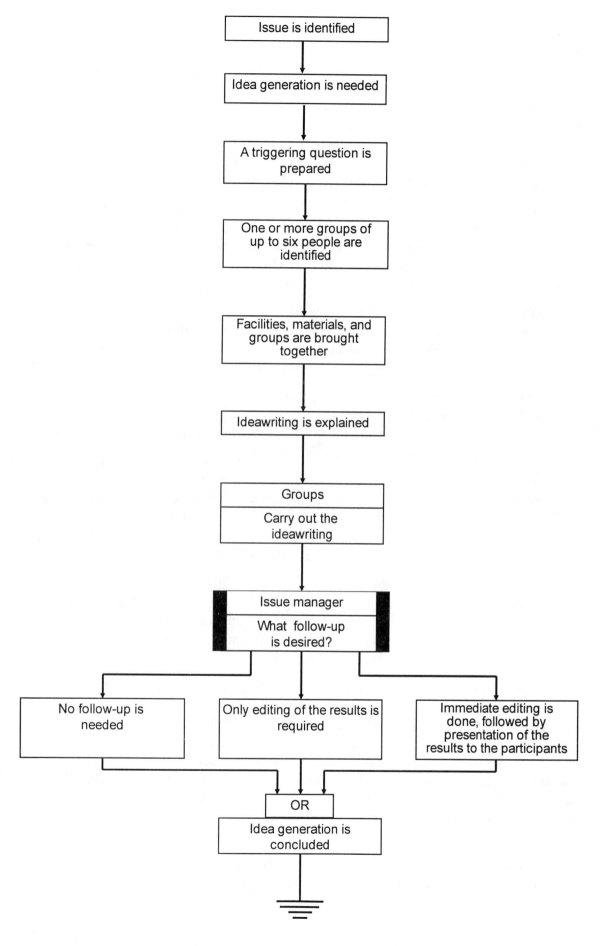

Figure 7.12 DELTA chart of ideawriting process. Copyright © 1982 SGSR.

Outcomes of this process will typically include a list of 20 to 150 ideas about an issue. There will be a greatly enhanced understanding of the components of the issue, an opportunity to assure that ideas of each member of the group become part of the context for future discussion, and a preliminary and rough assessment of the relative importance of the ideas that are produced.

Like the Ideawriting method, the NGT process is initiated by formulating carefully a **triggering** question. The ideas generated will be in response to this question. The ideas will be silently generated, and the written ideas will not be exchanged during the writing process. The quality and relevance of the generated ideas will be highly sensitive to thoughtful formulation of the triggering question.

After twenty to thirty minutes of writing of ideas, or whenever it appears that the participants have stopped writing, the facilitator will conduct a round robin recording of ideas, in which individuals present ideas one at a time. The facilitator will record the ideas on flip chart pages, and as each page is filled it is posted on the wall.

When all of the ideas have been displayed, the process continues with sequential clarification of each idea. Criticism of ideas is foregone. Some editing may occur to add to the clarity of an idea. Ideas which appear to overlap or to be identical may be pooled, if it is clear that nothing is lost thereby.

After all ideas are clarified and new additions to the list (if any) have been made during the clarification discussion, participants are asked to vote by written ballot. In this voting each participant selects the five ideas in the set that are deemed to be most important in respect to the issue, and ranks them in order of importance. The facilitator collects and records these votes.

In the NGT process as outlined in [4], a subsequent step may be carried out in which the votes are analyzed, and followed by a more exhaustive and definitive ranking. As applied in the Generic Design Science, this subsequent step is omitted from the NGT process. In its place, a more sophisticated method is used for structuring the ideas with computer assistance, as will be discussed in Sec. 7.5.

To carry out the NGT process, one requires a group leader trained as a facilitator who has some experience with the process. A carefully prepared triggering question drives the process. The participants consist (typically) of a group of between 6 and 12 individuals with issue-related expertise. Paper and pencils are required for each participant. A flip chart and felt-tipped pens are used by the facilitator. The meeting room should have table space for the group, comfortable chairs for all actors, and surfaces on which to tape the generated ideas where they will be in full view of the participants. A time period of about 3 hours for the process is the normal expectation.

Figure 7.13 shows a DELTA Chart that outlines the NGT. In Appendix 3 there is given a summary page useful for explaining the process briefly to participants.

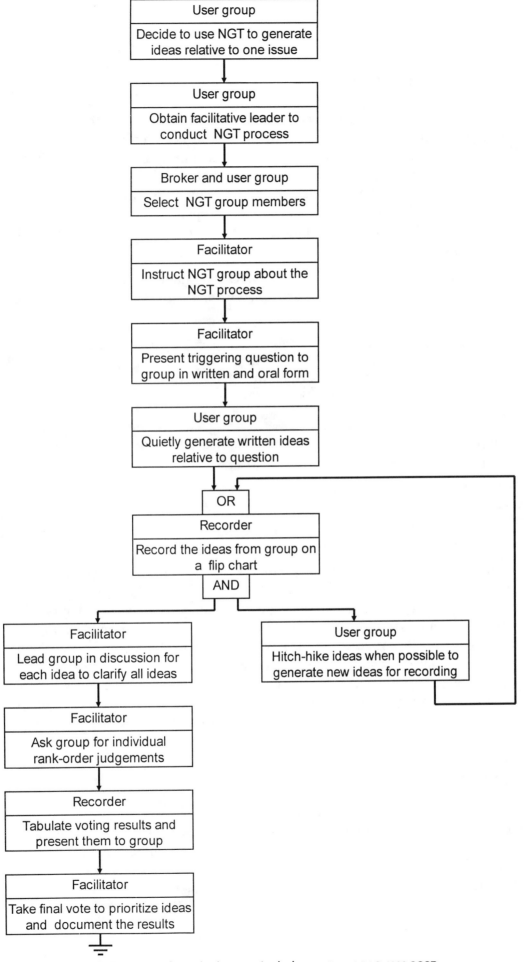

Figure 7.13 DELTA chart of nominal group technique. Copyright © 1982 SGSR.

The NGT process has been used regularly by the Center for Interactive Management for about eight years. During this time a variety of complex issues produced substantial data on such matters as numbers of ideas generated in a given time period, percentage of total ideas generated that were included in some participant's top five selections for importance, and duration of the process. Data are given in Appendix 5. In addition, as indicated in Appendix 5, analyses of the data have contributed to the theoretical background for Generic Design Science, as indicated in Chapter 6.

Table 7.1 shows mean values of several NGT parameters derived from analysis of 43 applications. The mean values are taken from Table A5.1, where the supporting data are presented.

Table 7.1
Mean Values of Some NGT Parameters

Parameter	Mean Value
Duration of Session	3.1 hours
Number of Ideas Generated	64 ideas
Number of Ideas Selected in Top Five	33 ideas
Diversity	5.6

As shown in Appendix A5, there is great diversity in the views of participants as to which five ideas drawn from the set of ideas that is generated and clarified by the group are the most important in relation to the issue under study. As explained in more detail in Appendix A5, a value of zero for Diversity means that the group is in full agreement about which of the ideas selected are the most important in relation to the issue being considered. A value exceeding five for Diversity typically indicates that the group is closer to perfect disagreement on relative importance than to perfect consensus. The mean value of Diversity is 5.6, which shows a significant and pervasive difference of view toward the issue, with this kind of difference tending to be present in any group that deals with any complex issue.

7.4 DELPHI.

The DELPHI Method, the oldest of the methodologies, is a means for generating, clarifying, structuring (in a limited way), and amending ideas. It is distinctive for its application when groups cannot or should not be in face-to-face communication, being served instead by a neutral information management group. As a rule, the DELPHI method is much slower in its use than the other methods, but it can be accelerated using modern communication and computer equipment at times. DELPHI is self-documenting.

The literature on DELPHI is extensive. While it meets the criteria set forth for the consensus methodologies, its truly distinctive feature is that it is applied with groups that do not work together in a face-to-face environment. It has been found experimentally in studies extending over a period of almost a decade that when groups are brought together, the benefits of direct interaction are great. Therefore DELPHI is seldom used in applying the Generic Design Science. For all these reasons, only a DELTA Chart of one version of this process is offered here. Figure 7.14 shows how this version might be carried out. Appendix 3 contains an additional summary sheet that may be useful in describing it to potential participants. For those who may wish to use it, reference to the extensive literature on it is recommended.

7.5 Interpretive Structural Modeling (ISM).

The Interpretive Structural Modeling (ISM) methodology provides the means to instrument the Theory of Relations, and thereby enables groups to structure information with computer assistance, while simultaneously clarifying the component ideas. It also allows for amendment of preliminary structures, again with computer assistance. This methodology can be used to produce certain standard Application Structural Types (Appendix 1) that are useful in a wide variety of situations. It is self-documenting.

In application, ISM provides the means to formulate a pattern or structure of elements associated with issue formulation. The elements may include needs, constraints, objectives, or options in a variety of fields such as education, public facility planning, city budget-cutting, or system design.

This method is useful when a complex issue is under study, and there are interactions among the diverse elements of the issue. A focused group discussion on the issue is needed on the way to the development of one or more relationship maps.

The relationships used in structuring must be transitive (see Sec. 2.4), and should be carefully chosen to arrive at the most useful outcome for purposes of interpretation (See Appendix 7). The elements that are structured as well as the relationships used to structure them are clarified by reasoning and discussion stimulated by the process. The quality of the results obtained depend upon skilled process leadership, which must be facilitative rather than issue-involved. Overemphasis upon the mechanistic and technical aspects of the process during its use is highly undesirable, while underestimation of the significance of its behavioral attributes by the facilitator may significantly weaken its utility.

The use of ISM produces one or more documented models of element interrelationships. Part of the product will include a carefully refined language with which to describe or discuss an issue or system. There will be a significantly enhanced understanding of the issue, accompanied by modification and clarification of initially-formulated elements and relationships.

219

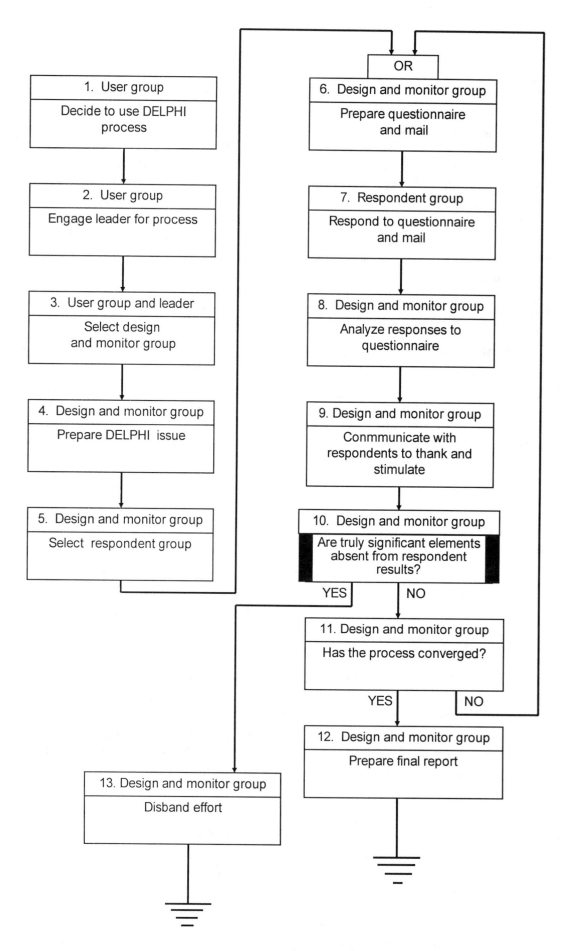

Figure 7.14 DELTA chart of DELPHI process. Copyright © 1982 SGSR.

In the application of ISM, an issue and a structuring theme are identified. A group and a process leader are chosen. Elements of the issue will be available from prior work, frequently as a consequence of use of the Nominal Group Technique. Part or all of the element set that is developed from the NGT activity (or other means of developing such a set) will be entered in a computer. The machine will present inquiries visually to the group, which discusses them and makes judgments about relationships of the elements. Following the completion of the computer-questioning and group discussion of the questions, the computer computes and displays a map of the relationship among the elements. The map is examined by the group and its interpretation is discussed. It may or may not then be amended (manually for simple amendments, or with computer assistance for more complex amendments). An example of one particular type of relationship map appears in Figure 7.15. This map is an "intent structure", showing how a set of objectives is related.

To initiate the ISM process, one typically begins with the set of elements, and with a chosen relationship chosen to be appropriate for exploration of the issue. The relationship chosen is then embedded in a **generic question** (see App. 7). There will be between 6 and 12 participants, an experienced group leader, a computer operator, and possibly other staff available to document key comments by the participants. The computer may be a time-sharing system, or may be a dedicated facility, but it must contain the software that supports and is part of the ISM process. A large wall display to present machine-generated questions to the group is achieved by a projection system driven from the computer. Copying facilities are needed to prepare and distribute results to the participants.

The time required for an ISM process depends upon the number of elements in the set and their complexity. Time periods from two to eight hours have been experienced.

The ISM process is the formal replacement for previously-used heuristic methods of organizing information. It replaces "rearrange and tape" methods, or other methods in the literature that lack a sound behavioral design which takes account of human limitations and other behavioral aspects already discussed in earlier Chapters.

Figure 7.16 shows a DELTA Chart that contains the major Events in the ISM process.

This process has been used in many settings since its invention in the early 1970's. Among the users was the Center for Interactive Management at George Mason University. In using this process with many complex issues and with a variety of groups, the Center accumulated data on its use, which are presented in Appendix 5. The analysis of the data has been helpful in formulating the Science of Generic Design.

Table 7.2 shows mean values of certain ISM process parameters drawn from 31 sessions, as tabulated in Table A5.2.

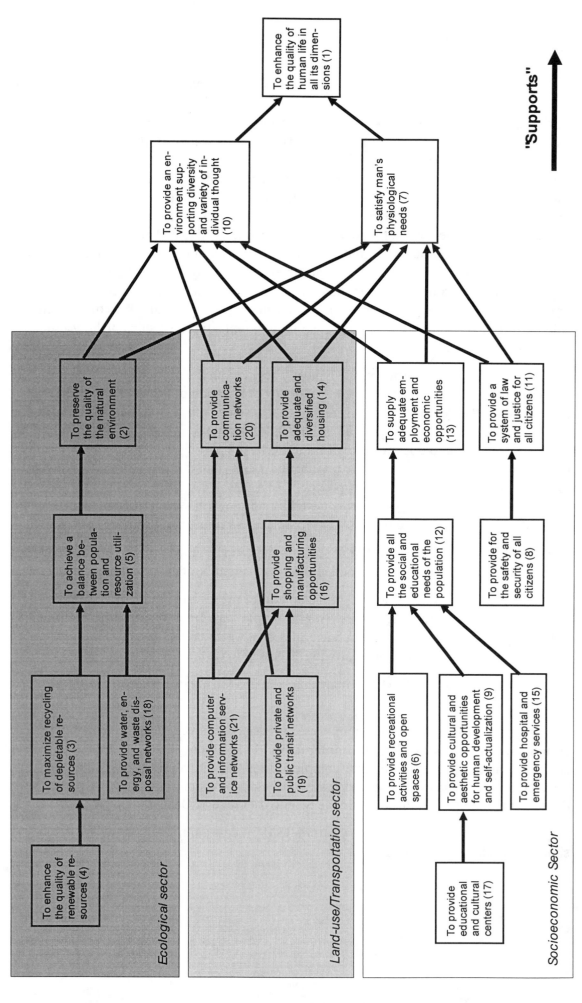

Figure 7.15 Intent structure.

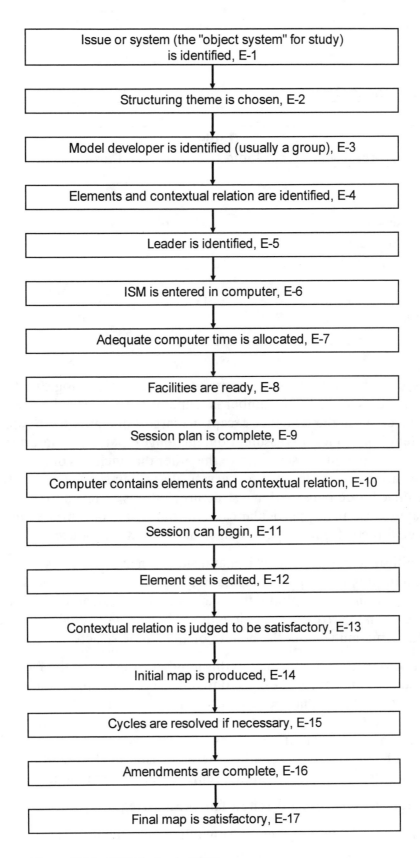

Issue or system (the "object system" for study) is identified, E-1

Structuring theme is chosen, E-2

Model developer is identified (usually a group), E-3

Elements and contextual relation are identified, E-4

Leader is identified, E-5

ISM is entered in computer, E-6

Adequate computer time is allocated, E-7

Facilities are ready, E-8

Session plan is complete, E-9

Computer contains elements and contextual relation, E-10

Session can begin, E-11

Element set is edited, E-12

Contextual relation is judged to be satisfactory, E-13

Initial map is produced, E-14

Cycles are resolved if necessary, E-15

Amendments are complete, E-16

Final map is satisfactory, E-17

Figure 7.16 DELTA chart of ISM process.

Table 7.2
Mean Values of Some ISM Process Parameters

Parameter	Mean Value
Duration of Session	3.1 hours
Number of Ideas Structured	22 ideas
Rounded-off Length of the Condensed Hierarchy	6
Rounded-off Interpretation Path Maximum Length	13

The last entry in this table is a measure of the deep or long logic that is involved in the structures developed. The number is found by the conservative method of assuming that all cycles in the structure except the largest one have been replaced with a proxy element [5]. Under this assumption, the longest path to be interpreted will be a path from one end of the structure to the other that includes only its largest cycle. This is an arbitrary way to get a conservatively-chosen single number to represent the cognitive burden involved in a structure, but it is believed to be a reasonable approach. In any particular case, of course, an appropriate number can be determined directly from the particular structure that is produced.

The significance of this number is that it shows on average a cognitive task to assimilate and interpret a logic pattern containing a path with 13 members, of which 7, on average, appear in a cycle. While this is a challenging assignment, it is much less of a challenge when the structure is visible than when an individual attempts to deal with the entire situation without the benefit of any visible structure.

Further conservatism is attached to this number by ignoring the fact that in all of the cases studied the data are restricted to only a portion (approximately half) of the ideas generated. Those that are structured are chosen from those selected by at least one participant to be in the top five in terms of importance. If the remaining ideas were also involved (as is often the case as a followup to the work tabulated in Table A5.2), path lengths would generally increase. This means that the deep or long logic is deeper or longer or both than that represented by a path length of 13.

The literature of this process is now fairly extensive [5-11].

A summary description is given in Appendix 3, which may be useful to describe the process to potential participants.

7.6 Options Field Methodology (OFM).

The Options Field Methodology and the Options Profile Methodology [12] provide means for thorough development of Design Situation descriptions and design Target descriptions. They involve discovery and identification of the dimensionality of the Situation (see Chapter 6), and facilitate matching the dimensionality of the Target with the dimensionality of the Design Situation, to satisfy the Law of Requisite Variety. Self-documentation is inherent and incremental, providing a constantly updated status of all design decisions. These two methodologies both use NGT and ISM as components. In this section the description of the Options Field appears, and the following section describes the companion Options Profile concept.

A Poly-Structure

The completed Options Field is a poly-structure. Its construction begins with the generation and clarification of a set of options. This set may be generated and clarified using the NGT, in response to a carefully formulated triggering question. This question defines the context and must, therefore, reflect substantial insight into the Design Situation. The question must be neither too broad nor too narrow. It must stimulate creative, productive responses, that do not stray from the topic under consideration.

Initial Structuring (Placing Options in Categories)

Once a set is developed, the initial structuring begins. The initial structuring is for the purpose of placing the options into categories, following the concepts set forth in Chap. 6 where the Theory of Dimensionality was given. The ISM process is used to carry out the structuring. A relationship that may be used for this initial structuring is "is in the same category as".

Naming the Categories

Following the placing of the options into categories, the options are displayed as sets, arrayed vertically in anticipation of developing a name for each category. options.

A standard comment that participants will make is that the categories should have been chosen first, and then the options should have been generated for each category separately. The standard response is that the disease called "hardening of the categories" is responsible for underconceptualization in many situations. To begin with the categories already specified will, no doubt, save time in options generation. The time spent in options generation is normally miniscule compared with the time spent later in designing, testing, installing, and operating the target system. It is the height of technomyopia to forego the opportunity to exercise imagination in developing the categories to fit the much larger set of options produced without being confined to prior fixations about pos-

225

sible outcomes. The reason for developing categories to characterize a set of already-existing options is to fight underconceptualization at the outset of the design task.

Identifying Design Dimensions

After the set of categories has been achieved, it is reasonable to believe that learning has occurred. At this point, it is appropriate to ask whether every category should be taken as a dimension of the design. The criterion for making this decision is to ask whether some option(s) in that category really must be specified in order to provide adequate definition of the alternative represented by choosing one or more options from each dimension, or whether any particular category is not essential to the definition of the Target. The purpose here is an economic one: to avoid using precious group time in working with a category that is non-essential to Target specification. Good processes leave room for groups to introduce superfluous information (within limits) in order to avoid cramping creative behavior, but later on provide opportunities to delete any intermediate outcomes that are deemed not to require further consideration.

Discovering Clusters of Dependent Dimensions

Once the group has settled on the dimensions of the Target, a second structuring occurs. Now it is the set of dimensions that is structured. Again the ISM process is used. The relationship used is "is dependent on". Two dimensions are defined to be <u>independent</u> if a choice of one or more options in one of the dimensions does not rule out any choices in the other dimension. The kind of independence being dealt with is "decision-making independence". If two dimensions are <u>dependent</u>, the choice of options in one can be restricted by the choice of options in the other.

Because of this kind of dependence, this structuring forms clusters of dimensions such that any two dimensions in the same cluster are dependent. Clearly it is desirable that the choice of options in a cluster be made in light of the interdependency within the cluster.

Following this structuring, there is defined a set of clusters, each cluster consisting of a set of dimensions, and each dimension consisting of a set of similar options.

Establishing a Choice-Making Sequence for the Clusters

Now the third structuring begins. This structuring takes the clusters as the elements to be structured. The structuring relationship involves the sequence in which choices of options should be made. Once again the ISM process is used. A suitable relationship is "should be considered first in making choices of options". At the conclusion of this structuring, the clusters will have been placed in a linear sequence.

Sequencing Dimensions Within Clusters

A fourth structuring now is carried out, which normally will not require the use of the ISM process, but which can use it if it appears necessary. In this structuring, carried out separately for each cluster, the initial decision-making sequence among the dimensions in each cluster is defined. If, for example, a certain cluster consists of dimensions A1, A2, and A3; at the conclusion of the structuring for this cluster, it may have been decided to choose options first from dimension A2, then from dimension A3, and finally from dimension A1. With such ordering done for each cluster, a linear sequence involving all the dimensions is achieved.

Displaying the Completed Options Field

It is then appropriate to organize the Options Field by placing the dimensions in the order determined, with the name of each dimension heading a list of the options in that dimension, and with the clusters clearly identified.

Examples of several Options Fields appear in Figures 7.17, 7.18, and 7.19. These come from specific studies, and are chosen to reflect the diversity of applications that have been carried out. Fig. 7.20 shows a DELTA Chart of the Options Field Process.

Note that in the representation of the Options Field, each option is preceded by a "bullet". The bullets have been found to be very useful in helping to distinguish each option from each other option (especially to distinguish an option from one appearing immediately below it and from one appearing immediately above it); and also to maintain a high quality graphical readability in the Options Profile, to be discussed next.

7.7 Options Profile Methodology (OPM).

The Options Profile is the visual representation of an Alternative, consisting of a set of chosen options, with at least one option coming from each Dimension in the Options Field.

Figure 7.21 shows a completed Options Profile. Note that each option that has been selected is so designated by a line drawn from the bullet in front of the selected option down to the "tie line". Options chosen in a given dimension may be single or compound. A compound option is a set of individual members of the set of options that constitute a given dimension.

In applications, it is common to construct several Options Profiles for a given Options Field. Each Option Profile represents one design Alternative.

In choosing options, choices are made in the sequence determined in formulating the way the Options Field is represented.

A1. Infrastructure

- Put in place a first Darpa's Initiative in Concurrent Engineering (DICE) architecture and development environment that we can use to develop DICE (1)

- Short-term co-location of task-oriented technical teams (3)

- Non-technical meetings to plan the center (4)

- Co-location of project management and business office (9)

- All decisions that will impact the center should first be discussed between General Electric (GE), West Virginia University (WVU), and government before other team members (12)

- Regularly scheduled meetings between GE and WVU to address individual tasks and the issues (25)

A2. Vision

- Center for Concurrent Engineering Research (CCER) should be organized so that GE develops an "ownership" (2)

- Joint preparation of joint long-range vision (6)

- Center for Interactive Management (CIM) or similar sessions for goal/consensus establishment (10)

- Immediate appointment of industrial advisory board to appraise long-range vision statement (14)

- Joint-team (WVU and GE) to address long-term center risk and risk resolution (15)

- Develop visible management strategic/public commitment (17)

- Preparation of a joint essay to clarify the significance of DICE for public dissemination (23)

- Early definition and assessment of key technologies and their status with respect to DICE (28)

- Create a five-year vision and technical plan, including finances, etc. (32)

- Establish a two-year plan (39)

TIE LINE

B. Teambuilding

- Exchange of technical seminars and workshops (5)

- Development of co-op program for WVU graduate and undergraduate students (7)

- Plan schedule of team-building sessions (8)

- One credit hour course modules (16)

- Technical and non-technical team sessions with customer and user community (18)

- Key WVU personnel attend GE Crotonville courses (19)

- Visits by key leaders to industry/university laboratories where pieces of DICE program which are currently operational (26)

- Send key GE researchers for a sabbatical/adjunct faculty to WVU for DICE and vice versa (31)

- Invite WVU researcher to appropriate GE activities (37)

- Schedule six quarterly CIM therapy sessions to sustain problem-solving (38)

C. Visibility

- National/government marketing of DICE vision (24)

- Technical milestone demonstrators and progress visibility (27)

- Increase the members and type of external technology transfer implementation partners (29)

- National Science Foundation support of emerging research issues (30)

- Establish a showcase of existing technologies at the cutting edge (GE) at the center (33)

D. Issues

- Academic release time for key WVU personnel (21)

- Resolve Travel and Living and peripheral issues associated with co-location (34)

- Enhance the access to DICE facility including transportation (36)

Figure 7.17 Example of an options field.

- Provide schedules (5)

- Make cross-program reviews of acquisition strategies to identify completeness, application of resources, and efficiencies (8)

- Assure no programmatic "dropballs" (17)

- Develop program schedules (23)

- Plan projects (26)

- Establish goals (39)

- Determine systemic, procedural, or policy problems (45)

- Direct long-term investment planning (50)

- Carefully assign work (59)

- Budget fiscal and personnel resources (74)

- A new technology is developed, integrated into a product, and offered to a customer (1)

- Identify future needs and assure within limited resources that programs are developed and survive that have high return on investment (3)

- Define technical requirements to meet the threats (10)

- Interpret and clarify directions and requirements (13)

- Help assure that the users'/operations' needs are met (21)

- Counter the threat (25)

- Translate engineering terminology into a description of military capabili... (31)

- Anticipate requirements changes (37)

- Justify a broad-based technology pr... gram to allow quick response to technology surprises (43)

- Insure research and development supports or leads to cutting-edge products (53)

- Monitor technology maturation (62)

TIE LINE

3. Resourcing (external focus)

- Defend budgets (4)

- Rob from the rich and give to the poor (6)

- Acquire resources (11)

- Fight for deserving programs Pentagon, Office of the Secretary of Defense (OSD), and Congress (20)

- Define economic position of project (22)

- Participate in the Program Objectives Memorandum (POM) process (30)

- Insure mission area is balanced and each program is executable (33)

- Aggressively defend programs against various staff levels in Washington (34)

- Define dependence on foreign sources (35)

- Clarify mobilization aspects of the project (47)

- Recruitment of people (51)

- Sponsor briefings/develop management consensus (54)

- Clarify industrial base capability for projects (55)

- Support competition (56)

- Clarify competing forces for industrial-based capability (61)

- Delineate model for resources and industrial capabilities (65)

Figure 7.18 Example of an options field. (Continued on next page)

229

4. Leadership

- Manage change (7)
- Strive to maximize value-added (12)
- Insure good communications (14)
- Develop trusting relationship with customers (16)
- Clarify accountability and expectations of personnel and organizations (24)
- Assess and manage risk (27)
- Keep customer satisfied and informed (28)
- Minimize in a vicious manner the number of people associated with the program (29)
- Develop business strategies (38)
- Perform liaison with other government activities, Congress, and contractors (48)
- Get around obstacles created by groups with divergent accountabilities (49)
- Mentor the young (57)
- Determine ways to get around the system (60)
- Develop ad hoc teams (64)
- Recognize when a program should go from specialized management to common Department of Defense (DOD) (67)
- Foster technology transition (69)
- Enjoy your work (71)
- Create an ethical environment (72)
- Reward technical excellence (73)

5. Foreign Military Sales

- Foreign military sales (68)

6. Program Execution

- Execute a program to deliver a quality product within schedule and budget and at a profit (15)
- Renegotiate contract terms (18)
- Monitor progress (19)
- Prepare and negotiate contracts (32)
- Report progress and accomplishments, and failures (40)
- Control engineer's desires for change after design established (41)
- In an autonomous mode, conceptualize, design, develop, produce, test, and support a product that meets or exceeds customers' needs (42)
- Conduct engineering investigations (44)
- Answer questions or write papers (46)
- Apply lessons learned to improve process (52)
- Review performance (58)
- Control technology transfer (66)
- Conduct design reviews (70)
- Assure no execution "dropballs" (75)

TIE LINE

Dimensions		Options
Production		• Totally automatic • Operator loads stock handle • Operator loads part into die
Mechanical		• Automatic part handling • Safety pawls • Device mountings
Electrical		• Plug-in devices • Standard off-inch-single-control • Remote control
Pneumatic		• Filtered and dried air • Normal shop air
Inspection		• 25% sample per week • Monthly unless weekly required • Variable period • Separate department
Maintenance		• According to request • Preventive maintenance • Regular overhaul
Safeguarding		• Barrier guards • Moveable gates • Light curtains • 2-hand controls
Supervisory		• Computer monitoring • Safety auditors • Variable monitoring by supervisor • Constant training

TIE LINE

Figure 7.19 Example of an options field.

231

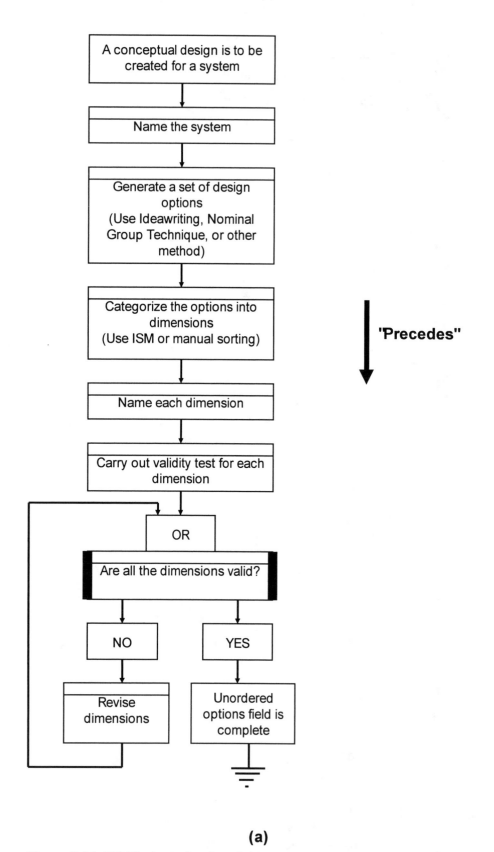

(a)

Figure 7.20 DELTA chart of options field methodology. (Continued on next page.)

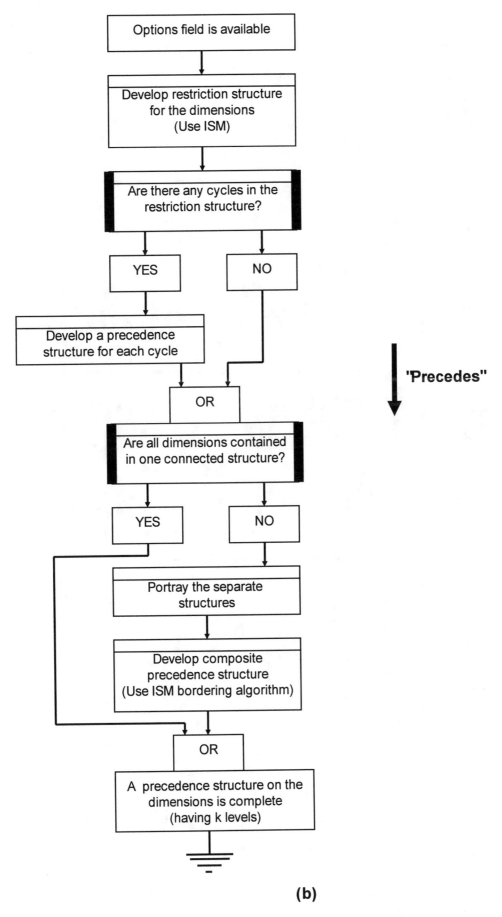

(b)

Figure 7.20 DELTA chart of options field methodology. (Concluded.)

1. Improved Agent/Service Relationships

- Establish transition plans from DARPA projects to project/system planning (33)
- Integrate DARPA projects to buying agency procurement schedule (36)
- Establish what an acceptable standard for DARPA procurement should be (37)
- Update DARPA/agent Memorandum of Understanding to highlight needs (38)
- Establish a rotating contracting officer position at DARPA (40)

- Have Defense Advanced Research Projects Agency (DARPA) do some public relations work with working level activities (22)
- Improve earlier coordination between DARPA and agents (25)
- Establish a DARPA priority system recognized by procurement activities for DARPA procurement (26)
- Have DARPA and agents do more things in parallel (28)
- Participation by the technical personnel at DARPA in DARPA/agent conferences (29)
- Use an overall procurement plan for DARPA (32)

2. Education

- Brief Assistant Secretary of Defense, Acquisitions and Logistics, and Defense Acquisition Regulations (DAR) council on the nature and problems of the tech based research and development (R&D) acquisition process (8)
- Convince Congress that tech based R&D warrants different acquisition laws from hardware development (13)
- Brief the technical community, e.g. DARPA, on Concracting in Competition Act (CICA) and procurement rules (15)
- Convince Department of Defense (DoD) executives and operating personnel that tech base research warrants different acquisition laws than hardware development (24)
- Establish a DARPA Congressional liaison position (42)
- Provide industry a primer for new plan (47)

3. Methods of Implementation

- Identify and rewrite confusing language in acquisition regulations (2)
- Establish responsibility for R&D advocacy within the existing DoD acquisition secretariat (3)
- Implement the recommendations of this task group through Secretary of Defense directives (9)
- Seek clarification from Congressional staffs with respect to those areas where interpretations of CICA don't acknowledge differences in R&D procurement (17)
- Establish a standing DAR council R&D committee to review proposed regulations (21)
- Get high-level DoD recommitment to DARPA charter (55)
- Charter a DoD group to rewrite tech base R&D acquisition regulation (57)

4. New R&D Acquisition Procedures

- Define a stream-lined R&D procurement process (6)
- Reduce Commerce Business Daily schedule for unsolicited proposals (20)
- Clarify "unique and innovative" as criteria for accepting unsolicited proposals for sole-source procurement (45)

TIE LINE

Figure 7-24 Completed options profile (alternative). (Continued on next page)

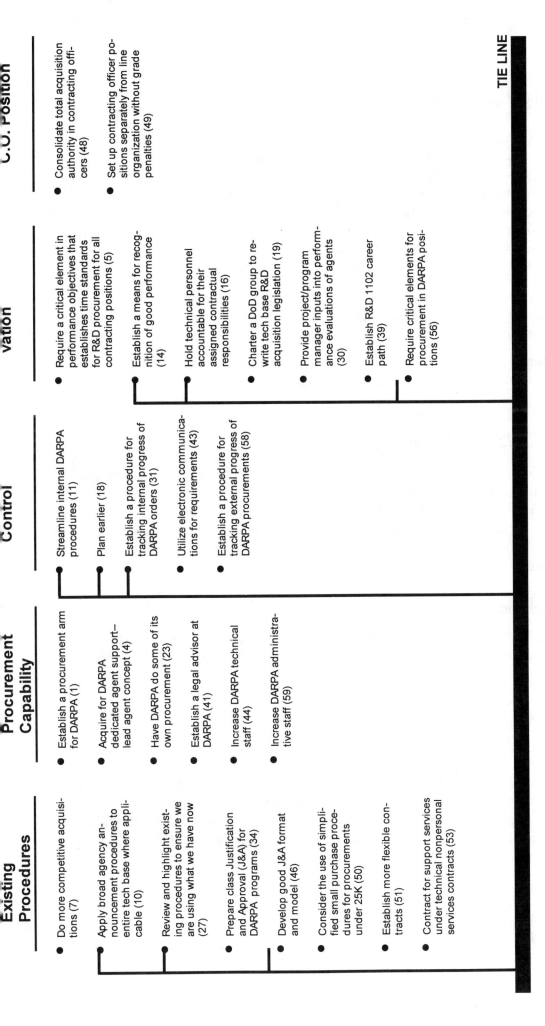

Existing Procedures

- Do more competitive acquisitions (7)
- Apply broad agency announcement procedures to entire tech base where applicable (10)
- Review and highlight existing procedures to ensure we are using what we have now (27)
- Prepare class Justification and Approval (J&A) for DARPA programs (34)
- Develop good J&A format and model (46)
- Consider the use of simplified small purchase procedures for procurements under 25K (50)
- Establish more flexible contracts (51)
- Contract for support services under technical nonpersonal services contracts (53)

Procurement Capability

- Establish a procurement arm for DARPA (1)
- Acquire for DARPA dedicated agent support—lead agent concept (4)
- Have DARPA do some of its own procurement (23)
- Establish a legal advisor at DARPA (41)
- Increase DARPA technical staff (44)
- Increase DARPA administrative staff (59)

Control

- Streamline internal DARPA procedures (11)
- Plan earlier (18)
- Establish a procedure for tracking internal progress of DARPA orders (31)
- Utilize electronic communications for requirements (43)
- Establish a procedure for tracking external progress of DARPA procurements (58)

...vation

- Require a critical element in performance objectives that establishes time standards for R&D procurement for all contracting positions (5)
- Establish a means for recognition of good performance (14)
- Hold technical personnel accountable for their assigned contractual responsibilities (16)
- Charter a DoD group to re-write tech base R&D acquisition legislation (19)
- Provide project/program manager inputs into performance evaluations of agents (30)
- Establish R&D 1102 career path (39)
- Require critical elements for procurement in DARPA positions (56)

C.O. Position

- Consolidate total acquisition authority in contracting officers (48)
- Set up contracting officer positions separately from line organization without grade penalties (49)

TIE LINE

Figure 7.21 Completed options profile (alternative). (Concluded)

235

Choice is made in the first dimension in the order, and the selected options are "tied down" to the tie line. Then choice is made in the second dimension, and so on. When an Options Field has many dimensions, it may occur that work will be interrupted at a point where choices have been made in the early dimensions in the sequence. These choices are designated by tying them to the tie line. When the group returns to resume work, they can see immediately the status of the work as they left it in a prior session, and can resume choice-making using the determined sequence. A DELTA Chart of the Options Profile Process is shown in Figure 7.22.

Of course there is nothing to prevent the group from making modifications in the Options Field, as a consequence of learning that goes on during the construction of the Options Profile.

When the decision is made that a sufficient set of Alternatives has been conceived, this set becomes the subject of tradeoff discussions, carried out using the Tradeoff Analysis methodology.

7.8 Tradeoff Analysis Methodology (TAM).

The Tradeoff Analysis Methodology (TAM) offers a means of choosing systematically one alternative from a set of several that has been produced using the previously-described methodologies. Like the others, this methodology is self-documenting. It may also use (a) the NGT process as a component to develop criteria for making choices and (b) the ISM methodology as a component for use in prioritizing those criteria.

Starting Conditions

The starting conditions for the use of the Tradeoff Analysis Method (TAM) are as follows. Two or more Alternatives (Options Profiles) are available. The group is prepared to choose one of these Alternatives as the recommended one to follow.

Development of Evaluation Criteria

The first step in the TAM is to generate ideas. The idea set that is desired is a set of Evaluation Criteria. These Criteria will be used as part of a systematic approach to the choice of a single Alternative. This set may be developed using any of the three methods described previously that produce sets of ideas in response to a suitable triggering question. The choice of which of the three will be used should be based on an understanding of the three processes and an awareness of the time available and relative complexity of the situation.

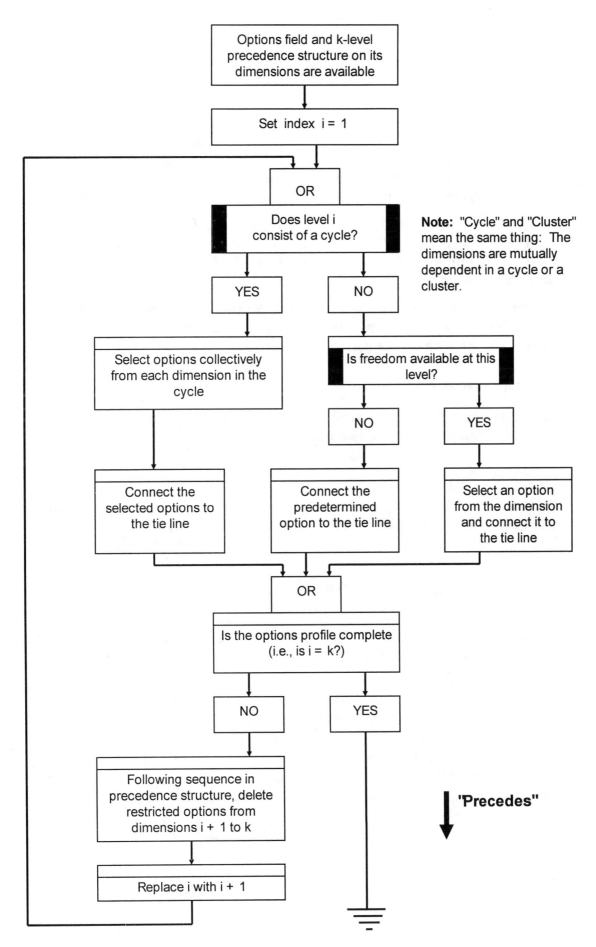

Figure 7.22 DELTA chart of options profile methodology. Copyright © 1982 SGSR

Criteria may be of two types: standard and non-standard. The standard criteria are those for which numbers are available that arise from a process of enumeration against accepted standards. For example, cost in dollars, area in acres, board-feet of timber, inches of topsoil, length of an artifact, number of horsepower, etc. The non-standard criteria are those criteria for which no suitable, accepted standards exist.

The non-standard criteria may be of two types: quantifiable and non-quantifiable. The former are those for which numerical values can be attained that reflect subjective opinion on a scale. The latter are those for which numerical values do not appear to have significance on any interpretable scale.

Then the criteria also can be said to fall into two other types: quantifiable and non-quantifiable. The former include both the standard criteria and the non-standard criteria which can be suitably quantified.

Choice of a Baseline Alternative

A single alternative can be arbitrarily chosen as a "baseline alternative", against which comparisons will be made.

Test for Dominance

Initially a table (matrix) will be constructed. The left side of this table will be indexed by the Alternatives, the Baseline Alternative being the first to appear in the index set. There will be one row in the table for each Alternative to be considered.

Across the top of this table will appear the Evaluation Criteria. There will be one column in the table for each criterion.

In the data cells of the table, there will be placed the quantified values for all those Evaluation Criteria that are quantifiable, one such value being tabulated for each Alternative.

For those Evaluation Criteria that are non-quantifiable, there will appear in each cell the rank of the particular Alternative in light of the particular criterion being applied. The ranks can be given in numerical form with 1 being the highest, and ties in rank must be permitted. Suppose, for example, that the criterion is "most beautiful". We know of no way to quantify beauty reliably. Nevertheless individuals may arbitrarily assign ranks, and the ranks may be averaged. What we are quantifying here is not beauty, but rather a perception that is likely to be different for each observer. Nevertheless this practice allows the table to be filled with numbers.

It is now possible to inspect the completely filled-in table to search for any dominance that may occur among the set of Alternatives. Any one Alternative # 1 is said to dominate another Alternative # 2 if and only if every numerical entry in the row corresponding to alternative # 1 is judged to be superior to or equivalent to the corresponding entry for alternative # 2.

If one Alternative dominates another, then the Alternative that is dominated is removed from the set of Alternatives, leaving a reduced set. It is conceivable that one Alternative will dominate all the other Alternatives. Should this occur, the TAM terminates and the dominant Alternative is chosen.

Computer software can be used to drive a display unit that presents the table to the group in a large wall display so that as entries and comparisons are made, all of the relevant data are constantly in view.

The following discussion, involving continuation of the TAM, is limited to the case where there are two or more Alternatives remaining after the dominance testing, and none of the remaining Alternatives dominates any of the other remaining Alternatives.

Difference Ranking

Select any two Alternatives for comparison. Each of the two Alternatives will now be examined by comparing them with respect to each Evaluation Criterion. Suppose the Alternatives are # 1 and # 2. Suppose that the Evaluation Criteria are A, B, C, and D.

Now examine the <u>difference</u> between alternatives # 1 and # 2 with respect to Criterion A. This difference can be designated D_A. This difference will be considered very carefully with respect to how each of the options chosen in the several dimensions relates to this difference. A similar comparison can be made for the differences D_B, D_C, and D_D. As this comparison is being made, it will become clear that it is possible to structure the differences according to their relative significance. It might turn out that differences are judged as of equal importance. In cases involving numerous criteria, the ISM process can be used to organize the structuring. A typical question might appear as follows:

> In the context of comparing Alternatives # 1 and # 2,
> is difference D_A at least as significant as D_B?

Notice that if it should happen that the two differences were regarded as equally significant, they would then lie in a structural cycle.

This process of structuring the differences continues until all differences lie in a structure that represents their relative significance in assessing Alternatives # 1 and # 2.

Scaling the Ranked Differences

After the differences have been ranked, they are scaled. The items to be scaled may be individual differences or cycles containing more than one difference. The item ranked most significant is assigned a scale value of 100. The item ranked next highest is assigned a scale value between 0 and 100, by judging its relative significance compared to the highest-ranked item.

The next most significant is then assigned a scale value less than (or possibly equal to) that just assigned, and so on, until all differences have attained a scale value between 0 and 100.

Scoring the Two Alternatives

Each of the two alternatives being compared can now be assigned a score for each of the scaled items. Suppose, for example, that Alternative # 1 is taken as superior to Alternative # 2 in respect to Evaluation Criterion A. Then there will be assigned to Alternative # 1 the scaled value attached to the item D_A, while a zero score would be assigned to Alternative # 2 with respect to that item. Similarly, the scaled values given to each difference are assigned to whichever of the two Alternatives being compared is judged to be superior on that particular difference. Of course it could occur that for some particular criterion there would be no difference. If this should occur, the difference would always be ranked lowest in significance and assigned a scale value of 0.

When all the scale values representing the items have been assigned as indicated, the scaled values assigned to each Alternative may be added together to form the total score for each Alternative. The Alternative getting the highest score is then declared to be the superior Alternative.

Structuring the Set of Alternatives

Note that, when two Alternatives are compared, one normally emerges as the one with the higher score. This Alternative would then be preferred to the first. By continuing to compare Alternatives in pairs, using the process just described, a relationship of preference is built up on the Alternatives. This means that one can draw a tentative preference structure for the set of Alternatives based on the paired comparisons of Alternatives. If there were four Alternatives being compared, one might find, for example, a preference ordering as follows based on the total scores: < 2,3,1,4> . This type of ordering could be found, for example, by four comparisons: (1,2), (1,3), (2,3), and (1,4). Nevertheless one should not automatically assume that the preference ordering found by these four comparisons is the last word.

Nothing in this process assures that transitivity will apply to the ordering so found. Experience with the TAM shows that transitivity almost always applies, but it should always be tested, because the mathematics of this process does not have a built-in guarantee of transitivity. This is because of the highly detailed process of comparison that is used.

Figure 7.23 shows a Delta Chart of the TAM. Because this process is relatively intricate, an example of its use will be given. This "movie example" is clearly a simplified one, from a design perspective. We take the design problem to be one of designing a strategy for going to the movies.

The Movie Example

Suppose that the process of designing a strategy for going to the movies has been brought to the point where the dimensions have been chosen, and the Options Field appears as shown in Figure 7.24.

Suppose further that three Alternatives have been selected, as indicated in Figures 7.25-7.27 inclusive.

Now suppose that the set of Evaluation Criteria selected is as follows: (a) The total portal-to-portal time required to attend the movie, (b) the cost of the movie, (c) comfort in the theater, (d) the number of people in the family who can attend, (e) how much sleep is lost, and (f) the expected quality of the entertainment.

Table 7.3 shows the descriptions of the three alternatives, A, B, and C, in terms of the six criteria just listed.

Given the data in Table 7.3, it is possible now to rank the alternatives on each of the criteria, as indicated in Table 7.4.

It can be seen by inspection of Table 7.4 that no Alternative dominates any other Alternative. Alternative A is ranked highest on all criteria except that of comfort, where it is ranked lowest. Alternative B is ranked lowest on four of the criteria, but is ranked highest on two of them. Alternative C is ranked highest on three of them, and does not rank lowest on any. However every Alternative ranks higher on at least one criterion than any other, which is sufficient to ensure that none of them dominates any other.

Having established that there is no dominance, the comparison of the Alternatives in pairs begins with an examination of the differences between them for each of the criteria. Table 7.5 provides this comparison for Alternatives A and B.

In order now to establish which of the two alternatives is best, the differences are ranked by the people who are going to attend the movie. The following is the ranking of the differences:

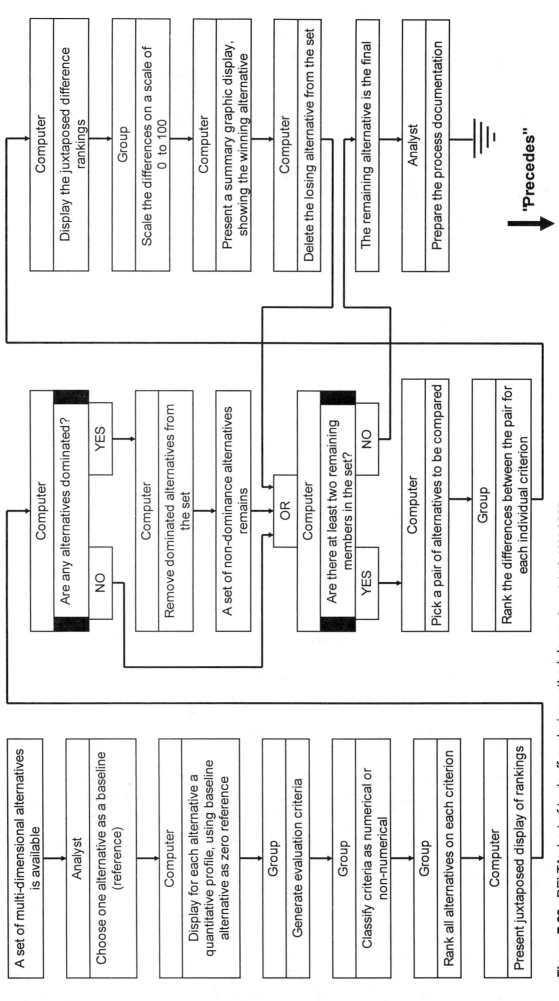

Figure 7.23 DELTA chart of tradeoff analysis. methodology. Copyright © 1982 SGSR.

Film

- Gone with the Wind
- The Strangler
- The Maltese Falcon
- Snow White
- Airport
- Thirty-nine Steps
- Casablanca
- E.T.
- Stanley and Living-stone

Theatre

- The Bijou
- The Fox
- Loews
- General Cinema
- Harper House
- Tenth Street
- Ritz
- Hot Flash

TIE LINE

Showtime

- Matinee
- Early show
- Late show
- Midnight show

Transportation

- Bus
- Walking
- Private car
- Bicycle
- Train
- Taxi
- Pogo stick

Figure 7.24 Options field for movie example.

244

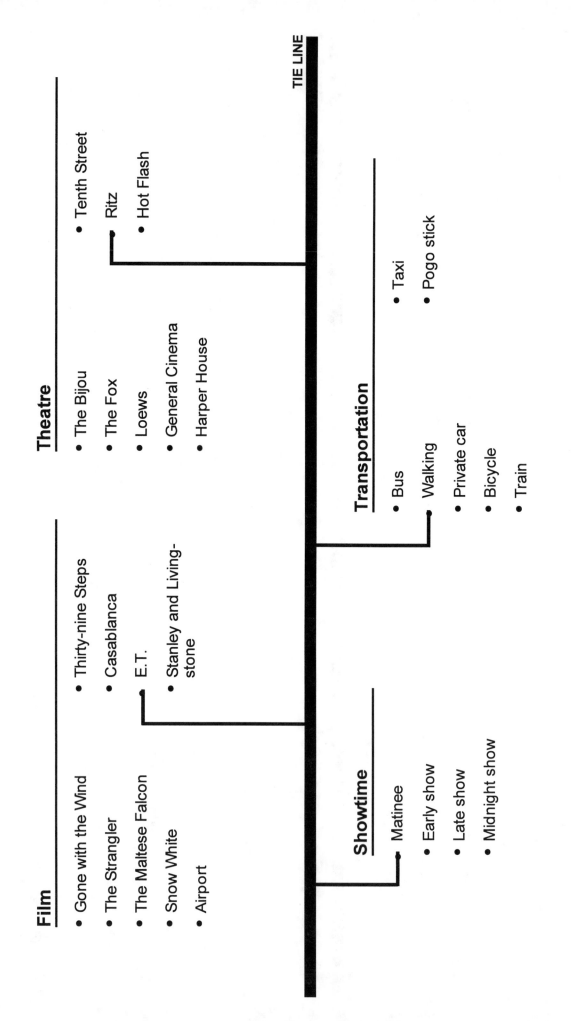

Figure 7.25 Alternative A for movie example.

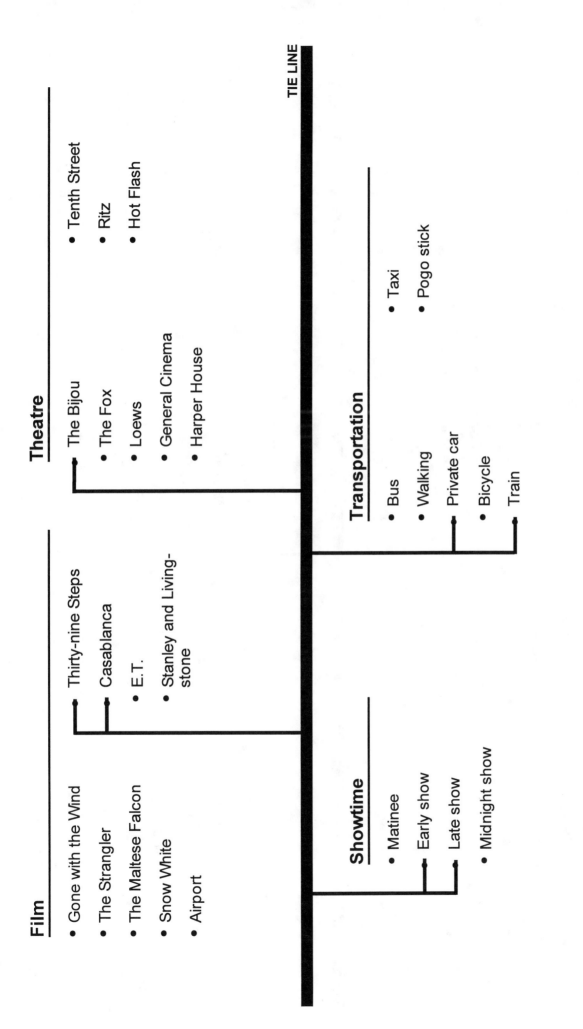

Film

- Gone with the Wind
- The Strangler
- The Maltese Falcon
- Snow White
- Airport

- Thirty-nine Steps
- Casablanca
- E.T.
- Stanley and Living-
stone

Theatre

- The Bijou
- The Fox
- Loews
- General Cinema
- Harper House

- Tenth Street
- Ritz
- Hot Flash

Showtime

- Matinee
- Early show
- Late show
- Midnight show

Transportation

- Bus
- Walking
- Private car
- Bicycle
- Train

- Taxi
- Pogo stick

TIE LINE

Figure 7.26 Alternative B for movie example.

245

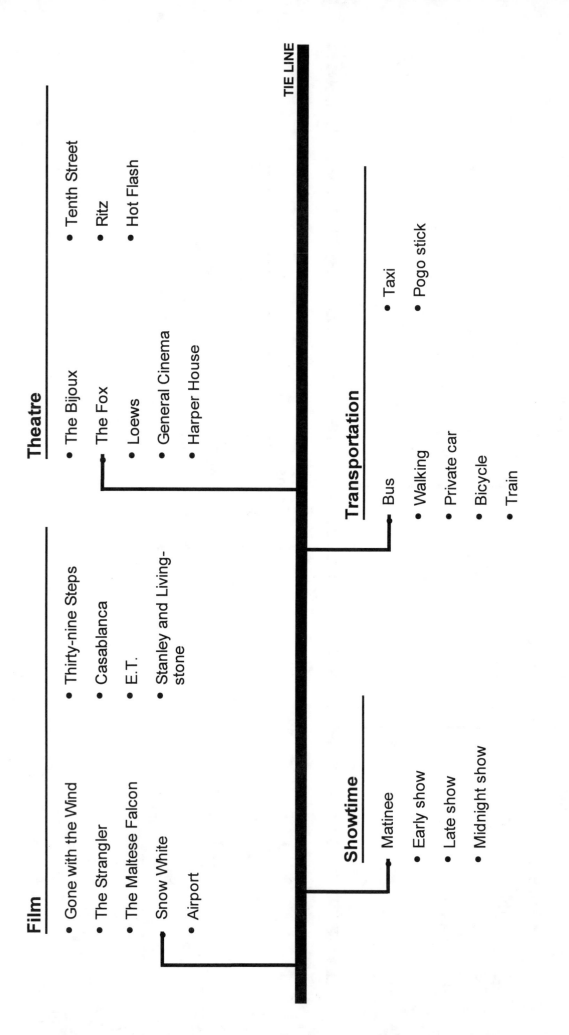

Film
- Gone with the Wind
- The Strangler
- The Maltese Falcon
- Snow White
- Airport
- Thirty-nine Steps
- Casablanca
- E.T.
- Stanley and Living-stone

Theatre
- The Bijoux
- The Fox
- Loews
- General Cinema
- Harper House
- Tenth Street
- Ritz
- Hot Flash

Showtime
- Matinee
- Early show
- Late show
- Midnight show

Transportation
- Bus
- Walking
- Private car
- Bicycle
- Train
- Taxi
- Pogo stick

TIE LINE

Figure 7.27 Alternative C for movie example.

Table 7.3
Relevant Data Concerning the Six Criteria
for Each of the Three Alternatives

Criteria -- Alternative	Time	Cost	Comfort	Attendees	Lost Sleep	Quality
A	2.5 hours	$16	Fair	4	None	High
B	6 hours	$19	Excellent	2	2 hours	High
C	3.5 hours	$18	Good	4	None	High

1. Comfort

2. Lost Sleep

3. Time

4. Attendees

5. Cost

The explanation for the ranking is as follows. The difference between Excellent and Fair in the Comfort criterion is judged to be more important than the $3 cost difference. The actors are willing to trade the extra $3 for the large difference in Comfort. Similarly, these actors are willing to accept the two-hour difference in lost sleep, and the 3.5-hour difference in the total time required, as being less important to them than the Comfort. They prefer A to B because the two children can accompany the two adults, but it is more important to them to be comfortable than to have the children attend.

Table 7.4
Ranking the Alternatives on the Six Criteria

Criteria -- Alternative	Time	Cost	Comfort	Attendees	Lost Sleep	Quality
A	1	1	3	1	1	1
B	3	3	1	3	3	1
C	2	2	2	1	1	1

Table 7.5
Comparison of Alternatives A and B

	Time	Cost	Comfort	Attendees	Lost Sleep
A	2.5 hours	$16	Fair	4	None
B	6.0 hours	$19	Excellent	2	2 hours
Difference	3.5 hours	$3		2	2 hours
Best	A	A	B	A	A

The second choice in their ranking of the differences is the lost sleep. The two hours of lost sleep that they would be able to avoid is considered important, because of the requirement to be at work early the next day.

The difference of 3.5 hours is not so important, because they have the time to spare; what is more important is the lost sleep that would be incurred.

The fact that the two children cannot attend is not as significant as the 3.5-hour time difference. And finally the $3 difference in cost is the least important of all the differences.

With this ranking, the scaling of the differences is not so hard to carry out. The comfort criterion gets automatically a score of 100, because it is highest ranked. The 2 hours of lost sleep that might be foregone by choice of Alternative A is judged to be only 70% as important to them as the greater comfort to be experienced by choosing Alternative B. Continuing, the scaling results are as follows for the comparison of A and B:

Comfort	100
Lost Sleep	70
Time	30
Attendees	10
Cost	5

These numbers are now allocated respectively to the alternative that is judged best on the several criteria. Based on this, Alternative B gets a score of 100 coming entirely from its excellent comfort rating. However Alternative A claims all of the other scores, because it is superior to B on the other four criteria.

Note that the criterion "quality" was not ranked, nor was it assigned a score, because the two Alternatives were rated equal on this criterion.

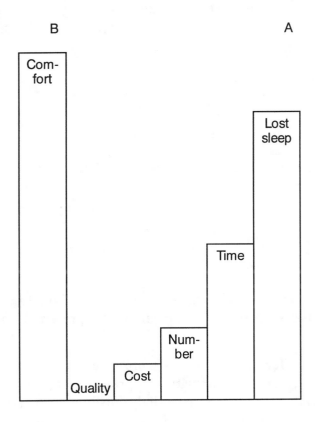

Scores: A 115; B 100. Thus, A is better than B.

Figure 7.28 Bar chart comparing alternatives A and B.

Figure 7.28 provides a visual bar-chart display of the scoring, in which the highest score for one Alternative appears at the left, and the highest score for the other appears at the right, with monotone decreasing bar heights showing the scores on the other criteria. This Figure shows visually exactly how Alternative A achieved a score that is superior to that of Alternative B, and enables a visual examination of what kind of adjustments would have to be made in the relative importance of the differences in order to cause a reversal of this rating.

Because Alternative A is selected as superior to B in this analysis, the winning Alternative is now compared with Alternative C, to see whether it also scores ahead of C.

In comparing A and C, it will be evident that the ranking of the criteria changes from what it was before. This comes about because the differences between the two Alternatives are being ranked, in terms of the several criteria.

In comparing A and C, only three criteria are to be ranked, because the two Alternatives are equal on three of the criteria.

The ranking of the differences now becomes:

1. Comfort (Good versus Fair)

2. Cost (A difference of $2)

3. Time (A difference of 1 hour)

The differences are now scaled, and the judgments about the relative importance of the differences are as follows:

Comfort	100
Cost	20
Time	10

Allocating these scores to the respective Alternatives gives a score of 100 to C, and a score of 30 to A. Figure 7.29 offers the summarizing bar chart representation of this choice.

Now it has been found that C is preferred to A, and A is preferred to B. Under these conditions, it is natural to assume that by transitivity, C is preferred to B as well. However as mentioned earlier, there is no assurance that transitivity will always hold. In order to test the hypothesis that C is the preferred choice, it will now be compared directly with B.

Table 7.6 shows the comparison of these two alternatives.e

Table 7.6
Comparison of Alternatives B and C

	Time	Cost	Comfort	Attendees	Lost Sleep
B	6 hours	$19	Excellent	2	2 hours
C	3.5 hours	$18	Good	4	None
Difference	2.5 hours	$1		2	2 hours
Which is Best?	C	C	B	C	C

The differences between the two Alternatives are now ranked as follows:

1. Lost Sleep

2. Comfort

C   A

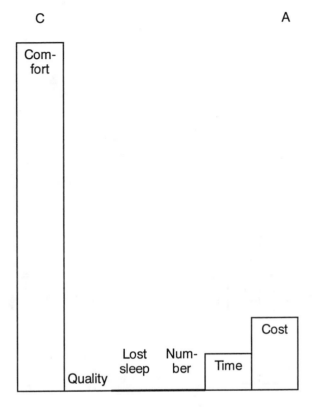

Scores: C 100; A 30. Thus, C is better than A.

Figure 7.29 Bar chart comparing alternatives A and C.

    3. Attendees

    4. Time

    5. Cost

Comparing this ranking with that applied to the comparison of Alternatives A and B, it is seen that the difference in comfort between Excellent and Good is not ranked as high as the previously considered difference between Excellence and Fair. The 2 hours of lost sleep now takes on more importance than any of the other differences.

The scores assigned to the differences are as follows:

Lost Sleep	100
Comfort	40
Attendees	40

251

C   B

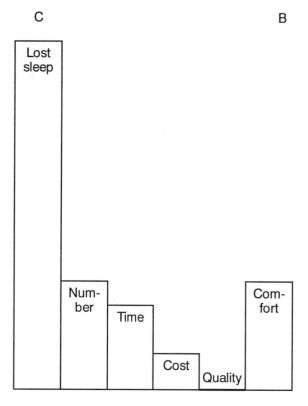

Scores: C 175; B 40. Thus, C is best.

Figure 7.30 Bar chart comparing alternatives B and C.

| Time | 30 |
| Cost | 5 |

Allocating these scores to the Alternatives according to which is rated best in Table 7.6 gives a score of 175 for Alternative C and 40 for Alternative B, as indicated in Figure 7.30.

Since C is clearly superior to B, the transitivity condition is satisfied in this case, and the final choice of C as the preferred Alternative is the outcome of the application of the Tradeoff Analysis Method.

SUMMARY

Methodology corresponds to process component prescriptions aimed at producing specific products related to problem-solving and design. Its priors are found in Theory and Foundations.

Methodology for Generic Design Science is viewed as a Division of Operations with Ideas. The primary such Operations are as follows:

- Generation of ideas
- Clarification of ideas
- Structuring of ideas
- Amending of ideas
- Implementing ideas

Seven methodologies have been selected to satisfy the requirements for Generic Design Science. They are: Ideawriting (also called Brainwriting), Nominal Group Technique (NGT), DELPHI, Interpretive Structural Modeling (ISM), the Options Field Methodology (OFM), the Options Profile Methodology (OPM), and the Tradeoff Analysis Methodology (TAM).

Two of these methodologies have been used sufficiently often, on a sufficient variety of complex issues, and with sufficiently varied groups of participants, that a statistical analysis of products has been made possible and meaningful. Appendix 5 presents Data from Applications, and some conclusions from analyzing these data. The data support key ideas of Generic Design Science, and emphasize that this Science is not limited to a theoretical perspective.

Examples of types of products produced from using the Methodology appear in Chapter 9, and examples of products from specific applications appear in Chapter 10.

REFERENCES

1. J. N. Warfield and J. D. Hill, "The DELTA Chart: A Method for R&D Project Portrayal", *IEEE Trans. Engr. Mgt.*, EM18(4), 1971, 132-139.

2. T. Inagaki and E. M. Himmelblau, "Hierarchical Determination of Precedence Order and Representation of Digraphs", *IEEE Trans. Syst., Man, and Cybern.*, 13(3), May/June, 1983, 406-413.

3. K. Sugiyama, S. Tagawa, and M. Toda, "Methods for Visual Understanding of Hierarchical System Structures", *IEEE Trans. Syst., Man, and Cybern.*, Feb., 1981, 109-125.

4. A. L. Delbecq, A. H. Van De Ven and D. H. Gustafson, *Group Techniques for Program Planning: A Guide to Nominal Group and DELPHI Processes*, Glenview: Scott, Foresman, 1975.

5. J. N. Warfield, *Societal Systems: Planning, Policy, and Complexity*, New York: Wiley, 1976 (reprinted, Salinas, CA: Intersystems, 1989.)

6. J. N. Warfield, "Interpretive Structural Modeling", Chap. 5 in *Group Planning and Problem Solving Methods in Engineering*, S. A. Olsen, Editor, New York: Wiley, 1982, 155-201.

7. Y. Sawaragi and K. Kawamura, *Participatory Systems Approach: Methods and Applications*, Tokyo: Daily Industrial Newspaper Company, 1982 (in Japanese).

8. N. Szyperski and M. Eul-Bischoff, *Interpretative Strukturmodellierung (ISM)*, Braunschweig: Vieweg, 1983 (in German).

9. A. Ohuchi, M. Kurihara and I. Kaji, "An Efficient Procedure for Transitive Coupling in ISM", *IEEE Trans. Syst., Man, and Cybern.*, SMC-15(3), May/June, 1985, 426-431.

10. J. N. Warfield, *Annotated Bibliography: ISM and Related Work*, Department of Electrical Engineering, University of Virginia, June 1980 (106 pp.), available through Interlibrary Loan from George Mason University, Fenwick Library.

11. J. N. Warfield, *Annotated Bibliography of Publications*, IASIS, George Mason University, May, 1988 (67 pages), available through Interlibrary Loan from George Mason University, Fenwick Library.

12. J. N. Warfield, "Organizations and Systems Learning", *General Systems* 27, 1982, 5-74.

QUESTIONS RELATED TO CHAPTER 7

1. For what is Sir Geoffrey Vickers noted?

2. What in the background of Sir Geoffrey Vickers would lead him to make a point of saying that "the word *system* is in danger of becoming unusable in the context of human history and human culture"?

3. What kind of subculture would preempt the use of the word "system" in such a way that Vickers' statement would be relevant to society?

4. What constitutes methodology?

5. What should steer the development and choice of methodology?

6. What actually steers the development and choice of methodology?

7. What is a likely consequence of developing methodology for use in specific, narrow contexts; and then presenting it in language specific to those contexts?

8. What area common to almost all human beings is chosen as the contextual base for the methodology for Generic Design Science?

9. What are the primary operations that are carried out with ideas?

10. Select a specific area of society where groups of people are constantly engaged in designing (e.g., Congress constantly engaged in designing legislation), and locate and describe a specific case in this area to develop a discussion of how the primary operations with ideas are actually dealt with in that case.

11. What furnish the criteria for choice of methodology in the Generic Design Science?

12. What does the Law of Gradation imply about the use of the methodologies of the Generic Design Science?

13. What are the seven methodologies that have been chosen for use through application of the Theory of Generic Design?

14. What do the letters represent in the acronym "DELTA"?

15. What is produced by using a hodgepodge of poorly-conceived graphics symbols on a chart?

16. What attributes does sheet music have that hold lessons for the choice of symbols and the design of language for dealing with complex systems?

17. Explain how sheet music satisfied the Law of Requisite Parsimony.

18. What are advantages of the DELTA chart, compared to other systems for giving a prescription for action?

19. Find a recipe in a cookbook. Make a copy of it to submit with your solution. Construct a DELTA Chart to substitute for the recipe. Write a descriptive comparison of the two ways of portraying the action sequence.

20. What are the three main ingredients of a DELTA chart?

21. What do the connectives on a DELTA Chart represent?

22. What three graphics principles are applied in the DELTA Chart concept?

23. Construct a plan for yourself for a selected day of the week, using the DELTA Chart to portray the plan.

24. Define "activity".

25. Define "event".

26. Define "decision".

27. Define "option".

28. Identify all of the walks on the DELTA Chart found in responding to Question 23 (above), and show their traces.

29. Which of the walks identified in responding to Quest. 28 are major walks, and which are minor walks?

30. What is meant by "realization of a walk"?

31. Identify the <u>major</u> walks on Figure 7.11.

32. Identify the <u>minor</u> walks on Figure 7.11.

33. What are the primary attributes of Ideawriting?

34. What roles are involved in Ideawriting?

35. Why should a triggering question for Ideawriting be formulated with care? (Hint: What will be some consequences of poor formulation?)

36. What are the four principal properties of the Nominal Group Technique?

37. What properties of the Nominal Group Technique are <u>also</u> found in Ideawriting?

38. What properties of the Nominal Group Technique are <u>not</u> found in Ideawriting?

39. What roles are involved in the Nominal Group Technique?

40. Construct a more detailed DELTA Chart of the Ideawriting process to show more of the actions involved in generating the events that make up the bulk of the description in Figure 7.12.

41. Discuss the concept of "Diversity" that is quantified in Table 7.1.

42. How does DELPHI differ from NGT?

43. What is the historical basis for the Interpretive Structural Modeling process?

44. What is meant when it is said that a process is "self-documenting"?

45. What capability does ISM bring to applications?

46. What is produced by using ISM?

47. What roles are involved in ISM?

48. What condition must be satisfied by a relationship that is chosen for use in ISM?

49. Sometimes authors who discuss ISM have not been completely sensitive to the importance or meaning of transitivity. For example, refer to: A.P. Sage, <u>Methodology for Large Scale Systems</u>, New York: McGraw-Hill, 1977, and especially to the Example 4.3-1 extending over pages 103 to 107, which is described on page 103 as "a simple example which will serve as a vehicle for presentation of

many of the central ideas of interpretive structural modeling". Explain why the relationship used in this example is not a transitive relationship, simply by using the situation described in the example.

50. Does the acronym "ISM" refer to a process, a model, or a product?

51. What is meant by a "generic question"?

52. What features apply for the Options Field Methodology and the Options Profile Methodology?

53. What two Consensus Methodologies are both a part of the Options Field Methodology and the Options Profile Methodology?

54. What justifies calling the Options Field a poly-structure?

55. Discuss the relative merits of (a) beginning with a set of categories and then placing options in each of them versus (b) generating a set of options, placing them in categories, and then naming the categories?

56. Is there any difference between a "category" and a "design dimension"? If so, what?

57. Which of the following are true, and which are false: a) Every cluster is a cycle, b) Every cycle is a cluster, c) A single dimension can be a cluster in a special case, d) Every dimension is a cluster, e) A cluster always represents a particular relationship, and no flexibility is available to alter that relationship, f) Sequencing of dimensions should precede the sequencing of clusters, for the purpose of ordering the choice-making part of the Options Profile process, g) Sequencing of clusters should precede the sequencing of dimensions, for the purpose of ordering the choice-making part of the Options Profile process?

58. Why is a tie line used?

59. What is the difference between an Options Field and an Options Profile?

60. Refer to Figure 7.21. Identify two options that were selected in designing an alternative, and identify two options that were rejected in designing an alternative.

61. Write a narrative presentation of the content of the Options Profile in Figure 7.21.

62. What two types of criteria are used in the Tradeoff Analysis Methodology?

63. What merit lies in comparing alternatives on the basis of the incremental differences between them, instead of comparing them directly on the basis of the options themselves?

64. What aspect of an Options Profile is illustrated by Alternative B, as contrasted with Alternative A, in the Movie Example?

65. Given all the results that were involved in developing Figure 7.28, and looking at the numerical scores, discuss what changes might be made in order to reverse the decision that A is better than B.

66. It seems reasonable to say that if A is better than B and if B is better than C, then necessarily A is better than C, because the relationship "is better than" is transitive. Why cannot this assumption of transitivity be justified in applying the results of the Tradeoff Analysis Methodology to arrive at the choice of a final alternative?

67. Discuss the significance of "referential transparency" in regard to Quest. 66.

68. Under what conditions could the transitivity of the relationship "is better than" be applied to arrive at a choice of a final alternative?

69. Discuss the Tradeoff Analysis Method in terms of the concept of Referential Transparency discussed in earlier Chapters.

70. Suppose a dominance analysis showed that the three alternatives in the Movie Example were in a dominance relationship, i.e., A dominates B and B dominates C. Could it be concluded from this that A dominates C? If the dominance relationship is transitive, why isn't the relationship "is better than" transitive, as used in the Movie Example?

71. If the ISM process were used to establish a preference ordering on the three alternatives shown in the Movie Example, what relationship should be chosen for use in the process?

CHAPTER 8

ENVIRONMENT AND ROLES
OF THE SCIENCE

"The eight symptoms of groupthink are: (1) an illusion of invulnerability, shared by most or all of the members, (2) collective efforts to rationalize in order to discount warnings, (3) an unquestioned belief in the group's inherent morality, (4) stereotyped views of rivals and enemies, (5) direct pressure on any member who expresses strong arguments against any of the group's stereotypes, illusions, or commitments, (6) self-censorship of deviations, (7) a shared illusion of unanimity...augmented by the false assumption that silence means consent, and (8) the emergence of self-appointed mindguards..."

--I. L. Janis

"I find it convenient to regard institutions as structures of mutual expectation, attached to roles which define what each of its members shall expect from others and from himself."

--Sir Geoffrey Vickers

Ordinary, everyday experience leads people to believe that it is normal to carry out design and related activities such as planning in almost any environment. If the design encompasses physical artifacts, the working environment may be minimally altered to provide the most obviously essential accessories. In the computer age, the ever-present publicity spurs the addition of computers to the working environment. But the idea that the environment should be subjected to the most detailed design, taking into account the Laws of Generic Design, and recognizing the potential benefits of creating an environment that offers enhancements and minimizes detractions will only very gradually be adopted.

Nevertheless it is essential to design, construct, and maintain an environment that maximizes the likelihood of success in design activity. As the number of large system failures continues to grow, more and more evidence will accumulate to support the ideas given here.

Similarly, the idea that one could design a model of a social system involving a set of roles and role interactions deduced from the most careful study of what is to be accomplished in system design, seems to be foreign. It is true, of course, that in the course of personnel recruitment, position descriptions are written, and that the past experience of the individual in similar positions (without too much regard to the success or failure of the individual in the position) is taken into account. But the concept of a systematic design of role sets and interactions in the light of requirements seems to be relatively rare or, perhaps, almost never found.

When success in some area seems elusive, and when the consequences of failure seem devastating, there is every reason to consider carefully the design of the environment and the design of the social system to operate in that environment.

In this Chapter, the environment is taken as the union of what will be called the Laboratory Environment (meaning the physical location in which the work is done, and the outfitting of that location) and the External Environment which includes the organization in which the physical location is present. A system of roles that is appropriate for the Laboratory Environment will be discussed. Then a specific instance of such an Environment designed in 1980 and implemented in several locations will be discussed, and the benefits of its use will be described. Some of the antecedents of this concept will be described. Finally, evaluation of the Laboratory Environment and roles will be discussed.

8.1 Divisions of the Environment.

The environment for carrying out and implementing generic design activities is divided into two parts: the Laboratory Environment, where the conceptual design activity is carried out and documented; and the larger External Environment from which motivation for the design process originates and into which the Target design is introduced and in which it performs.

The success or failure of a given Target design involves both the Laboratory Environment and the External Environment. The former can largely be specified, while the latter is largely self-determining. Nonetheless it is possible to articulate the desirable features of both, from the point of view of a dual-basis design philosophy.

One of the two bases in the dual-basis consists of those aspects related directly to the human being, and is called <u>anthropological</u>. The other of the two bases consists of those aspects related to language and the documentation of reasoning. This basis is called <u>logical</u>. (A third basis, used in much of the specific design science, is called <u>technological</u>. With this language, we have the anthropological, the logical, and the technological as the three primary bases for General Design Science defined in Chapter 3.)

The Laboratory Environment

The anthropological basis in the Laboratory Environment focuses upon eliminating detractions and providing enhancements. The logical basis in the same setting recognizes the need for a variety of communication aids and cognitive assistance means. Such an environment is designed in recognition of the need for personal comfort for human beings engaged in long and difficult tasks; of the need for well-conceived, large displays; of the value in making protracted logic visible; and of the need to relieve the actors of activities that take attention away from thought, listening, and communicating. It recognizes the need for cognitive assistance in organizing knowledge, and for dialog to develop the capacity for effective teamwork founded in understanding ideas.

A Laboratory Environment has been designed specifically to meet these needs. It is called "Demosophia", and will be described in Sec. 8.3.

The External Environment

The External Environment at present contains both components that (a) <u>do</u> look to scientific knowledge first, to discover methodologies that have passed rigorous screenings and (b) that <u>do not</u> look to such knowledge, but rather find other high- priority bases for their actions. In the long run, the latter must give way to the former. If the latter provide valuable results in Applications, they will find their way into the Science; while if they do not, the Science will gradually displace them.

This External Environment often carries cultural features that slight design and reward ad hoc and uninformed practices; and this Environment also has great variations in the distribution of power. The powerful will not always find that the Laboratory Environment described here will suit their purposes. Even when such an Environment is operational, cultural features may work against its use. Some detractors to design will yield only to wisdom displayed by individuals with significant power. Those who hold the power to promote change also often hold the power to prevent it or to steer it in bad directions.

In his study of many organizations, Chris Argyris has found that one of the major reasons for poor performance is reliance on the wrong fundamentals. In his concept of a proposed way out of the morass, he has conceived the Double-Loop Problem model discussed in Sec. 4.2. A strategy of "framebreaking and remodeling" was proposed by Argyris as a mode of intervention in organizations that is aimed at the fundamental difficulties. These recommendations are consistent with the generalization to the Poly-Loop Model (Sec. 4.9) that ties the corporate part of the External Environment to science as a basis for the remodeling. Redesign of the External Environment will benefit from the use of the proposed Laboratory Environment. It can be a setting both for redesigning the corporate part of the External Environment in the first instance, and for renewing it thereafter by incremental redesign.

8.2 Role Divisions.

The roles that are involved in the Generic Design Science and the Design Situation make up the Cast; and the Cast, together with the interactions among the roles, make up the social system. The Design Situation involves all aspects that are unique to a given social system.

A given set of roles is most effective when the environment is hospitable and supportive. A social system that expects good results from its designers will strive to make the environment supportive of effective design activity.

Roles in the Cast are <u>designed</u> roles, chosen on the basis of the findings of the Generic Design Science. The major roles are the following:

- <u>Participant-Designer</u>, a member of a design team who holds content knowledge relevant to the design task and is motivated to contribute to the design

- <u>Facilitator (Pilotos)</u>, a person who is intimately acquainted with the Science, and is able to manage the interaction among the members of the Participant-Designer group and the supporting actors and facilities, including the displays and the computer

- <u>Broker</u>, a person who is intimately acquainted with the Design Situation, and who selects the Participant-Designer group; and who also makes available the financial resources to carry out the design work; but who normally acquires these resources from sources in the Design Situation

- <u>Process Designer</u>, a person who formulates the process sequences to carry out the work in a given Design Situation, in collaboration with the Broker and the Facilitator, and who may also fill the Facilitator role

- <u>Top Manager</u>, a person who has the power to make available the resources needed to implement the design, as well as the power to prevent its implementation

- <u>Report Manager</u>, a person who manages the documentation and integrates it into a report of the activity

- <u>Implementers</u>, people who will play some role in the implementation of the design

- <u>Stakeholders</u>, people who will be affected positively or negatively by any design that is implemented

- <u>Supporting Process Roles</u>, people who manage the information displays, record the information that is generated by the Participant-Designer group, and provide various ancillary services to the group

While it is normal that one individual will fill just one role, it is also possible that in some situations an individual may play several roles. It is part of the general philosophy, however, that the actor who takes the role of Facilitator will not also take the role of Participant-Designer in a given Design Situation. The credibility and effectiveness of the role of Facilitator depends on adhering to this requirement.

Testing of these roles, in conjunction with the use of the Laboratory Environment to be described later, has taken place over a period of more than seven years in the Center for Interactive Management. This Center, first established at the University of Virginia in 1981, and subsequently moved to George Mason University in 1984, has been the primary testing ground for all of the Generic Design Science.

Other testing has taken place, however, at other locations that have adapted the Laboratory Environment pioneered by the Center for Interactive Management. Experience at these other locations indicates that the concepts, methods, roles, environments, and other aspects discussed in this book are not merely fantasies produced in a single organization.

Among the other locations just referred to, the following may be mentioned:

- Creation of the **Interactive Management Unit** at the City University of London, with leadership from Mr. Ross Janes

- An installation at the **Southwest Fisheries Center**, a fishery research organization, which is part of the National Marine Fisheries Service, itself a part of the National Oceanic and Atmospheric Administration (NOAA) of the U. S. Government, with leadership from Mr. David Mackett

- An installation in the **Futures Research Group** in the Department of Administration at the University of São Paulo in Brazil, with leadership from Mr. James T. C. Wright

- **The Aegean Seminar: Systems for Island Ecosystems**, involving the University of the Aegean, with leadership from Drs. Ioanna Tsivakou and Costas Sophoulis

- The **Institute for Decision Making** at the University of Northern Iowa, initiated by then Dean of the Business School, Dr. Robert Waller, who has made numerous contributions to the study of Interpretive Structural Modeling and its applications

- A **Systems Engineering and Cybernetics Centre** at Hyderabad, India, headed by Prof. P. N. Murthy, assisted by Mr. S. K. Batra and Centre staff. This Centre has been established as a part of Tata Consultancy Services (TCS), directed by Mr. F. C. Kohli, who has been instrumental in initiating the applications of systems sciences in the consultancy profession. TCS itself is a part of the Tata Group, whose history is inspiringly related in [1].

Leadership

Leadership is a word that describes the most critical aspect of the behavioral basis, whether it is the Laboratory or External Environment that is involved. The Bennis study of leadership (discussed in Sec. 1.6) found empirical evidence that people who are recognized as outstanding leaders, from a variety of fields, share four attributes. They know how to manage: (1) attention, (2) meaning, (3) trust, and (4) self. Inability to manage any one of these factors appears sufficient to invalidate leadership. Fortunately it is possible for people to learn how to manage these four things, should they be inclined to do so. The exercise of them is proionic, in that when they are exercised new phenomena arise that are not inherent in any one of them when exercised separately.

Leadership in generic design is not limited to any one individual. In the sense just defined, it can be practiced by every individual involved. Christakis and Prabhu [2] have proposed the name "Pilotos" to represent an individual who has "acquired the behavioral and technical skills to use computer-assisted methodologies in order to efficiently extract and organize ideas residing in the Phaneron and the Library, in accordance with the dictates of complex problem situations in the Residue which are amenable to change through design activity." This definition is an extension of the more familiar role of facilitator, which generally imposes considerably less demanding criteria.

8.3 Demosophia.

The Laboratory Environment that has been designed and tested for Generic Design has been given the name "Demosophia", meaning "wisdom of the people".

Research in psychology and sociology has revealed significant knowledge about individual and group behavior that bears strongly on problem-solving ability, as well as some simple logistical aspects of group activity.

Yet problem solving in groups usually proceeds almost as though this research had never been done, or as though its findings are wrong or irrelevant.

For this reason, it was determined early in the 1970's that it was critical to conceive of some means of ensuring that these research results did not lie fallow, but instead were carefully integrated into a scheme of problem-solving and design.

One of the five critical factors in problem-solving and design in areas of complexity is the physical environment in which such activity is carried out. (The other four factors have been discussed in Chapter 6.) It was determined that only by designing a special "situation room" unlike those that had already been developed in a few places, and which incorporated all the relevant research results, could the maximum benefits be achieved; and moreover it was believed (and later confirmed) that these benefits would be truly significant for the purpose. The advantages would not be incremental additions, but would reflect a giant step forward.

Accordingly in 1980 a design was developed for such an environment. It incorporated a number of key dimensions, ranging from simple "housekeeping" features (such as the coat rack to keep clothing out of the way of problem-solving activity) to sophisticated communication facilities involving software that carries out inference with information. (This inference is based in the Theory of Relations, and it was instrumented in 1973. The term "inference" itself is about the only thing that this process has in common with what is now called "artificial intelligence".)

The design was not carried out without relevant prior experience in environments that involved groups who were engaged in trying to solve complex problems or to design systems. Instead, a period of time extending from 1974 to 1979 had involved working in a variety of ad hoc settings, mostly consisting of rooms that were set aside as "meeting rooms", "conference rooms", or classrooms. Invariably these rooms had extremely bad attributes for problem-solving. It was after struggling to achieve results in group work under such unsatisfactory conditions that the insight needed to design an appropriate situation room was gained.

In short, two critical things went into the design of the room: (a) an understanding of the research results from social science revealing significant shortcomings that needed to be corrected in group work and (b) six years of experience working with groups in unsatisfactory environments.

In addition to the foregoing general benefits, the design was further informed by a number of specifics related primarily to methodology for group problem-solving that were gathered, developed, and tested during the period from 1970 to 1979. While designing to incorporate the research results and the experience, specific aspects of the design related directly to the methodologies being used. Thus the design of the room involved considerations not likely to be found in most other problem- solving facilities.

In addition to the main facility, the design involved an anteroom specifically conceived to be a strong supporting facility for what goes on in the main room. Operations in the situation room are supported on a real-time basis by operations in the anteroom. This is why the processes described in Chapter 7 can be self-documenting. The processes develop the necessary information. The actors who fill the various roles use the facilities of both rooms to provide the documentation in a real-time activity.

The first room to be developed was not completely faithful to the initial design. This was the decision-support facility at the University of Northern Iowa. There it was necessary to use an existing room that lacked some of the envisaged requirements. However many of the salient features were incorporated. Since its development in 1980, additional features have been added to make it more useful as a problem-solving environment. Also its use has not been limited to complex issues, but rather it has been applied to a variety of problems.

The second facility to be developed was almost totally done according to the original design insofar as the principal facility, the Demosophia, was concerned. The anteroom was considerably below desirable standards. Nevertheless this facility, developed at the University of Virginia, and placed in service in April of 1982, proved to be almost all that was hoped for in advancing the environmental needs for generic system design purposes.

As a result of experience gained with this design, its design was replicated by two client organizations in the period 1983-1985. These were the U. S. Forest Service Regional Office in Atlanta, Georgia, and the Southwest Fisheries in La Jolla, California (mentioned earlier). The former facility is no longer being used, because of cutbacks in the Forest Service. The latter facility continues to be used regularly by the Southwest Fisheries.

A room with most of the original design features was created in the period 1984-1986 at the City University of London. This facility incorporated some improvements in the equipment and in graphical capabilities.

Finally a well-equipped facility that was developed using the initial design was built at George Mason University in 1984-1985. This room had a much better anteroom than the one at the University of Virginia, providing for more efficient support services. It also had slightly more space, and its layout permitted better writing boards on the walls.

The name "Demosophia" was chosen for this room to distinguish it from other rooms that are also called "situation rooms" and to reflect the philosophy under which it was designed. Those who study situation rooms recognize that there are several types, characterized by different assumptions and underlying purposes [3].

The name "Demosophia" reflects the philosophy that the people who have difficult problems to deal with usually can do so with wisdom, provided they are supported by an appropriate environment, methodology based in sound theory, and staff people who are there to assist rather than to play out their own egos as superior problem solvers to those who "own" and who suffer from the problems.

Lasswell's Vision

While the design of Demosophia has been based on the background given in the preceding discussions, the original idea for such a room belongs to the late Harold Lasswell. This former Yale professor and political scientist was a well-known and well-respected scholar, teacher, and author. Among his better known books are *A Pre-View of the Policy Sciences* and *Politics: Who Gets What, Where, and When?*

In his early days as a faculty member, Lasswell was very interested in group problem-solving activity. One of the experiences that he had together with two colleagues, took place in a Peruvian mountain village. For three months the small delegation of faculty tried to communicate with and assist the inhabitants of this poor village to try to help restore the viability of the community. This took place with a group of Indians who did not speak English.

After several weeks, the discovery was made that communication could take place with a graphics language that was developed on the spot, using chalk drawings on the wall of a cave. Once this discovery was made, communication improved and significant progress was made toward restoring this village to health.

Years later, Lasswell articulated his concepts of a "decision seminar" and an "urban planetarium". The former was conceived as a specially designed room that emphasized major displays of information relating to policy development. In effect it was the modern version of the Peruvian cave. The urban planetarium was a larger concept. It would consist of a large building whose rooms and walls were so laid out and so covered with symbols, that a person could experience vicariously an entire urban center by simply walking through this building and experiencing its contents. In this way, it was thought that a citizen of a city could gain a feeling for the city as a whole and understand both its history and its current state, gaining an appreciation of the interdependence of its parts. By keeping an up-to-date status report, in graphical form, of numerous aspects of the city, citizens could know their city in a unique way. Even newcomers could gain rapidly an appreciation for the spirit and substance of the city. Possibly many of the self-serving actions that tend to destroy a city might be defeated if citizens perceived it more like an organism than only in terms of the individual's immediate situation. And possibly the individual might learn to appreciate the interdependence in the city and the possibilities for previously unenvisaged participation in its activities.

The vision of Lasswell was a significant motivation for the development of Demosophia, and the need for full information display was recognized as one of its main features.

Factors in the Design

By sorting out the room's attributes into principal design factors, it is possible to explain its concept and suggest how it is used. These are the main factors in its design:

- Physical Comfort. It should be possible for a person to sit in this room as a working participant for eight hours a day, and not be distracted from the task by any physical discomfort, the latter typically being found in "conference rooms" and most other settings where people are expected to work together

- Ample Table-Top Working Space. In many rooms developed for group activity, no thought is given to maintaining ample table-top working space. In many rooms, there is no place for winter garments to be stored, so the working space is preempted by coats and hats. Proper space utilization helps assure productivity.

- Flexible Table-Top Working Space. Some large conference rooms have access to ancillary small rooms, where large groups can be broken up into small groups, one small group per room. However in a university and in many business environments such space cannot be made available. Also many organizations lack eating facilities near the working areas. By having several smaller tables that can be fit together to form one large one, it is possible to have a group working around the large one, and later by separating the tables and moving them to corners of the room, several small groups can be accommodated to work in parallel. It is also possible to use one of the small tables to hold a catered lunch. This economizes on the use of the group's time.

- Design for Multiple Roles. There is ample evidence that for effective group work, (a) the group should be small -- perhaps 8 is the ideal size for effective verbal exchange -- but the group can vary from 6 to 12 without introducing undue difficulty, (b) since there is often a need to accommodate more people than the "small group", space can be provided for observers who do not require as much space as the participants, (c) processes may provide for breaks during which "caucusing" among participants and observers can be carried out [4], (d) the group must have a facilitator, someone who is highly-skilled in working with groups using the methodologies that the room is designed to implement, (e) for certain kinds of group work the cognitive burden may be alleviated by using the computer, so that provision is made for a terminal and an operator, and (f) there is a need to record and duplicate in order to document what goes on for quick dissemination and amendment. Accordingly, the room should be designed to accommodate the various roles, which means it must have space for each that is appropriate to do what must be done in the role and to provide any necessary equipment support. Figures 8.1 and 8.2 offer two photographic views of Demosophia, to supplement the prose description of this facility. In the Demosophia design, facilities are provided for about 10 participants, one or two facilitators, a computer operator, a computer terminal, up to twenty-five observers, and one or two scribes.

- Design for Display. Most of the walls are devoted to displaying information. The following modes are used: (a) manual display achieved by writing on butcher paper and taping it to the wall with masking tape, (b) manual display achieved by printing on cards, inserting the cards in magnetized holders, and manually placing them on the magnetic wall-board which holds them, (c) augmenting the card display by drawing lines that connect the magnetic card holders to show relationships among the elements that are displayed on the cards, (d) projection displays on a bare wall, which can be produced from an overhead projector or more commonly from a computer driving a projection system (By this means, the computer can communicate with the group. This removes some of the cognitive overload that otherwise would weaken the capacity of the facilitator to perform in certain aspects of group work), and (e) direct writing, with a marker pen.

- Design for Information Retention. While the ordinary conference room seldom carries provision for retaining any information, and thus serves the purposes of the executive who doesn't intend to spend more than an hour in the room, complex issues demand prolonged periods of work, which may extend over several days, and typically may involve several periods separated by intervening days to catch up on normal work. For this reason, it is important to design for retaining information in the form it exists when the group has to interrupt its activity. Information is retained on the walls so that when a group returns it is immediately cued in detail about its prior work status, and can resume work with little lost time. Information is also retained, when appropriate, in the computer, where it can be called up on demand for refresher purposes, or to amend it by addition, deletion or other editing.

- Production of Intermediate Results. Group work is demanding. On complex issues, it is very important to reproduce intermediate results as soon as they have been achieved. This is done off line in the anteroom, using the drafting and copying facilities. Hard copy can then be provided to participants, giving a deserved feeling of accomplishment, and a record to study as needed as the work evolves.

- Videotaping. For certain purposes, such as summarizing results of a long project, for showing trainees how they perform in group work, and for archival reasons, it is desirable to be able to make and display videotapes.

- Storing Possessions. One corner of the room, near the door, is set aside for hanging coats and leaving bags so they do not consume the work space and are available when leaving.

- Telephones. Persons using the room need to use telephones during breaks. Provision of them near but outside the working area is desirable.

269

Figure 8.1 Ford Motor Company Center for Interactive Design
(Photograph by Scott M. Staley, Ph. D., P. E., Ford Research Laboratory, Dearborn, MI).

- Report Preparation. Facilities are needed for preparing final reports on the work.

- Access to On-Line Software. Software for the ISM and TAM processes is needed to drive the processes, displaying questions and results.

It has been demonstrated repeatedly that through activity in such a Laboratory Environment, following the steering provided by a Science of Generic Design, the best features of the separate Virtual Worlds of the participants can be brought forth and integrated, and that the interaction among the participants provides a learning experience that dissolves the potential negative impact of the initially-divergent views about issues.

8.4 Precursors to the Design of the Laboratory Environment.

As indicated in Section 8.3, the Laboratory Environment designed for the practice of Generic Design has priors in the ideas of Harold Lasswell. He had a vision of physical facilities that he referred to by names such as "decision seminar room" and "social planetarium" [5]. A central idea in his thinking was that communication among people about complex issues required for its success a facility wherein the display of information was central. Beyond this, the content of the displays was to involve whatever factual information could be made available as a shared resource.

Figure 8.2 Southwest Fisheries Science Center Facility (photograph courtesy of David Mackett, Southwest Fisheries Science Center).

Other priors to the Laboratory Environment grew out of the concept called DE-MATEL, a **DE**cision-**MA**king and **TE**sting **L**aboratory. This idea, envisaged in the early 1970's by the Battelle Geneva Laboratories, and studied by Emilio Fontela and André Gabus, incorporated the assumption that world leaders needed to have a specially-designed environment where they could work together to solve difficult and interlocking problems, and where extensive enhancements would be provided. While such a facility was never completed as part of the DEMATEL project, some light was shed on why it was needed. A principal finding from analysis of results of an extensive questionnaire dealing with interactions among a defined set of "world problems", filled out by selected world leaders, was that there were no identifiable "schools of thought" on most major issues; rather each individual had a personal Virtual World from which these issues were interpreted, and all of the Virtual Worlds were different.

Additional evidence along similar lines is presented in Appendix 5. In this Appendix, data taken from use of the Nominal Group Technique in 43 projects (with different groups and different complex issues including design projects) show that there is major diversity of views among participants upon the relative saliency of factors related to the issues or designs. Their Virtual Worlds produce this diversity, and until some commonality is generated that is more than superficial, it will be difficult or impossible to get concerted action.

These results also illustrate C. S. Peirce's concept that at the outset of a problem-solving activity each individual carries an "unshakeable cognitive burden", making academic Descartes' prescription for problem-solving that one should empty the mind of all preconceptions at the outset. Experience in many group projects, and observations of many actors in these projects, shows that the mind in general does not have any way to "clear" itself (as a computer memory can be cleared), nor can it consciously even identify the preconceptions in many instances, as these have become so indelibly embedded in the psyche as to be indistinguishable from the nervous system in general.

8.5 Evaluation of the Environment and Roles.

Evaluation of the Environment and Roles is best carried out as part of a total evaluation of the application of the Science of Generic Design, when viewed in the context of the Sigma-N Concept described in Chapter 6 and elaborated through detailed discussion of Methodology in Chapter 7.

While seven factors were indicated as essential to success in the Law of Success and Failure for Generic Design, these can normally be partitioned into two groups. The first group consists of two of the factors: financial support and Target component availability. Very little can happen without financial support whether it be appropriated or in-kind, so financial support is normally a prerequisite to carrying out a design. The availability of components cannot be determined until the components are identified, so it is normally an issue that arises after the design activity is fairly far along; or at least, it cannot be definitively dealt with until a respectable Representation of the Target has been achieved.

The other five factors become part of a Sigma-5 pattern, as indicated in Figure 8.3, which serves as a reminder of the necessity to integrate these five factors in higher-grade design activity.

Accordingly, the Roles and the Laboratory Environment can be assessed as part of an overall Sigma-5 assessment. Such an assessment is to be carried out concurrently with design activity, with the results of this activity being used to assess the effectiveness of the Roles and the Laboratory Environment.

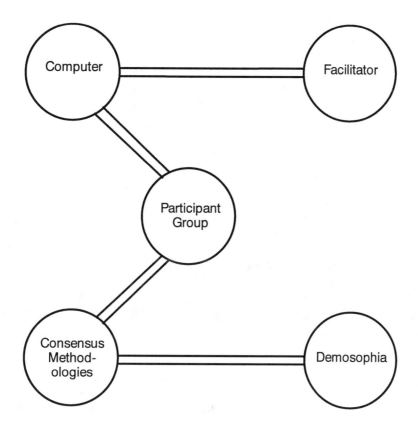

Figure 8.3 Sigma-five basis. Copyright © 1986 SGSR.

SUMMARY

The environment for carrying out and implementing generic design activities is divided into two parts: the Laboratory Environment, where the conceptual design activity is carried out and documented; and the larger External Environment from which the motivation for design activity originates and into which the Target design is introduced and in which it performs. The success or failure of a given Target design involves both the Laboratory Environment and the External Environment.

The Laboratory Environment designed for the practice of Generic Design has priors in the ideas of Harold Lasswell. He had a vision of physical facilities that he referred to by names such as "decision seminar room" and "social planetarium".

Another prior to the Laboratory Environment grew out of the concept called DEMATEL, a **DE**cision-**MA**king and **TE**sting Laboratory. This idea, envisaged in the early 1970's by Emilio Fontela and André Gabus of the Battelle Geneva Laboratories, bore the assumption that world leaders needed to have a specially-designed environment where they could work together to solve difficult and interlocking problems, and where extensive enhancements would be provided.

Roles in the Cast are <u>designed</u> roles, chosen on the basis of the findings of the Generic Design Science. The major roles are the following: Participant-Designer, Facilitator (Pilotos), Broker, Process Designer, Top Manager, Report Manager, Implementers, Stakeholders, and Supporting Process Roles.

Leadership is a word that describes the most critical aspect of the anthropological basis, whether it is the Laboratory or External Environment that is involved.

Leadership in generic design is not limited to any one individual. As defined by the results of the Bennis study, it can be practiced by every individual involved.

Circumstances are most favorable for effective design activity when the External Environment and the Laboratory Environment are both committed to achievement of high-quality design results.

Examples of the kinds of products that are produced in the Laboratory Environment appear in Chapter 9, and specific project results from example projects appear in Chapter 10.

REFERENCES

1. R. M. Lala, *The Creation of Wealth: The Tata Story*, Bombay: IBH Publishing Company, 1981.

2. A. N. Christakis and Y. Prabhu, "A New Role for Systems Scientists", *Proc. 30th Annual Meeting of the Society for General Systems Research*, Salinas, California: Intersystems, 1986, A48-A62.

3. Paul Gray, "Group Decision Support Systems", *Decision Support Systems* 3, 1987, 233-242.

4. Alexander Christakis, "The National Forum on Nonindustrial Private Forest Lands", *Systems Research* 2(3), 1985, 189- 199.

5. Harold Lasswell, *A Pre-View of the Policy Sciences*, New York: American Elsevier, 1971.

QUESTIONS RELATED TO CHAPTER 8

1. What eight factors are symptomatic of "groupthink"?

2. What is the Vickers definition of an "institution"?

3. A drama can be described partly as a "set of roles and role interactions". What other factors are normally required in order to stage a drama?

4. Consider the situation where a group of human beings gathers to design a complex system. Compare this situation to that of staging the play <u>MacBeth</u>. For example, compare the following: roles, role interactions, cast, script, setting, audience, author(s), difficulty. Is there any insight to be gained from this com-comparison? If so,what? If so, who needs to learn it?

5. What is meant by "Laboratory Environment"?

6. What is meant by "External Environment"?

7. What is meant by "Environment"?

8. What are the three primary bases for <u>General</u> Design Science?

9. In the Laboratory Environment, how are the three primary bases dealt with?

10. How are the three primary bases dealt with in ordinary group activity?

11. In 1990, NASA launched a vehicle to put into orbit the Hubbell Space Telescope. After it was in orbit, it was found that it did not work properly because one of the lenses was defective. When asked why the lens was not tested, NASA indicated that the costs of testing would have been too great, and that means of testing were un-certain. Later it was said that the lens could easily have been tested at modest cost. Discuss the environment related to this situation. Could this situation and others like it be the basis for legislation requiring that a "due process" be used in design of expensive systems, to provide public protection against waste of public funds?

12. In 1987, John A. Adam reported on the serious design flaws in the Sergeant York gun, and the waste of money incurred, in an article titled "The Sergeant York Gun: A Massive Misfire", in the <u>IEEE Spectrum</u>, February, 1987, 28-35. Discuss this situation in terms of the methodology used, and the nature of the environment related to this situation.

13. In 1984, Wm. L. Alpert reported on the waste of $230 million dollars associated with an attempt to design and construct (but not necessarily test) a new silicon chip, in an article titled "A $230 Million Turkey: The Sad Saga of Trilogy", in <u>Barrons</u>, August 27, 1984. Discuss this situation in terms of the methodology used, the nature

of the environment in this situation, and the possibility of groupthink at work.

14. In 1984, Francesca Lunzer described problems in the auto industry relating to design and quality control in the article "Does Your Car Have a Fan Belt?" in Forbes, December 3, 1984, pp. 222-224. Discuss this situation in terms of the methodology used, and the nature of the environment related to this situation. If you are familiar with the book On a Clear Day You Can See General Motors, compare what is in this book with what is involved in the article.

15. In 1985, Stanley Penn discussed a subway project in New York City in his article "How a Subway Project in New York Has Led to Doubt and Dismay" in the Wall Street Journal. October 25, 1985. Discuss this situation in terms of the methodology used and the nature of the surrounding environment.

16. In 1984, Claudia Ricci described problems with a computer network designed and marketed by the world's leader in telecommunications in her article "AT&T Plan to Market a Computer Network Hits Snags Repeatedly" in the Wall Street Journal, July 13, 1984. Discuss this situation in terms of the methodology used, and the nature of the environment related to this situation.

17. In 1987, Trudy E. Bell and Karl Esch discussed the disaster involving the Challenger explosion in their article "The Fatal Flaw in Flight 51-L", in IEEE Spectrum, February, 1987, pp. 36-51. Discuss this situation in terms of the methodology used, and the nature of the environment related to this situation.

18. In 1980, Dr. John G. Kemeny, a one-time member of the Institute for Advanced Study at Princeton University, a Professor of Mathematics at Dartmouth University, and the then-President of Dartmouth University, who had served as chair of the commission that studied the Three-Mile-Island nuclear accident, published an article titled "Saving American Democracy: The Lessons of Three-Mile-Island", in which he used the knowledge gained in studying that situation as a example of the massive problems of decision-making in the U.S. government, to try to spur some changes in how that government handles its affairs. Look at his article in Technology Review, June/July, 1980, pp. 65-75. Discuss this situation in terms of its relevance, if any, to Generic Design Science, and the environment related to this situation.

19. Pick a week at random from the last ten years. Go to a library that has a file of newspapers from that week. Look through the week's issue and choose the most absurd situation you can find that (a) is discussed therein, (b) involves significant misuse of funds or loss of life or both, and (c) gives adequate background for analysis. Write a short description of the situation and discuss its relevance to generic design and/or Interactive Management. If you can't find anything in that week's issues, try the week before or the week after.

20. What are the major roles in the Laboratory Environment?

21. Identify six locations where the Generic Design Science or components of it have been applied.

22. Why might the name "Pilotos" instead of the more common name "facilitator" be appropriate in discussing roles for application of Interactive Management?

23. Why might the special name "Demosophia" be more appropriate in discussing Interactive Management than the more common name "situation room"?

24. Can you find instances where the ideas presented in the writings of the late Harold Lasswell have been applied in designing environments other than those discussed in Chapter 8?

25. What are twelve factors that are incorporated in the design of Demosophia?

26. Why is it somewhat inappropriate to call Demosophia a "conference room"?

27. Visit a conference room at some local organization (preferably a new and state-of-the-art facility). Assess it in terms of the twelve factors mentioned in Quest. 25.

28. What are seven factors that are essential to success in large system design activity? Why are these factors separated into two groups in discussing applications of the Generic Design Science?

29. Consider the components of the Sigma-Five basis for group work on complex issues. Discuss the possible impact on group success for each individual factor, under the assumption that that factor is not permitted to be used in the group work.

30. In his survey paper on group decision support systems published in 1987, Professor Paul Gray did not mention the Demosophia or anything that has been published which concerns its use or the methods of theories attached to its design. (See the references at the end of Chapter 8.) Can you suggest various reasons for this omission?

31. The International Business Machines Corporation (IBM) has been supporting research at a university in Arizona for several years on group decision support. A special facility has been built there and replicated at other locations. In a survey article published by principals from that facility, no mention was made of any of the work discussed in this book. The University of São Paulo in Brazil has been using some of the processes described in this book since 1980 and, in fact, has been using ISM software written by IBM of Rio de Janeiro since about that time, with much success. Can you suggest any reasons for this apparent anomaly?

PART III

APPLICATIONS

"A scholar's activities should have relevance to the immediate future of our civilization."

--J. B. Conant

CHAPTER 9

PRODUCTS FROM THE PRACTICE
OF GENERIC DESIGN

"Our traditional patterns of problem-solving are flagrantly defective in presenting the future
in ways that contribute insight and understanding."
--Harold Lasswell

The products that arise from the practice of Generic Design can be classified as tangible and intangible.

The Cosmic Partition can be used as a way to further distinguish the products. We may say that many tangible products are contributions to the Library, i.e., that part of the Universe which involves contents of any form of media; while the intangible products are contributions to the Phaneron, i.e., that part of the Universe that involves ideas contained in the mind of anyone, anywhere.

The ultimate outcome of design activity will often be a modification of the Residue, that part of the Universe other than the Library and the Phaneron. Design has been viewed as a way of modifying the world by making changes in some of its physical features, such as roads, buildings, bridges, electronic systems, missiles, etc. Still a process whose primary outcome is to change what is in the Library and the Phaneron can also reasonably be thought of as design.

Any planned intervention in the world starts with perception; i.e., it begins with some kind of human response to what is seen as being worth changing or needing change. A process that inquires into what is needed in order to define exactly what is to be changed and how to do it is inherently part of a design process. One may aspire to develop a science in order to make such a process and its products higher in quality. The involvement of multiple actors, the conversion of the products into symbolic representation in the Library (which involves thinking through what the change should be and how to make it), and the activity that modifies the Phaneron are parts of such a process. Such activities enable those who will be involved in implementing the design to carry out their work and to explain it to others. Also benefiting are those who will interact with the finished design, and who need to know quite a bit about it in order to interact with it sensibly and responsibly.

The implementation of the design can and should be based on what is put into the Library.

Evaluation of the design outcome serves the purposes of judging (a) how well the design can be enjoyed or used and (b) what can be learned from it about future designs. Any weaknesses in the outcome can be assessed for possible relevance to amending the design science, in order to strengthen it.

In proceeding now to discuss the specific kinds of products that can be produced on the basis of the Science of Generic Design, it will also be appropriate to comment on factors that relate to the quality of these products. In assessing the Science, it is important to distinguish the extent to which the quality of those products or partial products depends on the Science, and the extent to which it depends upon factors that lie beyond the Science. Sections 6.8 and 8.5 have provided relevant background for making such distinctions.

9.1 Tangible Products.

Those tangible products that become part of the Library include various categories of information to be identified now.

Sets

The reader who has followed the arguments given previously in this book will appreciate the importance of working with collections of ideas grouped into sets. Sets of ideas are produced using any of the three Consensus Methodologies that involve idea generation. Ordered in terms of relative frequency of their use in applying the Generic Design Science, these are: Nominal Group Technique, Ideawriting, and DELPHI.

The sets produced with the Nominal Group Technique have the further distinction that they are clarified through extended dialog, in discussions managed by the Pilotos. The other two methods produce sets that should be regarded as unclarified.

In terms of quality, sets produced using NGT are frequently superior to those produced by Ideawriting or DELPHI because they have been clarified, and also because in the process there is often an editing to make the statements clearer. A major limit on the quality of the set of ideas always is the knowledge of the participants who generate the set. The methodology assures that a set will be produced. If clarifi cation is carried out, the methodology largely assures that the ideas will be understood. But the quality still depends on the knowledge of the participants, as well as the quality of the available language.

Relationship Maps

As related earlier, the ISM process is one whereby an initial idea set is converted into a map of relationship. Such a map always involves structuring of the idea set. Sets may be singly-structured or poly-structured through ISM. When they are to be poly-structured, unique representations may be conceived to find a mode of representation that most readily brings to the observer the benefits of the multiple structuring. An example of this is the Options Field, where each aspect of the multiple structuring is represented in a different component of a spatial scheme, minimizing cognitive burden on the user.

The quality of the relationship maps is likewise ultimately limited by the quality of the knowledge of the participants. However the use of the ISM process involves careful and systematic drawing out of participant thinking. Numerous applications of the process attest to the view that the maximum participant knowledge is very closely approached in the use of this process; and that en route to the development of the product, numerous ideas that originally may have been deemed correct by at least one participant were carefully examined and found to be lacking. Thus the quality of the product normally exceeds that which any single participant could have produced. Moreover it is normally higher than one would expect to attain by any method that lacks its systematic, cognitive-burden-reducing attributes.

Application Structural Types

Certain types of relationship maps recur in applications. They are identified as Application Structural Types. These are assigned distinctive names to permit discussion of their generic features and interpretations. The most common types are compactly tabulated in Table A1.3 for reference.

In the present Chapter, the principal types are identified and their characteristics given.

The DELTA Chart. The DELTA Chart portrays activities, events, decisions, and logic, to show planned or actual process sequences. It is appropriate for use in any situation where it is important to be able to portray how discrete elements are time-related. This type of representation permits flexibility in that it readily portrays contingency situations, where decisions are anticipated to occur at some later point in time, that will affect subsequent sequences.

The Intent Structure. The Intent Structure works with an element set whose members can be described as goals, objectives, aims, purposes, or intentions. Such elements are commonly encountered in developing plans. Many authors distinguish goals from objectives. To sort elements into these two categories is to suggest that planning involves a two-level structure. But as many examples of the development of Intent Structures readily show, planning often involves five to ten or even more levels, whereupon one is faced with the (pointless) question as to which levels should be goals and which should be objectives.

What is important is not the assignment of distinctive nomenclature to different elements, but rather to see how they are interrelated. Discussions about which are goals and which are objectives merely detracts from the hard work of penetrating the interdependence.

The Intent Structure shows how the attainment of success in achieving one goal or objective will or will not enhance the likelihood of success in achieving another one; at least to the extent that the participants in the development of the structure are able to foresee the interdependence. And while plans are not expected to be perfect, or to be followed blindly, certainly the ability to foresee is always critical to the success of planning.

The Intent Structure is appropriate as a vehicle for development and study in any situation where a clear benefit is seen to providing better articulation of goals or objectives, and where there is clear agreement that whatever is being considered for the future does not involve just one goal or objective, but involves multiple and interrelated goals or objectives [1,2]. For this reason, it is sometimes referred to as the "value system".

Priority Structure. Another common Application Structural Type is called a Priority Structure. While the DELTA Chart shows time sequence, and the Intent Structure shows favorable influence of one element upon another, the Priority Structure shows preference among a set of contemplated actions or other type of element. A typical relationship used to develop such a structure is "is of equal or higher priority than". It is important that the relationship allows for the possibility of cycles. Valid Priority Structures must show for any pair of elements A and B either that A has higher or lower priority than B, or that A and B have equal priority. Any relationship map that does not show one of these three outcomes is not a valid Priority Structure [3].

Priority Structures have been used by city and county governments to establish the priorities of budget line allocations. The ISM process has been used with sets of elements consisting of proposed municipal projects. In some instances, budgets involving a quarter of a billion dollars have been involved. Experience shows that the use of ISM in this way produces much greater understanding of the set of projects and their relative merits than the common methods of budgeting used in such jurisdictions. In typical budget prioritizing actions carried out in groups, experience has shown that most participants are knowledgeable only of some small subset of the elements which happen to be be prominent in their particular Virtual Worlds. Through the ISM process, all participants can become familiar with all of the elements being prioritized, which adds to the quality of the final decisions reached. Pioneering applications of this approach were made by Coke and Moore [4,5,6] and by Moore [7]. Jedlicka and Meyer carried out a unique application on a Mexican farm [8].

Problematique. A relationship map is called a problematique if the elements of the set are problems, and if the map indicates whether each problem may aggravate any other problem in the set.

Many such structures have been produced to deal holistically with sets of interlinked problems.

A typical relationship type for such a structure is "aggravates" or "increases the severity of". When a set of problems is structured in this way, some of the problems will lie at one extreme of the map and some will lie at the other extreme. One of the two extreme sets will typically be in the nature of "root difficulties" or "fundamental problems"; while the other extreme will be "surface difficulties" or "symptoms". Still others will be "intermediate".

Alexander Christakis has been a leader in advancing the study and application of this type of structure, and has helped many groups develop and interpret problematiques. Extensive use of the concept was made at the Battelle Geneva Laboratories [9,10] in their DEMATEL project.

Once again it is important that the relationship be such as to uncover any symmetry that may hold. If two problems aggravate each other, they lie in a cycle. It is very common to discover cycles in problematiques. It is common to see five or more problems in a cycle. One of the most valuable benefits of developing the problematique is to notice that problems lying in a cycle are best attacked as a unit. It is not very helpful to keep spending money to correct some problem that is in a cycle, while allowing the other members of the cycle to persist unchecked; because they continue to aggravate the very problem that is being singly addressed. The term "suboptimization" has sometimes been used to describe a situation where some part of a system is brought to an optimum state without regard to what this might cause for the system as a whole. But even this term is not appropriate to describe the activity involved in trying to correct one problem that lies in a cycle, while doing nothing about the others. The reason is that it may not even be possible to suboptimize for the single problem, just because of the continuing impact of the other problems. A better term to describe the concept of trying to solve one problem in a cycle of problems while ignoring the rest of those problems might be the search for a "sublution". The goal is to produce a solution, but almost certainly this will not be the outcome. Instead what is produced is considerably less than a solution, and could be called a sublution to remind us of that.

It has also been observed in repeated cases involving problematiques that a notable percentage of managers has become accustomed to believing that action should just involve a single problem and its supposed corrective measures. On several occasions, managers have had to be very patiently shown that staff had systematically discovered the interactions among the problems, and that corrective measures taken roughly simultaneously on several fronts often would produce outstanding results; while singly-corrective measures would produce sublutions that might be worse than doing nothing.

Among the cases in which such behavior has been observed are (a) a major defense agency whose procurement cycle had grown to about 450 days on average, and whose management had to be convinced that multiple actions were needed, with the ultimate result that the cycle was cut to about 260 days, and (b) a major farm machinery manufacturing firm that had been struggling for about a decade to correct defects in a pump and which, at long last, was able to make major improvements by making several simultaneous changes in the manufacturing situation.

Curriculum Sequence. Curricula always involve study sequences. If a set of elements is generated that is to form part of a study area, then the development of the Curriculum Sequence can be carried out, producing a structure for such a set. A particularly interesting application was carried out by Sato and his colleagues [11,12] who, working from the Nippon Electric Company Research Laboratories, collaborated with public school teachers to devise detailed curriculum sequences, including one to articulate carefully a study sequence for learning fractions in an early grade. Other curriculum studies have been carried out by Crim [13] and by Renckly and Orwig [14].

Solution Sequence. The development of algorithms (solution sequences) for mathematically-formulated problems has also benefited considerably from structural concepts. A study of El-Mokadem's econometric model of personal savings in the United Kingdom replaced a prior concept of how to solve a non-linear set of almost sixty simultaneous equations with a vastly simpler concept, as well as providing vastly superior insights into how to interpret the model [15].

Fields. Field structures can be viewed as classification structures in which elements are sorted into categories. For such structures, a suitable relationship is "is in the same category as", which is a symmetric relationship.

Design Quads Structured by Dependence. In applications, system dimensions are structured according to their dependence or independence which, e.g., helps formulate design quads by identifying the clusters of mutually interdependent dimensions.

Design Quads Structured by Preferred Choice Sequence. In applications, the sequence of making choices may have a significant impact upon the quality of the results. For this reason, dimensions may be sequenced using ISM by a group of participants who generate the logic that underlies the choice of such a sequence. The combined use of the Field Application Structural Type with the Design Quads Structured by Dependence and by Preferred Choice Sequence, is an example of polystructuring to reduce substantially cognitive burden, while increasing the quality of thought and documentation.

Alternatives Structures. Alternatives Structures, also called Options Profiles, provide visual displays of particular design alternatives showing what has been considered, what has been rejected, and what has been accepted as the basis for future design of a Target.

Complementary Structures. Two structures are said to be complementary to each other if one of them is based on a relationship associated with a relation R' and the other is based on a relationship associated with a relation R", where R' and R" are complementary (see Appendix A1 for the relevant definitions). Complementary structures have largely been neglected in applications, but they are destined to play a vital role in assessing the quality, correctness, and completeness of results of the use of the ISM process, as users become more acquainted with the advantages and relative ease of applying such structures. Modest additions to older software will provide this valuable capability.

9.2 Intangible Products.

Intangible products are those that arise in the Phaneron, i.e., they become part of the Virtual Worlds of individuals. Because in almost all applications of the Generic Design Science, the projects have been dealt with as applications, rather than as research projects that would impose extraneous conditions on the participants, the data collected from such applications are limited to what would necessarily surface as part of the process of applying the Science.

For this reason, statements made about the intangible products are almost all anecdotal in nature, representing the accumulated subjective judgment of people who have observed many such projects. Having said this, it seems appropriate to make certain claims rather strongly, given that the reader has been forearmed with the scientifically inadequate basis in data for making such statements. Only by making rather strong claims can the potential benefits be fully articulated in ways that both present valuable possibilities while pointing to the need for more definitive research on these matters.

Individual Orientation

Individual orientation toward complex issues is changed dramatically for the better. Virtual Worlds that were both contaminated by poor information and missing substantial components of context are cleansed and augmented. Moreover cognitive assistance is substantial in producing integration of previously disconnected or poorly-connected frameworks of thought.

Team Membership

A by-product of work to develop products in the modes discussed here is the development of teams. It is inevitable that people who share the same experience and the same set of integrative ideas concerning an issue with which they have had prolonged difficulty should find, upon developing together significant new insights and frames of knowledge, that they have developed certain bonds. These bonds provide a basis for moving ahead with further planning, definition, and implementation without the kind of mutually annulling activity that so often occurs in dealing with complex issues where there is diversity of belief (of the type discussed, e.g., in Appendix 5).

Mastery of Deep and/or Long Logic

One of the very specific products is mastery of the deep or long logic that is developed by the group. For many applications, there does not seem to be any substitute for this product of application of the Generic Design Science.

This includes the mastery of the cycles that are discovered, and many require the use of the more exotic aspects of ISM theory, such as the study of geodetic cycles and the hierarchy of geodetic cycles [16] (which are other commonly neglected aspects of the ISM theory).

Structural Metrics

The structural metrics allow quantitative measures to be attached to products, which permit gradual learning of how to assess relative complexity and make judgments in the light of past experience with Situations of greater or lesser complexity.

9.3 Product Development and Maintenance.

The development and maintenance of products of the use of the Generic Design Science can become a systematic practice, institutionalized in terms of such subjects as the Application Structural Types described in Section 9.1. By this means, organizations can, through maintaining up-to-date versions where appropriate, convey at any time with considerable ease substantial insights into their organizations, their programs, and their projects.

While some private-sector firms might feel the competitive need to avoid such openness, public sector organizations have an obligation to be open in their work and to be much more informative to their constituency than is commonly found in such organizations. In the past, the lack of efficient vehicles of communication has made such openness hard to achieve, but the availability of the Generic Design Science and, especially, of the Application Structural Types, now offers to greatly facilitate the documentation and communication process. Products such as those described are much more scientifically based, and much more integrated, e. g., than those described by Martin and McClure [17] as being in current widespread use in the computer industry.

SUMMARY

The tangible products of applying the generic Design Science can be enumerated as follows:

- Unclarified sets of elements
- Clarified sets of elements
- Maps of relationship
- Application Structural Maps (which may be either singly-structured or multiply-structured)
- Metrics (i.e., numerical measures pertaining to the products listed above)

The intangible products include the following:

- A greatly modified orientation of each participant to the Design Situation

- The development of a team of people who share the same orientation toward the Target of the design, and who have learned to work together on a common problem or issue

- A number of people who have collectively discovered and mastered the deep/long logic of the Design Situation, and translated that into a design Target description

Specific tangible products that make up the Application Structural Maps include the following kinds of structures: Intent Structures, Priority Structures, DELTA Charts, Problematiques (Aggravation Structures), Curriculum Sequences, Solution Sequences, Design Quads (as they appear after triple-structuring), Alternatives Structures, and Complementary Structures. Depending on the particular Design Situation, elections could be made from this list, or from a more general set of possibilities, and the development of those selected products would be a significant part of the work done in the Application.

For a contextual understanding of each of these types of product, it is helpful to see them illustrated in particular case examples, to be exhibited in Chapter 10.

REFERENCES

1. K. Kawamura and D. W. Malone, "Structuring Objectives in a Systematic Decision-Making Methodology", *Proc. 1975 Pittsburgh Conf. on Modeling and Simulation*, Pittsburgh: Instrument Society of America, 1975, 779-784.

2. R. W. House, "Application of ISM in Brazil's Alcohol Fuel Program", *Proc. 1978 International IEEE Conference on Cybernetics & Society*, New York: IEEE, 1978, 1008-1012.

3. J. N. Warfield, "Priority Structures", *IEEE Trans. Syst., Man, and Cybern.*, Vol. SMC-10(10), October, 1980, 642-645.

4. J. G. Coke and C. M. Moore, *Toward a Balanced Budget: Making the Tough Decisions*, Washington, D. C.: National Association of Counties, 1980.

5. J. G. Coke and C. M. Moore, Chapter 6 in *Managing Fiscal Retrenchment in Cities* (H. J. Bryce, Ed.), Columbus: Academy for Contemporary Problems, 1980.

6. J. G. Coke and C. M. Moore, "Coping with a Budgetary Crisis: Helping a City Council Decide Where Expenditure Cuts Should be Made", Chapter 5 in *Building City Council Leadership Skills: A Casebook of Models and Methods* (S. W. Burks and J. F. Wolf, Editors), Washington, D. C.: National League of Cities, February, 1981.

7. Carl M. Moore, *Group Techniques for Idea Building*, Newbury Park: Sage, 1987.

8. A. Jedlicka and R. Meyer, "Interpretive Structural Modeling: Cross-Cultural Uses," *IEEE Trans. Syst., Man, and Cybern.*, Jan. 1980, 49-51.

9. A. Gabus and E. Fontela, "Perceptions of the World Problematique," DEMATEL Report # 3, Geneva: Battelle Geneva Laboratories Research Report, 1975.

10. E. Fontela and M. Gilli, "Analysis of the Causal Structure of Economic Models", *Proc. 1978 International IEEE Conference on Cybernetics & Society*, New York: IEEE, 1978, 516-519.

11. T. Sato, "Determination of Hierarchical Networks of Instructional Units Using the ISM Method,", *Educ. Technol. Res.*, 3, 67-75, 1979.

13. Karen O. Crim, "Use of ISM in Environmental Studies at the Senior High Level," Univ. of Dayton Report, Grant No. G- 007700611, UDR-TR-79-27, April, 1979.

14. T. R. Renckly, and G. Orwig, "Curriculum Viewed as Binary System: An Approach to the Determination of Sequence -- A Project Report", presented at the Third Interservice/Industry Training and Equipment Conference, Nov. 30-Dec. 2, 1981, Orlando, Florida

15. A. M. El Mokadem, J. N. Warfield, D. M. Pollick, and K. Kawamura, "Modularization of Large Econometric Models: An Application of Structural Modeling", *Proc. 1974 IEEE Conf. on Dec. & Control*, New York: IEEE, 1974, 683-692.

16. J. N. Warfield, *Societal Systems: Planning, Policy, and Complexity*, New York: Wiley, 1976 (reprinted, Salinas, CA: Intersystems, 1989).

17. James Martin and Carma McClure, *Diagramming Techniques for Analysts and Programmers*, Englewood Cliffs: Prentice-Hall, 1985.

QUESTIONS RELATED TO CHAPTER 9

1. What are the two major types of products from the practice of Generic Design?

2. How can the products of the practice of Generic Design be related to the Cosmic Partition?

3. Is the concept of what constitutes design changed in any way from the normal perception by looking at design in terms of the Cosmic Partition? If not, why not? If so, are there any benefits to such a change? If so, what are they?

4. What are two valuable outcomes of the evaluation of a product of a design activity?

5. What are three main kinds of tangible products from design that become part of the Library?

6. Which consensus methodologies produce sets?

7. Which of the three Consensus Methodologies might produce the highest quality sets? Why?

8. Which of the Consensus Methodologies produces relationship maps?

9. Can you find a methodology with these properties: a) it is not one of the Consensus Methodologies and b) it produces relationship maps?

   If so, explain the methodology and compare it to the ISM process.

10. What are the principal Application Structural Types (AST'S)?

11. What characteristics do all the AST'S have in common?

12. Can you find any relationship maps that might be called "competitors" of the AST'S listed in Sec. 9.1? If so, compare them with those listed.

13. What four claims are made concerning the intangible products of applying the Generic Design Science?

14. What kind of evidence might be collectible, in principle, to validate or invalidate the four claims?

15. Select one of the AST'S and describe how its use might be institutionalized in some specific organization. Then discuss the advantages and disadvantages of doing so.

CHAPTER 10

APPLICATIONS OF THE SCIENCE

"Within the domain of neuroscience, questions at one level of generality inevitably provoke
questions at both higher and lower levels of generality."
--Patricia S. Churchland
"The whole of science is nothing more than a refinement of everyday thinking."
--Albert Einstein

Applications of the Generic Design Science will be found in any aspect of life where complexity, as defined in Chapter 4, is present. During the period from 1973 to 1994, hundreds of applications have been made that illustrate the application of aspects of this science, in spite of the fact that the science itself was not adequately congealed until about 1988. This was possible because of the way the components of the science evolved. The most distinctive aspect of the applications is that which uses the Interpretive Structural Modeling process that was discovered in the early 1970's and programmed subsequently into a wide variety of software configurations.

When the first edition of this book appeared in 1990, the applications to be discussed in this Chapter were naturally chosen from those that had been achieved up to that point in time by a variety of actors in a variety of locations. Since the first edition appeared, there have been many new developments. While it is not intended in this Chapter to extend the number of applications discussed, it is important to let them be seen now in the context that has expanded since 1990.

The developments that have taken place since that time can be described in three categories: (a) new applications, (b) new locations where applications have been made, opening up new types of applications, and (c) the development of a book titled A Handbook of Interactive Management. This book presents the system of management that has been developed to facilitate the quality-controlled application of the science of generic design. Incorporated into that book are short descriptions of numerous applications, including more than thirty that have taken place since 1990. Also included there is information concerning who carried out these applications, and the location in which they were performed. The names, addresses, organizations, and years of experience of key practitioners are included in Appendix 5 of the Handbook, along with additional information aimed at helping the reader to contact these persons. Included is a thorough description of what constitutes Interactive Management (IM), the kinds of outcomes that can be anticipated from its use, the five defined success levels to which a user can aspire, the three Phases of the process, the roles required to carry it out in accordance with the basis provided by the underlying science, the specific types of products that can be developed using IM, the component processes involved in its use, additional information concerning the facility partially discussed in Chapter 8 of this book, background on software that has been used and may be available for others to use, detailed descriptions of the three Phases of IM, and evaluation criteria for applications.

Also there is presented the results of a study aimed at making a detailed comparison of the methods that make up the IM process with methods long used in Japan and elsewhere that are intended to accomplish some of the same outcomes as those that are produced with IM.

An executive overview of IM is given, to help a new reader gain an overview of what constitutes IM in a short reading time. A detailed description of the DOS-based ISM software that has been in use since 1988 is offered, along with examples of its use spelled out in sufficient detail that a new user could follow through the examples in order to see simple examples of the application of this software. Discussions of group facilitation appear along with a case study coming from recent work in the automobile industry.

A great deal of the recent work in IM applications has been carried out in Mexico, through the leadership of Ing. Roxana Cárdenas, co-author of the Handbook. She has not only applied IM herself in significant applications, but also has originated a variety of educational programs in Mexico, enabling IM to flow out of the original campus of ITESM at Monterrey into many of the 26 branch campuses of that excellent academic institution. Included in the types of applications there are strategic planning for Mexican states, industrial management issues studies, and work with Indian tribes in northwest Mexico. This wide variety of application in Mexico has provided significant confidence in the powers of IM to be effective across a wide spectrum of activity.

Other important applications of IM have been carried out since 1990, including significant applications at the Ford Motor Company, Dearborn, Michigan, under the leadership of Dr. Scott M. Staley of the Ford Research Laboratory. Still others have been carried out at the National Railroad Passenger Corporation ("AMTRAK") under the leadership of Mr. Kenneth McIlvoy.

New centers of activity have sprung up, where activity seems destined to grow. These include a new center in New Delhi, directed by Mr. S. K. Batra, and new activity in England at the University of Humberside. Dr. M. C. Jackson, at the latter institution, has taken a very interesting approach to the study of systems methods, in which it is a goal to gain a strong overview of all such methods, and to offer constructive criticism of each of them in the hopes that improvements can be made, not the least of which could be new and novel syntheses in which aspects of various methods might be combined to form new conceptual frames or systems for application.

Professor Benjamin Broome of George Mason University has extended his previous work with IM to incorporate extensive activity involving various Native American tribes, in which he cooperates with LaDonna Harris, the President of Americans for Indian Opportunity (AIO). Through the terms of a Kellogg Foundation grant, AIO has been very active in developing leadership for tribal futures, and Professor Broome's work with the tribes using IM has been an important part of the larger aspects of the leadership program.

The firm Christakis, Whitehouse, and Associates (CWA), which was a private-sector followup to earlier nonprofit work at George Mason University, has undertaken a program of application of IM in various sectors. They have been a major player in recent years in the pharmaceutical industry located in the Philadelphia area, and that work has also catapulted them into interactions with the United States Food and Drug Administration.

Government applications in the Department of Defense have continued at a significant level, with leadership from Professors Henry Alberts and Stan Crognale at the Defense Systems Management College, Fort Belvoir, Virginia. Because of the extent and pace of their activity, an archive called the IASIS File has been located in the Library at the College. This File contains numerous application reports that go into much more detail than can be presented in this Chapter.

The applications discussed in this Chapter have been chosen to illustrate three aspects of the Science: (a) its generic nature, as indicated by the variety of applications and the variety of locations where it has been applied, (b) the kinds of tangible products that are produced in its application, and (c) specifics of application in five selected application areas.

The five areas chosen to illustrate applications are:

- Educational Systems
- Economic Development
- Human Service Systems
- Management in the U. S. Department of Defense
- Quality Control of an Industrial Product

For the convenience of the reader in comparing them, a particular case format is used:

- Summary: A brief overview of the case that highlights the nature of the design activity, the designer, the outcomes, and some indication of the effectiveness of applying the design methodology

- Background: Material to establish the context for the design activity and interpretation of the outcomes

- Stages in the Activity: A description of the products and outcomes in the sequence in which they were produced

- Use of the Products: A discussion of the use of the design outcomes, including testimony, interview excerpts, analyses, and consequences of the work (to the extent that these are possible in each case)

- Conclusions: The central conclusions that were reached based on the materials presented in the case study

Ideally applications to large-scale system design would be very thoroughly discussed, in line with the focus of this book. This is not possible, but the variety and scope of the applications to be discussed seems sufficient to document the application and utility of the Generic Design Science.

In what follows, numbers designating statements (e.g., # 25) are those originally assigned during the generation of the statements in applying the Nominal Group Technique. The numbers have no other connotation.

10.1 Applications in Education.

Four applications in education will be discussed: departmental planning for university departments (one in the United States and one in the United Kingdom), designing a mathematics curriculum for computer science, and designing for shared governance in school districts in Pennsylvania.

Case E-1. Departmental Planning for a University Department: the Communication Department of George Mason University [This Case description was contributed by Ms. Irene Cromer]

Summary. The methods of Generic Design Science were used to develop a strategic plan for the Communication Department at George Mason University. Applied in the context of an academic environment, the science yielded a comprehensive management and planning design for focusing administration and faculty efforts in future years.

The products include an Intent Structure (Chap. 9), alternative options for accomplishing the objectives, a three-year departmental plan, and a Mission Statement.

Professor Don M. Boileau, the departmental chairman, believes that the work benefited the Department by establishing a standard for continuous planning and design. Also the faculty identified priorities that guide the development of curriculum, research, and allocation of resources.

Background. George Mason University is a state-supported institution whose enrollment in 1989 was approximately 20,000. Both undergraduate and graduate degrees through the Ph. D. are offered in a variety of departments. The Communication Department offers undergraduate degrees and enrolls about 500 majors.

At the time the planning process started, a new chairperson, Don Boileau, had just joined the university. His previous position was Director of Educational Services at the national office of the Speech Communication Association. He had previously been affiliated with the department as Adjunct Professor, and in this role had taught several courses.

Past efforts at strategic planning had followed a traditional approach in university settings in the United States, devoting one-day sessions to solve one or two specific problems. A significant amount of faculty time was unnecessarily spent making decisions that could have been routinely made by the chairperson, if an adequate long-range plan had been in place. While the Department had traditionally taken a collegiate approach to problem-solving and decision-making, discussion was often unfocused and repetitive, with significant divisions occurring within the faculty on many issues of importance to them. The appointment of the new chairperson provided the impetus for initiating a systematic effort at long-range planning. He viewed the generic design process as a way to discover and elicit faculty perspectives on events within the University and in the Department. He also saw the process as a vehicle for helping faculty become more cohesive.

According to Professor Boileau, who participated in all of the sessions, the generic design process allowed the faculty to explore the entire spectrum of issues facing them, and especially the goals the Department should strive to achieve and the options for achieving them.

Stages. The work described here began in August of 1987 and continued intermittently through the 1987-88 academic year, terminating in June of 1988. Three phases of planning were involved in which a faculty member not affiliated with the Department who was skilled in the design methods facilitated the sessions. The sessions were held in the facility described in Chapter 8. Objectives were developed and organized into an Intent Structure (see Chapter 9). Options for meeting the goals were developed and organized as an Options Field. Then an Options Profile was developed that represented a three-year plan.

Phase 1. Developing an Intent Structure. The Nominal Group Technique (NGT) was applied, with the departmental faculty serving as participants, which produced 92 objectives. The triggering question was: "What should be the objectives (or goals) of the Communication Department of the future?" Two days were required to identify, clarify, and structure the objectives. Structuring was achieved using the ISM process to help the faculty develop an Intent Structure. This structure is shown in Figure 10.1.

The following generic question was applied as part of the ISM process:

"In developing the Communication Department of the future,
will the achievement of
objective A

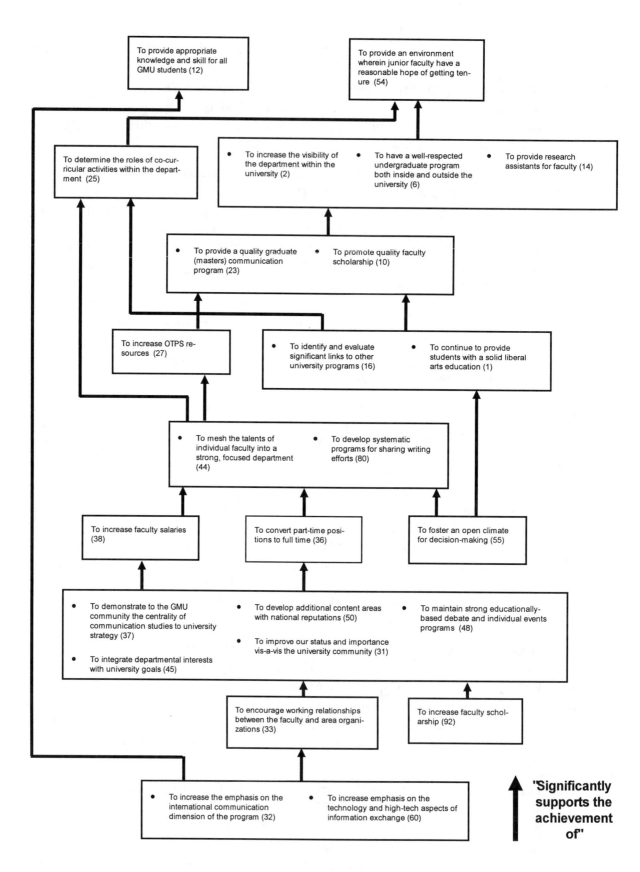

Figure 10.1 Intent Structure for Communication Department.

> support the achievement of
> objective B?"

From the 92 objectives generated, the participants chose 25 to be used in structuring, on the basis that they were the more important ones in the set.

The Intent Structure in Figure 10.1 indicates which objectives, if completed or acted upon, would help support the achievement of other objectives. The box-bullet form is used to represent cycles, i.e., objectives that are mutually supporting.

The faculty determined that the highest priority objectives were: to increase the visibility of the Department within the University (# 2), to demonstrate to the University community the centrality of communication studies to university strategy (# 37), to increase "Other Than Personal Services" resources (# 27), to promote quality faculty scholarship (# 10), and to improve faculty status and importance in the university community (# 31).

Phase 2. Developing an Options Field and a Mission Statement. The second phase involved generating and organizing options for achieving the objectives. This task required an additional two days. The NGT process assisted participants to generate, clarify, and edit a list of 120 options based on the triggering question "What are options for achieving the goals and objectives of the Communication Department of the future?"

The ISM process was used three times with three different relationships to assist in organizing the options. The generic question used to organize the options into categories was:

> "In the context of achieving the goals and objectives of
> the Communication Department,
> does option A
> belong in the same category as
> option B?"

After categorizing the options, and determining that the categories would form the dimensions of the Options Field, the group tested dependency of the dimensions, using the generic question:

> "Will choices in category A
> significantly restrict choices
> in category B?"

299

This work identified ten categories in which the option selections are relatively independent and 11 in which strong choice interdependencies were perceived to exist.

The ISM process was then used a third time, this time to organize the 21 dimensions for the purpose of sequencing the selection of options from the dimensions.

The generic question used for this purpose was:

"In developing plans for achieving the objectives of the
Communication Department,
should choices be made in category A
before choices in category B?"

The 21 categories of options, as they were sequenced by this process, were as follows:

A1. Mission

A2. Curriculum/Program Development

A3. Departmental Policies and Procedures

A4. Departmental Connections

A5. Co-Curricular Activities

A6. Basic Course

A7. Faculty Fiscal

B. Acceptance/Advising Policies

C. Internal/External Relations

D. Scholarship Development

E. Development Strategies

F. Part-time Staffing

G. External Funding Strategies

H. Other Than Personal Services Resources

I. Full-Time Staffing

J. Teacher Development

K. Conferencing

L. School of Continuing and Alternative Learning Issues

M1. Planning Horizon

M2. Lead Responsibility

M3. Informal Networks

Those categories labeled A1 through A7 are interdependent, as are those labeled M1 through M3.

Phase 3. Developing a Three-Year Plan. The final planning step was to develop an Options Profile by making choices from the Options Field. In the category A1, the faculty decided to choose only one option, that of creating a mission statement for the Department. They decided not to continue additional work until this statement was completed, because it would inform all further choices. The faculty met intermittently in unfacilitated sessions over a two-month period to complete this statement before resuming their formal design activity. Figure 10.2 shows the completed mission statement. It consists of a focusing sentence, followed by additional remarks that illuminate the mission; with views on teaching, research, and service spelled out separately.

The faculty then continued over a period of a day and a half to construct an Options Profile, guided by the mission statement. The faculty set a three-year planning horizon, and identified roles and lead responsibility for accomplishing the chosen options. A portion of the Options Profile is shown in Figure 10.3.

Use of the Products. The products (Intent Structure, Options Field, Options Profile, Mission Statement) facilitate the organization and effectiveness of the Department. They are kept in a single three-ring notebook which the Chairman refers to regularly. The Mission Statement guides the faculty in developing departmental by-laws and in evaluating members of the academic staff. The Dean of the College of Arts and Sciences has distributed it to other departments as a model of what other departments should have.

The Chairman's planning and management decisions are guided by the choices shown in the Options Profile and the priorities identified in the Intent Structure. The design work has been a driving force behind departmental activity, as illustrated by the following activities undertaken in the first year encompassed by the plan.

The Chairman allocated a high percentage of his time to accomplish objective # 2, "to increase the visibility of the Department within the University". With this in mind, he:

- Held three well-publicized faculty lectures on campus

- Scheduled periodic informal meetings between the chair and other University administrators

- Accepted a grant from the University of Kansas to host ten Korean journalists on campus

M I S S I O N   S T A T E M E N T

DEPARTMENT OF COMMUNICATION

The mission of the Department of Communication at George Mason University is to promote the development of theory and practice of communication in interpersonal, public, and mass media contexts through research, teaching, and service to the University, the GMU community, and the profession.

The Department of Communication studies the **centrality of communication** to human behavior. The faculty examine the artistic, humanistic, and scientific principles of communication. The department seeks to integrate historical perspectives and contemporary knowledge about communication.

Research and teaching reflect the broad spectrum of communication in a **variety of contexts.** Contexts mediated by the human voice and electronically mediated communication endeavors are considered essential to understanding the communication process. Thus, studies range from the dynamics of dyadic and small group communication to the complexities of organizational and public communication to the societal implications of print media, radio, television, and telecommunications. Communication processes are studied in families and friendships, groups and organizations, and across cultural boundaries.

The study and practice of communication contribute directly to the mission of the university, particularly to current emphases in general education, public policy development, and the humanities and performing arts. At the same time, the department helps students to improve communication in their daily lives, whether as citizens, as productive workers or in families and other personal relationships.

RESEARCH

The Department of Communication seeks to provide an environment in which its faculty can pursue research and scholarship that:

- Contribute to the development of theory and practice of communication;
- Enlarge the body of knowledge in the communication discipline;
- Incorporate research findings in classroom instruction; and
- Respond to the research needs of the GMU community.

TEACHING

The Department of Communication seeks to provide quality instruction that:

- Provides communication majors with a broad understanding of the discipline (interpersonal, public, and mass communication) as well as the opportunity to focus in a chosen content area;
- Prepares communication majors for entry-level professional work or for graduate study in communication or related disciplines;
- Offers graduate students at GMU opportunity to engage in advanced study in areas of departmental strength;
- Offers students not majoring in communication opportunity to learn communication principles and skills applicable to their personal and occupational interests;
- Offers students pursuing general education requirements opportunity to learn basic communication principles and skills;
- Enables students in communication courses to:

(a) develop critical and analytical modes of thought and to make rigorous, honorable decisions;

(b) interpret the complex questions facing them and society;

(c) interpret critical issues facing society from a global perspective;

(d) interact with others in a rhetorically-sensitive, empathic and self-confident manner;

(e) understand the impact of cultural diversity upon human communication as represented by differences in race, sex, national origin, or handicapping condition;

(f) understand the technological influences upon the delivery, creation and interpretation of messages;

- Enhances the GMU community's understanding of freedom of speech, the press, and the media as an essential element to a democratic society; and

SERVICE

The Department of Communication seeks to:

- Serve the students, department, college, and the university through activities such as advising, committee participation and leadership, media productions, public lectures, training, and consultation;
- Serve the communication profession and discipline by providing leadership in state, regional, national, and international organizations; and
- Serve as a resource to education, government, private enterprise, and associations in Northern Virginia, the Commonwealth, the nation, and internationally.

Figure 10.2 Mission Statement for Communication Department.

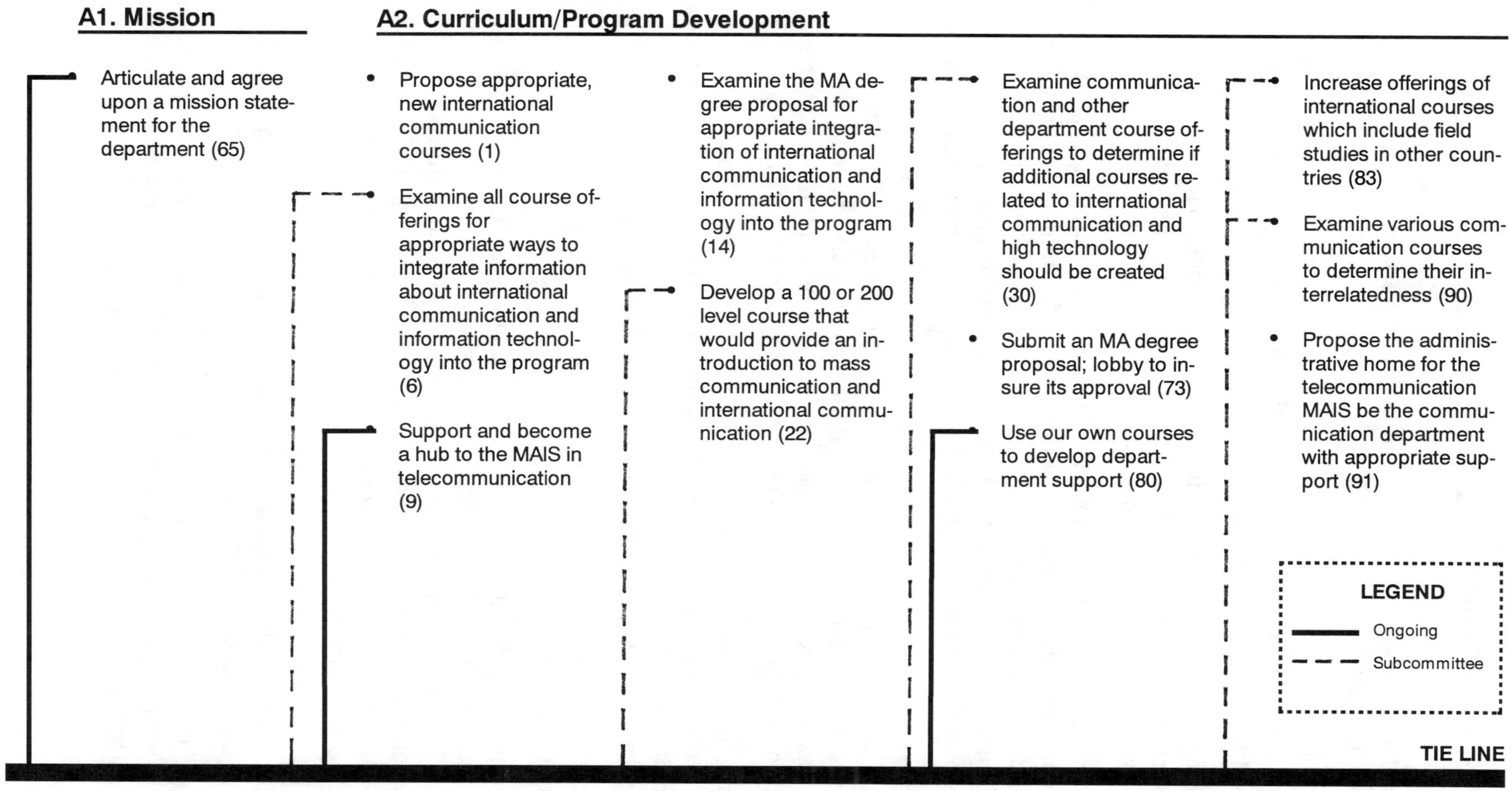

A1. Mission

Articulate and agree upon a mission statement for the department (65)

A2. Curriculum/Program Development

- Propose appropriate, new international communication courses (1)

  Examine all course offerings for appropriate ways to integrate information about international communication and information technology into the program (6)

  Support and become a hub to the MAIS in telecommunication (9)

- Examine the MA degree proposal for appropriate integration of international communication and information technology into the program (14)

  Develop a 100 or 200 level course that would provide an introduction to mass communication and international communication (22)

- Examine communication and other department course offerings to determine if additional courses related to international communication and high technology should be created (30)

- Submit an MA degree proposal; lobby to insure its approval (73)

  Use our own courses to develop department support (80)

- Increase offerings of international courses which include field studies in other countries (83)

  Examine various communication courses to determine their interrelatedness (90)

- Propose the administrative home for the telecommunication MAIS be the communication department with appropriate support (91)

LEGEND

———— Ongoing

– – – Subcommittee

TIE LINE

Figure 10.3 Partial options profile for Communication Department.

- Held a breakfast for the President of the University to speak to the Korean journalists

- Spent additional, voluntary, time working on several University committees when the opportunity arose, rather than limiting participation to only one pre-assigned committee

Some of the above items were not in the Options Profile. However the Chairman carried them out on his own initiative, because he knew the priorities of the Department, and was certain that the items were consistent with them.

In the area of curriculum development, the expressed concern of the faculty for an international dimension in their courses was the deciding factor in involving the campus international student group with undergraduate students in the Communication 100 class. When a question of whether to teach a course in policy control or global communication arose, global communication was chosen because of its international perspective.

Conclusions. The process facilitated the integration of diverse values, attitudes, and priorities of academic staff into a comprehensive departmental plan. Absence of stated objectives was replaced with presence of a logical structure of intent. Absence of articulated focus was replaced with a Mission Statement. Competition for resources and conflict over priorities were replaced with cooperation and coordination.

Some priorities could not be addressed in the first year and some unresolved issues remain. One instance arose involving resource allocation, in which it was clear from the planning process discussions that the faculty was divided. "Everybody knows they're divided" the Chairman reported, and he made the decision.

Priorities to be addressed in the second year are the bylaws, course loads, and curriculum for the major.

The Chairman states that the experience helped to build cohesiveness in the Department and to motivate the faculty. In his words, it was a "socially binding activity", helping to "create harmony" in the Department. Also, as he indicated, "I see other departmental chairpersons agonizing over things, but it is so easy for me to make some decisions as chairman because I've gone through that process. I have a different sense of department decision making that no other chairperson has."

Case E-2. Departmental Planning for a University Department: the Systems Science Department at City University [1]

Summary. The Department of Systems Science at the City University of London designed a plan for its future with a five-year planning horizon. The work was carried out in the Decision Support Laboratory located in the Department's facilities.

Initially a set of objectives was generated by the academic staff of the Department. A preliminary ranking of them was carried out. Next an Intent Structure and a Priority Structure were developed by the faculty. Finally a Mission Statement was constructed, consisting of a set of key goals.

According to the Head of the Department, the collegiate environment during the work relaxed "hidden tensions", and allowed participants to be "equal contributors to the decision making process." He further asserted that "the high priority given to research in the department was a surprise". He feels that "significant progress" has been made in implementing the top 14 of the objectives in the Priority Structure. During the process initial views about priorities changed dramatically. The establishment of a faculty appraisal scheme in City University means that all departments should have clear, well-defined objectives. This work provided the same for the Department of Systems Science.

One consequence of this work is that the University offered to pay the Department to carry out similar work with both administrative and academic departments who have requested the service. Three such studies have already been undertaken.

Background. Coincidentally, this case was initiated, like that in the Communication Department described previously, at a time when there was a change of leadership in the Department. Professor Philip M'Pherson, who was the founder member of the Department as well as its head, decided to retire. The appointment of a new head of department, Mr. Ray Jowitt, presented an opportunity to rethink the direction of both teaching and research. The department already had available the knowledge, facilities, and experience to carry out the work, since the facility had been established by Mr. Ross Janes, Senior Lecturer in the Department, and had been used to work with a number of clients in the United Kingdom. Thus it was only necessary that the Department make the decision to engage in the effort, in order to get it done.

Steps. The work took place in three separate occasions during the month of December, 1986.

Phase 1. Objectives Generation. On the first day, the participants used the NGT process to generate a set of objectives for the Department. The triggering question used was:

> "What should the Department of Systems Science be trying to
> achieve over the next five years?"

A total of 52 objectives was attained through this process. The NGT voting produced a subset considered to be the more important members of the set.

Phase 2. Development of an Intent Structure. On the second day, the participants used the ISM process to generate an Intent Structure (Chapter 4) showing how 19 of the 52 objectives were related to one another. The generic question format was as follows:

"Would accomplishing the objective A
help to achieve the objective B?"

This was to be answered in the context of the five-year planning time horizon chosen earlier. The Intent Structure is shown in Figure 10.4. The subset of 19 objectives was selected during the voting that took place in Phase 1.

Phase 3. Development of a Priority Structure and Mission Statement. On the third day, the group again used a subset of the objectives to produce the Priority Structure shown in Figure 10.5, using the ISM process. This subset contained 21 objectives chosen on the grounds that they have significant resource implications for the Department. In producing it, the key criterion was the assumption of limited resources.

After reviewing the objectives, the Intent Structure, and the Priority Structure, the faculty formed a set of key goals for the Department, to be used as the Department's Mission Statement.

The Mission Statement produced by the Department is as follows: To be recognized as a leading international centre for Systems Science by:

1. Developing a major research school in the areas of: Conflict Management, Decision Making, Engineering Management, Human- Activity Systems, Medical Informatics, Systems Theory, and Technological Change.

2. Developing teaching activities by: improving the undergraduate Management and Systems degree, and introducing a postgraduate degree programme focused upon Systems Management.

3. Developing the discipline of Systems Science.

4. Improving facilities for teaching and research, particularly in the areas of Information Technology and Decision Support Systems.

5. Promoting the skills and activities of the Department through the development of closer links with other institutions and organizations, e.g., by courses, contracts and consultancies.

6. Creating a management structure which facilitates the achievement of the goals listed above and promotes departmental cohesion.

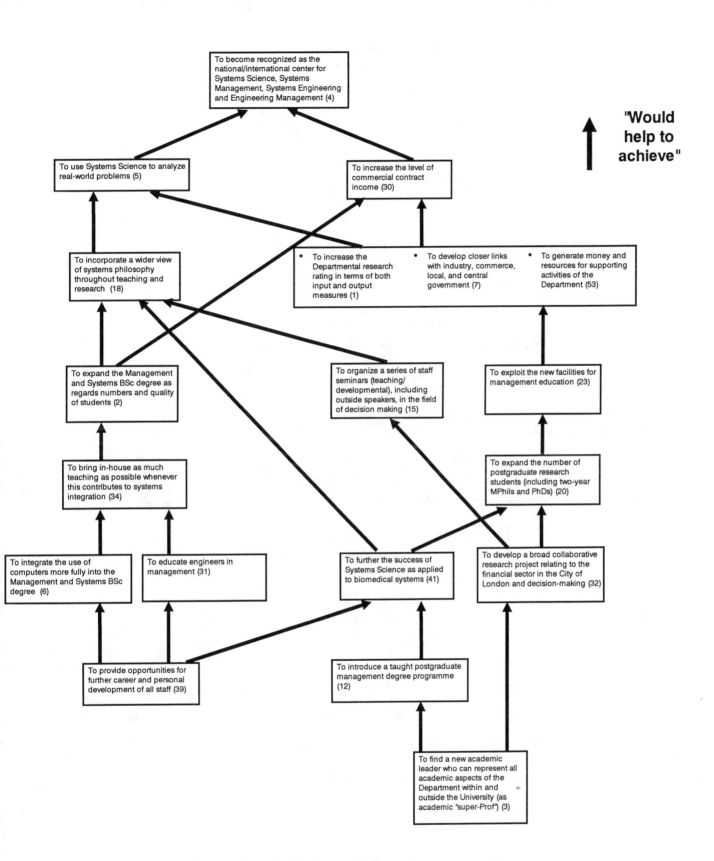

Figure 10.4 Intent Structure for Department of Systems Science.
Copyright © 1989 Plenum Press.

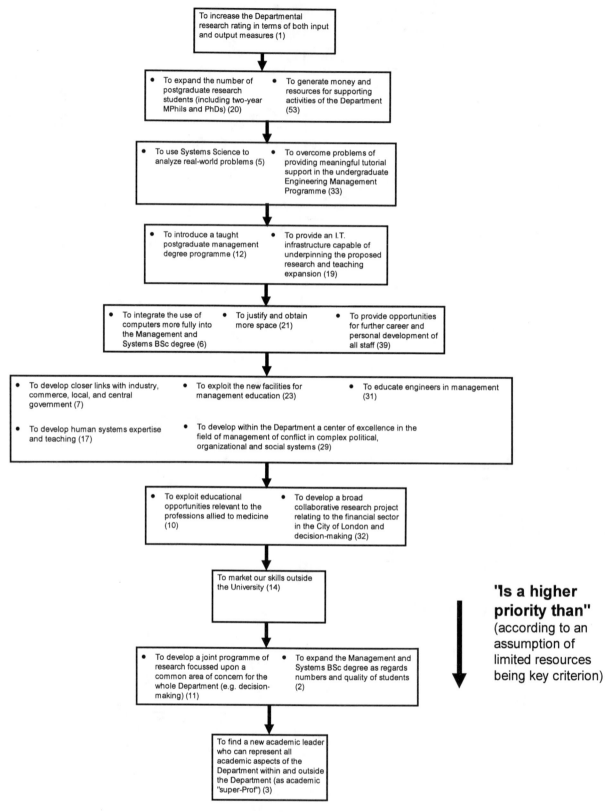

Figure 10.5 Priority Structure for Department of Systems Science
Copyright © 1989 Plenum Press.

Uses of the Products. Eighteen months after the completion of this project, the following uses of the products have been reported:

- To identify and share specific areas of existing interest and knowledge

- To assist in the identification of new areas for development

- To give the head of department confidence that he knows the views of all the participants

- To represent the views of the academic staff to the outside world

- To negotiate with and represent the views of the department to the central university authorities (Academic Registrar, Finance Officer, University Secretary)

- To enable the head of the department to allocate resources within the department

- To help design and coordinate the organizational structure within the department

- To assist in decision making

Conclusions. The sessions served to focus ideas clearly and to promote clarification and learning through structured discussion and argument. The participants understand the reasons for and logic behind the resulting products. They feel a sense of ownership and commitment to the objectives, priorities and mission statement. This was clearly evident in the way in which the priorities were implemented in the 18 months since the sessions took place.

It is not too much to expect that three days of hard work and dedication would be applied to set the course of an academic department for a five-year period. From this perspective, the activity was both efficient and effective.

Case E-3. Designing a Mathematics Curriculum for Computer Science

Summary. The methods of Generic Design Science were used to structure a proposed mathematics curriculum for students of computer science. Persons in computer science departments or mathematics departments or closely related industry formed most of the working group. The curriculum that was structured was developed from a consideration of major issues confronting the computer field, and was specifically tied to the amelioration of some of these issues. The results of the work were compiled in a report that was mailed to over 150 computer science departments in universities in the U. S. and abroad. The work was sponsored by, but not necessarily endorsed by, the U. S. National Science Foundation.

Background. The history of the United States is one of exploiting science, but not necessarily developing science or even appreciating the full significance of developed science. More recently, universities have opened curricula containing the word "science" in the name, without any significant exploration of whether the use of this word was justified. The field of computer science is one whose foundations are at best unclear or not agreed on by those who are allied with this field and, at worst, only poorly correlated with the responsibility that graduates are expected to assume.

The rapid growth of the computing industry has placed huge demands on education, and the pace has been such as to ignore the need for careful scientific underpinning in the rush to exploit the market for equipment and software which, in turn, generates the market for personnel.

In the defense arena, expenditures of the order of 15 billion dollars per year for software of dubious utility, along with report after report detailing the need for substantial improvement in software development, has still not produced any widespread demand for a scientific approach to software development. On the contrary, "experts" in the field have argued that all that is needed to correct the problems is effective management. It is not clear, however, what would constitute effective management in this field. In other areas of development, the effectiveness of management is closely allied to their capacity to take advantage of existing science and the practices that depend on existing science for their integrity and communicability.

In the belief that some of the many problems in the computer field, and especially in the software area, could be resolved by a better understanding of mathematics, it was decided to invite persons who were knowledgeable in the area to take part in a design workshop, in the hopes that the possibilities for better use of mathematics in computer science might be articulated.

Stages. The first two stages of the activity took place on November 10 and 11, 1986. In the **first stage**, the NGT methodology was applied, using the following triggering question:

> "What problems or issues must be dealt with in the future, in order
> to make computer science highly effective as a force in the
> computer and information systems industries?"

The participants in this activity generated and clarified 43 issues. Following this, each participant was asked to select the subset of five thought by that participant to be the five most important issues. A total of 21 issues received votes, yielding a Diversity measure of 3.2 (this situation is Case Number 16 in Table A5-1, and represents the third lowest Diversity found in any of the 26 cases represented in the Table).

In the **second stage** of the work, the ISM process was used to develop a problematique (see Chap. 9), based upon group member responses to the following generic question:

"In the context of the future effectiveness of
computer science,
does issue A
significantly aggravate (negatively impact)
issue B?"

The issues presented for structuring included those that received votes in assessing the five most important ones, along with two others that were generated during the structuring. However time did not permit structuring of all of these. Figure 10.6 shows the problematique that was produced.

At the conclusion of this stage, the participants were asked to comment on the structure that they had developed. Some of the comments were as follows (details and elaborations of these comments appear in the project report [2]:

- "Overall, I'm in sympathy with the structure."

- "I would have liked to have seen four threads: curriculum issues, industry interaction issues, formalism/mathematics, and human interaction issues."

- "I see three fundamental issues: development of algorithms, human-computer synergism, and technology transfer."

- "The fundamental threads are the need for more formalism, and the need to develop a theory of interaction between humans and computers."

- "It was interesting that the human ones came down at the bottom of the graph."

- "The text that is in the body of the graph does not reflect the debate which took place in the full meaning of the graph."

- "A much more solid connection between mathematics and formal thinking is indicated by the left two-thirds of the graph."

- "It has been difficult to know what was meant by these words. In terms of reformulations, I developed my own working model in my notes."

In the **third stage**, a survey was sent to the expected participants to (a) request a qualitative correlation between over 50 branches of mathematics (those that are identified as the branches of mathematics in the journal *Mathematics Reviews*) and the issues identified by the first participant group and (b) to identify those issues that appear to be most relevant to amelioration through appropriate application of mathematics.

311

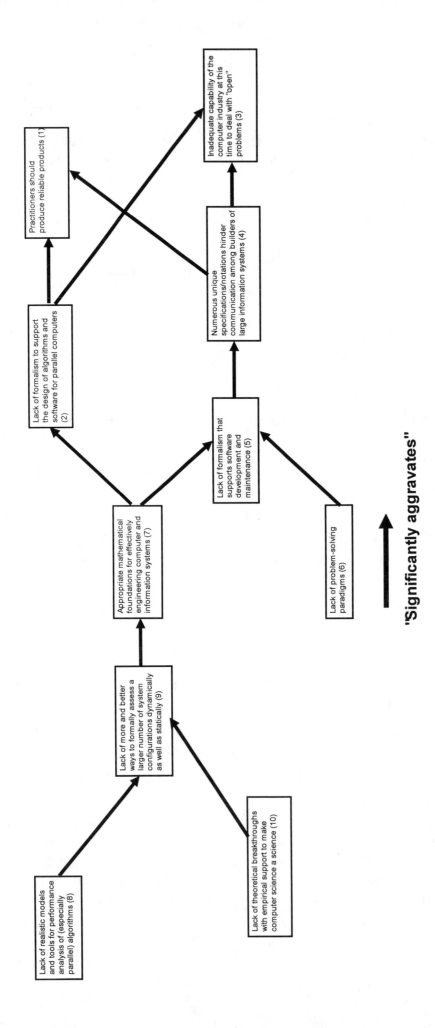

Figure 10.6 Problematique for the computer and information systems industry.

The survey identified the 15 branches of mathematics shown in Table 10.1 as having relevance to computer science in the foreseeable future.

The survey also identified 10 issues that appear to have high relevance to one or more branches of mathematics in the sense that these branches should help resolve the issues. Table 10.2 lists the issues.

In the **fourth stage** of the work, the ISM process was used with the following generic question:

> In the context of improving computer science,
> could the branch of mathematics called M
> be beneficial in helping resolve
> issue N?

where M represents one of the 15 branches of mathematics listed in Table 10.1 and N represents one of the 10 issues listed in Table 10.2.

Table 10.1
Branches of Mathematics with High Relevance to
Computer Science in the Foreseeable Future

---

1. Mathematics of Computing Machines

2. Logic and Foundations

3. Combinatorics and Graph Theory

4. Numerical Methods

5. Statistics

6. Set Theory

7. Sequences, Series, Summability

8. General Mathematical Systems

9. Approximations and Expansions

10. Linear Algebra

11. Order, Lattices

12. Probability

13. Finite Differences and Functional Equations

14. Fields and Polynomials

15. Mathematics of Information, Communication, and Control

Table 10.2
Issues Having High Relevance to Branches of Mathematics

1. Practitioners should produce reliable products.

2. Lack of formalism to support the design of algorithms and software for parallel computers.

3. Inadequate capability of computer industry at this time to deal with 'open' problems.

4. Numerous unique specifications/notations hinders communication among builders of large information systems.

5. Lack of formalism that supports software development and maintenance.

6. Lack of problem-solving paradigms.

7. Appropriate mathematical foundations for effectively engineering computer and information systems.

8. Lack of realistic models and tools for performance analysis of (especially parallel) algorithms.

9. Lack of more and better ways to formally assess larger numbers of systems configurations dynamically as well as statically.

10. Lack of theoretical breakthroughs with empirical support to make computer science a science.

Figure 10.7 shows the doubly-structured map with one of the relationships showing how one issue significantly aggravates another, while the other relationship shows how a branch of mathematics may help resolve one or more issues.

It can be seen from this map that five of the fifteen branches of mathematics were not perceived as having the power to help resolve any of the ten issues. Consequently these five branches appear as isolated elements in the structure.

In the **fifth stage** of the work, the ISM process was again applied, this time to structure branches of mathematics. The generic question used to carry out the structuring was:

> In studying computer science, should the branch
> of mathematics called Y
> be prerequisite to or corequisite with
> the branch of mathematics called Z?

In this question, Y and Z represent one of eleven branches of mathematics. The eleven branches include the ten branches shown as ameliorative in Figure 10.7, along with the added branch called linear algebra, which the group decided to include even though it appeared unconnected in Figure 10.7. The map shown in Figure 10.8 represents the prerequisite structure for the eleven branches of mathematics. Note that two of the branches were considered to be corequisites, as indicated by the cycle in Figure 10.8.

314

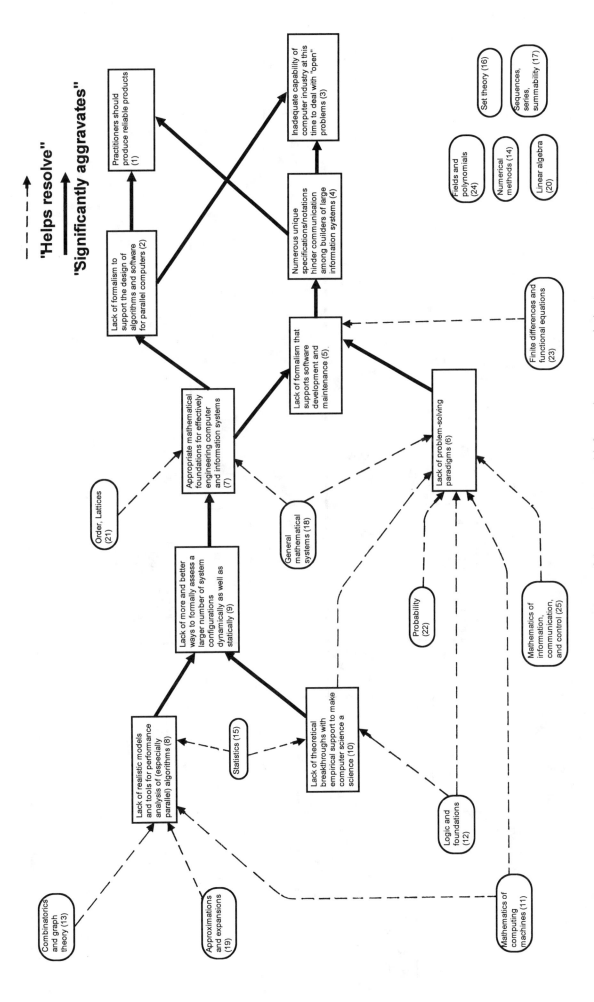

Figure 10.7 Relating branches of mathematics to problems of the computer and information systems industry.

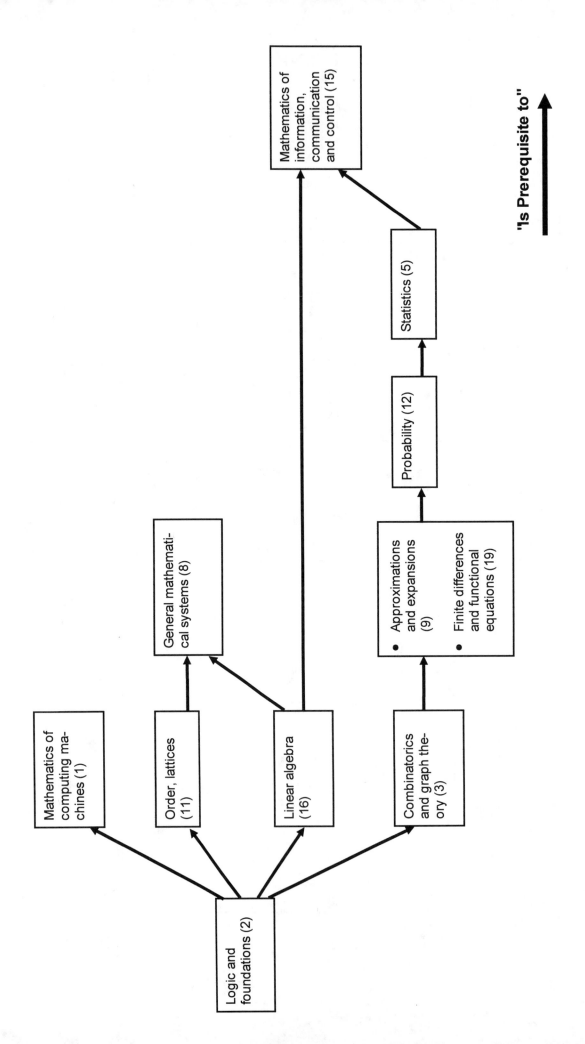

Figure 10.8 Mathematics curriculum structure for computer science.

The basis for making judgments pertaining to Figure 10.8 was that either it is necessary to know the prerequisite branch in order to learn the second branch, or that if a person could only learn one of the two, he should learn the first one because it is more important. (Whether these two distinct bases are logically compatible is left for the reader to judge.)

Following the conclusion of the foregoing, excerpts from some of the comments made by the participants were as follows (with the full text appearing in [2]):

- "Computer science is more of an engineering science than a natural science."

- "I think we are preoccupied with engineering these computer artifacts rather than focusing on computer science as a science."

- "I would have liked to have worked harder on the problem statements."

- "I don't think that the structure of the workshop helped to identify the correct problem."

- "Computer science is still largely viewed at the undergraduate level as an engineering science, but I believe there are many fundamental problems to be solved, especially in the areas of the link between logic and computer science, mathematics, etc."

- "I thought we might be producing a report for the secondary or primary school level rather than the college level."

- "I agree that the computer science problems are important and more needs to be done with them."

- "We need to replace the old mathematics with a newer computer science, machine-thinking type of mathematics."

- "I found this process and day extremely useful and it will be helpful to others."

- "I find the relationships among problem statements still unclear..."

- "I think we have learned also that we had better nail down our mathematics vocabulary."

- "I have thoroughly enjoyed today's activities... the question of training people in the conceptual areas (left-hand side) becomes a separate issue..."

Uses of the Products. While the products were distributed to over 150 departments of computer science, not one of them has volunteered to the originators of the report any comment about the use of them. Consequently the use, if any, remains obscure.

Conclusions. It was demonstrated that numerous issues are perceived to exist concerning the relationship between computer science and the computer industry, including applications of computers. Also it was demonstrated that there are perceived to be strong linkages between some branches of mathematics and these problems. Still the feeling persists that there remains inadequate definition, even of the basic concepts, so that attempts to resolve these matters with the current vocabulary of the fields suffer from a certain ambiguity. Applying the Law of Success and Failure to this area suggests that only a concerted effort to deal with the Universal Priors to all science will really bring this field to a state where, in the words of one of the participants, it is possible to "make computer science a science."

Case E-4. Designing for Shared Governance for School Districts in Pennsylvania [This Case was contributed by Harris Sokoloff, Ph. D., Executive Director of the Center for School Study Councils]

Summary. The Center for School Study Councils at the University of Pennsylvania Graduate School of Education is a partnership of the Graduate School of Education and some 68 school districts in Pennsylvania and New Jersey. These districts are divided into three separate Study Councils, to provide a context for school superintendents in each council to acquire the critical perspectives that they need to improve the quality of education in their districts.

The current educational reform movement focuses on the need to restructure education. The superintendents affiliated with the Center for School Study Councils see both the need for such restructuring and the social, political, and economic strength of current reform proposals. However, they also know that there is no clear consensus in either the research or the practitioner communities on what the key terms in this debate such as "teacher empowerment", "participatory management", and "shared governance" mean.

The methods of Generic Design Science were used to develop an understanding of the opportunities and inhibitors to realizing shared governance. The products include a structural model of the inhibitors and an options field for overcoming those inhibitors. These products will serve as the foundation for continuing long-term work to develop context-appropriate models for participating school districts.

Background. Public policy discussions about education in the 1980's in the United States -- in both the professional and popular press -- have focused on inadequacies of public education and proposals for improvement. The current wave of reform calls for transforming the organization of schooling. The normative transformation of the second wave of reform focuses on "empowering" teachers as professionals. Alternative versions of the transformation typically refer to "shared governance", "participatory management", and "site management". Experiments with such concepts are emerging in districts throughout the country where strong superintendents and strong teacher associations are willing to take bold steps.

These concepts are treated as if they were basically similar to organizational matters already solved: primarily representing issues of vertical organization that do not require reassessment of fundamental assumptions on which schooling currently operates.

Past history with similar reform activities suggests that current problems require participation of others (with different perceptions of the problems) to solve the current problems. The issues of governance raised in the second wave of reform present problems that are horizontal (as well as vertical) in their scope of involvement within the organization and are "unprogrammable" in relation to experiences with problems already solved. They require basic reassessment of fundamental assumptions and variables in our understanding of schooling and school administration.

Stages in the Activity. There were essentially three matters to clarify as the work began: a working definition of shared governance, a sense of the factors inhibiting its achievement in participating districts, and a strategic plan to overcome the inhibitors and to implement shared governance.

The **first stage** of activity took place in early July, 1988, in the conference room of one of the participating districts. In this first stage, the NGT process was used with the following triggering question:

"What are the characteristics of 'shared governance'?"

The eight participants in this activity generated and clarified 48 characteristics, of which 7 were eventually eliminated. Following this, the group worked to place these characteristics into groups. That work yielded a "definition structure" shown in Table 10.3.

It was intended that this structure would inform later work of identifying barriers to shared governance. Most of those who participated in this work expected to be (and were) available for the second stage of the work, in which barrier identification would take place.

In addition to the development of the structure, a short narrative description of shared governance was developed. This description was found acceptable to all participants. It reads as follows:

"Shared governance is a process -- including process tools, process structures, and process outcomes -- for organizing (or managing) part of a school district. These process tools, structures, and outcomes must be based on the district mission and its administration and implementation. In order for the processes to work, all major op-

Table 10.3
Working Definition of Shared Governance Descriptors and Categories

Pre-Process Conditions	Sustaining Conditions	Process Tools	Process Structures	Process Outcome
Metamorphosis (process of change)	Time, money, trust	Mutual respect	Clarity of types of decisions	Where control is located
Union: lack of consistent view	Impact on long-range planning	Democratic process	Involvement of actors in each type	Shared power
Formalized negotiations	District requirements	Expanded brain trust	Clearly defined rules of operation	Shared decision-making
Financial constraints	Support by administration	Peer discipline	Principal's role	Association willing to take responsibility for X
Support by administration, board, association based on district mission administration implementation requirements	Financial constraints

Hierarchy of authority | Quality Circles

Group techniques | Clarity of role descriptions

Variety of actors involved

Agreement on who/what makes final decision | Participants in fluence directions Ownership of decisions

Able and ready to live with results |
Reality of the future			Well-defined areas for a process	Collaboration and ultimately shared responsibility and benefits
Japanese chameleon (emulate Japanese model)			Clarity of areas open to shared decision-making/ governance	Increased bank of ideas and concepts
Fad, fiction, fact?				
Board of School Directors			Makeup of control group	
Union does not want shared responsibility				

erating stakeholders (the board, administration, teachers, and teachers association) must support the processes and be part of those processes. In addition, those processes must become part of long-range planning activities as well as the day-to-day activities in the district.

"Shared governance requires clear definition and agreement on:

- which areas are open to shared governance/decision making

- the types of decision and roles or levels of involvement of actors in each of those decision types

- the roles that different actors play and the responsibilities and accountability areas of actors in each of those roles

- guidelines and rules of operations

Agreement and implementation of these process structures as well as the use of a variety of process tools will lead to collaboration, ownership of decisions and, ultimately, to sharing responsibility, accountability and benefits of that collaboration."

The short description and the structure were both distributed to those who would participate in the second stage of the work.

The **second stage** took place on August 4 and 5, 1988, at the Center for Interactive Management at George Mason University. It was carried out in the Demosophia facility described in Chapter 8. The sessions were attended by six school superintendents, one assistant superintendent, one school principal, and one board member (the latter two attended along with their superintendent). The second stage involved two Phases. **Phase I** focused on generating, clarifying and structuring inhibitors to attaining shared governance. **Phase II** focused on identifying and organizing an options field for realizing shared governance.

One full day was used to accomplish the purposes of **Phase I**. The NGT was used to elicit a list of inhibitors associated with the realization of shared governance. Participants generated 44 inhibitors. They represent a broad range of concerns from financial, social, political, and historical forces to lack of knowledge of processes for accomplishing shared governance to lack of trust and a variety of social-psychological barriers.

Following clarification of the inhibitors, the NGT voting scheme was applied. Of the 44 inhibitors, 18 received no votes as being among the five most important, while four received three or more votes. Inhibitors receiving the most votes were: "demand for authority without accountability", "lack of trust", "lack of knowledge and acceptance of an operational definition of shared governance", and "dilemma of age".

The afternoon of the first day was spent with the intention of organizing the 26 inhibitors which received one or more votes into a graphic relationship. The generic question statement used with the ISM process to organize the inhibitors was:

"In the context of the shared governance concept,
does inhibitor A
increase the severity of
inhibitor B?"

Time constraints allowed organization of only 20 of the 26 inhibitors that received one or more votes in the NGT voting. Figure 10.9 shows the structure of inhibitors that the group produced. Development of this structure completed **Phase I**.

The second full day was dedicated to carrying out **Phase II** of the second stage in which an options field for realizing shared governance was identified and organized.

The NGT was used to generate a set of options (potential initiatives) which would ameliorate the inhibitors exposed earlier. The triggering question was:

"What are strategic options/initiatives which,
if implemented, will contribute to the realization
of the shared governance concept?"

Using NGT, participants were able to generate and clarify 30 options that would help to realize the shared governance concept.

The Options Field methodology was used to develop action plans. Participants first used the ISM process to organize the initiatives into similarity categories. The generic question used was:

"In the context of realizing the shared governance concept,
does option/initiative A
belong in the same category as
option/initiative B?"

where A represents one initiative and B represents another.

Initially all 30 initiatives were organized into 10 categories. Once these were displayed, the IM facilitator engaged the participants in the process of amending them. After amendments were finished, six final categories remained.

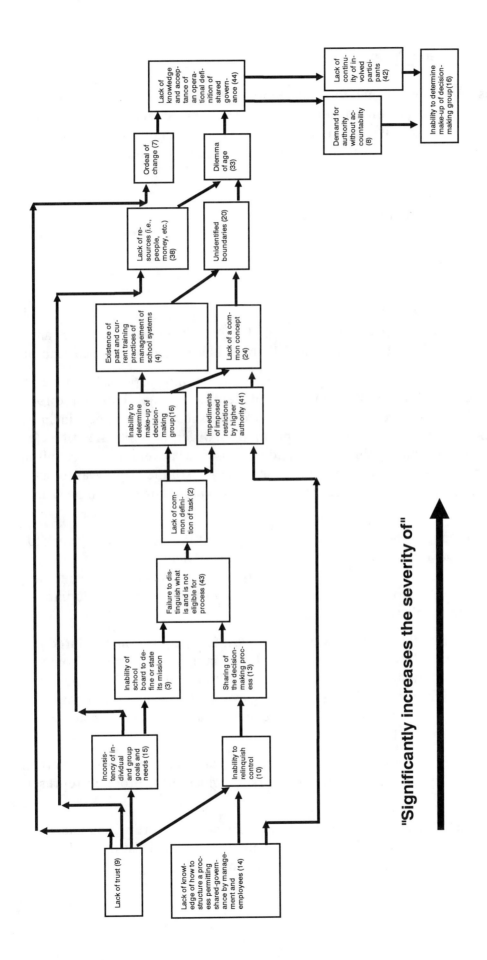

Figure 10.9 Structure of inhibitors to shared governance.

"Significantly increases the severity of"

Names were then assigned to the categories. The name of each category is important, because it shapes the conceptual image of each category. Also it captures the collective meaning of the individual options in each category. These categories then became recognizable as the dimensions of the system to be designed. The dimensions were named:

- Process of understanding
- Preliminary activities
- Roles/actors involvement
- Group selection
- Communicate
- Legislative mandate

Time did not permit construction of Options Profiles. These would represent alternative packages for taking actions toward the realization of the shared governance concept.

In the **third stage** of the work, the superintendents who participated in the second stage meet monthly in professional development workshops. During the 1988-1989 academic year, the workshops were focused on issues of governance, including models from industry and education, the positions of different political entities (e.g., unions, state departments of education), and processes for developing mechanisms for management to share governance functions. The goal of the group was to develop by the end of the academic year a "study council model or position on shared governance".

Use of Products. The products are a starting point for more focused work to realize the shared governance concept in participating districts, as well as in other districts that are affiliated with the study council organization. As the work continues, the products keep the group focused on problem identification and development of consensually acceptable solutions.

In the short run, the products serve as the basis for the position on shared governance that is being developed. The inhibitors and inhibitor structure become part of the internal institutional context of the group position and the foundation of the recommendations for action. The list of strategic options and the preliminary strategic Options Field form the basis of work to be done to develop a more concise choice of options for the formal position paper being prepared.

In the long term, the superintendents who participated in the workshop are investigating how they can best continue the work for which these products represent a beginning.

Conclusions. The workshop enabled the participants to concertize their understanding of shared governance, what inhibits its realization in school districts, and strategies for overcoming those inhibitors. The first cut at developing a working definition, a map of inhibitors, and a plausible strategic initiative indicates the complexity of the issue. The problems of which "shared governance" is a part are indeed complex, residing as much in the perceptions of the participants as in the structure of reality. Moreover, attempting to overcome those inhibitors with traditional strategic initiatives may well bring about change, but is unlikely to enable educators to realize the transformative potential of the second wave of reform.

In this context, the popular educational literature focus on examples of successful projects may not acknowledge the complexity of developing and implementing shared governance in school districts. Such articles typically start near the middle of the inhibition structure that was developed. Such questions as who will be in the decision-making group (# 16), what is and is not eligible for the process (# 43), and how adequate resources are secured (# 38) are all important issues. However, our work suggests that they are symptomatic of the more fundamental concern with setting up a process that permits/supports shared governance (# 14) and of a lack of trust (# 9).

The work represents an important initiative on the part of the seven involved districts. By addressing the issues in their complexity and uncovering the structure of that complexity, it is hoped to enable these and other school districts to develop successful shared governance projects in their districts. As one participant noted, "I think we have begun taking the first step out of X number of steps in a long, long conversation. But that conversation is to some extent threatening to all of us...and ultimately it is up to [us] to decide whether to continue it and how."

10.2 Application to Economic Development.

While several applications to economic development have been made, a single case is presented here, this being directed to planning for economic development at the local level in the State of Iowa.

Case ED-1. Planning for Economic Development in Iowa

[Establishing an Economic Development Program for the Fort Madison Economic Development Corporation through the assistance of the Institute for Decision Making at the University of Northern Iowa. This Case was prepared by Dr. William C. Wood of the School of Business, University of Northern Iowa, with technical assistance from Randal R. Pilkington, an economic development professional.]

Summary. After several years of frustration, community leaders from Fort Madison, Iowa, contacted the Institute for Decision Making at the University of Northern Iowa to assist the community in structuring a successful economic development program. Methods and concepts of Generic Design Science were integrated with a program structure for economic development to create a community-specific economic development plan for the city of Fort Madison. The plan was developed during four working sessions and incorporated Ideawriting, Nominal Group Technique, and a manual appli-

cation of Interpretive Structural Modeling. The first session assisted the group to identify and sequence the major issues facing them in the next several years. The following three sessions further assessed community needs and goals, and resulted in the
development of a short-term economic development plan to the level of action
steps. The action plan was completed in July of 1988. In the months that followed,
the community has been extremely successful in achieving economic growth through
the creation of new jobs and expanding the local tax base.

Background. The Institute for Decision Making is a university-based economic
development group that has been sustained by legislative funding for economic development from proceeds of the Iowa Lottery. The Institute does not charge communities for its services. Its primary purpose is to provide technical assistance to
Iowa communities which results in retaining and creating jobs. In economic development, jobs equals success.

The name "Institute for Decision Making" was chosen by Robert J. Waller
(NGT/ISM facilitator, author, and former dean) because it represented both the
long history and the potential of structured idea management and decision making
at the University of Northern Iowa. The professional staff of the Institute consists of
a former corporate vice president in international marketing, two economic development professionals, and one experienced practitioner of Generic Design Science.
The Institute is part of the External Services Division of the School of Business.
The resources of the Division, especially its Management Development Center, expand the capacity of the Institute well beyond what the operational funding alone
could provide.

With a client base of over 80 communities in two years, the Institute staff has
seen three major categories of economic development orientation. First, there are
those community groups who have little or no idea of what to do or how to do it. Individuals from these towns receive economic development training and are guided
into standard state-sponsored programs which are essential in preparing for economic development. Second are the communities which have had success with new
jobs in the past but are no longer successful, usually because the single individual
who was primarily responsible for the success has retired or died (Fort Madison fell
into this second category). The third category contains those communities that have
had solid experience in planning, but have reached a plateau and need to refocus
and re-energize their efforts. The Institute staff assists these communities with specialized projects or with broad, visionary community development plans which serve
as the context for revitalized, short-term economic development initiatives.

Although the Institute personnel deal differently with each type of community,
there is an overriding urgency with almost all of the Institute's clients. They are anxious
about their future, and don't know how to move forward. For them, "forward" means
economic recovery and growth that is consistent with their sense of community. When

unemployment is high, population is declining, storefronts are deserted, and schools are closing, the citizens and especially the leadership need short-term help upon which to build long-term hope.

The City of Fort Madison is a community of about 13,500 residents located in southeast Iowa along the Mississippi River. It is one of the oldest communities in Iowa, and had long enjoyed the best of times including riding the agricultural highs of the 1970's in Iowa. Just as the economy in Fort Madison (and Iowa) began to decline in the early 1980's, the long-time director of the Chamber of Commerce in Fort Madison passed away.

Since he had been so successful, no one else in the community had learned about economic development. With high expectations, the community leaders had consecutively hired two different Chamber Executives to run the economic development program. Both left after short tenures, due to lack of success. Most of the failure was directly related to the absence of direction and consensus in the community.

By 1987, the community had the highest (double-digit) unemployment rate in the state. The Fort Madison Economic Development Corporation (FMEDC) was created from a group of community leaders to develop a solution to this depressed situation. The FMEDC had received a proposal from a major consulting firm to prepare an economic development plan for the community at a price of $50,000. The stated purpose for the plan was to set forth necessary actions to make the community successful in economic development. While the FMEDC had raised $250,000 in cash and pledges for their economic development program, they were reluctant to spend 20% of the proceeds with no clear indication of immediate results.

The FMEDC had heard of the successes experienced by other clients of the Institute for Decision Making. They contacted the Institute in late 1987. Following initial discussions, the planning process with the Institute and Fort Madison began in February, 1988. The plan was completed in June, 1988.

Stages. At the time of this writing, the project has consisted of four stages of plan development: (1) Building consensus for the process and context; (2) Building consensus about the content; (3) Integrating economic development expertise with citizens' input; and (4) Revising, approving, and implementing the plan. Although the planning portion of the project occurred in these four separate stages, Fort Madison remains an active client of the Institute for further support and program development.

Stage 1. Building Consensus for the Process and Context. In February, 1988, a group of four community leaders and the newly-hired Chamber Executive traveled to Cedar Falls by private plane to visit the Institute for Decision Making. They wanted to learn about its services and hopefully to set forth a planning agenda for their community.

327

This introductory meeting was conducted in the External Services' Management Development Center of the School of Business at the University. This facility, a prototype of Demosophia, was designed specifically in the early 1980's to support effective and efficient group-decision-making sessions (see Chapter 8).

Using the NGT, the participants were asked to respond to the triggering question:

"What are the most pressing issues facing
Fort Madison in the next several years?"

Following discussion and the determining of relative priorities, 13 major issues were identified by the participants. This set of issues became the basis for determining the appropriate approach to initiate an economic development program. Following the NGT, the group engaged in a manual application of ISM to develop a chronological strategic approach to mitigate the 13 issues. The product of this initial session was a planning-process structural model which helped the participants determine the appropriate scope and useful sequence for attacking their pressing issues.

At the conclusion of this session, based on the model, the participants agreed that the City and FMEDC would benefit from a goal-setting workshop which would generate input from a broad, representative group of the community. They determined that this type of workshop would be important to ensure that they had the consensus of the community as their economic development plan evolved.

Stage 2. Building Consensus About the Content. The second session with Fort Madison was held in the community with about 40 community leaders and representatives of various sectors. An "ice-breaker" triggering question was used as part of the Ideawriting method, in order to help the participants become comfortable with each other, and to encourage interaction.

The question used was:

"What are your hopes and fears for Fort Madison?"

The group wrote responses to this question, and the responses were posted on newsprint as a transition to the next part of the workshop.

Then the group was led through another Ideawriting session to identify strengths and weaknesses of the community. The results are helpful to envisage what might be attractive or discouraging to a potential new business in the community. While some members developed and posted strengths and weaknesses, a smaller group of them worked on the development of a draft mission statement for the FMEDC. Though not formally applying the Options Field/Options Profile method, several options within key dimensions of a typical mission statement for an economic development corporation were provided to the smaller group. As the morning concluded, the workshop had identified the most significant strengths and weaknesses for Fort Madison and had produced a draft mission statement for the FMEDC.

Further work was conducted in the afternoon session with a smaller planning group, the executive committee of the FMEDC, most of whom had been present for the morning session. The group agreed that the purpose of their participation was to generate consensus on the most important goals for the FMEDC. Through a goal generation session using the NGT, the participants developed 40 goals which, for the most part, reflected the strengths and weaknesses that were developed in the morning session. Using the goals that were identified as most important for the FMEDC as evaluation criteria, the candidate mission statement of the FMEDC was validated and formally adopted.

Economic development program-area themes were then identified by a member of the Institute staff, and the participants grouped the goals by program area. These program areas and goals would be the basis for short-term economic development programs. The final portion of the day was devoted to prioritizing the amount of time that should be spent in each of the program areas.

Stage 3. Integrating Economic Development Expertise with Citizens' Input. Development of the plan with Fort Madison continued in the following month. The FMEDC leaders returned to the Institute to begin compiling the technical steps necessary to complete and implement an action-oriented plan. The session began with a detailed discussion of a sample plan for one program area which had been prepared by Institute staff. After modifying the sample plan, the group used the NGT to determine the specific objectives for each of the other program areas which would achieve the broad goals that had been generated in the previous phase of the project. Following clarification of the objectives, economic development implications and issues were addressed by Institute staff. Because of the economic development expertise of the staff, the group members were able to understand the requirements for implementation and some viable strategies. Finally, specific action steps were developed that detailed what had to be accomplished, by whom, and by when.

This level of detail was completed in the following areas:

- Sites and building inventory
- New business recruitment program
- Retention and expansion of existing businesses
- Tourism development
- Marketing plan/Target industry analysis
- Fundraising/Financing
- Riverfront development
- Entrepreneurship development
- Venture capital fund

From these nine program areas the first four were targeted for immediate action and the remaining five would be addressed in the second part of the year. Because of the ownership issue, i.e., the plan belonged to Fort Madison, the client group returned to Fort Madison with the newsprint and other raw output from the session. They were responsible for final decisions and documentation.

Stage 4. Revising, Approving, and Implementing the Plan. The FMEDC drafted the Economic Development Plan based on all the previous session reports and the output of Stage 3. Institute staff evaluated the draft. Feedback was given both in writing and later through frequent telephone conferencing. After the draft version was deemed acceptable, a special meeting of the Executive Board was called in Fort Madison to review the plan. The Institute also participated in this segment of the process to ensure that the Board members understood the plan and bought into what their specific responsibilities would be.

At this session, the local professional presented the plan in a thorough, step-by-step process. The economic development professional from the Institute helped turn the document into action by keeping perspective, explaining the rationale for action steps, answering questions, and discouraging the group from adding additional steps that were not needed. Before concluding the session, the Executive Board agreed on specific assignments of Board members to be in charge of each action area. The plan was then taken to the full Board which unanimously approved the plan.

Uses of the Products. This community created approximately 200 new jobs in 1988 as a direct result of the planning and implementation effort. The kinds of increases achieved are consistent with their sense of community. A summary of the achievements in Fort Madison is as follows:

- Lobbied for and obtained an 85-bed expansion to the State Penitentiary

- Successfully recruited two industrial companies to Fort Madison

- Achieved five local industrial expansions

- Achieved relocation (return) of professional employees to Shaeffer Pen divisional headquarters

- Created and funded a Convention and Tourism Bureau

- Extended infrastructure to previously unserved industrial park

- Developed community marketing materials

Conclusions. Generic Design Science assisted the participants of the FMEDC to understand that the problems facing their community were not insurmountable. Through the assistance of the Institute for Decision Making, the community was able to identify ways of overcoming the key impediments to success in the economic development arena. The planning process which integrated community expertise with professional economic development expertise enabled Fort Madison to move forward.

Fort Madison has accomplished objectives in each program area of the plan and it is no longer the Iowa city with the highest unemployment rate. The FMEDC members are confident that they have turned the corner. While the FMEDC has built its capacity to develop and implement almost any action plan, the Development Corporation still calls on the Institute for technical assistance. The next step is a more systematic and deliberate marketing effort.

10.3 Applications to Human Service Systems.

Four applications broadly grouped under the heading of human service systems will be described: (a) a review and analysis of the mission and objectives of a television broadcasting organization of a developing country, (b) designing the future of pediatric nursing in the United States, (c) developing strategic self-sufficiency plans for Native Americans, and (d) redesigning the National Marine Fisheries Service.

Case HS-1. Review and Analysis of the Mission and Objectives of a Television Broadcasting Organization of a Developing Country [This Case was contributed by Mr. S. K. Batra]

Summary. This case relates to the television broadcasting organization of a developing country. The objective of the study was to review and analyze the mission and objectives of the organization, hereinafter referred to as the TV Company. The study was carried out by a premier management consultancy organization, using methods from the Science of Generic Design. **Because of the terms of the signed agreement between the consultancy organization and the TV Company, neither organization will be specifically identified in this case presentation.**

The outcomes of the work included, among other things, an Objective Priority Structure, showing the hierarchical relationship among the stated global objectives and various policy-related issues that may influence the achievement of these objectives. The outcomes helped the TV Company and the consultants to arrive at a mutually acceptable set of key issues which needed to be addressed by the controlling Government department of broadcasting, to help ensure high organizational effectiveness of the TV Company. The study also enabled identification of key areas of management control for the chief executive of the TV Company, based on an analysis of the identified set of functions required to be carried out to meet the objectives at all levels in the Objective Priority Structure.

Background. The TV Company is one of the media units of the controlling Government department for broadcasting. It has an employee strength of over 11,000 personnel. The viewership of the TV Company programs is spread over 49% of the geographical area and 72% of the population of the country. The total annual outlay of the TV Company is around $270 million (U. S. Dollars).

The TV Company has become the most visible media unit of the Government in recent years, owing to a phenomenal growth in its program producing and transmitting capabilities. This growth has brought with it a high level of public expectations from the medium, thereby increasing sharply the complexity of its internal and external environment. As a result, there is constantly-increasing pressure on the TV Company to adapt itself to the needs of its environment. Ironically, the more it adapts to such needs, the more are the demands made on it. This has led to the TV Company operating as a task-oriented organization, shifting its priorities from time to time.

The perspective plan of the TV Company is geared towards providing new services, which will enable it to cater to the needs of the diverse language, culture, and intellectual groups in the country. However, the plan does not reveal any unified strategy towards integration of the hardware and software planning in the context of the stated objectives of the TV Company.

There is no ambiguity about the overall mission of the TV Company. It is to act as a catalyst for social change and development, as manifested in its stated objectives. However a need has been envisaged by the chief executive of the TV Company to systematically analyze the factors influencing the achievement of the mission, to obtain greater insight into the specific roles and functions that are required.

It was in this just-described context that the chief executive of the TV Company retained the consultants for a review and analysis of its mission and objectives. The consultants were also assigned the task of identifying areas of management control and designing a management information system.

Stages. To begin with, the consultants carried out literature surveys and held preliminary discussions with the chief executive and heads of various functions in the organization to obtain their perceptions on the mission and objectives of the TV Company. This laid the foundation of an intensive phase of the application of the methodologies of the Science of Generic Design.

The consultants conducted an NGT exercise with a group of 10 to 12 participants from within the TV Company, representing different functions such as engineering, programming, commercial and finance. The purpose was to generate a comprehensive set of ideas relevant to the achievement of the stated objectives of the TV Company. Table 10.4 shows some of the most important of the stated objectives of the TV Company.

The trigger question used for the NGT was:

"What, in your opinion, are the factors which
facilitate achievement of the stated objectives
of the TV Company?"

A set of about 40 ideas was generated during the NGT session, which was carried out during a period of about 4 hours distributed across two working days. Out of these, 25 ideas were selected based on a ranking of priority carried out by the group.

The next step in the process was to develop an intent structure of objectives. For this purpose the selected ideas were themselves edited into the form of objectives. Also additional objectives were developed from an analysis of the literature surveys and interviews carried out individually with the chief executive and heads of various functions at the beginning of the study. The intent structure was developed using the ISM methodology, with the following generic question:

> "In the context of successful achievement of the
> stated objectives of the TV Company,
> does the achievement of
> objective A
> facilitate the achievement of
> objective B?"

Forty-seven objectives were structured. This produced 10 hierarchical levels. The structure so produced was designated as the "Objective Priority Structure". Because of the size of the structure, it is reproduced in two parts. The upper half of the structure is shown in Figure 10.10. The lower half appears in Figure 10.11. In order to make clear the connections between the two halves, circled letters are used on each part. When correspondingly-designated letters are overlaid, the divided structure is thereby reconnected.

Table 10.4
Objectives of Television Company

- To act as a catalyst for social change
- To promote national integration
- To stimulate a scientific temper among the people
- To disseminate the message of family planning as a means of population control and family welfare
- To stimulate greater agricultural production by providing essential information and knowledge
- To promote and help in the preservation of environmental and ecological balance
- To highlight the need for social welfare measures including the welfare of women, children, and the less-privileged
- To promote interest in games and sports
- To stimulate appreciation of the country's artistic and cultural heritage

---

Uses of the Products. The Objective Priority Structure revealed a certain basic set of conditions which, if fulfilled, will eventually facilitate realization of the TV Company's mission more effectively. These basic conditions include:

a) Developing an internal system unique to the TV Company as a medium of broadcasting

b) Establishing distinct roles for the TV Company and its counterpart, the radio broadcasting organization of the country

c) Ensuring integrated hardware and software planning; and

d) Generating financial resources through commercialization.

It was also observed that there existed an ambiguity regarding the responsibilities of the controlling Government department of broadcasting vis-a-vis the TV Company in respect of functions such as commands and controls, monitoring, and coordination. It was suggested, as an inference from the Objective Priority Structure and an analogy with the neuro-cybernetic model of a human system, that the department of broadcasting should perform the role of a meta-system, embracing the functions of policy, planning, and overall monitoring and coordination for all of the media units under its control.

Areas of management control were identified by relating the functions presently being carried out in the organization with elements in the Objective Priority Structure. Some of the key areas of management control identified using the process were the following:

a) Allocation of transmission time

b) Viewership needs analysis

c) Quality of TV programs

d) Hardware expansion plan monitoring

e) Productivity of the TV Company's operations

f) Human resources management

g) New products and services

h) Exchange programs

i) Management of programs produced by outside agencies

j) Software research

k) Financial planning and control

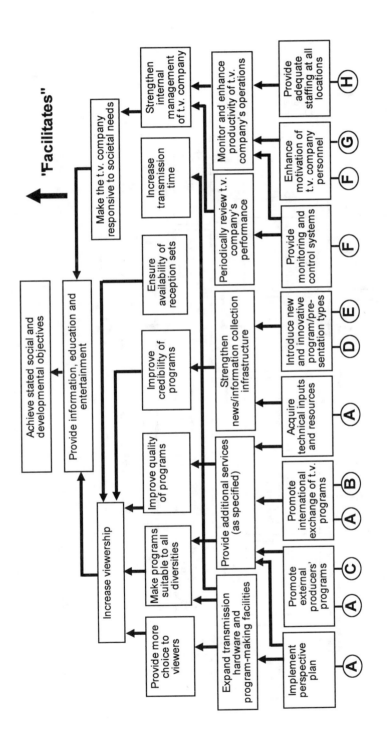

Figure 10.10 Objective priority structure for t.v. company. (Continued next page on Figure 10.11.)

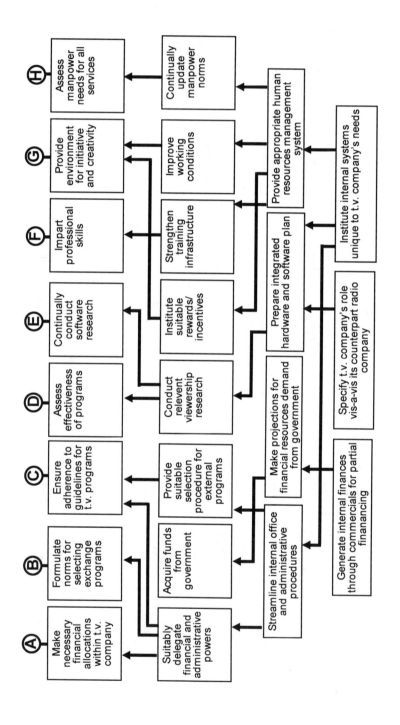

Figure 10.11 Objective priority structure for t.v. company. (Concluded)

The chief executive of the TV Company expressed the opinion that the Objective Priority Structure was an accurate representation of the complexity of the environment in which the TV Company operated and, at the same time, provided a systematic method of dealing with the complexity.

Conclusions. The process facilitated determination of a logical relationship between the social and developmental objectives of the TV Company and the basic issues confronting it. It was possible to demonstrate, through an objective evaluation inherent in the process, that resolving these basic issues is fundamental to effective organizational performance, in terms of achieving its stated objectives.

Case HS-2. Designing for the Future of Pediatric Nursing in the United States [This Case was contributed by Professor Veronica Feeg]

Summary. Experts in the field of pediatric nursing used the methods of Generic Design Science to design an agenda for the future for pediatric professionals, which focused on anticipated needs of pediatric health care consumers.

The participants produced a set of anticipated future needs and organized the need statements into similarity categories. A field of proposed short-term options for addressing the anticipated long-term needs was also produced.

The participants agreed unanimously that the process was productive and insightful. They responded positively to the format and structure of the discussion and generated nearly two hundred individual ideas to be integrated into the report on the forum. The group reached consensus on specific actions to be implemented relating to pediatric practice, administration, education, and research. They also suggested a future agenda for the journal, *Pediatric Nursing*, sponsor of the forum.

Background. *Pediatric Nursing*, a refereed bimonthly journal, sponsored the two-day forum, a closed invitational consensus-oriented conference, in May of 1988. Two groups of pediatric professionals were invited. One group was composed of twelve nationally-recognized experts in parent-child care or pediatric nursing, with emphasis on pediatric care. This group participated actively in the design work. The other group included experts invited to observe the group work and, if necessary, to provide replacements for any participants who could not attend on the second day.

Organizers began planning the forum in May of 1987. The selection of the participants was viewed by the Editor of *Pediatric Nursing* as critical to the success of the forum. The Editor sought to select a panel that represented diverse clinical and educational perspectives from different regions of the United States of America. Forum planners asked colleagues in pediatric nursing to respond to such questions as "Who would you consider to be the most well-respected or recognized person in pediatric nursing education (or home care or critical care or school health)?"

Working with the list from colleagues and collected invitation lists from other conferences, organizers completed their list of participants and observers for the forum. The final list included pediatric nurses from various areas of nursing practice, education, research, and administration. Clinical practice expertise included home, school, critical care, and developmental disabilities.

The purpose of the conference was to gain perspectives from national leaders in pediatric nursing on the future health needs of children and their families. *Pediatric Nursing* planned to share such perspectives with the pediatric professional community through published proceedings.

Stages. The design work was undertaken initially on May 16 and 17, 1988, in a facility described in Chapter 8. A skilled facilitator conducted the forum using the methods of Generic Design Science. A set of anticipated needs of pediatric health care consumers in the twenty-first century was produced first.

The need statements were then organized into eight similarity categories which the participants subsequently named. Options for meeting the anticipated needs were developed and organized into an options field.

A four-member ad hoc group collaborated on June 23, 1988 to complete the categorization of anticipated needs and to organize the short-term options into similarity categories. This committee was comprised of two forum participants and two solicited reviewers of the documents generated. The ad hoc group amended the original categories only to the extent of creating subcategories, while retaining the names.

Phase 1. Generation and Organization of Anticipated Needs. During the first day's work, participants used the NGT to generate and clarify 125 anticipated needs. The triggering question used to focus responses was:

"What are the anticipated needs for pediatric
health-care consumers in the 21st century?"

In responding to the triggering question, the experts were encouraged not to be constrained by images of the present state of pediatric health care, but rather to anticipate the future needs of children and their families before proceeding to make recommendations for the short-term future.

Approximately five hours were consumed in identifying and clarifying participant contributions. Initially the participants generated 111 anticipated needs. During clarification, 16 additional statements were produced and some statements were found to be duplications. The latter were deleted, leaving a total of 125 need statements.

To allow the group to focus their work in the time allotted, participants ranked the statements using a voting scale of one to five, one corresponding to an individual judgment of the most important need statement. Out of the total of 125, 34 received at least one vote.

The 34 selected statements were organized into similarity categories using ISM. The generic question chosen was:

In the context of the consumers,
does need A
belong in the same category with
(i.e., is similar to)
need B?

where A represents one of the selected need statements and B represents another of them.

The ISM work, conducted during the afternoon of the first day, took about 2 1/2 hours and produced eight similarity categories of needs. On the second day, an additional group of 42 statements from the set of 125 was placed within the categories.

(All 50 remaining statements eventually were incorporated in the categories by the ad hoc committee, which met about five weeks later. This group worked for about 2 1/2 hours to complete the classification of need statements using pairwise comparisons. The original eight categories were collapsed into five, using subcategories, and one new category was added.)

The categories are shown in Table 10.5.

Figure 10.12 presents the work completed by the forum participants and augmented by the ad hoc group. It displays the final six categories with lists of anticipated needs in each.

According to the judgment of the majority of the forum participants, similarity between statements warranted their assignment to the same category. For example, category B1, "Dimensions of Care: Practitioner Perspective" contains such statements as: "understanding and acceptance of cultural dimension of clients" and "knowledge and acceptance of diverse and changing family life styles". The listing of needs under each category does not represent any particular ranking or organization within the category.

Phase 2. Development of Options Field. The set of anticipated long-term needs which the participants generated the first day informed them in the next phase of work, the generation and clarification of options. The NGT methodology was used. The triggering question was:

What are short-term options which, if adopted, will
contribute to the fulfillment of the anticipated
needs of children and their families?

339

Table 10.5
Need Categories for Pediatric Nursing

A1 Comprehensive Health Care: Policy

A2 Comprehensive Health Care: Goals

A3 Comprehensive Health Care: Programs

B1 Dimensions of Care: Consumer Perspective

B2 Dimensions of Care: Practitioner Perspective

C1 Pediatric Nursing Profession: Issues

C2 Pediatric Nursing Profession: Environments

D1 Research: Demonstration and Evaluation

D2 Research: Program Initiatives

E Ethics/Decision-Making

F Pediatric Consumer Rights

The participants generated 71 short-term options. Because of time constraints, only 36 of these were clarified. The remaining options were listed in a separate table of the final report. The process of identifying and clarifying of short-term options took about 2 hours.

The ad hoc committee, which met on June 23, classified the short-term options into similarity categories using ISM. The generic question chosen was:

"In the context of the pediatric health care professional
does option A
belong in the same category with
option B?"

Six categories resulted in the Options Field after participants sorted the options into similarity categories. The Options Field appears in Figure 10.13, where the six categories of options can be seen. In contrast to the usual practice of assigning titles to these categories that reflect the contents of categories, what is done here is to assign titles according to what agent is likely to find the category falling within the agent's responsibility. This helps focus actions in particular arenas, and suggests also what the makeup should be of any group intending to design an implementation plan.

A1. Comprehensive Health Care: Policy

- Comprehensive national health policy for infants, children, youth and their families (17)
- A structure that links health care services in a comprehensive and coordinated manner (7)
- Dollars (59)
- Networks of supportive services for child-rearing families (18)
- A system designed to provide easy access to health services for all children (85)
- Sufficient health care resources (120)
- Availability of care providers (11)
- Child and family advocates (50)

A2. Comprehensive Health Care: Goals

- Provision of health care regardless of ability to pay (3)
- Comprehensive and continuous health care from conception to adulthood which will impact positively on healthful living behaviors throughout life (6)
- Health care which supports quality of life (20)
- More realistic and reliable reimbursement for a broad range of nursing practices (58)
- Preventive health care regimes (76)
- Least restrictive environment for children to promote their growth and development (81)
- Non-stigmatizing health care (88)
- A smokeless society for nurses as well as children and their families (93)
- A society which promotes supportive services to the disabled and mentally retarded (respite care) (96)
- Promotion of optimum development (108)
- A healthy psycho-social environment (114)
- Stronger partnership between society and family (117)
- Quality child care for the working parent (70)
- Quality child care for families who elect to use it (119)

A3. Comprehensive Health Care: Programs

- Children with chronic illness will need a spectrum of care (4)
- Family resource centers akin to farm program run by the Department of Agriculture (21)
- Development of variety of pediatric care delivery sites (28)
- Alternative care systems for young children whose parents are unavailable due to work or emotional problems (32)
- Ready availability of intensive nursing interventions (38)
- New models for well-child care which are environmentally and educationally oriented and intended to promote health for all children (45)
- Professional support for families facing exceptional stresses (65)
- Economical and effective technologies to monitor individual patients or groups of patients in other than hospital settings (67)
- Health, social and educational strategies that give children and families with poor starts a second chance (68)
- Techniques and strategies to prevent and treat various types of alcohol and substance use and abuse in families and children (72)
- Continued efforts to reduce adolescent pregnancies and teen suicide (school-based clinics) (78)
- Provision of home health care in a dual-career working society (83)
- Coalition building between the elderly and children for health care resources (101)
- Learning opportunities which utilize peer counseling and role modeling for behavior change (106)
- Research on coping with the aftermath of disasters (124)
- Provide supportive services for homeless and migrant families (127)

Figure 10.12 Anticipated needs field for pediatric health care consumers in the twenty-first century. (Items in grey boxes were judged by participants to be closely coupled.) (Continued on next page)

B1. Dimensions of Care: Consumer Perspective

- Knowledge and skills for greater autonomy within and without the health care system (1)
- Availability of assertive training (27)
- Need to normalize the life of children and families with health problems (30)
- Parent education/knowledgeable parents to guide children to optimal status (31)
- Assistance in developing a sense of integrity (34)
- Greater empowerment of the family or the child, when possible, to be an active participant or member of the health care team (39)
- Family education regarding the risks facing our children (56)
- Early health self-care by the child (60)
- Lifestyle options with dignity for individuals with mental retardation, dependency, or chronic illness (82)
- Knowledge, attitudes, skills, and habits (115)

- Opportunity for children, youth, and their families to learn and exercise their consumer rights: to be informed, to be safe and to choose (122)
- Health information packaging in usable formats (videotapes, audiotapes, CAI) (123)

B2. Dimensions of Care: Practitioner Perspective

- Understanding and acceptance of cultural dimension of clients (2)
- Need to promote wellness (8)
- Provision of atraumatic care (14)
- Need for high tech/high touch (19)
- Knowledge and acceptance of diverse and changing family lifestyles (36)
- Health care strategies which consider future as well as current problems (42)
- Environments that interface human care with machines (43)
- Coordination of care of sick children as they move to the wellness end of the continuum (44)
- Health care strategies addressing population-induced or intensified problems (51)
- Eradication of selected communicable diseases and reduction of unnecessary infectious diseases through good nursing practices (98)

- Prevention of sexually transmitted conditions in youth (107)
- Promoting healthy sexual development (121)
- Care of children whose parents are children (77)
- Care of children who are also parents (126)

C1. Pediatric Nursing Profession: Issues

- Need for appropriately prepared care providers in settings outside of the hospital (33)
- Professionals prepared to deal with new health conditions that evolve as a result of high tech (46)
- Incentives for nurses to practice in underserved areas (49)
- Nurses with advanced preparation in child development and family systems (52)
- Clarification of the role of acute care, long term care, and home health care and services delivered (62)
- More global networking and research by health professionals (63)
- Cadre of nursing leaders able to influence national and institutional health care providers educated to provide family centered care (66)
- Policies related to health care delivery systems (73)
- Prevention of burnout and support for nurses in stressful situations (74)
- Nursing leaders able to administrate complex health care systems (80)

- Validated nursing care which recognizes and takes into account the human responses of children and their families (84)
- Update of nurses' knowledge and skill in health promotion (95)
- A health care environment that supports the recruitment and retention of nurses (97)
- Accountable health care providers (99)
- A need for appropriately credentialed/certified health care providers (100)
- Nursing curricula which prepare nurses to accept role of family in promotion of self-care (shared responsibility) (102)
- The nurse as the evaluator of care (111)
- Professionals prepared to deal with new health conditions that evolve as a result of lifestyles (116)
- Provide an avenue for nursing to have input into the future marketing of pediatric care (126)

Figure 10.12 Anticipated needs field for pediatric health care consumers in the twenty-first century. (Items in grey boxes were judged by participants to be closely coupled.) (Continued on next page)

342

C2. Pediatric Nursing Profession: Environments	D1. Research: Demonstration and Evaluation	D2. Research: Program Initiatives	E. Ethics/Decision Making	F. Pediatric Consumer Rights
• Local area health care systems that are nurse-based (5)	• Child health status indicators that reflect function as well as dysfunction (12)	• Research to help understand the effect of giving or receiving care in ambulatory settings versus the hospital (64) *[grey box]*	• Support for decision-making in a complex environment (15)	• Safe physical environment (9)
• Severity of illness and care-setting placement (22)	• Interdisciplinary research to determine the predictors of positive family and child health (48)	• Research to clarify when services are/should be delivered (118) *[grey box]*	• Assistance with ethical decisions (25)	• A healthy physical environment (health protection) (29)
• Planned health care consultation in child care settings (24)	• Administration research to examine resource allocation of health professions (57)	• Use of information and computer technology for effective case management (89) *[grey box]*	• Ethical technology management (40)	• Freedom from abuse and neglect (55)
• Least restrictive environment for nursing practice (87)	• Better methodologies for recognizing early mental health problems in children (79)	• Use of new information in clinical decision-making from multiple alternatives (90) *[grey box]*	• Health care decisions which do not place children and their families in ethical dilemmas (94)	• Injury prevention (105)
• An environment for effective information processing by consumers and providers (103)	• Research to measure outcomes of nursing intervention (86)	• Immune banks (10)	• Appropriate decision making by health care providers regarding use/non-use of technology (104)	• Choices for families for health care delivery systems (37)
• Working with other health care professionals to come up with creative ways to provide health care in a complex environment (110)	• Application of research to nursing care (91)	• Single parents' family resource facility (35)	• Incorporate the right-to-know concept as it relates to patient, family, care providers, and others (113)	• Need to feel good (self concept) (41)
• Provide an environment for nurses to practice and make decisions based on sound nursing practices rather than legal and institutional constraints (125)	• Research to measure the true cost of health care for children and families (92)	• Child care for sick children (53)		• Early preparation for parenting and family life (47)
	• Knowledge of the long-term effects of illness and loss on families (16) *[grey box]*	• Adapted well-child services which take into account advances in genetic research (54)		• Protection of confidentiality and privacy (26)
	• Knowledge about health conditions and health care practices that take into account an appropriate time continuum in measuring outcomes (112) *[grey box]*	• Alternative health care systems for children with progressive and terminal health care problems such as AIDS (61)		• Successful academic achievement (23)
		• Traveling tutus (69)		• To die with dignity (75)
		• Community nursing organizations for children (schools, juvenile correctional facilities) (71)		

Figure 10.12 Anticipated needs field for pediatric health care consumers in the twenty-first century. (Items in grey boxes were judged by participants to be closely coupled.) (Concluded)

343

Use of the Products. The report of the proceedings of the forum was issued in 1989 as a special monograph by *Pediatric Nursing*. The major ideas and key concepts that were generated will become foci for concept papers for future discussion. These are:

- Changing sociodemographic trends in the next ten years
- Case managed/coordinated care
- Principles of atraumatic care
- Empowering the health care consumer
- Family resource centers
- Ethics and technology

Conclusions. Dr. Veronica Feeg, Editor of *Pediatric Nursing*, viewed the results of the forum as a "script" for the next century, a futuristic plan of options or recommendations. Dr. Feeg called for a new political activism by pediatric nurses, urging them to work to influence local, state, and national leaders who significantly address the needs of children and families. She also suggested that pediatric professionals engage others in discussing issues such as the "crisis of catastrophic illness", of "minimum-quality child care", or of "low wages for service providers in child-related facilities".

Specific recommendations for general action made by forum participants were in areas of pediatric nursing education, administration, research, and practice. They were:

- Increase minority enrollment in nursing education

- Influence J.C.A.H.O. in areas of accreditation to set standards of nursing credentials for pediatric facilities.

- Establish programs that unite pediatric nursing leaders to respond to the American Medical Association proposal for Registered Care Technicians

- Establish practices/policies in health-care settings to use principles of atraumatic care

- Develop a family Bill of Rights to be followed in all child-care settings

In addition, participants offered specific recommendations to the Editor of *Pediatric Nursing* to apply to editorial activities of the journal and the annual conference such as:

- Share the conference findings through publications

- Focus the 1989 conference on themes of ethics and cultural diversity

- Encourage advertisers to depict children/families in active consumer roles

A. Addressed to Pediatric Nursing Editor	B. Addressed to Pediatric Nursing Professionals	C. Addressed to Pediatric Nursing Education	D. Addressed to Pediatric Nursing Administration	E. Addressed to Pediatric Nursing Research	F. Addressed to Pediatric Nursing Practice
Share the findings of this conference through published materials, presentations at conferences, and promote the adoption of the findings with professional agencies or organizations (14)	Develop family bill of rights that is followed in all child care settings (3)	Increase minority enrollment into nursing education (9)	Influence the Joint Commission on the Accreditation of Hospital Organizations to have as an accreditation requirement that 20 percent of the nursing staff in any specialized area be prepared at the clinical specialist level appropriate to that area (M.S. in nursing) (36)	Encourage nurses to develop research and demonstration projects that address special initiatives (2)	Establish practices/policies in health care settings to employ principles of atraumatic care (12)
Focus the 1989 Pediatric Nursing Conference on cultural diversity and lifestyle issues (18)	Legislative lobbying for national health policy(ies) (7)	Tuition reimbursement for undergraduates plus stipends for graduate students (22)	Establish programs which unite research abilities of academicians with problem identification skills of clinical nurses (6)	Seek support for demonstration projects to assess alternative nursing practice settings (5)	Use media such as television to demonstrate assertiveness skills to families as applied to health care systems (21)
1989 pediatric nursing conference to include a focus on pediatric nursing ethical issues (24)	Form a coalition with A.A.R.P. on behalf of children and youth (11)	Develop programs which focus on the special needs of the critically ill child, his family, and his nurse (34)	Continue to develop innovative nurse-directed systems of care (31)	Develop and test culturally sensitive tools to assess positive aspects of child growth and development and family function (32)	Encourage nursing to apply the principles of public health for the health care of populations (23)
Prepare a series of articles on consumer rights with a comprehensive literature review to support why this should be a right (29)	Establish a national health fitness program (17)	Education of all nurses in development and influence of health policy (8)	Reimbursement for nurses providing services (4)	Establish longitudinal research methodologies which evaluate the long-term/future as well as immediate health care practices (35)	
Unite pediatric nursing leaders in particular to respond to the American Medical Association proposal for care technicians (33)	To establish child/family education programs within a variety of health care settings and community service agencies (25)	Encourage curriculum development in terms of the future dimensions of care, e.g., computer technology, risk benefit, cultural diversity, through the American Nursing Association, the National League of Nurses, and the American Association of Colleges of Nursing (20)	Establish consultant fees and referral networks between nurses (13)		
Encourage advertisers to depict children/families in active consumer roles (28)	Seek private sector support for child health care initiatives (16)	Target high school guidance counselors to educate them on the role of professional nursing (15)			
	Begin to merge professional organization meetings based on common conference themes (10)	Advanced academic preparation through extension in service agencies (1)			
	"Each nurse take one" health issue program by American Nursing Association (26)				
	Develop community "cultural sharing groups" to discuss traditions and beliefs (30)				

Figure 10.13 Options field for fulfillment of anticipated needs of children and their families.

Case HS-3. Designing Strategic Economic Self-Sufficiency Plans for Two Native American Tribes [This Case description was contributed by Ms. Irene Cromer]

Summary. Two Native American tribes applied the methods of Generic Design Science to address issues associated with strategic economic planning for the future of each tribe.

Members of the Winnebago Tribe of Nebraska participated in a 2-day session to produce an economic self-sufficiency plan. The products include a Priority Structure showing the relative priorities attached to barriers to implementing a plan, and options for addressing the barriers. The participants felt that the processes used were consistent with their traditional consensus-building practices and brought discipline to the discussions, enabling them to overcome interpersonal conflicts that had hindered previous planning activity.

Members of the Poarch Band of Creek Indians of Alabama participated in a 3-day forum to identify critical emerging issues facing the tribe in the next 5 to 10 years. The products include a Priority Structure of critical issues, options for resolving the issues, and responsibility assignments among segments of the community for implementing the options. The participants believed the forum was useful in helping to redirect the Tribe's priorities in the face of unprecedented economic growth, and to focus attention on communications among tribal constituencies.

The cultural, economic, and social histories of these two tribes differ markedly, which supports the decision to include both cases in this chapter.

Background for the Winnebago Project. According to Tribal Chairman Reuben Snake, the Winnebago Tribe throughout the mid-nineteenth century had been relocated frequently by the federal government, causing disruption or disintegration of traditional social structures and economic institutions, contributing to cultural and intratribal conflicts. These factors made it difficult for them to develop a strong base for economic development. In 1965, the Tribe was operating on a $6,000 a year development budget.

The Winnebago Tribe has suffered deleterious effects of economic underdevelopment including high unemployment, inadequate health care, substandard housing, high alcoholism rates, high infant mortality rates, and high incidence of diabetes. The Tribe's economic prospects changed when the federal War on Poverty was initiated in the late 1960's. With the influx of federal money, the Tribe began to develop housing and work programs. Twenty years later, the Tribe has become a multi-million dollar enterprise.

Yet, Federal programs have not been a panacea according to tribal leaders who recognized the need to improve the living conditions, health, education, and economic opportunities of their people. In 1980, the leaders developed a 20-year plan for attaining tribal self-sufficiency by the year 2000. Seven years later, the leaders felt it necessary to revisit the concept of self-sufficiency and to generate a plan based on community consensus.

In 1987, Reuben Snake recognized that the older plan had not received widespread acceptance in the community. Various social and cultural dissonances were inhibiting progress. He felt that a discussion on tribal self-sufficiency should engage different segments of the community to produce a consensus, leading to sound implementation of an action plan.

He had been a participant in a forum sponsored by Americans for Indian Opportunity (AIO) [3]. AIO, a national Indian organization, had introduced the generic design process to Indian country as part of their ongoing national analysis of the governance issues confronting tribes in contemporary times. In addition, AIO sponsored the two forums discussed in this case study. The forums were conducted by the Center for Interactive Management of George Mason University.

Stages in the Winnebago Project. The work was conducted in two days in July, 1987, in South Sioux City, Nebraska, with leadership from a facilitator experienced in the design processes. The 18 Tribal members who took part included members of the Tribal Council, the Administration, and community dissidents. The site was a hotel conference room that was temporarily converted into a facility similar to the one described in Chapter 8. The barriers to the implementation of a self-sufficiency plan were organized in a Priority Structure. Then participants worked in small teams to generate options for dealing with the barriers in accordance with the Priority Structure, and they reported their ideas at a clarifying plenary session.

Phase 1. Developing a Priority Structure. The first step in building consensus on a self- sufficiency plan involved definition of barriers to implementing such a plan. The Nominal Group Technique (NGT) was used to identify and clarify barriers. The participants generated 71 statements in response to the triggering question:

"What are the anticipated problems with (or barriers
to) the implementation of a Winnebago self-sufficiency plan?"

The 71 statements were then divided into two subsets through a voting process. Forty-eight were considered to be of greater importance, and 23 of lesser importance. The Interpretive Structural Modeling (ISM) process was used to organize the barriers into a priority structure. The following generic question was used:

"In the context of implementing a Winnebago self- sufficiency plan,
should barrier A
be addressed before or at the same time as
barrier B?"

Organizing the barriers into a Priority Structure improved the ability of the participants to organize their time. A total of 20 of the 48 higher-priority barriers appears in the Priority Structure shown in Figure 10.14. This structure is the version that followed discussion and amendment of the product from the ISM process. Several of the highest priority barriers related to community and collective action among tribal members.

Phase 2. Generating Options. Working in 3 small teams on the second day, participants used Ideawriting to generate options to alleviate the higher-priority problems. Each team responded to the following triggering question:

> "What are options which, if adopted, would alleviate
> anticipated problems with a Winnebago
> self-sufficiency plan?"

Phase 3. Reporting. They reported on their work in a plenary session, and then continued to work in small teams until all available time was used. The reporting and discussion during the plenary session improved participant learning, so that options proposed for lower-priority barriers were informed by proposed resolution of high-priority barriers.

<u>Use of the Products of the Winnebago Project</u>. The Tribal Government used the results to guide decisions on the use of resources and time. The Tribal Council defined specific roles and responsibilities for implementation of the options according to an agreed-on time schedule. Sixteen months after the conclusion of the two-day workshop, the following activities had been undertaken:

- The Public Relations Officer had created a "Winnebago Pride" Campaign to provide positive images of the Tribe and individuals to the general community
- The Tribal Mental Health Program had developed a proposal to create a Family System Therapy Center to work with total family units to resolve problems that create dysfunctions with individuals and families
- The Tribal Economic Development Division, working with the Tribal Credit Department, had held community seminars on Small Business Development for tribal members who wanted to become entrepreneurs with the aid of the Tribe's Long-Term Credit Program
- A community-based language program was funded by the Tribal government to generate involvement of members of the Tribe in cultural preservation efforts
- The Tribal government had taken the Federal government to task for its failure to work cooperatively towards tribal-specific health goals and objectives

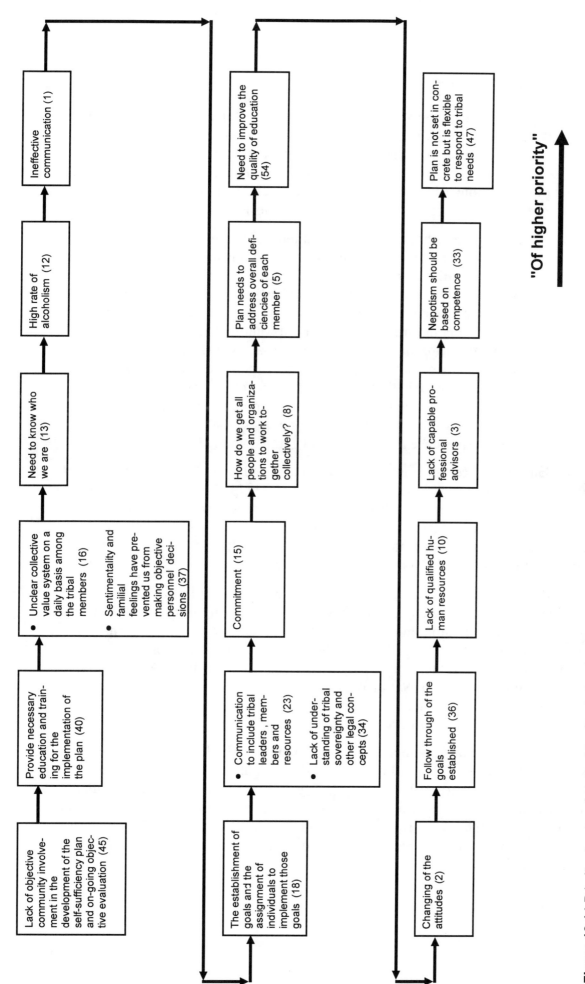

Figure 10.14 Priority structure for attacking barriers to implementation of a self-sufficiency plan for the Winnebago Indians.

Conclusions from the Winnebago Project. The Generic Design process enabled the participants to recognize root causes of their difficulties and prompted them to make specific suggestions for dealing with areas of dissonance. According to Chairman Snake, the process was a healing experience, analogous to the traditional pipe ceremonies in which everyone had an opportunity to speak and each person's contribution was respected. He said in his closing remarks:

> "Our grandfathers used to sit in a lodge. There would be a clan representative from each of the tribes of our nation and one of the grandfathers from my uncle's clan would light a pipe and that pipe would go around that circle...They had a firm conviction in their minds that what they were doing was very meaningful...Each one of them in turn would talk about what they thought and felt about the tribe or the nation. When all was said, they would understand the other very clearly and then they could make a decision. I thought that this process has some very closely-related relationships to the Indian way of developing a consensus. That's why I was so anxious to bring it over here, so that each one of you could experience this process and get that good feeling back" [4].

Comments received from other participants and observers were overwhelmingly positive. The consensus was that the process helped participants overcome interpersonal dissonances and substantive misunderstandings, and develop a consensual domain for tribal action. A communal spirit arose among the Tribal Council members and staff, along with a commitment to work collectively and cooperatively toward the achievement of tribal self-sufficiency.

Background for the Creek Project. The Poarch Band of Creek Indians has lived in southwestern Alabama for 150 years. The contemporary Poarch Creeks are descended from an autonomous community of "mixed-bloods" which formed in the late eighteenth century in southwestern Alabama. Most of the families in the community gained title to their improved, cultivated land under the 1814 Treaty of Fort Jackson. When the Creek Nation of Alabama was removed to Indian Territory in the 1830's, the Poarch Band remained and eventually settled permanently in distinct kinship-based settlements near Atmore [5].

The Poarch Band numbers over 1,800 members who live in three of the original settlements that still exist, and in nearby areas of Alabama and western Florida. The Reservation consists of 229.54 acres [6]. The Poarch Band has remained a highly cohesive community since its beginnings, although most cultural differences between the Poarch and their poor, rural, non-Indian neighbors declined in the late 19th century. The community became officially incorporated as the Creek Nation East of the Mississippi in 1971, and received federal recognition as a tribe in 1984 [7].

The Tribe has experienced rapid economic growth, largely because of an infusion of federal funds after federal recognition. They have business enterprises that include a hotel, restaurant and bingo palace. They have constructed a fire and rescue station, new housing for the elderly, a senior center and health center, new tribal headquarters, and a water tank. While they enjoy economic success, Chairman Eddie Tullis and other leaders have expressed concern as to whether they are adequately prepared for the challenges that future growth will bring. He sought a forum that would help the Tribe carry out its own planning activity.

Stages in the Creek Project. The project required 3 days in July of 1988, on the Poarch Band Reservation in Atmore, Alabama. The 20 participants included members of the Tribal Council, tribal staff, and key community members, some of whom are not Indian. Participants developed a Priority Structure of critical issues, generated options for resolving them, and assigned roles and responsibilities for implementing the options to various sectors of the community and Tribal Government [4].

Phase 1. Developing a Priority Structure. The Nominal Group Technique (NGT) was used to elicit from the participants a list of critical emerging issues facing the Poarch Band in the next decade. The triggering question:

"What are critical emerging issues for the Tribe
in the next five to ten years?"

stimulated the generation of 52 issues. This work was completed on the first day.

On the second day the participants organized 21 of the issues into a sequence for discussion purposes. The ISM process was used with the generic question:

"In the context of planning for the future of the Tribe
should issue A
be considered (for Forum discussion purposes)
before issue B?"

The Priority Structure that was produced is shown in Figure 10.15. This work was completed in the second morning.

Phase 2. Generation of Options. In the second afternoon, participants worked in three teams (denoted A, B, and C) to generate options for resolving critical issues (Figure 10.15 shows assignments of teams to issues or cycles of issues.). Ideawriting was used to conduct this small group activity. The triggering question used was:

"What are short-term options (activities) which,
if adopted, will address/resolve issue(s) X?"

where X refers to an issue or cycle of issues seen in Figure 10.15.

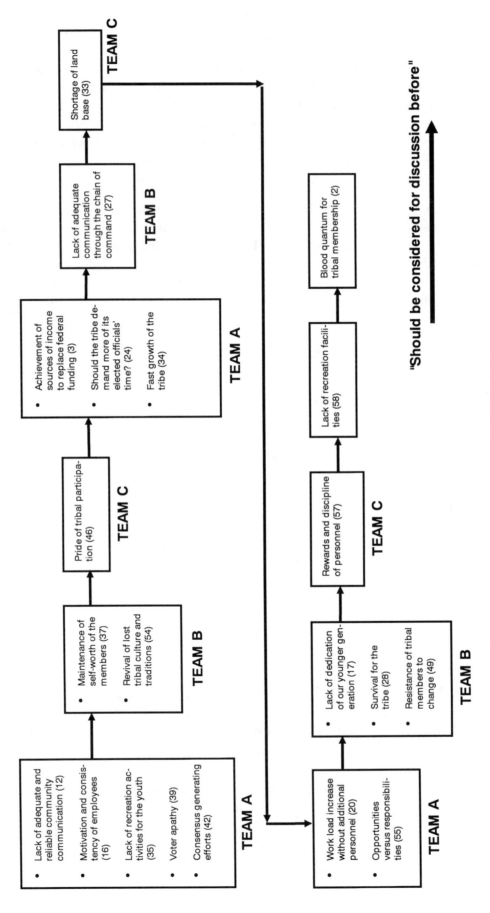

Figure 10.15 Priority structure for attacking issues critical to the Creek nation east of the Mississippi.

Each group worked for three rounds on their respective issues drawn from Figure 10.15. Because of time constraints the teams dealt with only 19 of the total of 21 critical issues, omitting the lowest items (# 58 and # 2) in the Priority Structure, and produced a total of 61 options for further consideration.

Phase 3. Assignment of Primary Responsibilities. When the teams had completed the generation of options, they were joined by the observers to form a larger group. This larger group was divided into five, each representing one key segment of the Poarch Creek community: Tribal Council, Administration, Social Services, Planning, and Community. These five groups proposed assignments of primary responsibility for implementing the options considered.

In the plenary session following the small group work, team members described their rationales for making assignments, and responded to questions. Large charts showing the assignments were drawn on newsprint and posted on the walls to assist teams to report on their work. Amendments were made in the assignments during the discussion.

The results show the participants were in <u>agreement</u> on 27 assignments, and in <u>near-agreement</u> on 18 assignments, out of the total of 61 options considered. This reflects a shared perspective as to what segment of the community should bear the lead role in achieving certain options. The group representing the community felt that the community was not involved enough in tribal activities. The group expressed the belief that people in the community are interested and willing to become involved with the Tribe, but that there is an apparent reluctance by other segments to take advantage of such a resource.

Table 10.6 shows examples of the assignments made to segments of the Poarch community for implementation of eight of the options relating to issues # 17, # 28, and # 49 in the Priority Structure. Lead responsibility is indicated by the column heading, while entries in the cells show which group or groups recommended the lead responsibility. For example, groups T, C, S, and P felt that lead responsibility for Option 1 should fall to the Tribal Council (T), while only the Administration (A) felt that it should fall to the Administration.

Table 10.6 also illustrates the concern of the C team representing the community that the Tribal Government should involve the community to a greater degree in tribal activities. Each entry in the column headed C that contains any letter(s) shows only a C in five of the six instances. This means that the Community team felt it should bear responsibility for implementing the options (numbers 2, 4, 5, 7, 8) but that no other team shared that feeling.

Uses of the Products of the Creek Project. The products of the work were moved to Tribal Council chambers for further planning and tracking.

Conclusions from the Creek Project. The group activity was intended to assist the Tribe to identify future issues. While this goal was accomplished, it became clear that many "future issues" are issues that threaten to polarize the community now.

Table 10.6 Implementation Assignments for the Poarch Community

Options	Tribal Council (T)	Administra-tion(A)	Community (C)	Social Services (S)	Planning (P)
1) It will be tribal policy that all training and/or seminars can be attended by non-participating observers.	T C S P	A			
2) When feasible, encourage tribal members to visit other tribes to review their development.	T A C S P	C	C	C	C
3) Inform and encourage (publicly) our youth to participate in decisions of the tribe.	T P	A	C S P		
4) Utilize excess property program to locate and obtain musical instruments for youth to utilize and participate in high school band and other musical activities.		T A C S P	C		
5) Bring in national role models to speak to the youth to encourage them to continue their education.	T S	A P	C		
6) Utilize appropriate means to educate tribal membership in the understanding that the survival of the tribe is not totally dependent on federal funds.	T	A S P			C
7) Continue to expand and perfect our youth work/learn program.	C	T A S P	C	C	
8) Tribal decision-making process should take into consideration impact of immediate decisions on five, six, seven generations of the tribe.	T A C S P	C	C	C	C

The most significant of these relates to poor communication within the community. Coupled with this perception is a strong sense of alienation from the governing process among large numbers of the tribal membership. Several participants believe that voter apathy is a result of this alienation.

Bobby McGhee, a Tribal Council member, stated, "I was surprised that people didn't know that all Tribal Council meetings are open except for a few closed sessions that involve discussion of personnel...I think it's our job and our responsibility to inform the people what we are going to have a discussion on." Other Tribal Council members share the belief that the discourse during the forum was constructive because it helped such issues to surface. The Tribal Administrator, James T. Martin, said "...We have to remember that...we have been in a crisis situation in the past five years. I feel energetic about this process because we've been able to identify people issues."

Overall, the participants expressed enthusiasm and renewed hope for continued and increased involvement of tribal members in community issues. The Tribal Council acknowledged the concerns expressed by participants. Chairman Eddie Tullis stated, "We haven't solved our problems today. We've just put our problems up where everyone can look at them...this is only the beginning of a process and we can get more people involved if we can find the people who will assume the responsibility."

Case HS-4. Redesigning the National Marine Fisheries Services [This Case description was contributed by Ms. Irene Cromer]

Summary. The National Marine Fisheries Service (NMFS) used the methods of Generic Design Science in a ten-day executive seminar series to redesign the NMFS for the 1990's. The impetus for change came from outside the agency, including Congress and higher levels of management at the U. S. Department of Commerce and the National Oceanic and Atmospheric Administration in which NMFS is located. Conflicting regulations and policies of these and other agencies of the federal government hindered the effectiveness and efficiency of the NMFS.

During the design process, 28 senior and upper-level NMFS managers were successful in generating anticipated problems of the 1990's, and in articulating and organizing long-range goals and objectives of the NMFS into an Intent Structure. They also proposed initiatives or options for redesigning the agency to enhance its capabilities to respond to anticipated future problems and roles.

A survey of the effectiveness of the process indicated that managers felt better informed about the organization. The openness of communication during the stages of design work contributed to their understanding of the complexity of the issues facing them. Sensitivity to current and future organization-wide changes enabled managers to develop their plans and programs in a more informed manner within the context of long-term goals and objectives.

Background. The National Marine Fisheries Service (NMFS), which began as the U. S. Fish Commission in 1871, is an organization of the federal government assigned to conserve and protect living marine resources through responsible regulation and management. The Fishery Conservation and Management Act of 1976 (Public Law 94-265) moved the agency into a significant regulatory role for the first time in its history. Before then the mission of the agency was primarily to conduct research on living marine resources in the coastal areas of the United States and up to 200 miles off-shore. The new role required increased interaction with the State Department, commercial fisheries, recreational fisheries, private research organizations, private fisheries associations, and state and local governments, with emphasis on regulation. In response to the new demands, the agency grew incrementally and reactively, creating new divisions or offices as the needs arose.

At the time the design work was undertaken in October of 1985, the NMFS was operating in a very turbulent environment created by diverse constituent needs, contradictory priorities, and legislative policy changes -- all strong motivators for organizational redesign. According to the agency director, managers at all levels within NMFS headquarters were faced with severe organizational and managerial problems, including:

- Diminishing relative capacity of a given individual (top manager or otherwise) to comprehend the overall management system
- Increasing levels of unexpected and counter-intuitive consequences of policy action
- Declining legitimacy of leadership
- Increasing challenges to basic value premises
- Increasing system rigidity and inflexibility
- Increasing demand for public participation in decision-making

Several studies of these problems had been conducted for NMFS over the years, but they had failed to yield long-term resolutions. Total study costs were about $120,000. Senior management responded in October of 1985 by re-examining the broad underlying philosophies and directions of the current NMFS and redesigning the NMFS organization for the 1990's.

Mr. William Gordon, the Director of NMFS during this period, chose the Generic Design processes to enable managers to identify current and future organization-wide problems and to adopt a proactive approach to organizational change.

The choice was made in the light of previous activity with the Southwest Fisheries Center, San Diego, California, one of four fisheries research centers of the NMFS, which had come to the attention of the larger agency with headquarters in Washington, D. C. The Southwest Fisheries Center had been so pleased with the results of that activity that they had installed their own Demosophia, and had learned to conduct their own working sessions, with leadership from Dr. Izadore Barrett (the Director of the Southwest Fisheries) and facilitation by Mr. David J. Mackett [8].

Stages. The work required 10 days in three blocks of time (3 days, 3 days, and 4 days, respectively), during the period from October, 1985 through January, 1986. The sessions were held in the Demosophia facility described in Chapter 8. A Problematique for the agency was produced first. Then an Intent Structure was developed. Options for the conceptual redesign of the NMFS of the future were then generated and organized into an Options Field.

Phase 1. Developing a Problematique. The first 3-day session focused on establishing a context for defining many of the anticipated problems. A need for a common ground for discussion was envisaged. As became apparent early in the process, NMFS managers must deal with inconsistent, contradictory demands on their resources. Turf-building and internal competition are part of the response. Consequently, establishing a problem context was promoted as an opportunity for all participants to express individual departmental needs and to develop a collective understanding and appreciation of the internal and external environment. A desire by senior managers to promote and instill an anticipatory problem-solving posture in rising managers was present. The desire to close the gap between anticipated problems and current and projected practices is a stimulus to use planning and design as an ongoing strategy.

The Nominal Group Technique was applied to generate and clarify anticipated problems, with 28 upper- and senior-level managers serving as participants. They generated 84 statements in response to the triggering question:

"What are the anticipated problems of the NMFS
of the 1990's?"

The Interpretive Structural Modeling process was used to develop the structure of the Problematique. The generic question used for this purpose was:

"Does anticipated problem A aggravate
anticipated problem B?"

357

From the 84 problem statements generated, the participants chose 27 to structure on the basis that they were the most important ones in the set. Figure 10.16 shows which of these problems aggravate other problems. A group of statements in a single box represents a cycle of mutually-aggravating problems.

Phase 2. Developing an Intent Structure. Following the analysis of the Problematique, the Nominal Group Technique was applied again, this time to develop a list of goals and objectives. Participants decided that goals would be defined as long-range intentions and objectives would be defined as short- range intentions. The triggering question was:

"What should be the goals and/or objectives
of the NMFS of the 1990's?"

A subset of 28 of the elements generated was chosen for developing the Intent Structure. The following generic question was used:

"Does goal or objective A significantly support
goal or objective B?"

Figure 10.17 shows the Intent Structure that was developed. The entries on the right side were interpreted by the participants to be long-range goals, and those at the left end were generally seen as short-term objectives aimed at attaining the longer-term goals. The three highest-level components in the structure, numbered 36, 8, and 13, were seen as the highest priority long-range goals. Elements numbered 24, 41, and 16, were seen as supporting objectives deserving early project work.

The development of the Intent Structure required 3 days of work, as had the development of the Problematique. The products and learning from these 6 days enabled the participants to develop a consensual image of the anticipated problems and direction for NMFS. To prepare for the remaining 4 days, during which solution ideas would be generated and organized, the participants overlaid the goals and objectives on the major divisions in the current organizational structure to identify shortcomings in existing plans, programs, and responsibilities. The results of this work appear in Figure 10.18. The three major divisions of the agency and a Mission Statement for each division of it were developed by the participants in small group work. They assigned the components of the Intent Structure to the divisions that would have lead responsibility for implementing them.

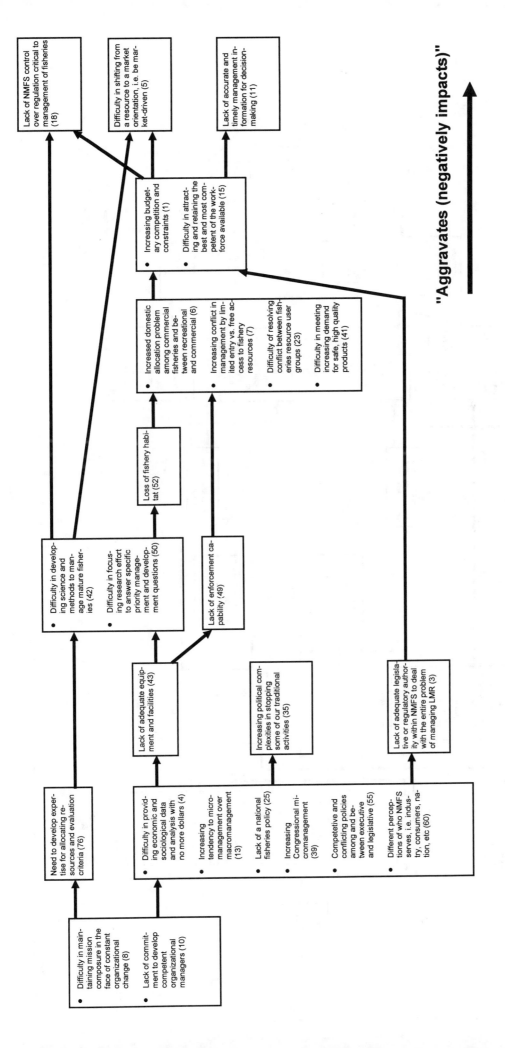

Figure 10.16 Problematique for the National Marine Fisheries Service.

"Aggravates (negatively impacts)"

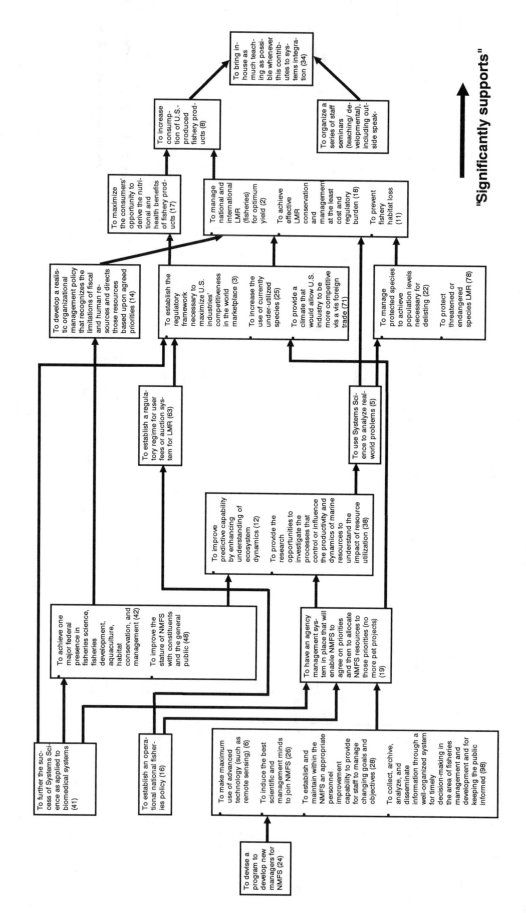

Figure 10.17 Intent structure for the National Marine Fisheries Service.

During this work, objective 90 was split to form objectives 90A and 90B. Those components that were not naturally matched to existing NMFS divisions and those which overlapped divisions provided a basis for amendments that related to possible reconfiguration of departments, as well as new roles and responsibilities.

Phase 3. Developing an Options Field. The third phase of the work involved generating and organizing design options aimed at developing the scope of the organization and other factors deemed critical to the redesign.

The 4 days devoted to this activity began with the use of the NGT process to generate, clarify, and edit 126 options based on the triggering question:

> "Does design option A belong in the same
> category as design option B?"

After developing and labeling the categories, the participants reviewed the categories to decide if they all were necessary to design an NMFS of the 1990's. Those categories judged to be necessary were classified as "design dimensions". Finally, to facilitate choice-making among the dimensions and the options within each of the dimensions, the dimensions were sequenced, to reflect both choice precedence and interdependence. The generic question used in applying the ISM process to arrive at the choice precedence relationship was:

> "Should a choice in dimension A precede a
> choice in dimension B?"

The structure developed from this question yielded a sequence for choosing options from each dimension so that the most salient options are chosen from the first dimension, then options are chosen from the second dimension in the light of the choices made in the first dimension, and so on. Figure 10.19 shows about one third of the completed Options Field.

The 15 design dimensions, presented in the order in which they were sequenced, with letters used to indicate clusters (i.e., cycles of interdependent dimensions), are as follows:

> 1. Policies/Legislation/Roles
>
> 2A. Data/Information
>
> 2B. Living Marine Resources Management
>
> 3A. Federal Structure
>
> 3B. Habitat
>
> 3C. Priority/Planning
>
> 4A. Trade/Development

4B. Internal Organization/Efficiencies

5. User Conflicts

6. Personnel

7. User Fees/Revenues

8A. Law Enforcement

8B. Information Dissemination

9. Advisory Bodies/Public Appointments

10. Academic Outreach

Use of the Products. The products provided the director and senior managers with printed documentation of where the agency stood at a certain point in time, namely, January of 1986, and where it perceived its future to lie. A videotape on the executive seminar series was produced. This allowed the director to distribute copies of the videotape, interpreted as an "electronic memorandum", to others in the agency to help them understand the process used in the redesign work. Specific assignments were made following the prescriptions shown in Figure 10.18.

Conclusions. The work helped managers of NMFS to identify significant anticipated problems to be confronted in the future. It helped them organize the direction in which the agency should move ahead, and assess its current positioning to accomplish goals. While the time did not permit choice of options, the Options Field remains available to develop several design alternatives that can be compared through tradeoff analysis, if desired.

The Generic Design processes provided a forum for sharing views, for learning about NMFS programs, and for creating group cohesiveness. The majority of the managers noted that the processes facilitated open and effective communication. They believe perspectives changed that produced clearer understanding of agency direction. The Director stated that "Many participants have given up turf and have looked at a broad range of issues. The process got people thinking, just as it was supposed to...We have done an excellent job of laying out [the problems and options] and putting them in fairly decent order."

A followup survey conducted six months after the conclusion of the work shows that 18% of the participants believed that some of the objectives produced during the work had been achieved as a direct result of the work. When asked about improvements in their decision-making ability, 9% of those sur-

Fisheries Management

Mission Statement: To maintain or improve levels of real economic return for fisheries through programs designed to conserve and manage living marine resources and their habitats at the least cost and regulatory burden, and programs to improve utilization of U.S. fishing resources and maximize consumer benefits. In conducting these programs, F/M will make maximum use of advanced technology, seek user fees, and minimize conflicts among users.

- To manage national and international LMR (fisheries) for optimum yield (2)

- To establish the regulatory framework necessary to maximize U.S. industries' competitiveness in world markets (3)

- To resolve user conflicts (5)

- To make maximum use of advanced technology (6)

- To increase consumption of U.S.-produced fishery products (8)

- To achieve effective LMR conservation and management at the least cost and regulatory burden (10)

- To prevent fishery habitat loss (11)

- To implement a national fisheries policy (16)

- To provide maximum opportunity for consumers to derive the nutritional and health benefits of fishery products (17)

- To manage protected species to achieve population levels necessary for delisting (22)

- To increase the use of underutilized species (25)

- To recruit and maintain the best scientific and management minds (26)

- To establish and maintain the staff capability to manage change (28)

- To maintain or improve real economic return to users (36)

- To prevent the loss of fisheries habitat through management, abatement, and alternative development (41)

- To collect resource user fees (63)

- To provide a climate that would allow U.S. industry to be more competitive in foreign trade (71)

- To protect endangered or threatened species (78)

Fisheries Sciences

Mission Statement: To provide data, information, and expertise in an effective and efficient manner for decision-making.

- To resolve user conflicts (5)

- To make maximum use of advanced technology (6)

- To increase consumption of U.S.-produced fishery products (8)

- To improve predictive capability by enhancing understanding of ecosystem resource dynamics (12)

- To implement a national fisheries policy (16)

- To provide maximum opportunity for consumers to derive the nutritional and health benefits of fishery products (17)

- To recruit and maintain the best scientific and management minds (26)

- To establish and maintain the staff capability to manage change (28)

- To provide the best data to meet agency objectives (90A)

- To implement an effective, efficient information system (90B)

Fisheries (Director)
(Program Planning, Congressional Affairs, Management and Budget)

Mission Statement: To provide the leadership and environment and to accomplish all agency goals and objectives.

- To resolve user conflicts (5)

- To make maximum use of advanced technology (6)

- To restrict the government role to those matters which the industry cannot do for itself (13)

- To allocate fiscal and human resources consistent with realistic policies (14)

- To create an organic fisheries policy (15)

- To implement a national fisheries policy (16)

- To have no more pet projects (19)

- To develop new management team (24)

- To recruit and maintain the best scientific and management minds (26)

- To establish and maintain the staff capability to manage change (28)

- To maintain or improve real economic return to users (36)

- To achieve one federal fisheries presence (42)

- To improve NMFS stature and image (48)

- To collect resource user fees (63)

- To implement an effective, efficient information system (90B)

Figure 10.18 Assignment of intentions to offices or units of the National Marine Fisheries Service.

1) Policies/Legislation/Roles

- Evaluate existing legislation and authorities dealing with fisheries and habitat (1)

- Clarify role of government in common property resources (7)

- Develop a strategy for gaining acceptance by the administration, Congress, and our constituents for our new mission (#36), goal (#8), and objectives (#17, #2, #10, #11) (9)

- Create inter-industry commission to develop national fisheries policy (15)

- With the Office of Management and Budget, develop and seek Congressional passage of a comprehensive organic fisheries act that defines federal fisheries role (16)

- Realistically examine our current activities with a view of stopping or transferring those inconsistent with our mission goal and objectives (23)

- Identify National Marine Fisheries Service control and catalytic roles (28)

- Establish operational policies commensurate with changing times and legislation (30)

- Improve management institutions/infrastructure by focusing on end-use/users (36)

- Develop the means to honestly broker the termination or transfer of unneeded or inconsistent activity (38)

- Amend Fisheries Conservation and Management Act to define optimum yield in terms more beneficial to the consumer (43)

- Reassess our international fisheries objectives (62)

- Establish a national Fisheries Management Council review body to deal with conflicts between Councils and national management problems (79)

- Gain passage of marketing council legislation to provide industry the basis to handle all marketing activities (86)

- Establish a long range science policy and program (90)

- User referendum system for Living Marine Resources decisions (98)

- Place into the private sector fishery development (10)

- Identify and continually address our public trust responsibilities (102)

- Promote legislative clarification and simplification of national policies to guide National Marine Fisheries Service programs (104)

TIE LINE

2A) Data/Information

- Participate in an international system for the collection of economic, social and political data, e.g. to enhance international trade (58)

- Establish as number one priority a data management system to allow proper collection and use of fisheries data (67)

- Establish a national mandatory reporting system for all marine resource users (89)

- Establish a national fishing craft/vessel federal permit system (95)

- Establish a non-enforcement domestic inspection service to reduce vessel survey (97)

- Develop a nation-wide commercial and recreational statistics collection system using uniform data collection methodologies and procedures and based on a uniform funding mechanism (126)

2B) Living Marine Resources Management

- Improve management/regulatory process (National Marine Fisheries Service and Councils) (61)

- Improve mechanisms to rapidly assess and adjust fishery management measures to meet goals/objectives (71)

- Have an informed regional/national fisheries management decision body that takes into account the stock assessment, social/economic, and resource utility options (73)

- Establish management regimes sensitive to variable biological, social, and economic conditions to achieve comprehensive balanced management of all fishery elements of large ecosystems (77)

- Where practical, transfer harvest rights and resource management responsibilities to user groups (92)

- Legislatively establish property right concept for all fisheries cost of maintenance to be born by owners/commissions established to arbitrate inter-fisheries conflict (108)

Figure 10.19 Part of the options field for designing the National Marine Fisheries Service of the 1990's. (Continued on the next page)

5) User Conflicts

- With Council participation, establish a process to develop policies to resolve user conflicts (18)

- For priority resource units, specify and report options to minimize or mitigate conflict among resource user groups (65)

6) Personnel

- Promote greater interchange of personnel between National Marine Fisheries Service and state agencies, related federal agencies, the Office of Management and Budget, and Congressional staff (6)

- Develop a program to send National Marine Fisheries Service to work in industry (17)

- Promote hiring/training to increase the acceptance of economic/business expertise in Living Marine Resources decision-making (26)

- Develop specific mobility and training requirements for employee development (33)

- Devise system for hiring scientists, allowing pay scales and career ladders at higher levels so that they may remain in science (44)

- Establish an equitable performance-based personnel system throughout fisheries (45)

- Enhance employee productivity incentives by specifying criteria for bonus awards (48)

- Structure and initiate a comprehensive training program to prepare our managers for the l990s (52)

- Develop a career training program for stock assessment, socio- economic, decision-maker types within the agency to meet the needs of the priority resource units (91)

- Require rotation within program area and among Fisheries Management Councils for promotions above GS-12 (103)

- Increase the use of temporary (1 to 2 year) assignments to other federal, state and public agencies (105)

- Increase contacts between National Marine Fisheries Service and industry, particularly at the GS-7 through GS-12 levels (107)

7) User Fees/Revenues

- Establish a team to make recommendations concerning user fees/auction systems (32)

- Identify and gain acceptance for user-fees as a means of financing all our programs (63)

- Provide for public access to real-time and historical data under user-pay system (84)

- Replace the foreign allocation system with an auction system (94)

TIE LINE

Figure 10.19 Part of the options field for designing the National Marine Fisheries Service of the 1990's. (Concluded) veyed stated that their ability to make decisions in their departments had improved significantly, while 41 percent stated that their ability had been "somewhat improved". Of those surveyed, 45% reported "no change", and 5% said that their ability had "somewhat decreased". No further followup has been possible.

10.4 Applications to Program Management in the United States Department of Defense.

Three applications to Program Management in the United States Department of Defense are included: (a) designing an information system for the Defense Advanced Research Projects Agency (DARPA), (b) developing a conceptual design for improvements in defense systems acquisition, and (c) defining the job of the program manager in the Department of Defense.

Case PM-1. Designing an Information System for the Defense Advanced Research Projects Agency (DARPA) [This Case description was contributed by Dr. David Keever and reviewed by Mr. Brian Sosdian of DARPA]

Summary. The conceptual design of a computerized information system (IS) at the Defense Advanced Research Projects Agency (DARPA) was initiated to develop a consensus on the system goals and user requirements. A senior management group identified 32 critical issues for a next-generation design configuration, developed 44 management goals, and organized 24 of these goals in a support structure.

Using this information, DARPA's User Group, a formal committee representing agency-wide user needs, developed 260 functional options/requirements, organized these into 19 functional categories, and prioritized the categories. A group of computer system specialists developed a preliminary translation of selected goals and requirements into technical options for conceptual prototyping based on the management and User Group information.

As a consequence of this conceptual design activity, a new $2 million computer system was selected and ordered by senior management, consistent with the design requirements.

Background. DARPA is a U. S. Department of Defense agency entrusted to sponsor annually approximately $1 billion of industrial and university research projects to keep the U. S. defense community alert to new and emerging sciences and technologies. To assist the approximately 100 program managers and 75 support staff members in tracking and managing several hundred multi-year, multi-million dollar projects, a computerized information system has been used since the early 1970's.

The long-term planning and redesign of an IS for DARPA has been a festering problem for over 15 years. Issues of standardization, employing the latest technology, networking, and software capabilities are in a continuous state of planning and re- evaluation, rendering the current information system unsatisfactory to many of the users. Before the project described here began, a long-range planner at DARPA spent about two man-years and $300,000 applying conventional methods (surveys, time-motion studies, external consultants, etc.) to develop a conceptual design of the next generation IS. As of May, 1987, he had yet to get a consensus on overarching goals and design requirements among senior managers and the DARPA user community.

Stages. The application of the Generic Design Science for the conceptual design of the IS at DARPA involved a 3-part, 8-day strategy comprised of participative design activities involving different stakeholders. First, senior DARPA managers established, during a one-day session, a consensus on the critical issues and goals for the next generation IS through a combination of NGT and ISM. Second, the User Group (already established within DARPA) developed, over 7 days, all functional requirements of the proposed next-generation IS using the Options Field/Options Profile methodology. Working with the goals and functional requirements, a group of computer consultants and contractors (both within and outside of DARPA) further developed the specifications for many of the requirements. Finally, an outside support contractor incorporated the requirements into the agency's current update of its information systems plan.

Phase 1. Goal Setting for the Next Generation Information System. To prepare the senior managers for the development of goals for the next generation information system, the Deputy Director of DARPA, Dr. Craig Fields, provided the context and two primary criteria for the design project. Most important was the need to save the time of DARPA program managers in dealing with non-technical and administrative tasks. Next in importance was the need to develop a sophisticated, attractive IS which would aid in recruiting high-quality program managers and support staff. System cost constraints were minimal, but it was important to develop a reasonable set of prototype designs within six to nine months.

Given these more important points as the context for the design activity, 11 senior managers and program managers assembled for one day to identify critical issues and management goals for the system. The NGT was applied to generate and clarify a list of 32 critical issues affecting the development, installation, and operation of the system. The triggering question was:

"What are the critical issues in designing the
DARPA information system?"

367

In responding to this, participants developed a common understanding of critical concerns. Next the NGT was again applied with the same group responding to a different triggering question:

"What management goals should be achieved in the
design of the DARPA information system?"

A total of 44 goal statements was obtained and clarified. The ISM process then was used to develop a support structure among 25 of the top vote-getting goal statements. The structure produced is shown in Figure 10.20.

The following generic question was used as part of the ISM process:

"In the context of designing the next-generation
DARPA information system,
does achievement of goal A
significantly support
achievement of goal B?"

The need for improved, flexible communication through the use of integrated databases was one of the major goals of the senior managers. Many senior managers were being hampered by an existing computer system that required too much learning time of users; had awkward, isolated databases and structures; and was more of a hindrance than a support to their program management activities.

Phase 2. Development of Functional Requirement Options. The DARPA User Group, composed of 12 staff members and 2 program managers, assembled for 7 days to develop the functional requirements of the IS based on the critical issues and goals established by the senior managers. Having reviewed the materials developed by the senior managers, the User Group members were asked to generate design options using NGT and the triggering question:

"What are design options for the next-generation
DARPA information system?"

The design dimensions were sequenced for purposes of choice-making among options using ISM and the following generic question:

"In the context of designing the next-generation
DARPA information system,
is the choice of an option in
category A

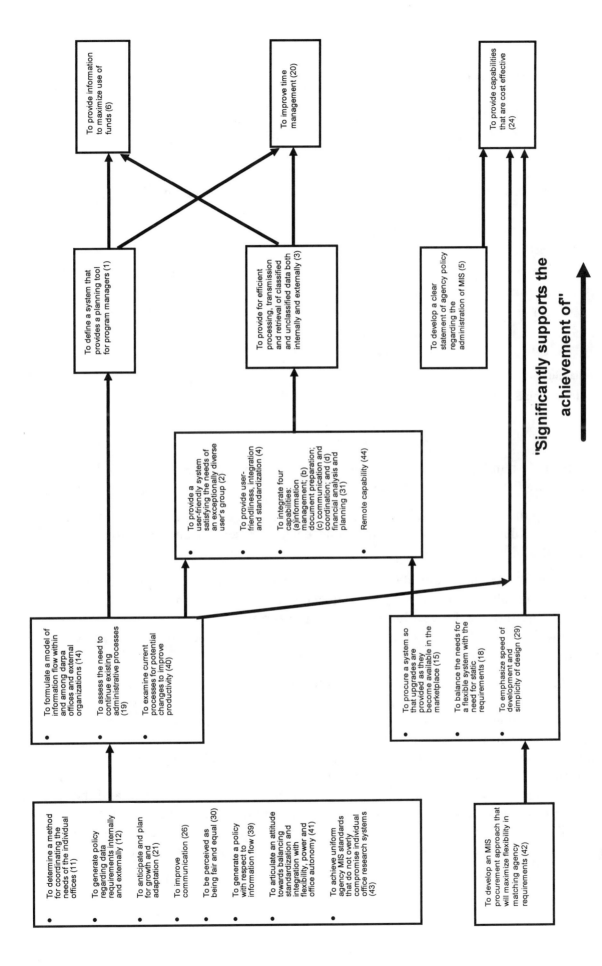

Figure 10.20 Intent structure for DARPA information system.

> of higher relative significance than
> the choice of an option
> in category B?"

The sequenced design dimensions that were produced by this means were:

1A. Program Execution	1B. Image	2. Program Control
3. Programmatics	4A. User Friendly	
4B. System Response	4C. Data	5A. Access
5B. Communication	6. Policy	
7A. External Database	7B. Administrative Support	
7C. Tools	7D. Document Automation	
7E. Database Access	7F. Storage	8. Security
9. Reliability and Maintainability		
10. Information Exchange		

Serially-numbered dimensions, such as 4A and 4B, indicate strong interdependence during the selection of options.

Using the Options Field, the User Group members developed two preliminary Options Profiles of functional requirements, each representing an Alternative Design for the Information System.

Phase 3. Development of Conceptual Technical Prototypes. A group of eight technical specialists worked independently with the two Profiles developed by the User Group to guide the development of technical prototypes. This 6-month activity was coordinated by the Broker and initially involved briefing sessions of the activities of the senior managers and the User Group.

Phase 4. Selection of the Preferred Information System Alternative. Selection of the final configuration was made easier for senior managers by the technical specialists' development of just two alternatives. Both configurations used a mini-computer as the central depository for a collection of integrated databases for tracking, budgeting, and scheduling DARPA research programs. Connected to this central computer were a local area network and about 100 personal computers. The two design alternatives differed in the type of personal computers to be selected and the interfacing software. The preferred alternative was chosen mainly because of its capability to tap the central database with ease, involving minimal user training, and its capability to produce business graphics for program manager presentations.

Uses of the Products. The outcomes from this design project include:

- An integration of managerial views into a DARPA-wide consensus on the next-generation IS

- Development of functional requirements consistent with top-management goals for IS and organizational information-handling requirements

- Identification by technical specialists of technical considerations

- Avoidance of unproductive, seemingly endless, planning meetings to discuss information systems

Conclusions. A consensus was reached on goals and functional requirements for the next-generation DARPA information system. The preferred configuration that emerged consisted of about 150 microcomputer work stations connected to each other and to a microcomputer through a local area network. It will contain centralized databases for project budgeting, scheduling, and tracking. This configuration was significantly different from the one proposed 18 months earlier by an external consulting organization.

During the design activity, the Broker noticed and reported several findings. The most difficult problem encountered was the bridging of the user-technical group interface caused by different vernacular, incomplete description by users and technical specialists of technical needs, less than full participation by various stakeholders (DARPA program managers and technical consultants), and a reluctance to abandon design methodologies that had failed in the past.

Among the outcomes were the recognition (a) that the critical issues were about 80 percent human-based and only about 20 percent technically-based, (b) that the strategy of addressing critical management issues early was more important than premature detailed delineation of technical specifications (which is contrary to typical information system design practice), and (c) that the Generic Design Science provided a proper foundation for conducting a complex system design effort.

Case PM-2. Developing a Conceptual Design for Improvements in Defense Systems Acquisition. [This Case description was contributed by Dr. David Keever]

Summary. The United States Department of Defense (DoD) became engaged with the methods of Generic Design Science in a series of five workshops to improve program management of smart munitions acquisition. The workshops were conceived in response to a directive by the Under Secretary of Defense for Acquisition, USD(A), for recommendations for aggressive changes in the acquisition process for smart munitions, to produce a more effective program.

During August and September of 1988, four three-day workshops were conducted in collaboration with the Defense Systems Management College (DSMC) to assist groups of program managers from various mission area programs to:

1) Identify and clarify inhibitors to meeting the objectives of the smart munitions acquisition program

2) Organize the inhibitors in an influence structure

3) Generate and organize options for improving the performance of smart munitions acquisition program managers

4) Develop alternative design profiles (recommendation packages) for improving smart munitions acquisition program management

Participants in the four workshops were chosen from four distinct smart munitions programs, which were:

- Air-to-Surface
- Surface-to-Surface
- Surface-to-Air/Anti-Submarine Weapons (ASW)
- Air-to-Air/ASW

There were 41 program managers in the four mission area workshops. Of these, 19 represented the defense industries and 22 were from the government.

At the conclusion of the four workshops, 295 critical factors that inhibit fulfillment of cost and schedule objectives were defined, 274 solution ideas were proposed, and 14 alternative design profiles were advanced.

During October, 1988, a Task Force of representatives from each mission area workshop and senior officials representing acquisition management organizations from within the Office of the Secretary of Defense and the Services, was convened to synthesize the results of the previous four workshops and to design specific action programs. The objectives of the Task Force design activity were:

1) To review and understand the solution ideas (options) proposed in the mission-area workshops

2) To organize the options into specific projects for implementation

3) To specify roles and responsibilities among the various entities in the acquisition management arena

The Task Force developed support structures for implementation of options in three project areas and assigned responsibility for implementation to the major entities involved in the acquisition system.

Participants felt that the design experience was educational, permitting managers of diverse backgrounds from industry and government to share different perspectives on common problems. The fact that the workshops were held represented a strong commitment from the Office of the Secretary of Defense (OSD) "to increase attention, focus, and importance of smart munitions programs", in the words of one participant. The majority of the participants expressed reservations, however, that their efforts would result in any substantial changes in the existing smart munitions acquisition system. Nevertheless, they felt that the openness of communication during the workshops enabled them to reach consensus on many problems and proposed solutions.

Background. In October, 1987, the Deputy Secretary of Defense directed the Under Secretary of Defense for Acquisition to conduct a Secretarial Performance Review of Smart Munitions Programs. The review, conducted in May of 1988, identified deficiencies in the areas of cost, schedule, and performance. In response to the findings, the Chairman of the Conventional Systems Committee (CSC) of the Defense Acquisition Board (DAB) was asked by the Under Secretary to recommend changes in the smart munitions acquisition system.

Under the direction of OSD, a series of workshops to address program deficiencies and generate solutions was planned jointly by the Center for Interactive Management (CIM) and DSMC, the agency responsible for educating program managers. DSMC selected program managers from both government and industry to serve as participants in each of the four mission-area workshops. The Task Force was composed of representatives of each mission-area workshop and senior officials from OSD and the Services.

According to the Brokers for this work, Mr. Anthony Melita of OSD and Professor Henry Alberts of DSMC, the Generic Design processes were chosen for this series of workshops because past experience with these processes had demonstrated their applicability to complex problem resolution.

Stages. Five three-day workshops were held in a 2 1/2 month period extending from August 1, 1988 to October 14, 1988. All were conducted by a facilitator skilled in the design methods, and all sessions were held in the Demosophia facility described in Chapter 8. A total of 41 acquisition program managers from industry and the Services participated in the four mission-area workshops, representing smart munitions programs from each of the mission areas. The Task Force, consisting of 12 participants, was assembled following the four mission-area workshops to address the entire set of proposed solutions. The intent was to synthesize the results produced by mission-area participants and translate the ideas into a set of implementable action projects.

Each of the four workshops produced an influence structure of inhibitors. Options for improving performance were generated and organized into similarity categories. Finally, working in two teams, each mission-area workshop produced two Options Profiles.

The Task Force reviewed the options in each of three major project categories: "Improving Program Manager Authority", "Budgetary Consideration", and "Improving Requirements", and made extensive amendments. After amendments and augmentations by the Task Force, 15 projects had been defined. The participants then developed support structures for implementation of options in each of these. After developing the structures, the Task Force identified individual or collective agencies that should have primary responsibility for implementation of each option in each structure.

The present case study discusses one mission area workshop (Air- to-Surface) and the results of the Task Force effort in one project area, "Improving Program Manager Authority".

Phase 1. Developing a Structure of Inhibitors. Nominal Group Technique was used to generate lists of inhibitors to meeting cost and schedule objectives of the smart munitions acquisition program. The triggering question used to focus responses was:

"What are the critical factors which inhibit your ability
to meet cost and schedule objectives?"

The process of identifying and clarifying contributions from participants in each of the four workshops took approximately three hours. The participants in all mission-area workshops generated a total of 295 critical issues through the NGT process, representing a broad spectrum of concerns.

The participants in the Air-to-Surface workshop generated 93 issues and then voted on the relative importance of the issues in order to establish a subset of inhibitors for structuring. Thirty-four issues received at least one vote and were included in the subsequent structuring. The ISM process was used in the next step. The generic question was:

"In the context of improving your ability to meet
cost and schedule objectives, does
factor A
significantly increase the severity of
factor B?"

The structuring sessions in each workshop typically lasted about 3-1/2 hours. The structure developed in the Air-to-Surface workshop is shown in Figure 10.21. As shown there, an aggravation relationship was used. In the judgment of the participants, the existence of a specific issue may aggravate or increase the severity of one or more other issues. The two most basic inhibitors are "Dilution of program manager's authority (# 3) and "Absence of specification tailoring" (# 13). The inhibitors in this cycle of critical factors are mutually aggravating, i.e., the existence of # 3 aggravates # 13 and vice versa. It was also the judgment of participants that these two inhibitors individually and collectively increase the severity of all other inhibitors appearing in the structure.

Structural maps displaying the same relationship were produced in similar fashion by participants in the other three mission-area workshops.

Phase 2. Developing an Options Profile. The second phase involved generating and organizing design options for improving program manager ability to meet cost and schedule objectives in the smart munitions acquisition system. This task required two full days of group work. Using NGT, managers generated, clarified, and edited 274 options based on the triggering question:

> "What are options (solution ideas) which,
> if implemented, will improve your performance
> as program manager?"

The options were organized into similarity categories using the ISM process in each mission-area workshop. The following generic question was used:

> "In the context of developing plans for
> improving your performance as program managers, does
> option A
> belong in the same category
> as option B?"

After judgments of similarity were complete and dimensions were established, participants were asked to develop a sequence for use in choice making. The following generic question was used:

> "In the context of developing plans for
> improving your performance as program managers, should
> a choice of an option in category A
> be made before or at the same time as
> a choice of an option in category B?"

The resulting structure developed in the Air-to-Surface workshop is shown in Figure 10.22. The dimensions from the Options Field are arranged in sequential order for choice making (select options first in dimension A, next in dimension B, and so on),

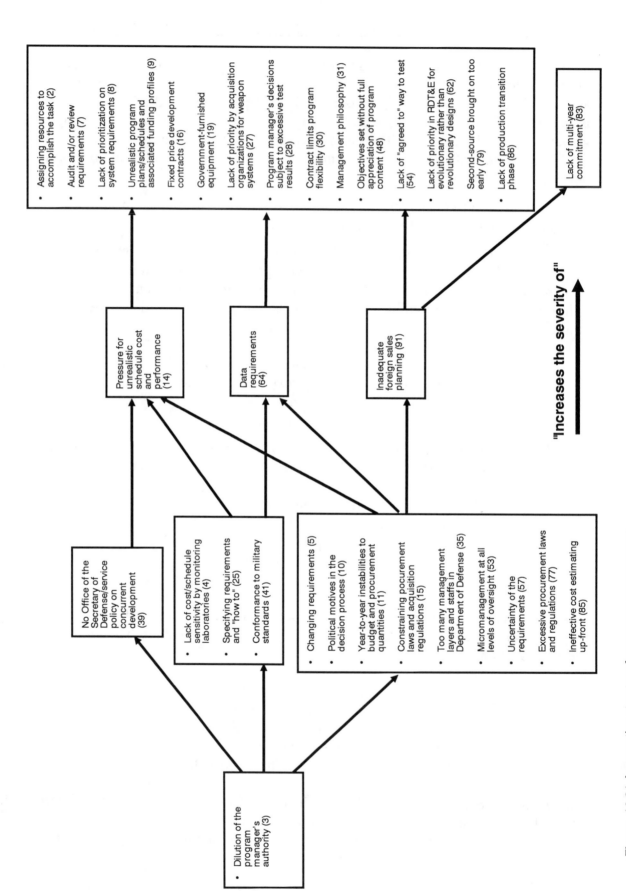

- Assigning resources to accomplish the task (2)
- Audit and/or review requirements (7)
- Lack of prioritization on system requirements (8)
- Unrealistic program plans/schedules and associated funding profiles (9)
- Fixed price development contracts (16)
- Government-furnished equipment (19)
- Lack of priority by acquisition organizations for weapon systems (27)
- Program manager's decisions subject to excessive test results (28)
- Contract limits program flexibility (30)
- Management philosophy (31)
- Objectives set without full appreciation of program content (48)
- Lack of "agreed to" way to test (54)
- Lack of priority in RDT&E for evolutionary rather than revolutionary designs (62)
- Second-source brought on too early (79)
- Lack of production transition phase (86)

Lack of multi-year commitment (83)

Pressure for unrealistic schedule cost and performance (14)

Data requirements (64)

Inadequate foreign sales planning (91)

No Office of the Secretary of Defense/service policy on concurrent development (39)

- Lack of cost/schedule sensitivity by monitoring laboratories (4)
- Specifying requirements and "how to" (25)
- Conformance to military standards (41)

- Changing requirements (5)
- Political motives in the decision process (10)
- Year-to-year instabilities to budget and procurement quantities (11)
- Constraining pocurement laws and acquisition regulations (15)
- Too many management layers and staffs in Department of Defense (35)
- Micromanagement at all levels of oversight (53)
- Uncertainty of the requirements (57)
- Excessive procurement laws and regulations (77)
- Ineffective cost estimating up-front (85)

- Dilution of the program manager's authority (3)

"Increases the severity of"

Figure 10.21 Aggravation structure for program management.

A1. Acquisition Executive Responsibilities

- Establish policy to strengthen the acquisition function within the services and Office of the Secretary of Defense (1)
- Streamline program managers reporting to service acquisition executor (3)
- Satisfy program cost and schedule impacts to policy and directive changes at the implementation point (5)
- Provide concise program manager charter (12)
- Eliminate layers of those who can micromanage (14)
- Insulate authorized program funding from micromanagement by Office of the Secretary of Defense/service comptrollers (15)
- By policy, reduce matrix influence on a program decision (25)
- Streamlining initiatives (26)
- Authorize program managers funding flexibility and real-time tradeoffs (27)
- Require audits and program reviews be directed only by acquisition executives (29)
- Base decisions on real data (34)
- Avoid fixed-priced in development contracts (40)
- Streamline program documentation reviews (41)
- Eliminate layers of staff management (43)
- Streamline on-going program reviews to deal with only parameters outside of established limits (44)
- Select experienced, successful leaders as key program managers (45)
- Use established criteria for selection of program managers (46)
- Allow flexibility in regulations with- out excessive approval process (53)
- Require Department of Defense and service staffs to focus on policy vice programmatic issues (70)
- Simplify the decision process for joint service procurement (75)
- Streamline contract negotiations and award procedures (78)
- Require better flowdown direction for implementing procurement policy legislation (81)
- All policy and directive changes affecting acquisition programs must be issued by Office of the Secretary of Defense/service acquisition executors to the PEOs to the Program Managers (82)

A2. Laws

- Deconflict laws and regulations (31)
- Reduce the level of social program efforts within acquisition direction (56)
- Reduce congressional staffs (67)
- Reduce debilitating laws and regulations (71)
- Eliminate Small Business Administration requirements when not cost effective (76)
- Eliminate competition requirements when not cost effective (77)

B. Independent Test and Evaluation

- Permit testing to return to basics (38)
- Limit the independent testers' roles and powers (47)
- Consolidate "independent" test agencies into a single responsible and responsive organization (52)
- Establish a policy on testing smart weapons (61)
- Independent test agency must be responsible directly to Office of the Secretary of Defense acquisition executive (83)

C. Program Stability

- Stabilize the requirements (2)
- Baseline and commit to long-term program financing (11)
- Use established programming and budgeting process to support requirements (20)
- Establish a difinitive written plan encompassing schedule, funding, and progress measurement (21)
- Encourage multi-year commitment (28)
- Use planning tools which establish macro limits on critical program requirements (32)
- Define program quality and reliability goals at program initiation (50)
- Establish realistic success criteria (54)
- Require development of logistics and related support elements at program initiation (58)
- Consider foreign military sales potential at program initiation (59)
- Provide a better balance of priorities for weapons versus platforms (62)
- Commit to the acquisition strategy/philosophy formulated at program milestone one (66)
- Establish configuration audit plans at initiation (80)

TIE LINE

Figure 10.22 Options field for design of alternatives. (Continued on next page)

D. Program Manager Authority	E1. Program Flexibility	E2. Innovation		E3. Costing Improvements	E4. Teamwork
• Hold monitoring laboratories responsible for cost/schedule impact (4)	• Place more emphasis on the use of Contractor Furnished Equipment versus Government Furnished Equipment hardware (39)	• Identify several programs as test cases for implementing new ideas. (6)	• Emphasize evolutionary design through improvements to existing weapon systems (68)	• Emphasize need for production transition cost and schedule implications (17)	• Allow more open military/industry interaction (19)
• Eliminate matrix management at the program office level (7)	• Require joint review of applicable specifications with every solicitation (13)	• Use air force "model installation program" procedures to reduce nay-sayers influence DOD-wide (10)	• Develop means for military services to combine procurement of like components (72)	• Improve the cost estimating function/process (35)	• Make selected contractor team a key partner and responsible participant in Department of Defense team (33)
• Establish and staff program office with authority and responsibility (9)	• Require tailoring consideration of all applicable specifications (16)	• Encourage innovation (22)	• Emphasize P³I initiatives (73)	• Enhance methodologies for the cost/technical estimators (36)	
• Stabilize personnel assignments within the program offices (24)	• Task government and industry Special Projects Offices (SPO's) to jointly tailor mil-standards now (18)	• Establish an environment that encourages risk-taking without fear of retribution (23)	• Promote contractor quality program incentives (74)	• Recognize and provide management reserve budgets (48)	
• Allow program managers more flexibility in hiring, rewarding, and retaining qualified personnel (65)	• Increase the use of procurement to performance specifications versus data packages (37)	• Develop and implement an on-going approach that sorts the easily achievable requirement objective from the more difficult (30)	• Implement realistic contractor incentives and penalties for contract performance (79)		
• Allow program managers to incorporate critical changes quickly (69)		• Allow mistakes (49)			
		• Develop a policy that permits concurrent development and production (55)			
		• Allow test/demonstration of innovative acquisition approaches (63)			

Figure 10.22 Options field for design of alternatives. (Concluded)

except that, by convention, choices in dimensions that lie in a given cluster (e.g., A1 and A2) should be made collectively because of the interdependence of the choices. The Options Fields for each of the other workshops were interpreted similarly.

With the Options field in hand, participants divided into two small groups and generated two sets of Options Profiles. The selection of options was based on criteria established for this work by Mr. Anthony Melita (OSD), namely, "specificity" and "priority".

Phase 3. Developing a Support Structure. Before the Task Force convened, a "project team" comprised of Mr. Melita (OSD) and Prof. Alberts (DSMC) classified the universe of options from the four mission workshops into 11 preliminary project categories. As the Brokers for this work, present at each workshop, Mr. Melita and Prof. Alberts had the continuity and context expertise needed to make these preliminary judgments. Classification was based on the team's recollection of the explanations accompanying each option, using the participants' comments as reflected in the workshop reports as memory aids. The preliminary project categories were developed as a way to give a starting point to the Task Force work. The Task Force was not constrained by these preliminary categories. The participants were encouraged to make augmentations and amendments as they saw fit. Members reviewed a list of 79 options in the category "Improving Program Manager Authority". Substantial changes were made in the preliminary list. After additions, deletions, or movement to other project areas, 21 options were left in the project area "Improving Program Manager Authority". In voting on the relative significance among the 21 options, 18 received at least one vote as being among the 5 most significant. Due to time constraints, the Task Force support structure contained just 14 of the options.

Participants used ISM to organize the 14 options. The following generic question was used:

"In the context of improving program manager authority, will
option A
help achieve
option B?"

After the support structure was produced, the Task Force assigned responsibility for implementing each option to the major players in the acquisition arena, namely, the Office of the Secretary of Defense, the Services, the Office of the Joint Chiefs of Staff, the Congress, and Industry, according to their understanding of existing law and accepted practice. The result of this work is shown in Figure 10.23.

Use of the Products. The products of the first four workshops were used by the Task Force, after amendments and augmentation, to develop support structures for three project areas [9]. The influence structures and options profiles developed in all four mission-area workshops appear in appendices to a comprehensive report to the Under Secretary of Defense for Acquisition [10]. The support structures devel-

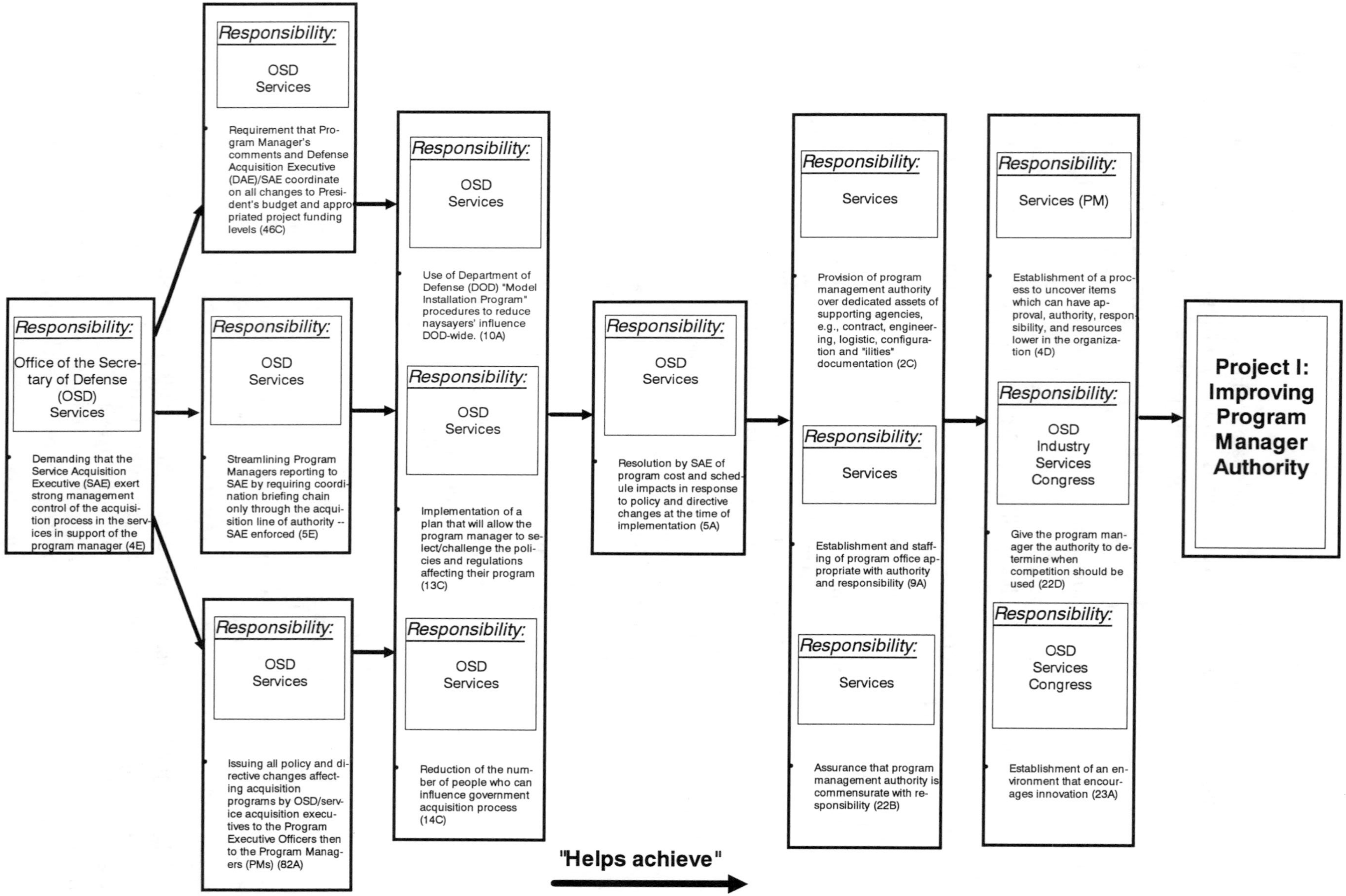
Responsibility:
Office of the Secretary of Defense (OSD) Services
Demanding that the Service Acquisition Executive (SAE) exert strong management control of the acquisition process in the services in support of the program manager (4E)
Responsibility:
OSD Services
Requirement that Program Manager's comments and Defense Acquisition Executive (DAE)/SAE coordinate on all changes to President's budget and appropriated project funding levels (46C)
Responsibility:
OSD Services
Streamlining Program Managers reporting to SAE by requiring coordination briefing chain only through the acquisition line of authority -- SAE enforced (5E)
Responsibility:
OSD Services
Issuing all policy and directive changes affecting acquisition programs by OSD/service acquisition executives to the Program Executive Officers then to the Program Managers (PMs) (82A)
Responsibility:
OSD Services
Use of Department of Defense (DOD) "Model Installation Program" procedures to reduce naysayers' influence DOD-wide. (10A)
Responsibility:
OSD Services
Implementation of a plan that will allow the program manager to select/challenge the policies and regulations affecting their program (13C)
Responsibility:
OSD Services
Reduction of the number of people who can influence government acquisition process (14C)
Responsibility:
OSD Services
Resolution by SAE of program cost and schedule impacts in response to policy and directive changes at the time of implementation (5A)
Responsibility:
Services
Provision of program management authority over dedicated assets of supporting agencies, e.g., contract, engineering, logistic, configuration and "ilities" documentation (2C)
Responsibility:
Services
Establishment and staffing of program office appropriate with authority and responsibility (9A)
Responsibility:
Services
Assurance that program management authority is commensurate with responsibility (22B)
Responsibility:
Services (PM)
Establishment of a process to uncover items which can have approval, authority, responsibility, and resources lower in the organization (4D)
Responsibility:
OSD Industry Services Congress
Give the program manager the authority to determine when competition should be used (22D)
Responsibility:
OSD Services Congress
Establishment of an environment that encourages innovation (23A)
Project I: Improving Program Manager Authority
"Helps achieve"

Figure 10.23 Support structure (project sequence) for improving program manager authority.

oped by the Task Force appear in the main body of that report. It contains recommendations for changes in the smart munitions acquisition system in the areas of program manager authority, budgetary considerations, and requirements. Recommendations for assignments of primary responsibility for implementation of such changes also appear in the report.

Conclusions. According to Mr. Melita, the structure of high-priority factors that inhibit program manager ability to meet cost and schedule objectives yielded a deep logic portrayal of the interrelationships among the inhibitors for each of the mission-area workshops. This deep logic pattern is a valuable source of information for decision making in the acquisition system (primarily defined in terms of roles, responsibilities, and resources). By structuring the high-priority inhibitors using an aggravation relationship, the participants were able to identify and distinguish between symptomatic and fundamental concerns.

There was also a realization that the problems in meeting cost and schedule objectives were generic to acquisition within the DoD, and not merely specific to the smart munitions arena. Many of the problems and solutions developed by the participants were a restatement of inhibitors and solutions already set forth in previous studies of the DoD acquisition system (e.g., studies by the Grace Commission, the Packard Commission, and the Carlucci Initiatives). Evidently it remains to be seen whether the leadership and management strength needed to carry out these recommendations can be found within the federal government.

Case PM-3. Defining the Job of the Program Manager. [This Case description was contributed by Professor Henry Alberts]

Summary. The Defense Systems Management College (DSMC) used the methodology of Generic Design Science to:

- Define tasks performed by Defense Acquisition Program/Technical Managers

- Develop significantly improved understanding of critical issues

- Generate suggestions to improve performance of those tasks

As a result of this initial application of Generic Design Science, change in form and content of a major educational effort was accomplished.

Background. The Defense Systems Management College is responsible for professional education of individuals who serve as Program Managers for Defense "Major Acquisition Programs". A Major Acquisition Program is defined as one which is expected to exceed $200 million in Research, Development, Testing, and Evaluation (RDT&E) funds, or $2 billion in procurement (manufacturing and subsequent phases of system life cycle) funds. The kind of education required by Program Managers clearly depends upon the demands of the job they will perform.

During the period from 1981 to 1983, the U. S. Navy conducted a survey of many of its Program Managers and their supervisory chains of command. The questions were formulated to permit construction of the nature of the Program Management job from their responses. The basic survey tried to determine the kinds of "tasks" performed by Program Managers, and the percentage of time they spent in performing those tasks. Respondents were also asked to state particular kinds of training or education which they felt would help them to perform those tasks better. As a result of that effort over 400 discrete tasks were "identified" and grouped within some general heading categories such as "administer/monitor contracts".

An analysis was also carried out to determine how much time was spent in performance of the various tasks identified. This analysis was inconclusive in that no pattern could be found which appeared to be useful in devising a curriculum perceptively better than that already in place. Respondents' suggestions for training and educational opportunities were generally within already existing DSMC curriculae.

During June of 1987, DSMC recognized an opportunity to examine the issue again. The Technical Managers Advanced Workshop (TMAW) had been designed in response to a 1982 market survey conducted by DSMC among Technical Management persons serving within the Department of Defense and industrial organizations [11]. TMAW had been traditionally structured as a one-week ("short") course: morning sessions of lectures and discussions, followed by afternoon sessions during which participants chose and pursued subjects for group study and issued reports on their work.

During the years between 1982 and 1987 there had been substantive changes both in Program Manager operating environment and the application of the technical disciplines to defense acquisition. There had been increasing Congressional involvement in the management details of particular acquisition programs, and computational technology had advanced rapidly. June of 1987 seemed a good time to redefine the educational needs of Technical Managers and design a course format and content around them.

An additional factor was the exposure in December, 1986, of some of the DSMC faculty to the Generic Design processes and their subsequent judgment that the processes might be useful for specialized kinds of educational functions within DSMC. In order to capitalize on this kind of thinking, the TMAW Course Director decided to gather together a small number of specially-selected representatives from each Service, DoD agencies, and the Congressional Staff, to redefine the functions which Program and Technical Managers perform, and to generate ideas for helping them to become more efficient in performing those tasks. The desired end results of TMAW 88-1 were to:

- Understand Program/Technical Manager tasks and performance inhibitors at a broader level than had been possible from the previous Navy study

- Develop a set of needs for improved educational emphasis

There was one further consideration. It was hoped that by focusing on major acquisition problems and potential problem solutions, the work would be useful during transition between the Reagan and (what was to become) the Bush administrations.

Stages. The work can be viewed as taking place in two stages. In the first stage, an operational definition of the development activities performed by the Managers was found and placed in perspective. In the second stage, initiatives for improving the conduct of the work were generated, organized, and placed in perspective.

Stage 1. Initially the NGT was used to elicit a list of descriptors of the work performed by the Managers. The triggering question was:

"What are descriptors of the acquisition work we do?"

Three hours were spent identifying and clarifying the contributions made by the group members. The 74 descriptors generated by the group appear in Table 10.7. The numbers in the Table refer only to the order in which the ideas were generated by the group.

Table 10.7
Descriptors of Defense Acquisition Managers' Tasks

---

1. A new technology is developed, integrated into a product, and offered to a customer.
2. Manage a seven-step process for system acquisition.
3. Identify future needs and assure within limited resources that programs are developed and survive that have high return on investment.
4. Defend budgets.
5. Provide schedules.
6. Rob from the rich and give to the poor.
7. Manage change.
8. Make cross-program reviews of acquisition strategies to identify completeness, application of resources, and efficiencies.
9. Identify scopes for systems and environments of projects.
10. Define technical requirements to meet the threats.
11. Acquire resources.
12. Strive to maximize value-added.
13. Interpret and clarify directions and requirements.
14. Ensure good communications.
15. Manage a program to deliver a quality product within schedule and budget and at a profit.

16. Develop trusting relationship with customers.
17. Assure no programmatic "dropball".
18. Renegotiate contract terms.
19. Monitor progress.
20. Fight for deserving programs, Pentagon, OSD, and Congress.
21. Help assure that the users'/operators' needs are met.
22. Define economic position of project.
23. Develop program schedules.
24. Clarify accountability and expectations of personnel and organizations.
25. Counter the threat.
26. Plan projects.
27. Assess and manage risk.
28. Keep customer satisfied and informed.
29. Minimize in a vicious manner the number of people associated with the program.
30. Participate in the "Program Obligation Memorandum (POM) Process".
31. Translate engineering terminology into a description of military capability.
32. Prepare and negotiate contracts.
33. Ensure mission area is balanced and each program is executable.
34. Aggressively defend programs against various staff levels in Washington.
35. Define dependence on foreign sources.
36. Manage the procurement process for acquiring and delivering systems.
37. Plan for requirements changes during period of deployment.
38. Develop business strategies.
39. Establish goals.
40. Report progress and accomplishments, and failures.
41. Control engineers' desires for change after design is established.
42. In an autonomous mode, conceptualize, design, develop, produce, test, and support a
    product that meets or exceeds customers' needs.
43. Justify a broad-based technology program to allow quick response to technology surprises.
44. Conduct engineering investigations.
45. Determine systemic, procedural, or policy problems.
46. Answer questions or write papers.
47. Clarify mobilization aspects of the project.
48. Perform liaison with other government activities, Congress, and contractors.
49. Get around obstacles created by groups with divergent accountabilities.
50. Direct long-term investment planning.
51. Recruitment.
52. Apply lessons-learned to improve process.
53. Ensure research and development supports or leads to cutting- edge products.
54. Sponsor briefings/develop management consensus.
55. Clarify industrial base capability for projects.
56. Support competition.
57. Mentor the young.
58. Review performance.
59. Carefully assign work.
60. Determine ways to get around the system.
61. Clarify competing forces for industrial-based capability.
62. Monitor technology maturation.
63. Acquire technical information.
64. Develop ad hoc teams.
65. Delineate model for resources and industrial capabilities.
66. Control technology transfer.

67. Recognize when a program should go from specialized management to common DoD.
68. Foreign military sales.
69. Foster technology transition.
70. Conduct design reviews.
71. Enjoy your work.
72. Create an ethical environment.
73. Reward technical excellence.
74. Budget fiscal and personnel resources.

Following the identification and clarification of the task elements, each group member was asked to identify the 5 most important tasks in the set of 74. Those considered of highest importance were then placed into similarity groups (dimensions) using the ISM process with the following generic question:

"In the context of our acquisition work,
does descriptor A
belong in the same class with
descriptor B?"

More than 5 hours elapsed in carrying out this activity, including considerable modification to the initial set of categories arrived at with the ISM process. Ultimately six dimensions were defined by the group, and each of the descriptors was incorporated within some member of this set of dimensions. The group then selected names for the dimensions. Figure 10.24 shows the Task Field produced by this work.

Participants were then asked to order the dimensions according to the relative difficulty of carrying out the tasks. Using ISM a second time, the generic question was:

"In the context of our acquisition work,
is dimension A
of higher relative difficulty than
dimension B?"

Figure 10.25 represents the order of difficulty of performing tasks in each dimension, as perceived by the TMAW 88-1 group. Although Foreign Military Sales was initially selected as the "least difficult" category of tasks performed, it was later separated from the mainstream of tasks and placed alone as a separate, but important, part of all work done. At this point, the first stage of the work was completed and it was time to proceed to the second stage.

1. **Planning and Programming (Internal Focus)**

- Provide schedules (5)

- Make cross-program reviews of acquisition strategies to identify completeness, application of resources and efficiencies (8)

- Assure no programmatic "dropballs" (17)

- Develop program schedules (23)

- Plan projects (26)

- Establish goals (39)

- Determine systemic, procedural, or policy problems (45)

2. **Requirements Definition and Technical Proposals**

- A new technology is developed, integrated into a product and offered to a customer (1)

- Identify future needs and assure within limited resources that programs are developed and survive that have high return on investment (3)

- Define technical requirements to meet the threats (10)

- Interpret and clarify directions and requirements (13)

- Help assure that the users'/operators' needs are met (21)

- Counter the threat (25)

3. **Resourcing (External Focus)**

- Defend budgets (4)

- Rob from the rich and give to the poor (6)

- Acquire resources (11)

- Fight for deserving programs: Pentagon, Office of the Secretary of Defense, and Congress (20)

- Define economic position of project (22)

- Participate in the Program Obligation Memorandum process (30)

- Insure mission area is balanced and each program is executable (33)

- Aggressively defend programs against various staff levels in Washington (34)

- Define dependence on foreign sources (35)

- Clarify mobilization aspects of the project (47)

- Recruitment of people (51)

- Sponsor briefings/develop management consensus (54)

- Clarify industrial base capability for projects (55)

- Support competition (56)

Figure 10.24 Task field for defense program management. (Definition of the acquisition work technical managers perform.) (Continued next page)

4. Leadership

- Manage change (7)
- Strive to maximize value-added (12)
- Insure good communications (14)
- Develop trusting relationship with customers (16)
- Clarify accountability and expectations of personnel and organizations (24)
- Assess and manage risk (27)
- Keep customer satisfied and informed (28)
- Minimize in a vicious manner the number of people associated with the program (29)
- Develop business strategies (38)
- Perform liaison with other government activities, Congress, and contractors (48)
- Get around obstacles created by groups with divergent accountabilities (49)
- Mentor the young (57)
- Determine ways to get around the system (60)
- Develop ad hoc teams (64)
- Recognize when a program should go from specialized management to common Department of Defense (67)
- Foster technology transition (69)
- Enjoy your work (71)
- Create an ethical environment (72)

5. Foreign Military Sales

- Foreign military sales (68)

6. Program Execution

- Execute a program to deliver a quality product within schedule and budget and at a profit (15)
- Renegotiate contract terms (18)
- Monitor progress (19)
- Prepare and negotiate contracts (32)
- Report progress and accomplishments, and failures (40)
- Control engineer's desires for change after design established (41)
- In an autonomous mode, conceptualize, design, develop, produce, test, and support a product that meets or exceeds customers' needs (42)
- Conduct engineering investigations (44)

Figure 10.24 Task field for defense program management. (Definition of the acquisition work technical managers perform.) (Concluded)

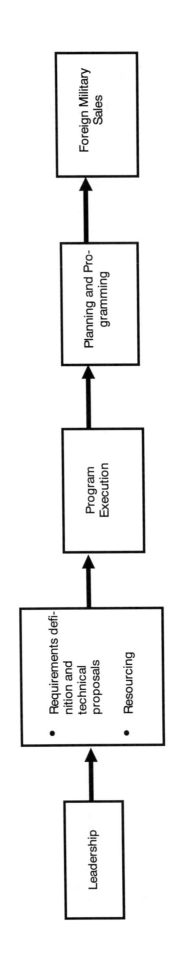

"Is of higher relative difficulty than"

Figure 10.25 Relative difficulty structure for dimensions.

Stage 2. The group was then asked to generate ideas about how the acquisition process might be improved. The NGT triggering question was: "What initiatives will foster (improve) the work we do in acquisition?"

About four hours were spent in identifying and clarifying 80 initiatives, which appear in Table 10.8.

Table 10.8
Initiatives for Improving Defense Acquisition Work

---

1. Create sound economic policy and strategy.
2. Appropriate one lump sum to each Military Department.
3. Plan to realistic expectations.
4. Strive for stabilized funding.
5. Focus the program technical tasks to the limit of budget stability.
6. Develop baseline programs at the highest national level.
7. Establish a rigorous presumption against new starts.
8. Give the project manager authority appropriate to responsibility.
9. Simplify acquisition rules.
10. Must stabilize program resourcing.
11. Provide stability of program funds.
12. Change rules on appropriations to allow flexibility.
13. Generate Requests for Proposals which will allow more free rein for solution.
14. Have a centralized requirements bureau to define a global strategy to meet the threat.
15. Revise the method by which funds reductions are allocated.
16. Decrease the number of people who say "no" and hold those who do accountable.
17. Enhance the ability to monitor the systems and allow fruitful communications to flow up and down.
18. Define functional/operational interfaces to demonstrate technology advantage.
19. Do not allow yourself to get locked into defining programs too early.
20. Establish a system of accountability that will assure the public that poor performers are held accountable without creating disincentives to risk-takers.
21. Develop a meaningful incentive system for the management team.
22. Establish realistic common goals.
23. Disestablish DCAA and DCAS; incorporate DCAS functions into PMO acquisition management improvements.
24. Lessen inter-Service requests for funds for similar equipment.
25. Allow each service to keep 15% management reserve for funding changes for new starts.
26. Judicious use of MIL Standards and MIL Specs.
27. Commercialize doing business with the government.
28. Move waiver approval for non-executable legislative requirements to a lower management level.
29. Rationalize or reduce the number of efforts; decrease FSED starts.
30. Improve leadership skills to include motivation of people.
31. Establish a single DoD acquisition agency.
32. Index economic determinants for program duration.
33. Standardize Service approaches and requirements.
34. Utilize Strategic Business Units (SBU) technique in program formulation.
35. Deal with the influence of traditional associations, industry and individual congressmen on military procurement and facilities.
36. Reduce non-productive reporting requirements.

37. Incentivize contractors to bring a good product to the market--do not legislate the product.
38. Apply AFR 800-29 to more programs.
39. Increase our ability to reward people/performance (do away with GM system).
40. Improve PM tools to make corrections.
41. Accept the European-Japanese model and make managerial and technical competence a criterion for manager selection.
42. Make people aware of consequences of politicizing programmatic investment.
43. Grant a 5-year budget program on acquisition.
44. Contractor visit and understand the user in the trenches.
45. Prioritize programs--cut the ones you can't afford.
46. Defend and budget for P3I and formalize T2 (Technology Transfer).
47. Enhance ability to keep up with threats and projected threats.
48. Review and revise life-cycle concept.
49. Develop common knowledge base for all projects in special office.
50. Improve systematic flexibility.
51. Require DoD to conduct more controlled test of acquisition management improvements.
52. Reduce the number of government checkers.
53. Mechanize system to minimize time from program initiation to program incorporation.
54. Foster dialog with users, developers, industry, technologists.
55. Eliminate the DoD/IG, DoD level test guys.
56. Accept rational expectations for project performance and explain rationale to public (be honest).
57. Enhance the dialog within services.
58. Loosen restrictions on travel and communications systems.
59. Provide each service a budget to spend to the plans they have presented.
60. Reduce impediments to information flow.
61. Make scapegoats a professional category.
62. Create a more capable workforce.
63. Improve the quality of threat projections.
64. Focus on building trade with Russia, China, and Third World.
65. Do not require that we see proof of the threat before we counter it.
66. Provide more public evidence of threat.
67. Require each Service to cut down the number of systems being developed.
68. Streamline data releasability to friendly nations.
69. Have value-added gate on new legislation.
70. Allow military officers and acquisition personnel no continuous staff duty.
71. Cut Congressional staff and OSD by 50%.
72. Review rules affecting the retired military.
73. Ask the development community for anticipated impact prior to implementing new legislation.
74. Limit Requests for Proposals to five pages.
75. Assess the cost impact of specifications, standards, and procedures implementation.
76. Rationalize our organizational structure.
77. Make managerial competence a prerequisite for managerial positions.
78. Get people in program office and staff out to the field.
79. Delineate clear functions, responsibilities, and accountability.
80. Require foreign content analysis related to political/economic impact statements.

Each group member was asked to select the five initiatives that he felt would help most to improve acquisition performance. Then participants were asked to structure the initiatives according to how they were interrelated through the use of ISM with the generic question:

"In the context of fostering our work,
will implementation of initiative A
significantly support
implementation of initiative B?"

The map (support structure) that resulted from this work appears in Figure 10.26.

Use of the Products. The products were made available in a report issued to all of the Managers who attended. The managers asserted that the results were extremely valuable.

Conclusions. The results of TMAW 88-1 were far-reaching in an educational sense. Each subsequent TMAW has used the methodology of Generic Design Science to explore acquisition issues first developed in TMAW 88-1. Specifically,

1) TMAW 88-2 addressed the issue of managing change -- that single descriptor of acquisition management selected as of high importance by 8 of the 15 group participants.

2) A series of 5 additional workshops was held during the period from July through October of 1988 to address particular problems of Smart Munitions Acquisition Programs (see Case PM-2.)

3) TMAW 89-1 used the same approach to explore the question "How can the effect of change be predicted before that change is instituted?"

The TMAW Course Director believes that the methodology provides an extremely useful means to examine and structure complex issues, and he has taken initial steps aimed at developing the capability to use the methodology routinely within DSMC.

10.5 Design for Quality Control of an Industrial Product.

This case describes work carried out by Mr. Steve Landenberger, with consulting assistance from Dr. Robert Waller, on behalf of a large midwestern manufacturer. This work involved an industrial pump. The work brought the acceptance rate at the end of the production process from 49% to 85%.

Summary. A department in the factory of a large midwestern manufacturer was engaged in assembling and testing hydraulic pumps. The pump test machine was rejecting 51% of the pumps arriving at the test machine. A task force was created to determine what was causing the high reject rates. Management set a goal to

391

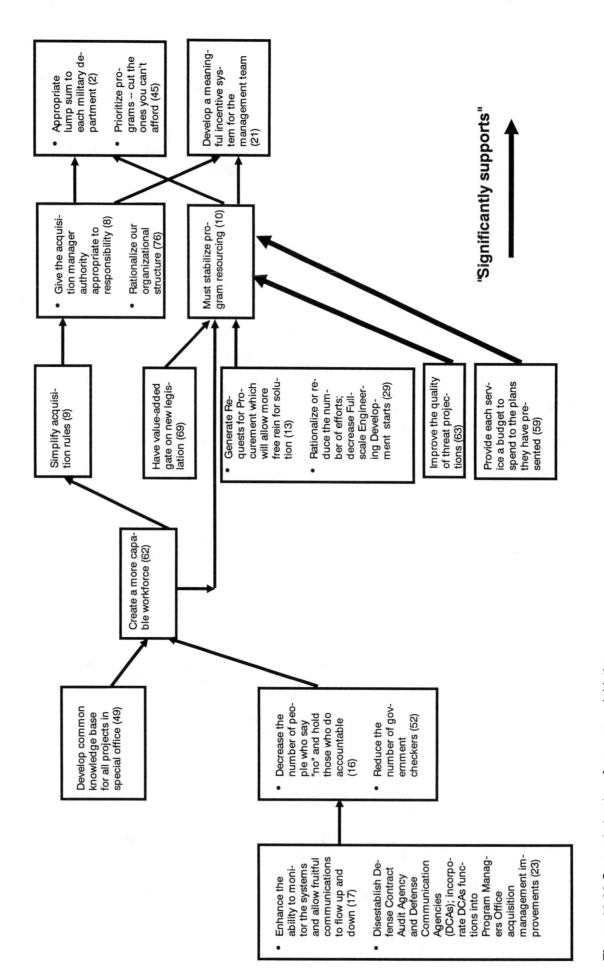

Figure 10.26 Support structure for program initiatives.

achieve 85% acceptance without retest. The task force objective was to develop a plan to achieve the goal of 85% acceptance. Once the plan was approved by management, the task force was responsible for implementation. The task force was able to achieve these goals by creative use of multiple methods.

Background. Extensive and informed use of statistical quality control has been acclaimed as one of the major factors in the ascendence of Japan as a manufacturer of quality products. Well-managed American manufacturers likewise apply statistical quality control. However this approach is best suited to determining that something is wrong in manufacturing, and the magnitude of the problem, and is of lesser significance in determining precisely how to correct the problem.

Mr. Steve Landenberger [12] decided to use a hybrid methodology in which, once statistical quality control practices had identified the severity of the problem, follow-up methods would be used for arriving at a proposal to correct the problem.

Stages. The work was carried out in six stages: (1) use the NGT process to develop an element list of items thought to be contributory to pump rejects, (2) use the ISM process to construct a problematique, showing a hypothesized relationship among the problem elements, (3) use the Kepner-Tregoe (TM) decision analysis technique to decide which elements should be studied and attacked first, (4) gather data to support the proposed implementation sequence, (5) consolidate all the prior information to formulate the required plan, including estimates of impact on reduction of pump rejects, estimated cost, and estimated time to implement and (6) use the consolidated information to develop the recommendations to management.

Stage 1. Generate the element list. The task force, consisting of a product engineer, a manufacturing engineer, a quality control engineer, and a production supervisor were presented with the triggering question:

> What elements are causing rejects on the pump
> test machines?

The group produced the element list shown in Table 10.9.

Stage 2. Constructing the Problematique. The group used the ISM process to structure the 26 elements, using the generic question:

> Does problem A
> contribute to the severity of
> problem B?

Here A and B refer to any two members of the set of 26 elements.

Figure 10.27 shows the structure developed by this process.

Table 10.9
List of Elements Thought to Contribute to Rejection

1) Stroke control valve not stable

2) Sticky pistons

3) Standby pressure setting

4) Piston bore wear

5) Machine controlled outpressure

6) Standby input power of the pump

7) Standby input power of the test machine

8) Contamination

9) Endplay adjustment

10) Pump shaft groove

11) Inlet oil temperature variation

12) Machine inlet pressure variation

13) Test specifications (tolerances)

14) Misalignment of bores on SCV housing

15) Seal drain flow in the pump

16) Valve leaks and/or line leaks in the machine

17) Program not sensitive to break-in

18) RPM variation

19) Auxiliary pressure control, servo control

20) Faulty electrical sensing equipment

21) No feedback from malfunction test stand components

22) Poorly seated stroke control valve

23) Seal drain flow in the test machine

24) Erratic partial flow control of load run

25) Out-of-calibration machine

26) Low pump efficiency

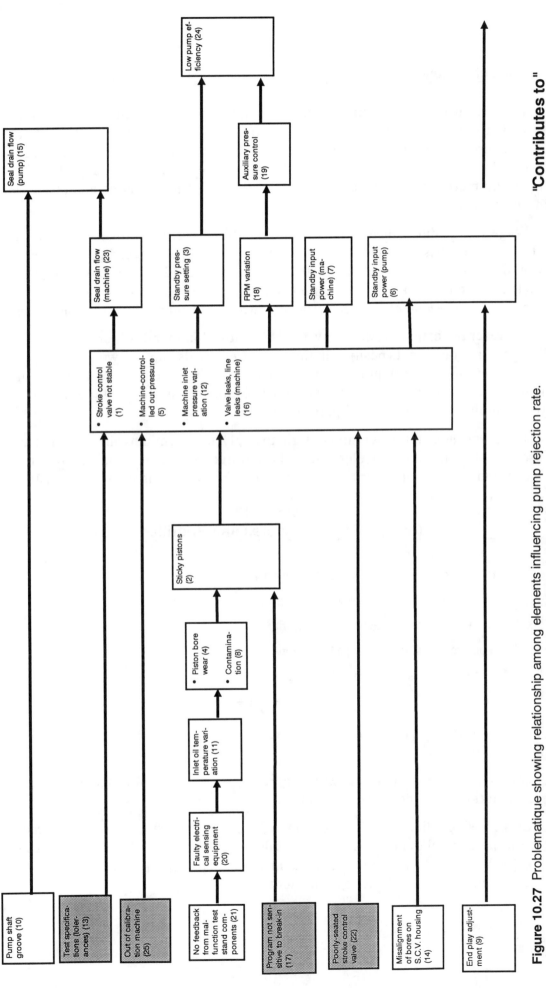

Figure 10.27 Problematique showing relationship among elements influencing pump rejection rate. (Shaded boxes were selected as key problems in resolution of the pump problem.)

"Contributes to" ("aggravates")

Low pump efficiency (24)

Seal drain flow (pump) (15)

Auxiliary pressure control (19)

Seal drain flow (machine) (23)

Standby pressure setting (3)

RPM variation (18)

Standby input power (machine) (7)

Standby input power (pump) (6)

• Stroke control valve not stable (1)
• Machine-controlled out pressure (5)
• Machine inlet pressure variation (12)
• Valve leaks, line leaks (machine) (16)

Sticky pistons (2)

• Piston bore wear (4)
• Contamination (8)

Inlet oil temperature variation (11)

Faulty electrical sensing equipment (20)

Pump shaft groove (10)

Test specifications (tolerances) (13)

Out of calibration machine (25)

No feedback from malfunction test stand components (21)

Program not sensitive to break-in (17)

Poorly-seated stroke control valve (22)

Misalignment of bores on S.C.V. housing (14)

End play adjustment (9)

The structure is of the hybrid type, incorporating two cycles, one with 2 members, and one with 5 members. Members of a cycle negatively influence each other. The condensed structure is a hierarchy of length 8. (The minimum-maximum path length including only the largest cycle is 13, which is the same as the rounded mean value of this metric found by averaging over 31 ISM sessions, as discussed in Chapter 7 and Appendix 5.)

Stage 3. Deciding which elements should be studied first. If Figure 10.27 were used as the sole basis for deciding which elements should be attacked first, element 21 would be the first choice, element 20 would be the second choice, and so on, because the element 21 that has no incoming lines negatively influences many other elements, and the element 20 negatively influences many other elements, and so on.

However the extent to which any one element will influence other elements will depend not only on its position in the structure, but also on its own intensity. Moreover, even if an element is very influential, it may involve great cost and a long time to correct. Thus the choice of a sequence should be based on criteria that go beyond simply what is shown in Figure 10.27.

The team chose three decision criteria to apply in determining the sequence to be used to attack the problem elements. These were: impact on rejects, cost to implement, and time to implement. These three criteria were assigned weights of 10,

---

Table 10.10
Top Five Element Scores and Priorities

22. Poorly seated stroke control valve, 175, Priority 1

17. Program not sensitive to break-in, 160, Priority 2

16. Valve leaks, line leaks, machine, 155, Priority 3

13. Test specifications (tolerances) 153, Priority 4

25. Out of calibration test machines 145, Priority 5

10, and 5 respectively. The application of these criteria produced the results shown in Table 10.10.

Stage 4. Gather data. Data were gathered to support the proposed plans for implementation of the prioritized elements.

Stage 5. Consolidate the information to formulate the plan. All of the preceding work was applied to produce five proposals, one for each problem listed in Table 10.10. Each proposal showed the estimated impact on pump reject reduction, estimated cost, and estimated time to implement.

Stage 6. Develop recommendations to management. It was recommended that management approve the parallel approach to deal with the five high-priority problems. The analysis shows that if these five were pursued along the lines recommended, the acceptance rate could be raised from 49% to 87%. Management approved the recommendations.

Use of the Product. The recommendations became the basis for the quality improvement program. This program was completed, with results very close to what was predicted, as the acceptance rate on the pumps rose to 85%.

Conclusions. The pump quality control problem incorporated complexity that is comparable to that found in numerous studies of problems that do not yield to normal methods. By constructing an approach that relied on systematic application of design tools specifically appropriate to dealing with complexity, in a sequence that recognized the logical foundations of the issue, a favorable result was achieved.

SUMMARY

Applications of the Generic Design Science can be found in any aspect of human life where complexity is present.

Applications have been described in the following five areas: education, economic development, human services, management of defense systems acquisition, and quality control in manufacturing. These applications show the variety of settings in which it has already been applied and illustrate, thereby, the generic nature of the science.

The variety of applications continues to grow and, as the applications develop, the learning that occurs is used to review and, if necessary, modify and update the Science, in line with the concepts set forth in relation to the Domain of Science Model.

As the applications grow, other organizations begin to apply the Science with good results, both within the United States and in other nations of the world.

REFERENCES

1. F. R. Janes and R. Jowitt, "Applications of Interactive Management in Planning for a University Department" in *Systems Prospects* (Proceedings of the International Conference of the United Kingdom Systems Society), Plenum Press, 1989.

2. Roger Volkema (Editor), "Curriculum Workshop: Mathematics for Computer Science", George Mason University, Center for Interactive Management, 1987 (report on National Science Foundation Grant DMC-8615486, John N. Warfield, Principal Investigator).

3. B. J. Broome and A. N. Christakis, "A Culturally-Sensitive Approach to Tribal Governance Issue Management", *International Journal of Intercultural Relations* 12, 1988, 107-123.

4. I. Cromer and R. Kirrish, "Issue Management Forum for the Poarch Band of Creek Indians", unpublished report of the Center for Interactive Management, George Mason University, July, 1988.

5. U. S. Department of the Interior, Bureau of Indian Affairs, letter to Assistant Secretary--Indian Affairs from Deputy Assistant Secretary--Indian Affairs (Operations), 29 Dec., 1983.

6. *Federal Register* 50(75), 18 April, 1985, p. 15502.

7. *Federal Register* 49(113), 11 June, 1984, p. 24083.

8. David J. Mackett, "Strategic Planning for Research and Management of the Albacore Tuna Fishery", *Systems Research* 2(3), 1985, 201-210.

9. M. A. Fiore and A. N. Christakis, "First Report on Improving Smart Munitions Acquisition Management" (Aug., 1988); "Second Report on Improving Smart Munitions Acquisition Management" (Sept., 1988); "Third Report on Improving Smart Munitions Acquisition Management" (Sept., 1988); "Fourth Report on Improving Smart Munitions Acquisition Management" (Sept., 1988); Center for Interactive Management, George Mason University.

10. United States Department of Defense, Office of the Secretary of Defense, "Improving Smart Munitions Acquisition Management", 1989.

11. Dr. Joel Rakow, Vice President of American Training Institute, Manhattan Beach, California, performed the survey work in 1982. It was delivered in 1983, and was the basis for some later study ideas at DSMC.

12. Steve A. Landenberger, "Using Decision Making Tools to Solve Quality Problems", unpublished manuscript, 24 September, 1984.

QUESTIONS RELATED TO CHAPTER 10

1. What three aspects of the Generic Design Science are intended to be illustrated in Chapter 10?

2. What are the five areas chosen to illustrate applications?

3. What are the types of improvements that the examples of applications in education address?

4. Compare Figures 10.1 and 10.2. Discuss how the portrayal in Figure 10.1 relates to that in Figure 10.2.

5. Convert Figures 10.4 and 10.5 into a portrayal like that in Figure 10.2.

6. Convert Figures 10.7 and 10.8 into a prose essay.

7. Convert Figures 10.10 and 10.11 into a prose essay.

8. Discuss whether pediatric nursing can be considered to be a "large-scale system" and a "sociotechnical system". Take advantage of any evidence that might be extractable from the relevant case study.

9. Classify each of the figures in Chapter 10, first as to whether it is an AST and, if it is, to what type of AST it belongs.

10. In relation to Figure 10.21, discuss a possible strategy for correcting problems represented in this map.

11. In relation to Figure 10.23, discuss a possible strategy for carrying out activities shown there. Discuss especially the management of such an activity in terms of such things as who should be in charge, who should monitor the work, who should judge its progress, and who might be involved in trying to scuttle the activity and why.

12. Discuss the case described in Section 10.5 in terms of the "framebreaking and remodeling" considerations and whether this scheme may have been followed in the case.

PART IV

AMPLIFICATION

APPENDIX 1

RELATIONS, LATTICES, STRUCTURAL TYPES, STRUCTURAL METRICS

A1.1 Relations.

The mathematics of relations had its qualitative beginnings with Plato and Aristotle, and revolved around what could be inferred from given or assumed information. The exploration of the various modes of the syllogism was carried forward for hundreds of years in a qualitative and argumentative manner.

After about two thousand years of such studies, it was recognized by Leibniz in the late 17th century that the fragilities and ambiguities resident in natural language were themselves sufficient to denigrate such studies. Instead of condemning science to continue to be constrained by what C. S. Peirce was later to call "the deceit of language", Leibniz proposed the need for a language especially designed for science.

About a century and a half later, in 1847, George Boole published his algebra of logic, and in the same year Augustus De Morgan published a treatise in which he used, for the first time in recorded science, a generic symbol for a relation(ship). Subsequently his work on the theory of relations was extended by others such as Frege, C. S. Peirce, and Schröder. Whitehead and Russell used this developing theory as the basis for the famous *Principia Mathematica*. Soon after its publication, the young Norbert Wiener clarified more precisely the way to interpret the meaning of the term "relation" in mathematics. Kuratowski showed later that the Theory of Relations and the Theory of Sets were largely interchangeable.

Still later, Harary showed that the Theory of Relations could be mapped into the Theory of Binary Matrices [1], and that either could be mapped into the Theory of Digraphs, giving three different mathematical languages that collectively form three languages of relationships.

Later, Warfield [2] developed the theory of a process whereby a large set of elements could be placed into a relationship that satisfied critical conditions of consistency, using the idea of transitivity [known to Peter Abelard in the 12th century, (Sec. 2.4)], that was declared by Peirce to be the essential condition for the validity of the syllogism. This process was designated Interpretive Structural Modeling but, in retrospect, it might better have been called "relationship mapping".

Warfield showed that another theory could also be mapped into the Theory of Relations, this being the Theory of Boolean Inequalities. The capacity to express an extensive set of relationships in any of four mathematical frameworks, and to transform such a set from one language to another, provided great flexibility in choosing the special language that is most suitable for some particular audience or purpose. Moreover this set of four languages of relationships provided a kind of composite generic language to satisfy Leibniz's purpose, capable of being specialized to any particular discipline of science or applications of science.

As a result, it became possible to engage people and computers in collaborative work to develop relationship maps that allow the portrayal and interpretation of deep/long logic. Such portrayals and interpretations are critical to developing, assessing, and overcoming complexity.

The ability to engage people in this way followed after Warfield developed the theory of Interpretive Structural Modeling. This theory, in effect, provided people who wished to deal with complex issues a form of automated Western logic that placed no mathematical demands on them, but merely guided and documented the process of creating the logical structure of a complex issue in any of a large number of possible ways.

One area of study that then assumed importance is how to assure that all of the perceived content of the working space in which the maps are developed can be captured simply by reading walks on maps. In proceeding now to address this topic, some of the pitfalls associated with this topic will be illustrated. Useful supporting theory will be developed in which the familiar relations of arithmetic will be applied in examples. The discussion will also be used to develop a formal understanding of "linear reasoning" which, frequently practiced, tends to promote the mistaken belief that all of the information content of a working space can be perceived intuitively by reading only one map.

The information content of a working space will be defined, and it will be shown that all of the content of the working space can be read from either two or three maps, depending upon the nature of the defined relationships.

A distinction will be made between correctness of a map and completeness of a map. These distinctions provide guidance to those who manage the process of map development, helping to ensure that both correctness and completeness are considered at the time the map is developed and in possible later amendments of the initial map.

Preliminaries [†]

Collection of Elements. Suppose there is given a collection S of elements.

Cartesian Product (Working Space). The Cartesian product S x S = T is called the working space of the structural model (map).

Relation. The statement "R is a relation in the working space" can be stated symbolically in either of the following ways:

a) $R \subseteq T$

b) For all x, the statement that x is contained in R implies (i) the existence of some y contained in S and (ii) the existence of some z contained in S, such that (c) x is equal to the ordered pair (y,z). The ordered pair (y,z) of elements of S is called an edge of the working space.

Transitivity. A relation R is said to be transitive if, given any two edges (a,b) and (b,c) in R, it is also true that (a,c) is in R. Historically, this principle was recognized by Peter Abelard in the 12th century, and arose later in connection with C. S. Peirce's analysis of the syllogism, in the situation where the elements a, b, and c are all different. Yet the standard definition of transitivity does not require that they all be different. The effect of this is to deny easy use of transitivity for any relation that does not contain edges of the form (a,a).

3-Transitivity. We say that a relation R is 3-transitive if it does not violate the standard definition of transitivity, given that it is applied only to the case where the terms a, b, and c are all different.

Transitive Closure. If a relation R is not transitive, there exists in the working space T some increment ΔR such that the union of R with ΔR is transitive, and such that no edge appears in ΔR that is not necessary to make the union transitive. Then $R \cup \Delta R$ is called the transitive closure of R. (An algorithm for finding the transitive closure appears in [2].)

3-Transitive Closure. By analogy with transitive closure, we say that a relation R has a 3-transitive closure R', the latter being found by uniting with R only those edges required to make R' 3-transitive.

[†]   Adapted from J. N. Warfield, "Complementary Relations and Map Reading", Institute of Electrical and Electronics Engineers, Transactions on Systems, Man and Cybernetics, June, 1980, 285-291. Copyright © 1980 IEEE.

Digraph of R. We designate by D(R) a digraph of R, where there is an edge in D(R) for every edge in R except those edges of R whose two elements are identical.

Walk on D(R). A walk on a digraph is a directed path on the digraph with an origin and termination consisting of vertexes of the digraph.

Nontrivial Walk on D(R). A nontrivial walk on D(R) is any walk on D(R) that includes at least two distinct vertexes.

Statement on D(R). By a statement on D(R) we mean an expression of the form aRb, where a is the origin and b is the termination of a nontrivial walk on D(R).

Content of D(R). The content of a digraph D(R) is the set of all statements on D(R).

Valid Statement on D(R). A statement on D(R) is described as valid with respect to a judging group, if that group declares it so by majority vote. (This criterion is simply the normal criterion for judging whether some result is part of a science, i.e., that it be open for inspection and validation, and that a community of scholars tentatively accepts it as valid, without prejudice to future findings; except that because the validity may be a local judgment of restricted import, common sense dictates that the size of the judging community may be considerably smaller than that which pertains to science as a whole, in general being determined by that part of the population that has a motivated interest in the matter being discussed.)

Correct Digraph of R. A digraph D(R) is correct, provided all of its statements are valid. (Later completeness will be distinguished from correctness.)

Partition of a Set. A partition of a set is a collection of its nonempty subsets, called blocks, such that the union of the blocks is equal to the set and the intersection of any two blocks is empty.

Cycle. A cycle in S is a universal relation on a collection $C \subseteq S$. A universal relation on a collection C consists of all members of C x C.

Reachability Matrix of a Digraph. A reachability matrix M of a digraph is a matrix whose main diagonal is filled with ones, such that an entry of one appears in the cell indexed by (a,b) (where a is not equal to b), if and only if there is a walk on the digraph from the origin a to the termination b; otherwise a zero appears in the cell. If there is a walk from a to b, then b is said to be reachable from a.

Digraph Levels. An ordered partition exists on the set of elements of a digraph, the form of the partition being $L_1; L_2; ...; L_n$, where n is the number of levels of the digraph. The blocks of the partition are called levels. Elements in a level are reachable from other elements in the same level if and only if all such elements lie in a cycle. L_1 is the top level and L_n is the bottom level. No element in a given level is reachable from any element in a higher level. For further details, see [2].

406

<u>Condensation of a Digraph</u>. A condensation of a digraph D' is a digraph D", which is formed from D' by replacing every maximal cycle in D' with a single "proxy" element, while preserving all the reachability in D'.

<u>Skeleton Matrix of a Digraph</u>. A skeleton matrix of a digraph is found by (a) finding the condensation matrix of the digraph and then (b) replacing with zeros all those ones that are not essential to preserve reachability. For an algorithm to do this, see [2].

<u>Map</u>. A map is an enlargement of a digraph, where each vertex is replaced by an associated prose statement (that may contain mathematics components) representing the element that corresponds to the vertex, and where a relationship is associated with each walk on the digraph. For convenient reading, the prose statements will normally be enclosed in boxes, and the arrows will be drawn from the top of each box to the bottom of the box(es) that it reaches; or if the map is drawn horizontally, the arrows will be drawn from the right side of each box to the left side of the box(es) that it reaches.

<u>Disjoint Relation Pair</u>. If R' and R" are any two relations in the working space T, we say that they are disjoint if their set intersection is empty.

<u>Covering Relation Pair</u>. If R' and R" are any two relations in T, we say that they are a covering relation pair, provided their union is equal to T.

<u>Complementary Relation Pair</u>. If R' and R" are any two relations in the working space T, we say they are complementary (or they are a pair of complements), if they are both a disjoint pair and a covering pair.

The Edge-Classification Partition

It turns out to be very helpful for later analysis if we introduce the idea that a relation R in T induces a partition Π on the working space, called the edge-classification partition, defined as follows:

$$\Pi(T) = I_1; I_2; I_3; I_4; I_5$$

where

(1) For all s such that $s \in S$, (s,s) is contained in I_1, and for all (y,z) such that y is not equal to z and such that (y,z) is contained in T, the following conditions hold:

(2) (y,z) contained in R and (z,y) contained in R implies that both (y,z) and (z,y) are contained in I_2

(3) (y,z) contained in R and (z,y) not contained in R implies that (y,z) is contained in I_3

(4) (y,z) not contained in R and (z,y) contained in R implies that (y,z) is contained in I_4

(5) Neither (y,z) nor (z,y) contained in R implies that both of them are contained in I_5

Names of Edges. Edges of the working space are classified as shown in Table A1.1. The names are assigned to edges according to how the edges relate to the relation R that induces the partition $\Pi(T)$.

Table A1.1
Classification of Edges of the Working Space T

Block of the Partition	Name of Contained Edges
I_1	Trivial
I_2	Cyclic
I_3	Up-Oriented
I_4	Down-Oriented
I_5	Foreign

Pairs of Relations

We now define several types of relation pair.

Definition 1. A Pair of Opposites. We say that R' and R" are a pair of opposites in the working space, provided they are either symmetric opposites or antisymmetric opposites.

A pair of symmetric opposites satisfies (i) $R' = I_1 \cup I_2$ and (ii) $R" = I_5$. An example of such a pair is R' (=) and R" ($\neq$), as interpreted in arithmetic. If a collection S consisted only of integers, then any edge from the collection would fall into one or the other relation, hence this pair would be a covering pair. Any two integers either would be equal or not equal, and no two integers could be both equal and not equal.

A pair of antisymmetric opposites satisfies (i) $R' = I_3$ and (ii) $R" = I_4$. An example of such a pair is R' (<) and R" (>), as interpreted in arithmetic. Such a pair cannot be a covering pair, because all edges having identical elements are missing from the pair.

As interpreted in arithmetic, the antisymmetric opposites would be transitive and hence would be 3-transitive. The symmetric opposites, on the other hand, are not necessarily even 3-transitive. Suppose, for example, that I_5 consists of (3,4),(4,3), (4,5), and (5,4). It is not 3-transitive as seen by the absence of the edge (3,5). On the other hand it would become 3-transitive if the edges (3,5) and (5,3) were appended. It is impossible that any non-null I_5 can be transitive because it cannot contain an edge whose two elements are the same, yet such is necessary for it to be transitive.

Definition 2. A Pair of Converses. We shall say that R' and R" are a pair of converses in the working space, provided:

(i) R' = $I_1 \cup I_3$ and (ii) R" = I_4. An example of such a pair is R being the less than or equal to relationship, and R" being the greater than relationship, both as interpreted in arithmetic. This pair can be covering only when I_2 and I_5 are empty.

Definition 3. A Pair of Cohorts. We shall say that R' and R" are a pair of cohorts in the working space, provided:

(i) R' = $I_1 \cup I_2 \cup I_3$ and (ii) R" = $I_1 \cup I_2 \cup I_4$. An example of such a pair is R' being the less than or equal to relationship, and R" being the greater than or equal to relationship, both as interpreted in arithmetic. The example pair is not disjoint, but would be a covering pair should I_5 be empty. As typically used in arithmetic, both relations would be transitive.

We refer to these pairs in subsequent developments.

Condensibility of Digraphs

We now present two theorems relating to the condensibility of digraphs, which are significant in terms of how reasoning is carried out.

Theorem 1. If I_5 is empty, each level of a digraph D(R) is condensible to a single element.

Proof. Necessarily, if a level of a digraph D(R) is to be condensible to a single element, it must consist of a single cycle (which could be a single element). Suppose that some level is not condensible to a single element. Then there must be at least two elements in that level that are not connected within the level. But then these two elements would represent two foreign pairs (see Table A1.1) in Π and I_5 would not be empty, which violates the premise.

Theorem 2. If I_5 is empty and D(R) has at least two levels, then D(R) is condensible to a linear hierarchy (Chap. 2).

Proof. If I_5 is empty, then by Theorem 1, every level is condensible to a single element. Since every level is necessarily connected to some adjacent level, the condensed structure is necessarily a linear hierarchy. (In the trivial case where D(R) has only one level, D(R) is condensible to a single element, the limiting case of a linear hierarchy).

Linear Reasoning

Linear reasoning can be understood as a form of reasoning that relies on a structure of information corresponding to a digraph which is condensible to a linear hierarchy, i.e., to a situation where I_5 is empty.

That linear reasoning is the basis for arithmetic reasoning can readily be interpreted in the sense mentioned, insofar as the antisymmetric opposites are concerned. For them, I_5 typically is empty, and R' can be interpreted as the order defined on the number system using the relationship "is less than", while R" can be interpreted as the order on the number system using the relationship "is greater than".

A similar interpretation is readily developed for the converse pair where, once again, I_5 is empty, and a like situation holds as well for the cohort pair.

Only in working with symmetric opposites do we observe a situation where I_5 is not necessarily empty. Using the arithmetic relationships "equals" and "does not equal" as an example, we note that the digraph of each member of a pair of symmetric opposites consists of a single level, and that the relationship "does not equal" is, in general, intransitive.

We conclude that when the condition that I_5 is not empty applies, it can be taken as a signal that reasoning should depart from ordinary intuitive assumptions and rely on more careful structural analysis. Such reliance is made possible by an understanding of how to read information contained on digraphs, which will be discussed subsequently.

Also it is noted that in general none of the opposites, converses, or cohorts are covering pairs, which is further reason to be suspicious of applying methods commonly associated with structures that are condensible to linear hierarchies.

Content of the Working Space

In its most general form, we mean by the content of the working space T all of the valid statements that can be constructed using edges from T. This means literally that all conceivable relationships involving edges of T are part of the content of T.

In what follows we restrict the meaning to consist of all of the valid statements that can be constructed using a relation R and its complement R_c, except for trivial statements involving edges like (a,a). The exclusion of the trivial edges is for convenience and can be relaxed in particular applications. However, relaxation would require modest amendments to what follows.

The restriction to a single relation and its complement involves no loss of generality. If we are able to develop a method for finding the content corresponding to a single complementary pair, the same method can be applied to all other relations, thereby satisfying the need to conduct poly-relational studies.

To proceed with the specific discussion of content, we find it convenient to define the <u>primary relation R</u> in the working space as $R = I_1 \cup I_2 \cup I_3$, and we assume henceforth that the primary relation is transitive. (Such an assumption is consistent with the use of the Interpretive Structural Modeling process to produce a transitive relation, thereby rendering a relation that can be taken as primary.) With this assumption, I_2 and I_3 are necessarily 3-transitive. We define the <u>secondary relation</u> in the working space to be the complement of the primary relation $R_c = I_4 \cup I_5$. Because the primary and secondary relations form a covering pair and are disjoint, if given either it is possible to compute the other. Thus if a modeling group arrives at the primary relation, a computer can determine the secondary relation.

If the primary relation is judged to be incorrect, the group can always amend it by deletion. However the primary relation may be correct without being complete. Correctness can be judged simply by reading walks on the map of R, using a method to be discussed. Completeness cannot be so judged. A correct relation may be incomplete simply because the existence of one or more edges that should be in R may not have been perceived while the group was engaged in developing the primary relation.

In the interests of being concise, we now bring together in one theorem many of the conditions concerning how to assure that a relation is complete or correct.

<u>Theorem 3</u>. Given that R is transitive, a necessary and sufficient condition that

(i)   R is complete is that R_c is correct

(ii) R_c is correct is that R is complete

(iii) D(R) is complete is that R is complete

(iv) R is complete is that D(R) is complete

(v)   R is correct is that D(R) is correct

(vi) D(R) is correct is that R is correct

(vii) D(R_c) is correct is that R is complete and R_c is 3-transitive

(viii) D(R_c) is correct is that R_c is both correct and 3-transitive.

Theorem 3 helps establish the relationships between the relations and their digraphs. Notice that the conditions that apply to the primary relation do not generally apply to the secondary relation. The former is transitive, while the latter is not.

411

Completeness is of concern only with respect to R and D(R). If these are complete, this assures that R_c is correct, but it does not assure that $D(R_c)$ is correct. This will be illustrated in an example to follow.

The completeness of D(R) refers to the condition that all valid statements of the form aRb in T are represented by walks on D(R). The fact that completeness of D(R) and completeness of R are equivalent stems from the assumed transitivity of R.

Additional insight may be gained into the differences between the primary and secondary relation through Theorem 4.

Theorem 4. Given that the primary relation is transitive, the content of T can be obtained by reading all of the statements on D(R) and $D(R_c)$ provided R is complete and I_5 is empty.

The proof of this Theorem appears in [3].

Reading a Map Via Walks

While most of our discussion involves digraphs, in practice we are more interested in maps (Interpretive Structural Models) based on digraphs. Let us consider an example that will be used first to illustrate map reading and, later on, to illustrate the general theorem that will be offered for obtaining the content of the working space.

Example. Figure A1.1 shows a reachability matrix M corresponding to a certain primary relation R.

Figure A1.2 shows the corresponding skeleton matrix [2].

$$
M = \begin{array}{c|ccccccc}
 & 1 & 2 & 3 & 4 & 5 & 6 & 7 \\
\hline
1 & 1 & 1 & 0 & 0 & 0 & 0 & 0 \\
2 & 1 & 1 & 0 & 0 & 0 & 0 & 0 \\
3 & 1 & 1 & 1 & 0 & 0 & 0 & 0 \\
4 & 1 & 1 & 0 & 1 & 0 & 0 & 0 \\
5 & 1 & 1 & 1 & 1 & 1 & 0 & 0 \\
6 & 1 & 1 & 0 & 1 & 0 & 1 & 0 \\
7 & 1 & 1 & 1 & 1 & 1 & 0 & 1 \\
\end{array}
$$

Figure A1.1 Reachability matrix M. Copyright © 1980 IEEE.

	1	2	3	4	5	6	7
1	0	1	0	0	0	0	0
2	1	0	0	0	0	0	0
N = 3	1	1	0	0	0	0	0
4	1	1	0	0	0	0	0
5	0	0	1	1	0	0	0
6	0	0	0	1	0	0	0
7	0	0	0	0	1	0	0

Figure A1.2 Skeleton matrix of reachability matrix M. Copyright © 1980 IEEE.

Figure A1.3 shows a map of the relation R where elements contained in a cycle are shown in the box-bullet form. Also shown there are the levels (i.e., the subsets of S as organized on the map).

It is easy to derive by inspection either of M or of the map, the edge-classification partition induced by R on T. Specifically, the blocks of the partition $\Pi(T)$ are:

$I_1 = \{(1,1),(2,2),(3,3),(4,4),(5,5),(6,6),(7,7)\}$ — dia (x,y) reflex

$I_2 = \{(1,2),(2,1)\}$ — block sym

$I_3 = \{(3,1),(3,2),(4,1),(4,2),(5,1),(5,2),(5,3),(5,4),$
$(6,1),(6,2),(6,4),(7,1),(7,2),(7,3),(7,4),(7,5)\}$ — 0's   ok asym

$I_4 = \{(1,3),(1,4),(1,5),(1,6),(1,7),(2,3),(2,4),(2,5),$
$(2,6),(2,7),(3,5),(3,7),(4,5),(4,6),(4,7),(5,7)\}$ — 1's   asym

$I_5 = \{(4,3),(3,4),(6,3),(3,6),(6,5),(5,6),(7,6),(6,7)\}.$ — sym 0's

Every entry of one in M of Figure A1.1 corresponds to a walk on $D(R)$ and to a statement involving R. By counting ones in M not on the main diagonal, or by counting members of I_2 and I_3, we observe that there are 18 nontrivial walks, hence 18 statements, represented by the map in Figure A1.3.

These can be read systematically. If there are any cycles, they can be read first, one at a time. In the example, we read 1R2 and 2R1.

413

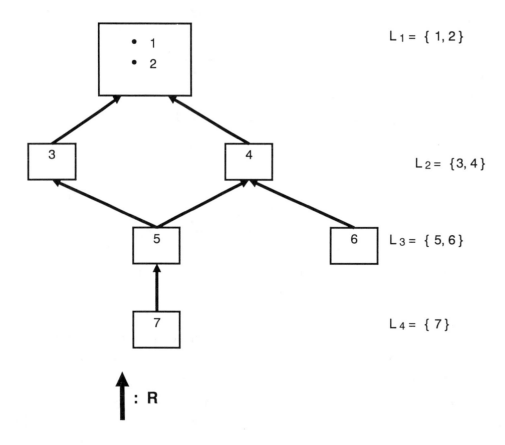

Figure A1.3 Relation map illustrating box-bullet form for cycle. Copyright © 1980 IEEE.

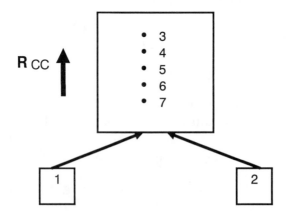

Figure A1.4 Mediator map. Copyright © 1980 IEEE.

We can then read from each lower level to each upper level. For example, from level 2 to level 1 we read 3R1, 3R2, 4R1, 4R2. From level 3 to level 1 we read 5R1, 5R2, 6R1, 6R2. From level 4 to level 1 we read 7R1, 7R2. From level 3 to level 2 we read 5R3, 5R4, 6R4. Continuing in this way, we can systematically read all of the statements represented by walks on D(R) or on the map in Figure A1.3.

General Approach to Content

Now we turn to the question of the general approach to gaining the content of the working space T. We assume that a primary relation is available and is known to be correct, but is not necessarily complete. We further assume that I_5 is not empty, in general. While R is assumed to be transitive R_c is <u>not</u> assumed to be 3-transitive.

<u>Definition 4. Increment Relation</u>. To any secondary relation R_c there corresponds an increment relation ΔR, defined as that relation which must be united with R_c to form the 3-transitive closure of R_c.

Definition 5. <u>Mediator Relation</u>. We define $R_{cc} = R_c \cup \Delta R$ as a mediator relation. It is clearly 3-transitive.

<u>Theorem 5</u>. Any increment relation is 3-transitive.

<u>Theorem 6</u>. If R is complete, then $R_{cc} - \Delta R$ is correct, when interpreted through the secondary relation R_c.

Proofs of both Theorems 5 and 6 appear in [3].

The significance of Theorem 6 is that it furnishes the basis for (a) determining whether R is complete, (b) amending R if it is not complete to make it complete, and (c) reading all of the content of the working space with use of at most three maps. Let us return to the previous example to illustrate these matters.

Suppose that Figure A1.3 represents a correct but not complete map of a primary relation R. From the information in R we are able to find both a mediator map and an increment map as shown in Figures A1.4 and A1.5 respectively. Notice that the latter is a submap of Figure A1.3, as expected.

Now we superimpose the increment map on the mediator map, as illustrated in Figure A1.6. This Figure can be read in the manner given earlier for reading maps, except that those statements corresponding to dashed lines will not be read, as they are known to be invalid when interpreted in terms of R_c.

Suppose now that in reading the mediator map we discover that the edges (1,3) and (5,7) represent invalid statements. That is $1R_c3$ and $5R_c7$ are judged invalid. The respective edges should then be united with the primary relation. Since the latter is required to be transitive, and since uniting these edges with it does not assure that the result is transitive, the transitive closure of the altered primary relation

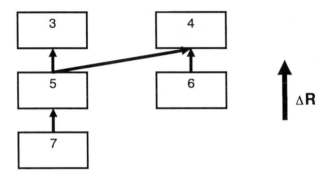

Figure A1.5 Increment map. Copyright © 1980 IEEE.

should be formed, which may take still more edges away from the mediator map. In the example, this requires that edges (2,3),(4,3), and (6,3) be appended to the primary relation and removed from the secondary relation.

The process just described is continued until it is established that all remaining statements on the mediator map other than those represented on the increment map are valid. When this is done, the content of the working space is then fully represented by walks on the primary map (as revised) and the mediator map (as revised), exclusive of those walks on the mediator map that correspond to the increment.

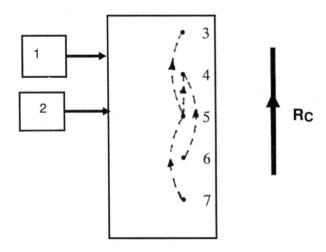

Figure A1.6 Increment map superimposed on mediator map. Copyright © 1980 IEEE.

416

If we envisage a situation where a computer is available to do the necessary structural calculations and present the maps for inspection, we can also imagine that often it will not be feasible to show directly on the mediator map the dashed lines representing the increment map. Thus we can imagine that instead all three maps, the primary map, the mediator map, and the increment map will be made available. Under these circumstances we can summarize what has been said, in Theorem 7.

Theorem 7. When R is transitive and complete, the content of the working space can be read entirely from walks on the primary map and the mediator map, reading only those walks on the mediator map that are not walks on the increment map.

In interpreting Theorem 7, it is only the origin and terminal of a walk that appear in any statement, hence if two walks have the same origin and terminal, they represent the same statement.

Returning to the example, if we assume that no further change is required in R other than what has already been discussed; the revised primary map, the mediator map, and the increment map will finally appear as shown in Figure A1.7.

Association

It is common in the application of mathematics to carry out an operation of association between some concept of importance and some term or concept in a particular mathematical language. Not only is it common, but all of the applications of mathematics depend on this (often-implicit) operation. If, for example, x represents an unknown, one may associate with this symbol the meaning "interest rate", and may then assign to this meaning the value of 6%. Association and assignment are distinct operations, for one attaches meaning, while the other merely attaches an attribute to the meaning.

It is possible to have an abstract "mathematical relation" and to associate to this a specific kind of relationship from a natural or designed language. This is how the Theory of Relations becomes amenable to Applications. As soon as such an association occurs, it becomes possible to begin to assign elements to that relationship that are perceived as being related by it. This is why computers can be used, under appropriate conditions, to manipulate relationships and test their consistency, as well as compute their structural form. This is also why computers can help people organize their qualitative reasoning, and compute a structure of it that displays the deep/long logic. It is also why a generic science can be created, because any generic science requires that one be able to choose from among many concepts the particular one or ones that are to be associated with a given specially-designed language.

The mathematical types of relation can be classed as reflexive, symmetric, asymmetric, transitive, etc. As one must have the flexibility to associate a contextual relation, i.e., a relationship from natural language, with a mathematical relation, the

417

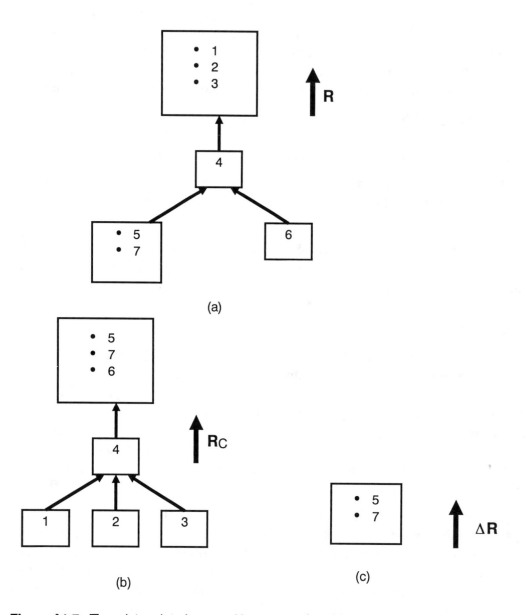

Figure A1.7 Three interrelated maps with content of working space. Copyright © 1980 IEEE.

term "relation" is applied to represent the abstract mathematical type, and the term "relationship" is used to represent a less abstract or more concrete type that comes from the natural language such as "causes", "prefers", "is greater than", "is north of", "is relevant to", "is included in", etc.

418

A1.2 Lattices.

Extensive relationships are portrayable by digraphs. A lattice is an expression of a particular kind of digraph. It is possible, for example, to define rigorous meanings for analysis and synthesis, in terms of lattices.

Analysis

In the purest form of analysis, a high-level concept is divided into a set of second-level concepts, each of which is contained in (or otherwise related to) the higher-level concept. The second-level concepts are then divided into third-level concepts, and so on until further division is judged to be pointless. While such a division has some similarities to what is called "reductionism", such a process is <u>not</u> reductionism. (It <u>could become</u> reductionism, if the lowest level in the structure were taken to represent completely the highest-level concept, and further if the behavior of those lowest-level members, acting in isolation, were interpreted to represent entirely the behavior of the top-level concept.)

This form of analysis by division, invented by Plato and Aristotle, was originally intended to be a means of defining how one concept could be distinguished from another. Notably, to distinguish one concept from another, it is only necessary in principle to demonstrate a sufficient set of attributes or components such that no other concept has that identical set. If, however, the definition is intended to distinguish a class, then all members of the class will have the attributes, but only members of that class may have all of them. The class then has a set of attributes or components such that no other class has that identical set. Individual members of the class may have additional attributes not shared by other members of the class.

While this form of analysis can be taken to define what is meant by qualitative analysis, it should be clear that no restriction was placed upon the division to say that it could not include numerical attributes. To make it clear that this form of analysis is a generic form, one notes that in addition to the development of the lattice, it is possible in some instances to attribute numerical descriptors to some members of the various levels, and that the means of arriving at such numerical descriptors may be through computation or counting. Furthermore, there is no intention to limit the hierarchy to members and classes. On the contrary, the developing branch of mathematics called "category theory" now recognizes an indefinite number of types, with names having been invented for four or five types.

While category theory is in its mathematical childhood, it seems destined gradually to become the successor to the Theory of Relations, though it will itself be founded primarily in that theory. Category theory will relate to the Theory of Relations much as calculus relates to algebra and geometry.

Studies by Hartmanis and Stearns [4] and others, show that divisions themselves can be classified as covers or partitions, and that algebras can be devised that take covers and partitions as the operands. Such divisions thereby become amenable to formal manipulation by computers, if desired.

By applying the mathematics of combinatorics, it is possible to count and tabulate the number of possible partitions of a concept into a prescribed number of blocks. Such means permit decisions to be made on what kinds of partitions appear to be most useful, and on what tradeoffs appear wise between the width and the height of a lattice, in relation to compatibility with human cognitive apparatus.

Consider the question: in how many distinct ways can a set containing n members be partitioned into k blocks? Let the notation $\Pi(n,k)$ symbolize the answer to this question. Then the following theorem [5] applies:

Theorem 8. It is possible to compute the value of $\Pi(n,k)$ from the recursion equation:

$$\Pi(n+1,k) = k\Pi(n,k) + \Pi(n,k-1)$$

and the initial conditions that $\Pi(n,0) = 0$ and $\Pi(n,1) = 1$ for any positive integer n, and any positive integer $k \le n$. (The proof of this Theorem is rather long. Readers who want to see the proof can write to the author for a copy of it.)

Using Theorem 8, values of $\Pi(n,k)$ can be tabulated for small values of n and k as shown in Table A1.2.

Table A1.2
The Number of Ways n Things Can Be Partitioned into k Blocks

n	k	1	2	3	4	5	6	7	8	Sum of Row
1		1	0	0	0	0	0	0	0	1
2		1	1	0	0	0	0	0	0	2
3		1	3	1	0	0	0	0	0	5
4		1	7	6	1	0	0	0	0	15
5		1	15	25	10	1	0	0	0	52
6		1	31	90	65	15	1	0	0	203
7		1	63	301	350	140	21	1	0	877
8		1	127	966	1701	1050	266	28	1	4140

Let us interpret the significance of some of the numbers in the Table. We see, for example, that if n = 3 (i.e., there are 3 members in the set S), there are only 5 possible partitions to consider. Each of them conceptually is an alternative way to imagine working with the set S on some problem or some design task. If the number n is increased by 1 to equal 4, the total number of possible partitions jumps to 15. This value exceeds what the short-term memory can work with, as discussed in Chapter 2. Advancing n to 5 gives a total number 52 of possible partitions.

We see in this brief analysis one of the fundamental reasons why so much suboptimization occurs. People may not consciously decide in the light of a problem situation to restrict the problem so they can adjust to their human limitations. Rather they may just automatically restrict it under the influence of those limitations, and thereby suboptimize.

Among the wide variety of possible examples one can give of situations where the foregoing material is systematically ignored is in the design of high-level computer language. The old language ALGOL 60, for example, incorporates as part of the design of its syntax a situation requiring that the mind recursively (cyclically) comprehend 14 items. That is, if one is to understand any of the 14, one must understand all the others [6]. And this statement does not recognize the further need to understand still others in the same context that are not recursively defined.

Not to be outdone, one version of the newer language Pascal involves syntactic cycles having, respectively, 19, 12, 12, and 5 elements. The cycle of 19 must be understood as a precursor to understanding one of the cycles having 12 elements. Figure A1.8 shows the details of the (inner) cycle having 19 members.

It is true that many computer programs have been written in the languages mentioned, especially in Pascal. Can it be, then, that the capacity to retain fewer concepts in short-term memory than is required to comprehend the meaning of terms in the cycles in the syntax is somehow being circumvented by those who program in the language? Lacking any detailed empirical research on the specific question, one can only respond to this question in terms of the general experience with computer software. There is abundant experiential information to show that the number of errors in much computer software is very high. One author has indicated that the vast majority of software written under U. S. defense contracts, for example, has not been successful.

In a report of a Task Force appointed by the U. S. Defense Science Board, it was stated that before significant advances in software can be expected, it will be necessary to deal with the fundamental issue -- "designing intricate conceptual structures rigorously and correctly" [7]. Such a view appears to be completely consistent with what is being proposed as a Science of Generic Design.

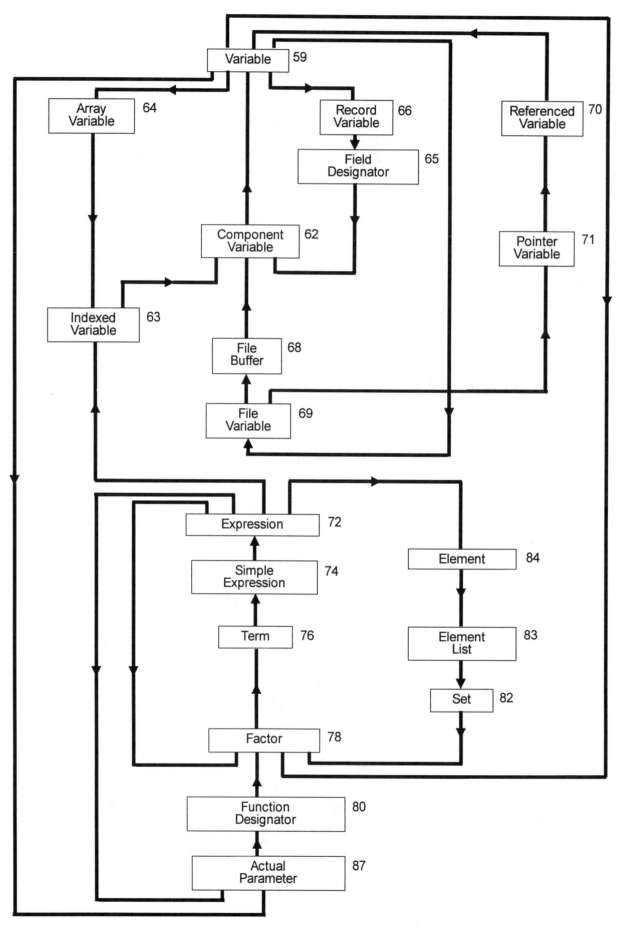

Figure A1.8. An inner cycle for the Pascal computer language syntax.

Synthesis

Lattices also form the foundation of synthesis. The process of synthesis involves the combination of a set of elements lying at some conceptual level into a single element at the next higher conceptual level, and continuation into higher levels until a stopping point is reached. This process of synthesis is, therefore, the reverse of the process of analysis, and both processes are rooted in the lattice concept.

Lateral and vertical replication of this kind of activity produces a lattice of subsets, and is completed with a single high-level element representing the whole, of which the lower-level elements are parts. Subsets also can satisfy various algebras, including the algebra of the Theory of Relations. If divisions and subsets did not satisfy the algebra of the Theory of Relations, such an algebra would be of little significance. But because they do, activities of analysis and synthesis that do not take advantage of the Theory of Relations are overlooking the principal available formalism to improve the results; results that display major flaws in the absence of it.

In both analysis and synthesis it is important to keep in mind what may be called proionic encounters. For example, in synthesis, it may occur that totally new elements can emerge that have properties quite different from those of the elements that encounter each other.

Definition of Lattice

To understand a lattice, it is helpful to recognize that it can be described in several quite different ways. First of all, it can be regarded simply as a conceptual system that satisfies certain operations. In this abstract light no appeal is made to visual interpretation. But a second way of describing it is heavily visual, and thus provides an intuitive approach to its understanding.

Every lattice includes a set S of elements. But the lattice is more than a set. It also incorporates a relation H among the elements of the set. If given a set S and a relation R involving the members of the set, the pair (S,R) can be examined to determine whether it is a lattice or not by examining the relation R to see if it meets the description of the relation H.

The relation H must satisfy these conditions (and certain others to be discussed):

- It is reflexive [i.e., for all $s \in S$, $(s,s) \subseteq H$].
- It is antisymmetric [i.e., if s and t are both contained in S, and if $(s,t) \subseteq H$, then $(t,s) \subseteq H$].
- It is transitive [i.e., if $(s,t) \subset H$ and $(t,u) \subset H$, then $(s,u) \subset H$].

These conditions are sufficient to provide a visual, or intuitive, concept of a lattice. Any relation H that satisfies the conditions given so far must correspond exactly to a map that either (a) is a connected hierarchy (contains no cycles having two or more elements) or (b) it is the trivial form of such a hierarchy, consisting of a single element or (c) it is a collection of connected hierarchies none of which is connected to any other one. A lattice will, then, have to be a structure that is free of cycles (except for self-loops on single elements).

Additional conditions on H restrict further the concept of lattice. Specifically, if s and t are any two elements contained in the set S, then necessarily:

or

    (a) Either (s,t) is contained in H or (t,s) is contained in H (but not both)

    (b) There are elements u and v contained in H such that (s,u) and (t,u) are contained in H and (v,s) and (v,t) are contained in H

From a visual or intuitive point of view, these additional conditions tell us that the map of the lattice must be connected. If it were not connected, we could always find two elements s and t such that neither condition (a) nor condition (b) could be satisfied.

The final restriction involved in the relation H is that if condition (b) applies and we are able to find more than one u that satisfies the condition, the set of such u's constitutes a linear hierarchy with a unique member at the lowest level, and this is called the <u>least upper bound</u> for the pair of elements s and t; and similarly if we are able to find more than one v that satisfies the condition, the set of such v's also constitutes a linear hierarchy with a unique member at the highest level, and this is called the <u>greatest lower bound</u> for the pair of elements s and t.

This completes the conditions applicable to the relation H, allowing us to test any given relation R to see if it corresponds to a lattice.

Among the implications of the foregoing are that any finite lattice L will have an identity element and a zero element. The identity element is the single member of the top level of the hierarchy and the zero element is the single member of the bottom level of the hierarchy.

The lattice of all partitions on a set, for example, includes as its top-level, identity element a partition with a single block containing all members of the set; while the bottom-level, zero element is a partition with exactly one member of the set in each of its blocks.

The lattice of all subsets of a set S, for example, includes as its top-level, identity element the set consisting of all members of the set S; while the bottom-level, zero element is the empty set.

From these considerations, we see that a map of a finite lattice will always have only one member in both the highest and lowest levels of the hierarchy, and will consist of a connected hierarchy. Moreover, any element on the map will always fall upon a path from the bottom level to the top level of the hierarchy. For additional formality related to lattices, please refer to [4].

A1.3 Structural Types.

By noting that certain kinds of relationship among certain types of elements tend to be required frequently in applications, it becomes possible to define specialized "Application Structural Types" of relationship. For example, if the elements are objectives and the relationship is "supports", one is discussing the particular Application Structural Type called an "intent structure". Likewise the relationship "precedes" can become the basis for a "sequential structure", showing the long logic of a situation. The DELTA Chart described in Chap. 7 is such a structure.

The advantages of working with a selected Application Structural Type include: (a) one need only learn the characteristics of that type in order to use it, and need not become familiar with the broad, general theoretical basis for the creation of many types of structure and (b) by repeated development and interpretation of a given type, one becomes expert in interpreting and applying it. Also one can begin to build a mini-science around such a type, based on the accumulated experience with it in a variety of situations. Thus such types become a kind of interface between a theoretical system and a user, insulating or buffering the user who wishes to be insulated from the theoretical system that underlies any particular application.

On the other hand, to retain the Referential Transparency all the way back to the fundamentals of logic, one must be willing to study and learn those fundamentals. Nevertheless local Referential Transparency, specific to an application, comes from the deep and/or long logic displayed in one or more particular Application Structural Types.

Knowledge Organization

Knowledge organization can be approached initially by identifying fundamental structural types upon which the Application Structural Types can be based. But one principle to be followed is that the fundamental structural types should be translatable into other forms, including prose.

To introduce the idea of a translatable graphic, consider Figure A1.9. Here is shown a prose sentence expressed in the conventional way, a second form in which the prose sentence is replaced with a "graphics sentence", a third form in which the same statement is encoded in the language of set theory, and a fourth form in which the statement is represented by the popular Venn diagram.

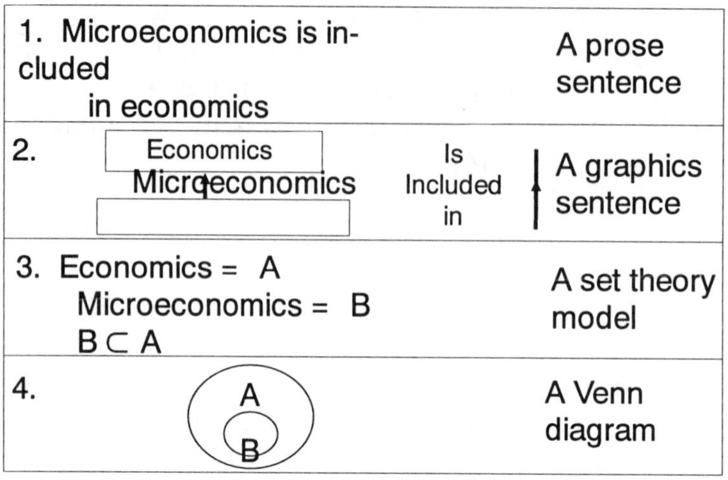

1. Microeconomics is included in economics		A prose sentence
2. Economics / Microeconomics	Is Included in	A graphics sentence
3. Economics = A Microeconomics = B B ⊂ A		A set theory model
4. (A (B))		A Venn diagram

Figure A1.9 Four modes of expression. Copyright © 1979 IEEE.

When large amounts of information are expressed in these four ways, three of them fail. The structure of the information is masked in a mass of prose. The substance of the information is coded in a mass of set theory notation and becomes inaccessible to most readers. The Venn diagrams become unreadable due to excessive overlap. Only the digraph-based structural notation preserves the substance of the information and highlights the structure of it.

The utility of the digraph-based structures is greatest precisely when it is most needed, i.e., when the relationships propagate, due to transitivity.

The fundamental structural types have been designated in [8] as follows:

- Isolated element
- Array (a set of isolated elements)
- Linear Map
- Multilinear Map
- Hierarchy
- Cycle
- Hybrid (Mixed-structure, multilevel map)

These types are illustrated in Figure A1.10.

426

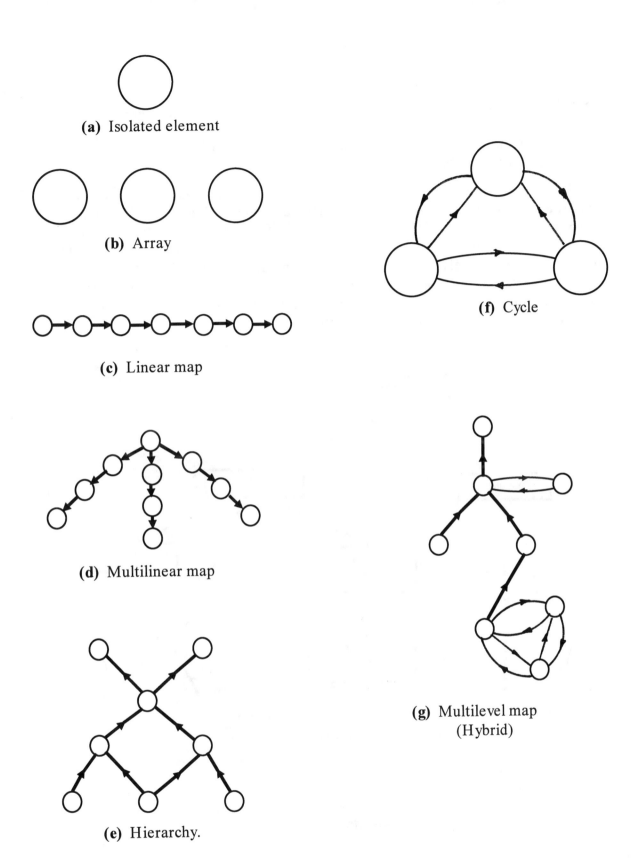

(a) Isolated element

(b) Array

(c) Linear map

(d) Multilinear map

(e) Hierarchy.

(f) Cycle

(g) Multilevel map
(Hybrid)

Figure A1.10 Fundamental structural types. Copyright ©1979 IEEE.

The relationship among the types shown in Figure A1.10 is indicated by means of the inclusion structure shown in Figure A1.11.

Further indication of the unsuitability of Venn diagrams is given in Figure A.12. Here there are shown two different Venn diagrams and one digraph. The digraph shows an inclusion relation among four elements. This same digraph would correspond to either of the two Venn diagrams shown in the Figure. The Venn diagrams do not translate uniquely into prose in terms of the inclusion relation, while the digraph does. Because the inclusion relation is of great importance throughout science, any system of representation that fosters confusion by non-uniqueness in representing this relationship cannot be taken as fundamental.

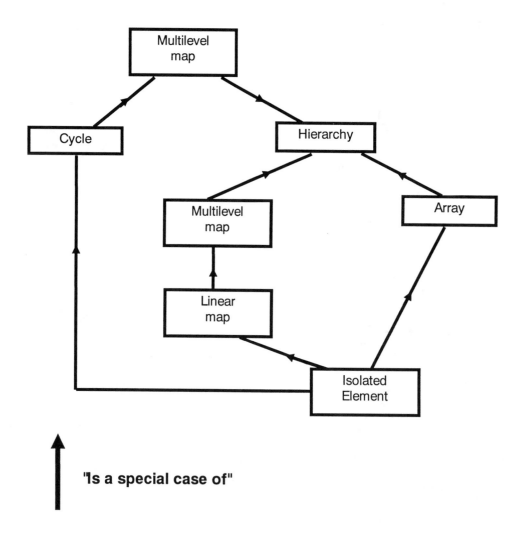

Figure A1.11 Inclusion structure for structural types. Copyright © 1979 IEEE.

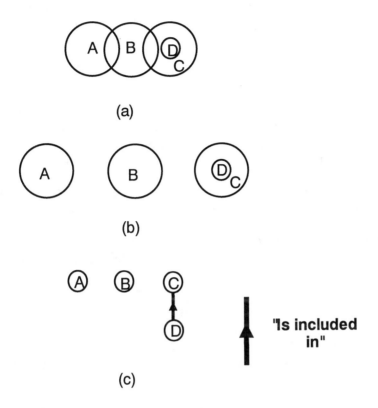

Figure A1.12 Unsuitability of Venn diagrams for general use. Copyright © 1979 IEEE.

Frequently it is important to try to develop a representation where the various blocks do not overlap, i.e., none is included in another. For this purpose the concept of field has been defined, and a theorem has been given to show how a process called Iterative Array Mapping [8] can produce a representation where the blocks do not overlap.

A <u>field</u> F(S) is defined as a breakout of S into n blocks such that (a) no two blocks are equal, (b) the union of the blocks is equal to S, and (c) every block intersects at least one other block unless n = 1. A collection of non-intersecting blocks of S is called a <u>degenerate field</u>. In the limiting case, a field may be entirely degenerate (much as a point is the degenerate version of a line), in which case it constitutes a partition. If a field contains no degenerate subfield, it may be further distinguished by calling it a <u>proper field</u>.

These designations offer maximum flexibility in working with a variety of breakouts of S.

Three types of field appear to have importance in organizing knowledge. In order to distinguish these types, the concepts of "nested pair" and "contaminated pair" were introduced [8]. A pair of elements is nested if and only if one member of the pair is completely included in the other. A pair is contaminated if and only if the pair overlaps partially.

Then a field is said to be uncontaminated if and only if it contains no contaminated pairs. It is said to be contaminated if and only if every pair of blocks in the field is contaminated. And if it is neither uncontaminated nor contaminated, it is said to be partly-contaminated.

Then the theory of Iterative Array Mapping furnishes a theorem that allows substantial simplification as a way of diminishing or eliminating contamination.

Specifically, let F(S) be a field with n blocks. Let Π(S) be an unknown partition of S into m blocks. By a constructive mapping of F into Π is meant a mapping such that

- $m \leq n$
- F dominates Π

(i.e., every block in the second representation Π is a subset of some block in the first representation F).

Theorem 9. Any field F(S) can be mapped algebraically into a partition Π(S) through a constructive mapping, hence it can be mapped graphically into an array.

The proof of this theorem is given in [8] along with examples of its use.

All of the foregoing is relevant to the design and application of Application Structural Maps. However all of the foregoing can be converted into computer programs that mask the operations from the user, so that the user needs to work only with the substantive information germane to the problem or design situation.

Application Structural Types

Application Structural Types offer modularity to the organization of information. When people become familiar with a particular type, it becomes very useful in operations involving information.

Table A1.3 identifies ten Application Structural Types, each of which involves a single kind of relationship.

As an example from Table A1.3, an intent structure is a particular kind of Application Structural Type. Such a structure relates goals, objectives, and aims, all lumped together as "intents", each intent being stated in a well-defined prose syntax.

Table A1.3
Application Structural Types

Type of Structure	Element Class	Relation Type	Specific Relation(s) Used in Applications
Intent Structure	Objectives, Goals, Intentions	Influence	"supports", "helps achieve"
Priority Structure	Budget Line Items	Comparative	"is of equal or higher priority than", "is of equal or higher value than"
DELTA Chart	Activities, Events, Decisions	Temporal	"should precede or coincide with"
Problematique	Problems	Influence	"aggravates"
Curriculum Sequence	Learning Modules	Temporal	"should be learned before or coincident with"
Solution Sequence	Unknown Variables	Influence, Temporal	"is a function of", "should be computed before"
Field	Option	Definitive	"is in the same category as"
Design Quad	Dimension	Influence, Temporal	"is dependent on", "should be explored first in making design choices"
Complementary	Any	Any	"is the complement of"

The elements are related through a relationship of the "influence" type, a common choice being "helps achieve". Then two adjacent members on such a structure might represent the following prose statement:

"Attaining objective A helps achieve attainment of objective B"

where the structure would include the details of A and B.

While all of the types shown in Table A1.3 involve only a single kind of relationship, it is perfectly possible to define other Application Structural Types that represent the union of more than one relationship. Such structures have been discussed or illustrated in several places in this book.

A1.4 Structural Metrics.

The structures (maps) that flow out of the application of the Theory of Relations have features that can be quantified. These include the height, width, length, and numbers of levels or stages in a map; the number of cycles in a map; the number of elements in a cycle; and, in one particular measure, the "structural complexity" of the map, based on only its structural features [9]. Certain assessments of such metrics enable various general empirical results to be attained by studying how the metrics compare across sets of applications. Some data of this type and some of the conclusions drawn therefrom appear in Appendix 5.

Software as an Illustrative Situation

The suggestion that maps based on digraphs might be the basis for a set of software metrics was made by Schneidewind [10]. Metrics that are based only on the form or structure of a map without invoking the details of the content of the map can properly be called structural metrics. Of course the structure itself is a consequence of the way in which the content has been organized. But it is important to realize that people put together content intuitively, and ordinarily do not even overtly perceive the structure of the organized content. They do not know that it is possible to extract the "bare" structure from a congealed combination of content and structure, possibly because they have been accustomed to thinking of them as inseparable.

Because structure can be extracted from content, much as a skeleton remains after the vulture has peeled away the flesh; and because this statement is valid whatever the subject matter, structural metrics are discipline-independent and profession-independent. They possess one of the critical properties that is needed to construct a language that goes across disciplines and professions. They cannot belong to the "turf" of any one discipline or profession. Perhaps this is one reason they have been slow to gain acceptance.

The metric to be discussed here is intended to be one of several possible measures of complexity, and it is founded only on the structure. For this reason, it cannot be a complete measure of complexity. It has two properties that are especially relevant to computer software. First, it measures the complexity of learning a high-level language, without regard to what might be done with it if one learned it. And second, it measures the complexity of trying to use such a language to develop other software, through its correlation with what is known about bounded rationality and cognitive burden.

The syntax of high-level computer languages is often given in what is called the Backus-Naur Form (BNF); a mode of expression that maps directly into the Theory of Relations, but which is universally treated as an innovation without historical precedent, thereby implicitly denying its universal character.

When the syntax of a language is fully expressed in the BNF, it is easy to develop the structure that shows how the understanding of a single term on the left side of one of the many equations making up the syntax requires an understanding of the several terms appearing on the right side of the same equation. When the entire set of equations making up the BNF is so examined, it is possible to construct a reachability matrix, a skeleton matrix, and finally a digraph that shows the learning dependencies in the BNF representation.

Structures have been developed to show these learning dependencies for Algol 60, Pascal, C, and Ada. Several of them appear in two references [6,9]. For the several structures, one can define a structural metric to measure complexity.

A fundamental assumption was made in developing this metric, to the effect that the complexity of a cycle varies exponentially with the number of elements in the cycle. With this assumption, the "raw" complexity measure for a cycle is computed by the formula 2^{n-1}. This sets the complexity to the value 1 when the cycle has only 1 member, offering a good reference point. With this assumption, the raw complexity of a cycle with 2 members is 2, with 3 members is 4, with 4 members is 8, and so on.

The adjective "raw" is used in anticipation that a logarithmic measure of complexity is probably more useful, and it will be shown later in this section.

A second assumption used in assessing complexity dealt with the complexity occasioned by levels in a hierarchy. This assumption is that multiplication of complexities of terms that are adjacent in a map is an appropriate way to transmit complexity vertically in the map. If a map consists of a linear hierarchy, with one member in each level, the complexity of each individual level would be 1, because each level would contain a (trivial) cycle consisting of 1 member. If multiplication were the only algebraic operation involved, one might imagine multiplying together a set of 1's, one for each level, and arriving at a complexity of 1 for the entire hierarchy; an unreasonable situation, giving the same value for the long hierarchy as for a single member. Thus it was concluded that it is appropriate to start at the lowest member in a hierarchy, and when computing the complexity at the adjacent higher level to arrive at a single- element figure by the formula $1 + c_1c_2$, where the product is the complexity of each member taken as an isolated member. The 1 is added to reflect the effect of the levels, so if two linearly connected single elements are involved, giving a linear hierarchy of length 1, the complexity of the hierarchy would be 2.

Studies of several hybrid structures using these assumptions show that in many instances the complexity of a structure is dominated by the presence of cycles and, most particularly, by the presence of cycles in walks. Thus it was found appropriate to estimate the syntactical complexity of computer languages in terms of the structural metric, by simply ignoring all parts of the structures of the respective syntaxes except the cycles that appear in walks [9]. It is also possible to ignore the addition of

1 to reflect movement from a lower level to the next higher level, because the exponentials become very large compared to one for cycles with more than a few members.

After computing complexities on the basis of these thoughts, it was decided that it was most appropriate to use a logarithmic measure, taking logarithms to the base 10, to get orders of magnitude of relative complexity that would be consistent with Claude Shannon's philosophy of using a logarithmic measure of information. This also correlates with the long-established idea in physics of using "orders of magnitude" for comparisons when precise values involve very large numbers and may be much less meaningful than the orders of magnitude.

With all these understandings, it was shown in [9] that Ada, the newest of the languages studied, was about 10 orders of magnitude more complex than Pascal, largely because the syntax of Ada contains four cycles in a linear hierarchy, having 34, 3, 6, and 26 members respectively. Pascal, it was found, was about 2 orders of magnitude more complex than the oldest language Algol 60, largely because Pascal had three cycles in a linear hierarchy having 19, 12, and 5 members respectively. The oldest language also had three cycles in a linear hierarchy, but their cardinalities were 12, 2, and 14 respectively. Analysis of the language C shows that its syntax is 6 orders of magnitude simpler than Algol 60, the simplest of the other languages studied, and 16 orders of magnitude simpler than Ada [11].

It is not intended here to give anything approximating a full treatment of software complexity. Instead it was the goal to use widespread developments in the software field to illustrate how measures of complexity are ignored, how they can be determined just from the structure, and to suggest the need for paying much more attention to such approaches, without regard to the field from which complexity stems.

Appendix 5 shows some general data concerning the incidence of cycles in structuring complexity, and gives some average numerical results that may point the way to further study and interpretation.

The value of structural analysis of syntax in developing learning strategies remains largely unexploited.

REFERENCES

1. F. Harary, R. F. Norman, and D. Cartwright, *Structural Models: An Introduction to the Theory of Directed Graphs*, New York: Wiley, 1965.

2. J. N. Warfield, *Societal Systems: Planning, Policy, and Complexity*, New York: Wiley, 1976 (reprinted, Salinas, CA: Intersystems, 1989.)

3. J. N. Warfield, "Complementary Relations and Map Reading", *IEEE Trans. Syst., Man, and Cybern.*, June, 1980, 285-291.

4. J. Hartmanis and R. E. Stearns, *Algebraic Structure Theory of Sequential Machines*, Englewood Cliffs: Prentice-Hall, 1966.

5. J. N. Warfield, "The Magical Number Three -- Plus or Minus Zero", *Cybernetics and Systems* 19, 1988, 339-358 (First presented at the 1987 annual conference of the International Society for General Systems Research, Budapest).

6. J. N. Warfield, "Structural Analysis of a Computer Language", *Proc. l7th Southeastern Symposium of System Theory*, New York: IEEE, 1985, 229-234.

7. F. Brooks, (Chair), *Report of the Defense Science Board on Military Software*, Office of the Under Secretary of Defense for Acquisition, Washington, D. C. 20301, September, 1987.

8. J. N. Warfield, "Some Principles of Knowledge Organization", *IEEE Trans. Syst., Man, and Cybern., June, 1979, 317- 325.*

9. J. N. Warfield, "A Complexity Metric for High-Level Software Languages", *Proc. International Conference on Systems, Man, and Cybernetics*, New York: IEEE, October, 1987, 438-442.

10. N. F. Schneidewind, "Software Metrics for Aiding Program Development and Debugging," *Proc. National Computer Conference*, 1979, 989-994.

11. A. Ohuchi, I. Kaji, and J. N. Warfield, "Structural Analysis and a Complexity Metric for High-Level Software Languages", *Proceedings of the Conference of the Japan Information Processing Society* (in Japanese), 1988, 646-647.

QUESTIONS RELATED TO APPENDIX 1

1. What individual's life divided the period of <u>acceptance</u> of received language as the basis for studies in logic from the period of <u>design of language</u> as the basis for studies in logic.

2. What was the proposal of Leibniz for dealing with the "deceit of language"?

3. What two authors published in the year 1847 major books dealing with the use of language as it relates to logic?

4. What three nineteenth-century mathematical languages are interchangeable from the point of view of information content concerning the language of relationships?

5. In assessing the three mathematical languages, is there any basis for distinguishing one from another depending on the particular way in which each could be used?

6. What condition did Charles S. Peirce assert was necessary for the validity of the syllogism?

7. What fourth mathematical language was added in the 1900's to complement the three mathematical languages that were discovered in the 1800's?

8. What mistaken belief is sometimes used in working with relation maps?

9. Define "Cartesian Product of a set S".

10. Define "working space" of a map.

11. Give two definitions for "relationship in the working space".

12. Distinguish transitivity from 3-transitivity.

13. Define the transitive closure of a relation R.

14. Define the 3-transitive closure of a relation R.

15. What is meant by a digraph of R?

16. What is meant by a <u>walk</u> on a digraph?

17. What is meant by a <u>statement</u> on a digraph?

18. What is meant by the <u>content</u> of a digraph?

19. What is meant by a <u>valid statement</u> on a digraph?

20. What is a correct digraph of R?

21. What is a partition of a set?

22. What is a cycle?

23. What is a <u>reachability matrix</u> of a digraph?

24. What is meant by the <u>levels</u> of a digraph?

25. What is meant by the <u>condensation</u> of a digraph?

26. What is meant by <u>skeleton matrix</u> of a digraph?

27. What is meant by a map?

28. What is meant by <u>disjoint</u> relation pair?

29. What is meant by <u>covering</u> relation pair?

30. What is meant by <u>complementary</u> relation pair?

31. Identify the blocks of the edge-classification partition of a working space T and give the name of each block.

32. What is meant by a pair of <u>opposites</u>?

33. What is meant by a pair of <u>converses</u>?

34. What is meant by a pair of <u>cohorts</u>?

35. Are the distinctions among opposites, converses, and cohorts part of the common natural language usage?

36. When is a digraph condensible to a <u>single element</u>?

37. When is a digraph condensible to a <u>linear hierarchy</u>?

38. How is linear reasoning defined with respect to the edge-classification partition?

39. What kind of reasoning is the basis for arithmetic reasoning (i.e., reasoning about the relative size of numbers)?

40. Explain why the relation "equals" is transitive and illustrate why the relation "does not equal" is not.

41. Is there any connection between the practice called "bean counting" and the condition that the block 5 of the edge-classification partition is not empty?

42. How is a <u>primary</u> relation in a working space defined?

43. How is a <u>secondary</u> relation in a working space defined?

44. What does Theorem 4 say about how many maps must be read for completeness, under what conditions?

45. Construct a binary reachability matrix, its skeleton matrix, and the blocks of the edge-classification partition for the matrices.

46. What does Theorem 7 say about how many maps are sufficient to enable all of the content of a working space to be read?

47. In applying mathematics to problems, what is meant by "association"?

48. What was the purpose of "analysis by division" as practiced by Plato and Aristotle?

49. In how many ways can 5 things be partitioned into 3 blocks?

50. In how many ways can 8 things be partitioned into 5 blocks?

51. Which (if either) of these statements is always true: (a) a relation is a lattice, (b) a lattice is a relation.

52. What can be said about every map of a finite lattice?

53. What is meant by a "translatable graphic"?

54. Which of the four modes of expression shown in Figure A1.9 is open at scale? Explain your answer.

55. What is the most complex structural type?

56. List nine examples of Application Structural Types.

57. Which of the AST's shown in Table A1.3 are illustrated in one or more applications in Chapter 10?

APPENDIX 2

A GRAPHICALLY-INTEGRATED LANGUAGE SYSTEM (GRAILS)

Design of language seems to be a neglected activity. Still this activity takes place in implicit activity constantly in all high-technology operations involving new systems. The implicit nature of this activity virtually guarantees that any given large organization will have parts involved in constructing languages that will not be compatible with one another, thereby contributing to highly-defective organizational linguistics, and to all succeeding activity anywhere and everywhere the products of the involved organization are purchased and applied. Among the perils arising from the neglect of linguistic design are those that have to do with hierarchies of information of all types, ranging from the simplest to the most complex, wherein compatibility among levels is almost essential.

A2.1 System Components.

A Graphically-Integrated Language System (GRAILS) consists of an eight-level, prose-augmented, graphics language called G; computer-implemented algorithms that facilitate the production of Applications Structural Types; processes that involve human-oriented techniques for eliciting, clarifying, and structuring information; and a facility designed to maximize the interactive benefits of the foregoing.

The Graphics Language G

The eight-level language G is developed from a fundamental level, where only graphic symbols appear in structured form, to the highest level where only a small number of overview "Box Structures" is organized to represent very large systems of ideas.

Application Structural Types

Application Structural Types reflect frequent incidence of situations where some well-defined structural type fills a particular representation requirement. Several such types have been published in connection with exemplary applications. Table A1.3 described ten such types. Each of them can be developed directly, beginning with algorithms involving the language G.

Processes

The processes that can be used to develop the Application Structural Types are those that are identified in Appendix 3, namely the Consensus Methodologies.

A Facility

Best results in complex design situations are achieved when the physical facility for conducting design is itself designed in the light of the various components of the Design Situation. Such a design serves the purpose of creating near-optimal conditions for the necessary component interaction. A similar situation exists in regard to the production of documentation and the amendment of existing designs.

The Integrated System

The Language System is a complex of components whose purpose is to facilitate and document communication. The purpose, when achieved, typically involves two sets: (a) Set 1, the Transmission Set: {Message Generator, Message, Transmission Medium, Sender, Receiver, Interpreter}, and (b) Set 2, the Ingredient Set: {Objects, Symbolic Representation of Objects, Relations Among Objects, Syntax, Semantics, Structure}.

Whatever else may be true about such a system, communication will not be of high quality unless the Interpreter is able to extract the meaning which the Sender intended. This requirement places stringent conditions upon the design of the other members of the two sets.

Technomyopia incorporates the symptom that the afflicted individual does not conceive of the full communication requirement, but may believe that it is only necessary to communicate with persons highly trained in a field. Yet with large systems many of the requirements for operation, maintenance, and even interpretation may fall upon persons who do not have that education. Operators of nuclear plants have been known to fall asleep, or to engage in playing electronic games while ostensibly keeping watch over a complex system.

In the computer software field, one finds such complaints as the following: software that cannot be understood by clients, software development times that greatly exceed schedules, low productivity, software that cannot be re-used, software that cannot be maintained, inability to compare competing software products in order to make good purchasing decisions, lack of metrics, and lack of good decision-making bases. But most of all one finds lack of adequate documentation.

A2.2 Layers in the Language G.

The GRAILS concept has the power to correct most, if not all, of the origins of such complaints. The language G is developed in 8 layers, each of which offers certain benefits. Taken as a whole, these benefits produce a synergistic means of creating, measuring, explaining, and documenting software. And this will be true whether it is computer software or any other kind of intellectual product whose integrity cannot be directly tied to the universal referents coming from physical science.

Table A2.1 illustrates each of the 8 layers in G, and sets forth the special benefits of each of the layers.

A2.3 Standard Production Graphics Symbols.

The building blocks shown in Table A2.2 are candidates for standard production graphics symbols. They are designed to represent the various Application Structural Types, providing functions that accompany whichever of the six types of relationship given in Table 2.7 happens to be relevant to a particular type of application. Entries of U in Table A2.2 indicate that no designation has been given to the symbol for the particular relationship type that is involved. These undesignated cells leave open the possibility of extending the utility of the language G and its standard production graphics symbols as future research and experience may indicate is needed.

Moreover, the one-to-one correspondences that relate these symbols to mathematical constructs allows programming of the layout, sizing, and drawing of the structures, thereby giving a sound representational basis for documentation, and thereby furnishing the means of interpreting the structure and meaning of complex sets of relationships that are involved in complex systems.

Table A2.1 *Eight Layers of the Graphics Language*

Layer 1	Pure Graphic	
	This layer allows purely structural metrics to be defined, and used as a means of characterizing the relative structural complexity of the topic represented by this structure. The only elements of the graphic are vertexes and edges, thus:	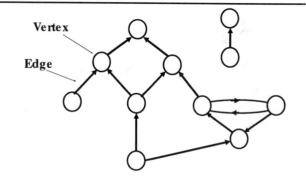

Layer 2	Indexed Graphic	
	This layer incorporates an index set from which a unique assignment is made to each vertex. This allows one-to-one follow-up assignments to be made to vertexes, allows computer renaming of vertexes, allows reference to specific vertexes in programs, allows cycles to be represented as specific vertex-edge structures.	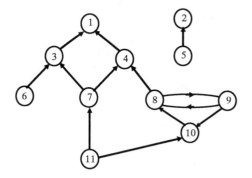

Layer 3	Box-Cycle Indexed Graphic	
	This layer differs from Layer 2 only in that each cycle is shown in a box with a bullet preceding each index. This representation can be used for very large cycles without any confusion, while the vertex-edge notation becomes unreadable when cycles have many vertexes. Also this notation can be used when prose assignments replace the index notation.	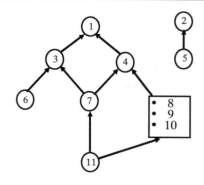

Layer 4	Resolved-Cycle Indexed Graphic	
	This layer differs from Layer 4 in that for each cycle there is substituted its "resolved" form. The resolved form of a cycle portrays the vertexes and edges, but only those for which "adjacency" has been established in the relationship. This allows a deeper level of analysis and permits computation of geodetic subcycles, as well as a hierarchy of geodetic subcycles for each resolved cycle, to aid in interpretation.	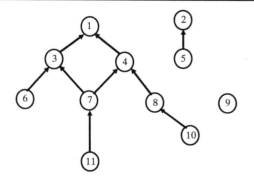

442

Layer 5   Mathematics Assignment

In this layer, an assignment to each index of some mathematical statement is carried out, and an assignment of the same mathematical relation to every edge is carried out.

This automatically corresponds to representing, by the graphic, a set of statements, one for each walk on the structure.

Also each vertex is now drawn as a box and is sized to allow the mathematical statement to be enclosed by the box.

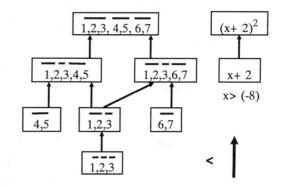

Layer 6   Prose/Mathematics Assignment

In this layer, an assignment is made to each index of a statement that can be prose, mathematics, or a combination; and an assignment of the same contextual relation is made to every edge. This automatically corresponds to representing, by the graphic, a set of statements, one for each walk on the structure. Each vertex is now drawn as a box and is sized to allow the combined prose/mathematics statment to be enclosed in the box. The box format may be varied, when justified, to convey readability.

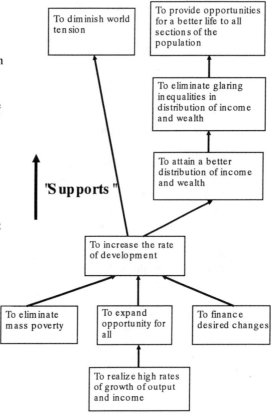

443

Table A2.1 *Eight Layers of the Graphics Language (Concluded)*

Layer 7 **Logic-Augmented**

This layer is identical with Layer 6, except that logic boxes can be inserted to convey more precisely composite relationships involving AND and OR logic operations.

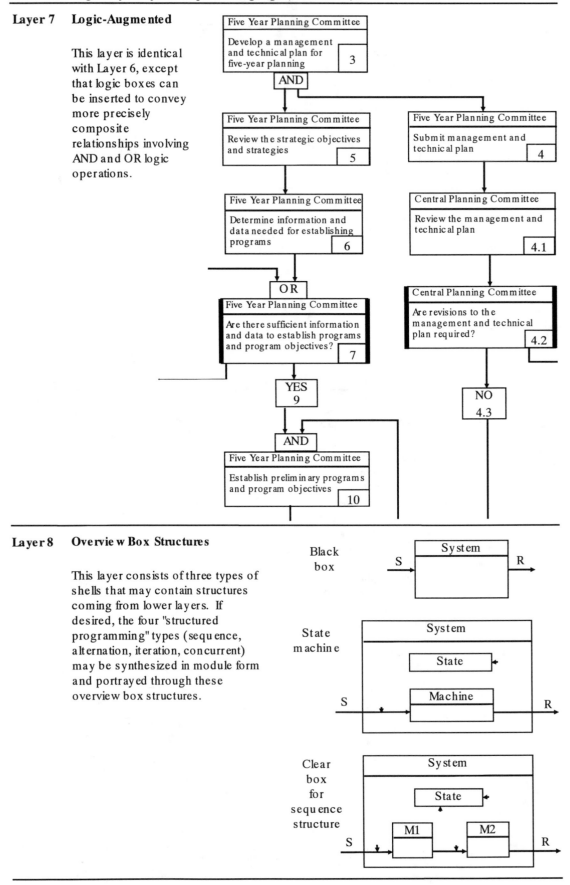

Layer 8 **Overview Box Structures**

This layer consists of three types of shells that may contain structures coming from lower layers. If desired, the four "structured programming" types (sequence, alternation, iteration, concurrent) may be synthesized in module form and portrayed through these overview box structures.

Table A2.2 *Illustrative Standard Production Graphics Symbols*

Symbol Number	Graphic Representation	Interpretation of the Graphic Representation by Type of Contextual Relation					
		Definitive	Influence	Comparative	Temporal	Spatial	Mathematical
1		Element	Element	Element	Event*	Element	Date
2		∪	∪	∪	Upper part: Role/actor; Lower part: activity*	∪	∪
3		∪	∪	∪	Upper part: decider; Lower part: decision* to be made	∪	∪
4		Member of basis set	Fundamental influence	∪	Special event (milestone)*	Border element	∪
5		Comment	Comment	Comment	Comment	Comment	Comment
6	AND OR ***	Logic boxes	Logic boxes	Logic boxes	Logic boxes	Logic boxes	Logic boxes
7		Contextual relation	Contextual relation	Contextual relation	Contextual relation	Contextual relation	Contextual relation
8	... **	Cycle	Cycle	Cycle	Cycle	Cycle	Cycle
9		∪	∪	∪	Termination of a sequence	∪	∪

*   Subject to strict syntax controls
**   Illustrative for three members
***   Represents the exclusive OR

QUESTIONS RELATED TO APPENDIX 2

1. What are the four major components of a Grahically Integrated Language System?

2. Describe the eight-level graphics language G.

3. What are the benefits of the layers in G?

4. Explain the information contained in line 1 of Table A2.2.

5. How might language G be significantly improved?

APPENDIX 3[†]

CONSENSUS METHODOLOGIES

The purpose of this Appendix is to consolidate, in a standard format, information about each of seven "consensus methodologies" that forms part of the working repertoire in applications of the science of generic design. To satisfy this purpose, each of the seven is separately described in the form of a "portfolio", rendering information about each in several complementary formats.

Before describing these seven, an explanation will be given to provide responses to certain questions that keep recurring concerning them. Here are the questions that will be discussed:

1. Since there are many methodologies described in various literature, such as planning literature, why are only seven identified here? It would seem that this unduly limits what people might want to use and to do.

2. Why do you call them "consensus methodologies"? It does not appear that some of them (or perhaps any of them) produce consensus.

3. What features do these seven have that caused them to be chosen?

4. From what I have read, it seems that some of the seven are used much more frequently than others. Is that true and, if so, why? What are the approximate frequencies of use?

5. I understand that you use and recommend most of the steps in the Nominal Group Technique, but you do not use the very last step, which is the one where final decisions on priorities are made. Is this true and, if so, why?

The Choice of Seven.

The inventor of methods or methodologies is anxious to add to the list of "tools" available to users. Academics like to publish books that are filled with such tools, believing that they are serving the interests of users who, like themselves, are anxious to learn many methodologies and explore the wonders that can be attained through their use. Such a view overlooks the fact that most users are only interested in getting results that add value, and are not in a position to review the historical records on dozens or hundreds of methods while trying to master their subtleties, in order to make choices among large sets of options that lie outside of their normal activities.

---

†   All Portfolios shown in Appendix 3 first appeared in *General Systems*, Vol. 27, © 1982 SGSR.

Such an individual can benefit by having the individual who chooses and recommends methodologies display the logic of choice, and make it easy for the person or organization with the problem to take advantage of demonstrably productive and well-designed and tested methodologies.

The number of methodologies to be included in a comprehensive repertoire should be as small as possible while still allowing the user to do what needs to be done in a given situation, since this minimizes the learning time for everyone and allows refinement of methodologies and immediate feedback of products of their application from staff who are intimately acquainted with the chosen few.

The Choice of Title

The explanation of the title "consensus methodologies" is given in this book in the Postscript, as a response to referee comments.

The Features

It is desired to have methodologies that do not impose artificial intellectual barriers between the user and the explanation of the results. For this reason methods that may produce similar results are excluded from use when they apply exotic mathematical techniques to get the results which preclude lay explanations. For example, the Analytic Hierarchy Method is sometimes used instead of the ISM method for arriving at priorities. But the former uses eigenvalues from mathematics that insert opaqueness in the system, while the latter only uses articulated human reasoning and dialog to arrive at the results. It is also desired to use several different ways for idea generation to add flexibility to the collecting of information, based upon time and location of participants. However a similar flexibility is not appropriate for the logical structuring of ideas, which can only be responsive, in this context, to well-established "Western logic".

Frequency of Use

Frequency of use approaches 100% for the Nominal Group Technique (as modified) and for Interpretive Structural Modeling. For the other methodologies, the frequencies are estimated as follows: Ideawriting (10%), DELPHI (5%), Options Field (40%), Options Profile (25%), Tradeoff Analysis Methodology (2%). Normally both the NGT and the ISM processes are integral subprocesses of the use of the Options Field Methodology, and may also be used with the Tradeoff Analysis Methodology. The DELPHI Method is used only when it is believed that there is no significant benefit to using face-to-face group interaction.

Truncation of the Nominal Group Technique.

The last step in the Nominal Group Technique involves collective voting on priorities. This step is not used, because it is believed to be cognitively unsound to ask people to rank collectively many items. Interpretive Structural Modeling is believed to be much more appropriate for this purpose, and is so used.

Consensus Methodologies.

A set of methodologies called Consensus Methodologies was partly selected and partly invented to meet the requirements for effective group design activity. These methodologies satisfy a dual-basis condition. This means that they meet the anthropological requirements that enhance human effectiveness and meet human aspirations, while simultaneously satisfying the logical requirements associated with language and reasoning through relationships.

In contrast, most methodologies examined for relevance to generic design science deal openly only with one basis or the other, to the detriment of either satisfaction or productivity or both.

Figure A3.1 shows a chronology of the development of the Consensus Methodologies. Also shown in this Figure is the "Brainstorming" process, which is not one of the Consensus Methodologies.

There are two reasons for including Brainstorming in the chronology. The first is that it pioneered the specific incorporation of knowledge from behavioral science in group processes, specifically the requirement that no criticism be allowed during idea generation, because of its known impact in inhibiting creative behavior. This same feature has been incorporated in the later methods that are used for generating ideas, including the three that are included in the Consensus Methodologies. Thus it is an ancestor that deserves to be acknowledged as such.

The second reason for including Brainstorming is to call attention to the fact that the other three processes that involve idea generation: DELPHI, Ideawriting, and Nominal Group Technique differ significantly from Brainstorming (and from each other, as well).

Why is it important to note the significant differences? The answer is that it has been observed empirically in numerous applications projects that many people have never been sensitized to a simple fact: two processes that may appear to be very similar from a technological point of view may be extremely different from a behavioral point of view. The technological point of view may be primarily focused on the mechanics of the processes and their products. If the mechanics appear similar and the types of product are very similar, there may be a tendency to assume that the processes are virtually equivalent. One of the consequences of this point of view is

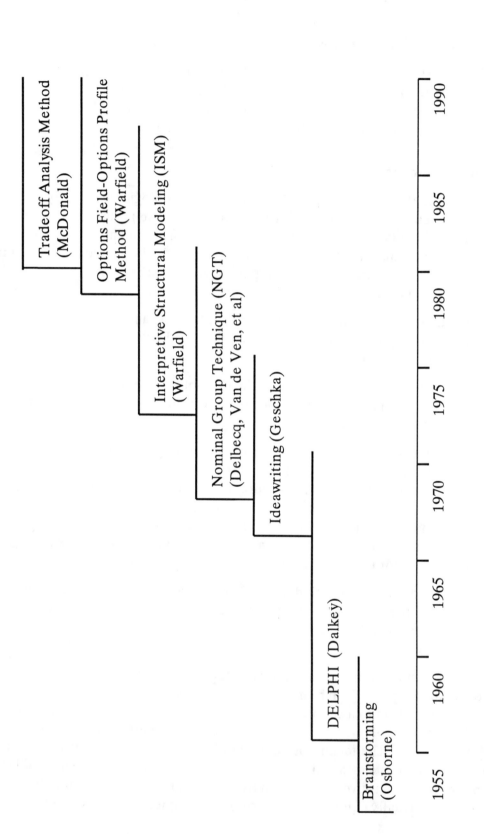

Figure A3.1 Evolution of consensus methodologies.

that technological changes that affect severely the behavioral side of the process design may be inadvertently introduced that have a major impact on the effectiveness of the process, and this may go unrecognized. Alternatively, people may direct the use of the processes without understanding that the behavioral part of the process design is at least as important as the technical part and, unknowingly, decimate the process by introducing what they perceive as a minor change, or as a way to improve the efficiency of the process. When the changes they introduce cause unrecognized consequences, they may assert that the process is not effective, and that the claims made for it should be disregarded. This sequence of events is a multiple disaster, brought about by insensitivity to the behavioral side of the process of design. People who do not understand this should not try to manage the use of the consensus methodologies.

While these methodologies are described in Chapter 7, this appendix is intended both to amplify the descriptions given there, and to locate in one convenient place capsule descriptions of these methodologies for prospective users. Three kinds of descriptive materials are given for each of the seven: (a) a capsule overview in a single prose sentence, (b) a more elaborate, but still condensed, prose overview and (c) a graphic that gives a pictorial image of the process sequence.

(Readers who would like to copy only this Appendix for use as a Portfolio of processes can take advantage of the liberal copying policy shown on the Copyright Page of this book.)

PORTFOLIO 1

IDEAWRITING (BRAINWRITING)

AN EFFICIENT METHOD FOR GENERATION OF IDEAS BY GROUPS

PORTFOLIO I

IDEAWRITING (BRAINWRITING)

A method of collective inquiry useful in generating ideas about some issue or question. The method is helpful for idea generation by small groups. Ideas are individually generated in response to a trigger question and then shared with others to encourage the generation of additional ideas.

APPROPRIATE CONDITIONS FOR USE

There is a need to collect ideas or elements relevant to some issue, in little time.
The information desired is spread among various people.
It is desired to eliminate the potentially inhibiting influence of dominant personalities.
People are available and willing to take part in the idea generation.

APPLICATION AREAS

Generally appropriate for all efforts where collective idea generation is of value and especially useful for issue formulation, including problem definition, and identification of objectives.

RESULTS

Spontaneous occurrence of ideas, triggered by other ideas.
A list of 50 to 150 ideas about an issue or question. Increased understanding of ideas generated by collective inquiry.

RESOURCES REQUIRED

A specific trigger question that is to be the basis for idea generation.
A group leader who has mastered the process and is willing to act as process facilitator.
No more than six people for a single ideawriting (brainwriting) process. Any number of simultaneous processes may be held.
Each group needs a table and chairs and a quiet room, as well as paper and pencils.
At least 15 minutes, typically 45 minutes and certainly no more than two hours of time.
Funds, if required, to compensate participants and leader.

(continued next page)

PORTFOLIO 1

IDEAWRITING (BRAINWRITING)

(continued)

HOW THE METHOD IS APPLIED

Silent generation of ideas in writing by individuals for about 5 to 10 minutes in response to a carefully prepared trigger question. Exchange of sheets of paper and continuation of idea generation for 5 to 10 minutes; continued exchange of sheets of paper until all participants have examined all papers.
Ideas are edited and organized for presentation.

IMPORTANT ATTRIBUTES AND FEATURES

Potential for generation of many ideas concerning organizational, behavioral and other aspects of an issue. Potential for encouraging contributions from those normally noted for reticence and quietness. Potential for greatly enhanced stakeholder input into the planning process. Not useful for negotiation or simple information exchange.

RELATED METHODS

There are no methods prerequisite to use of ideawriting (brainwriting). Alternatives are brainstorming, synectics, charette, survey, nominal group technique and DELPHI.
The ideas generated by ideawriting generally represent useful elements for further analysis and impact assessment.

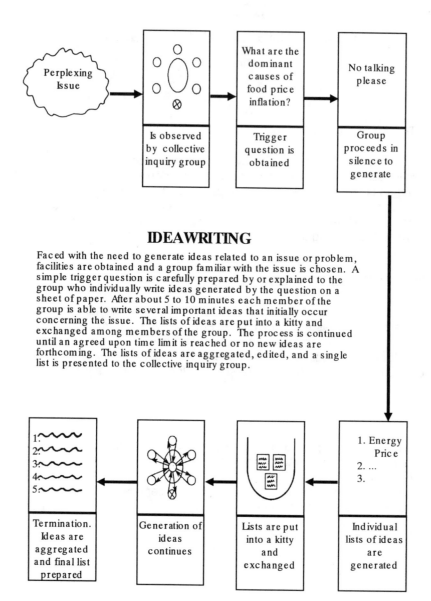

IDEAWRITING

Faced with the need to generate ideas related to an issue or problem, facilities are obtained and a group familiar with the issue is chosen. A simple trigger question is carefully prepared by or explained to the group who individually write ideas generated by the question on a sheet of paper. After about 5 to 10 minutes each member of the group is able to write several important ideas that initially occur concerning the issue. The lists of ideas are put into a kitty and exchanged among members of the group. The process is continued until an agreed upon time limit is reached or no new ideas are forthcoming. The lists of ideas are aggregated, edited, and a single list is presented to the collective inquiry group.

PORTFOLIO 2

NOMINAL GROUP TECHNIQUE (NGT)

AN EFFICIENT METHOD FOR GENERATING IDEAS IN GROUPS, FOR CLARIFYING THE GENERATED IDEAS, FOR EDITING THE GENERATED IDEAS, AND FOR DEVELOPING A PRELIMINARY PARTITION OF THE SET OF IDEAS INTO THOSE DEEMED BY AT LEAST ONE PARTICIPANT TO LIE IN THE TOP FIVE IN IMPORTANCE, AND FOR RANKING THEM.

PORTFOLIO 2

NOMINAL GROUP TECHNIQUE (NGT)

An efficient method for generating ideas in groups, for clarifying the generated ideas, for editing the generated ideas, and for developing a preliminary partition of the set of ideas into those deemed by at least one participant to lie in the top five in importance, and for ranking them.
A method for collective inquiry, individual ideas and judgments are generated and effectively aggregated. The technique is helpful in identifying problems, establishing priorities, and postulating and exploring policies and problem solutions.

APPROPRIATE CONDITIONS FOR USE

A need to collect ideas relevant to some issue.
Controversy and uncertainty exist concerning the nature of an issue or problem and its possible resolution.
It is important to neutralize the effect of dominant individuals in generally small group meetings.
A first selection or prioritization of ideas or elements is desired.

APPLICATION AREAS

Generally appropriate where collective idea generation is of value, and therefore especially useful for issue formulation.
Business and government planning.
Fostering stakeholder participation in planning.

RESULTS

A list of 20 to 100 ideas about an issue.
A preliminary prioritization of these ideas according to a specific relation.
Increased understanding of generated ideas.
Opportunity to assure that ideas of each member of the group are part of the output.

RESOURCES REQUIRED

A carefully prepared trigger question.
Six to 10 task-oriented individuals with issue-related expertise.
A group leader who is willing to act as a process facilitator, not a substantive expert.

(continued next page)

PORTFOLIO 2

NOMINAL GROUP TECHNIQUE (NGT)

(continued)

RESOURCES REQUIRED (continued)

Papers and pencils for each participant; flip chart and felt tip pen for
process leader.
Brief training of group leader(s).
Meeting room with adequately sized table, chairs, and surfaces on which to
tape ideas.
Sixty to 120 minutes time for the process.

HOW THE METHOD IS APPLIED

Silent generation of ideas in writing by individuals in response to oral
presentation of a carefully prepard trigger question.
Round robin recording of ideas in which individuals present one idea at a
time.
Spontaneous hitchhiking of ideas is encouraged, but no discussion or
justification of ideas.
Serial discussion of the resulting list of ideas.
Voting on the priority of generated ideas.

IMPORTANT ATTRIBUTES AND FEATURES

Potential for generation of many ideas concerning organizational,
behavioral and other issues.
Potential for encouraging contributions from those normally noted for
quietness.
Greatly enhanced stakeholder input into the process.
Not useful for negotiation.
Ideas and/or elements need to be thoroughly discussed and analyzed by
the group before the evaluation or prioritization takes place.

RELATED METHODS

Alternatives include brainwriting, brainstorming, synectics, surveys,
charette, and DELPHI.
Any of several voting schemes may be used in conjunction with nominal
group technique.

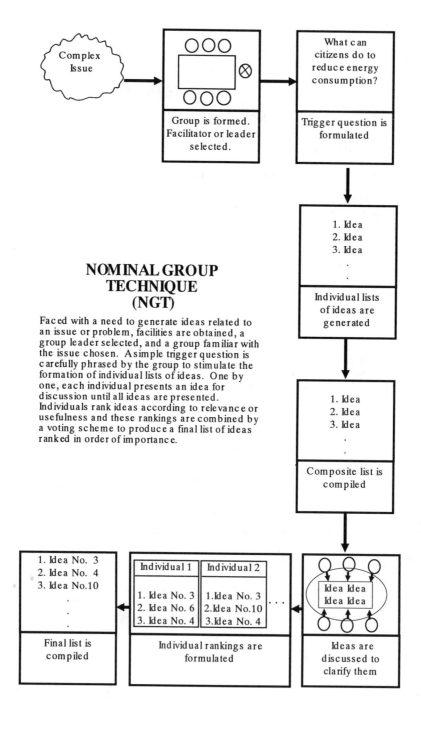

**NOMINAL GROUP
TECHNIQUE
(NGT)**

Faced with a need to generate ideas related to
an issue or problem, facilities are obtained, a
group leader selected, and a group familiar with
the issue chosen. A simple trigger question is
carefully phrased by the group to stimulate the
formation of individual lists of ideas. One by
one, each individual presents an idea for
discussion until all ideas are presented.
Individuals rank ideas according to relevance or
usefulness and these rankings are combined by
a voting scheme to produce a final list of ideas
ranked in order of importance.

PORTFOLIO 3

DELPHI

A METHOD FOR GETTING VIEWS OF PEOPLE WHEN THERE IS NOT A PRACTICAL MEANS FOR BRINGING THE PEOPLE TOGETHER IN ONE PLACE AND HAVING THEM ENGAGE IN A CONSTRUCTIVE DIALOG.

PORTFOLIO 3

DELPHI

**A method for getting ideas of people when there is not a practical means
for bringing them together in one place and having them engage in
a constructive dialog. A method for syst ematic development of the views
of a panel of individuals, generally experts, with regard to some issue.
To minimize the influence of dominant personalities, to remove
geographic limitations, to allow input from persons who might
otherwise not be able to participate, and to allow anonymity
among the panel (if desired), written responses to a sequence
of correlated questionnnaires are obtained. The results of each
questionnaire are fed back to the panel by the monitoring
group, which strives gradually to develop
consensus among the panel members.**

APPROPRIATE CONDITIONS FOR USE

There is a need to collect and evaluate ideas, forecasts, or opinions relative to some issue. Face-to-face participation and interaction is not feasible or not desired. Expert opinions and knowledge are the prime sources of information. The experts should learn from each other.

APPLICATION AREAS

The DELPHI method is appropriate for idea generation, description, and evaluation. Examples of application include technological and social forecasting, water resource management, and technology assessment.

RESULTS

Increased understanding, clarification of positions, and explanations of differences of opinion among experts. A supply of elements, events, and possible dates of occurrence for further analysis. A final report summarizing the process.

RESOURCES NEEDED

Design and monitor group of 1 to 10 people. Supporting staff to type and mail questionnaires, receive and process results. A respondent panel of 5 to 100 people whose judgments are sought, and who possess reasonable written communication skills. A process leader to coordinate the design and monitor group, the supporting staff, and the expert panel. Physical facilities for housing and supplying the monitor group.

(Continued on next page)

462

PORTFOLIO 3

DELPHI

(continued)

HOW THE METHOD IS APPLIED

An issue and a process leader are chosen. The design/monitor group is chosen, and the panel is chosen. An initial questionnaire is developed and mailed to the panel. Panel replies are received and analyzed. A revised questionnaire is mailed to the panel. The process continues iteratively until convergence is achieved or sufficient information is obtained. A final DELPHI process report is prepared and distributed.

IMPORTANT FEATURES AND ATTRIBUTES

Individuals in the respondent panel participate on an equal and anonymous basis. Iteration and controlled feedback between iterations are provided. Statistical group response by aggregation of individual opinions of the panel can often be developed. Does not require respondent panel travel or prolonged effort at any particular time, since the time allowed typically varies from one month to a year.

RELATED METHOD

If anonymity is not required and short-term results are essential, one may use Ideawriting, Charette, or Nominal Group Technique in place of DELPHI. When sufficient data and theory are available, various modeling methods can be used as alternatives to DELPHI questionnaire data.

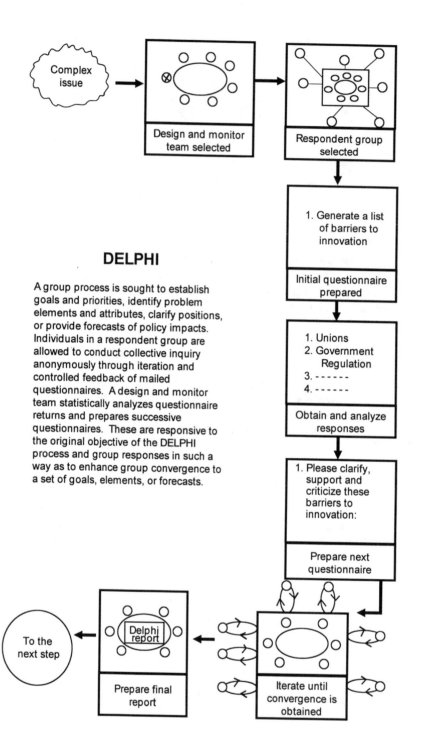

DELPHI

A group process is sought to establish goals and priorities, identify problem elements and attributes, clarify positions, or provide forecasts of policy impacts. Individuals in a respondent group are allowed to conduct collective inquiry anonymously through iteration and controlled feedback of mailed questionnaires. A design and monitor team statistically analyzes questionnaire returns and prepares successive questionnaires. These are responsive to the original objective of the DELPHI process and group responses in such a way as to enhance group convergence to a set of goals, elements, or forecasts.

PORTFOLIO 4

INTERPRETIVE STRUCTURAL MODELING (ISM)

A COMPUTER-ASSISTED LEARNING PROCESS THAT CULMINATES IN THE DEVELOPMENT OF A STRUCTURE OF AN ISSUE, PROBLEM, PLAN, PROJECT, OR DESIGN. THE STRUCTURE IS DEVELOPED BY A GROUP OPERATING WITH THE ASSISTANCE OF A SKILLED PILOTOS WHO, IN TURN, IS ASSISTED IN THE DETAILED SEQUENCING OF THE AGENDA BY THE COMPUTER-DRIVEN DISPLAY.

PORTFOLIO 4

INTERPRETIVE STRUCTURAL MODELING (ISM)

A computer-assisted learning process that culminates in the development of a structure of an issue, problem, plan, project, or design. The structure is developed by a group operating with the assistance of a skilled pilotos who, in turn, is assisted in the detailed sequencing of the agenda by the computer-driven display, a computer-assisted learning process that enables an individual or a group user to develop a structure or map showing interrelations among previously determined elements according to a selected contextual relationship.

APPROPRIATE CONDITIONS FOR USE

A complex issue is under study, with interactions among diverse elements.
A focused group discussion on the issue is needed.
A multilevel relation map is wanted.

APPLICATION AREAS

Linking of elements associated with issue formulation such as needs, constraints, or objectives, in a variety of fields, such as education, public facility planning, and city budget cutting.

RESULTS

A documented model of element interrelations.
A carefully refined language with which to describe or discuss an issue or system.
Modification and clarification of elements and relations used in the study.
Enhanced understanding of the issue.

RESOURCES REQUIRED

A set of elements relating to the issue.
A contextual relationship, which is appropriate to interrelate the elements.
Up to 8 willing and able participants, as well as a group leader familiar with interpretive structural modeling, and a computer operator.
Participants should have a genuine concern for the issue and capability to contribute through participation.
A time-shared digital computer that contains the programs for structuring.
A large screen display is helpful.
Costs include participants' time, and equipment costs which are approximately $50 per hour.
The time required for an exercise depends upon the number of elements in the model and their complexity. A ten-element exercise may take as long as one to two hours.

(continued next page)

PORTFOLIO 4

INTERPRETIVE STRUCTURAL MODELING (ISM)

(continued)

HOW THE METHOD IS APPLIED

An issue and structuring theme are identified.
A group and a process leader are chosen.
Elements and contextual relations are obtained.
The group responds to computer-posed inquiries concerning element interactions.
The computer displays the obtained map.
The map is iterated and edited for group satisfaction with the structure.

IMPORTANT ATTRIBUTES AND FEATURES

Contextual relations must be transitive, and carefully chosen.
Elements and relations are clarified by reasoning and discussion stimulated by the process.
The quality of the results obtained is strongly dependent upon process leadership, which must be facilitative rather than issue- oriented.
Overemphasis on the mechanistic and technical aspects of the process is undesirable.

RELATED METHODS

Nominal group technique, brainwriting, brainstorming, DELPHI, charette, extensive literature search, or a combination of these may provide elements and contextual relations for the process.
In very simple situations "rearrange and tape" and other heuristic non-computer assisted methods may be used.

INTERPRETIVE
STRUCTURAL
MODELING
(ISM)

The method takes a set of elements and a transitive contextual relationship as its inputs. The computer asks questions, one at a time, which are discussed by the group and ultimately answered by a "yes" or "no" response. The computer makes significant use of logical inference to decrease the number of questions to be asked. Also the computer determines which question has the best chance of providing maximum information, in order to minimize participant time in evolving the structure. The method develops the structure of the model for the model building group and allows for modification or amendment of the structure so that final group satisfaction with the evolved structure is obtained.

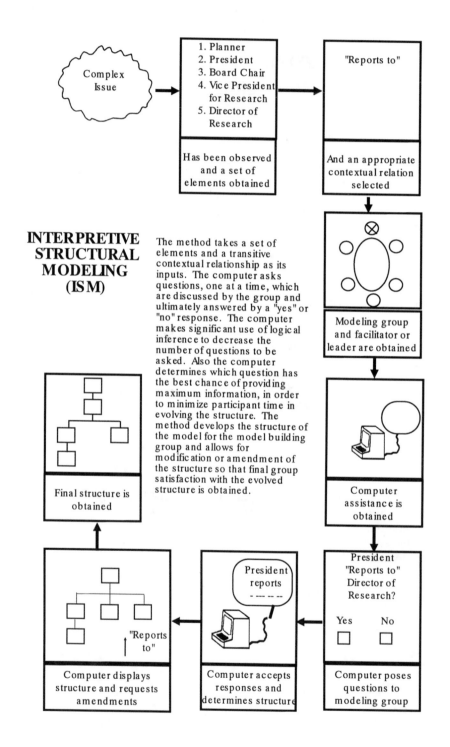

Complex Issue

1. Planner
2. President
3. Board Chair
4. Vice President for Research
5. Director of Research

Has been observed and a set of elements obtained

"Reports to"

And an appropriate contextual relation selected

Modeling group and facilitator or leader are obtained

Computer assistance is obtained

President "Reports to" Director of Research?

Yes ☐   No ☐

Computer poses questions to modeling group

President reports - --- -- --

Computer accepts responses and determines structure

"Reports to"

Computer displays structure and requests amendments

Final structure is obtained

PORTFOLIO 5

OPTIONS FIELD METHOD (OFM)

A METHOD FOR PORTRAYING ALL THE CONCEIVED DIMENSIONS OF A SITUATION OR A PROSPECTIVE TARGET OF DESIGN, INCLUDING THE SIMPLE OPTIONS AVAILABLE IN EACH DIMENSION; AND SHOWING THE CLUSTERS OF INTERDEPENDENT DIMENSIONS. THE CLUSTERS ARE ORDERED IN THE SEQUENCE IN WHICH DESIGN CHOICES ARE TO BE MADE, AS ARE THE DIMENSIONS WITHIN EACH CLUSTER.

PORTFOLIO 5

OPTIONS FIELD METHOD (OFM)

A method for portraying all the conceived dimensions of a situation or a prospective target of design, including the simple options available in each dimension; and showing the clusters of interdependent dimensions. The clusters are ordered in the sequence in which design choices are to be made, as are the dimensions within each cluster. A means for developing, organizing and displaying the options, dimensions, and clusters that are relevant to a design problem. The display of the options field is intended to provide an adequate basis for group dialog concerning a design, and further to provide the means whereby a group design can be continuously updated until all of the decisions needed to establish an alternative design have been made.

APPROPRIATE CONDITIONS FOR USE

A requirement to develop a design has been agreed on. Contributions to the design process are required from a group, usually involving six or more individuals. A top-down design process is to be used.It is important to maintain continuous display of past design decisions.Documentation of what was considered is needed, to show not only what was chosen but what was rejected; along with the sequence of design choices.

APPLICATION AREAS

Product designs, curriculum designs, system designs, organization designs, process designs, experiment designs, program designs, project designs.

RESULTS

An organization of the key design information in a display format that will facilitate design decision-making. An input to the Options Field Method which carries the design to conceptual completion.

RESOURCES REQUIRED

Knowledge of options. Large wall for display purposes. Facilitator with thorough knowledge of the Options Field Method (OFM). A group of persons familiar with the design goals and objectives. A person to develop the wall display. Methods for options generation and classification.

RELATION TO OTHER METHODS

Option generation can be carried out with brainwriting, nominal group technique, or DELPHI. Manual sorting methods may suffice for aggregating options into dimensions.

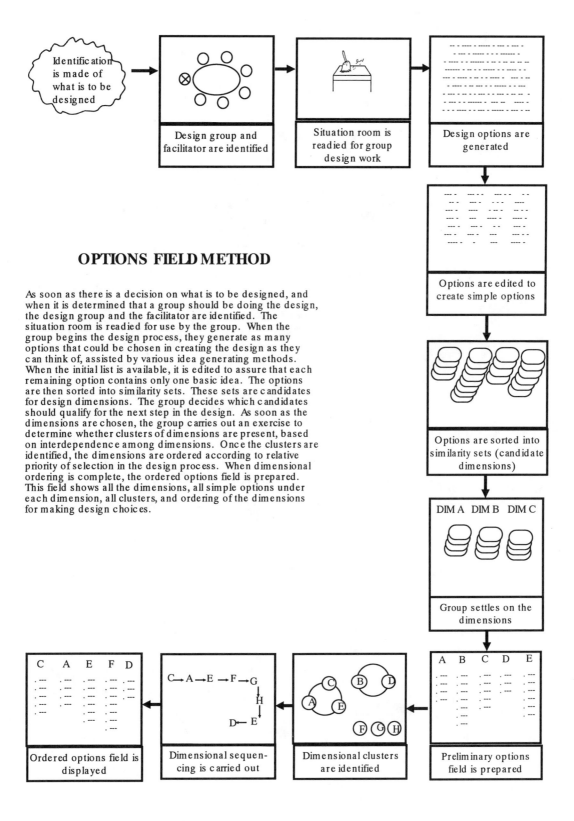

OPTIONS FIELD METHOD

As soon as there is a decision on what is to be designed, and when it is determined that a group should be doing the design, the design group and the facilitator are identified. The situation room is readied for use by the group. When the group begins the design process, they generate as many options that could be chosen in creating the design as they can think of, assisted by various idea generating methods. When the initial list is available, it is edited to assure that each remaining option contains only one basic idea. The options are then sorted into similarity sets. These sets are candidates for design dimensions. The group decides which candidates should qualify for the next step in the design. As soon as the dimensions are chosen, the group carries out an exercise to determine whether clusters of dimensions are present, based on interdependence among dimensions. Once the clusters are identified, the dimensions are ordered according to relative priority of selection in the design process. When dimensional ordering is complete, the ordered options field is prepared. This field shows all the dimensions, all simple options under each dimension, all clusters, and ordering of the dimensions for making design choices.

PORTFOLIO 6

OPTIONS PROFILE METHOD (OPM)

A METHOD FOR DEVELOPING A TOP-DOWN DESIGN, BEGINNING WITH AN OPTIONS FIELD, AND ENDING WITH A SPECIFICATION OF ALL OF THE OPTIONS SELECTED TO FORM THE SET OF DESIGN CHOICES. THE OPTIONS PROFILE IS A REPRESENTATION OF ONE DESIGN ALTERNATIVE. REPEATED DEVELOPMENT OF ADDITIONAL OPTIONS PROFILES IS EQUIVALENT TO GENERATING NEW DESIGN ALTERNATIVES.

PORTFOLIO 6

OPTIONS PROFILE METHOD (OPM)

A method for developing a top-down design, beginning with an options field, and ending with a specification of all the options selected to form the set of design choices. The options profile is a representation of one design alternative. Repeated development of additional options profiles is equivalent to generating new design alternatives.

APPROPRIATE CONDITIONS FOR USE

An Options Field has been generated to be used as the basis for a top-down design.
A group is available to do the design.
A facilitator is available to lead the group design effort.

APPLICATION AREAS

Same as for the Options Field Method.

RESULTS

A portrayal of an alternative top-down design, showing the sequence in which choices were made, which options were chosen, and which options were rejected.

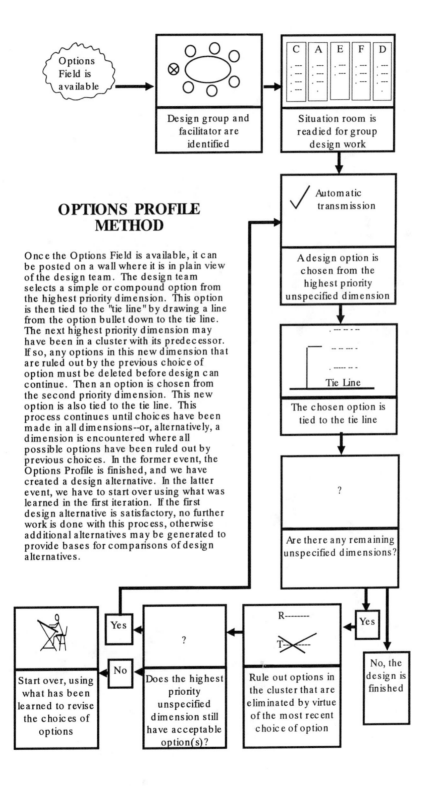

OPTIONS PROFILE METHOD

Once the Options Field is available, it can be posted on a wall where it is in plain view of the design team. The design team selects a simple or compound option from the highest priority dimension. This option is then tied to the "tie line" by drawing a line from the option bullet down to the tie line. The next highest priority dimension may have been in a cluster with its predecessor. If so, any options in this new dimension that are ruled out by the previous choice of option must be deleted before design can continue. Then an option is chosen from the second priority dimension. This new option is also tied to the tie line. This process continues until choices have been made in all dimensions--or, alternatively, a dimension is encountered where all possible options have been ruled out by previous choices. In the former event, the Options Profile is finished, and we have created a design alternative. In the latter event, we have to start over using what was learned in the first iteration. If the first design alternative is satisfactory, no further work is done with this process, otherwise additional alternatives may be generated to provide bases for comparisons of design alternatives.

PORTFOLIO 7

TRADEOFF ANALYSIS METHOD (TAM)

A METHOD FOR CHOOSING ONE ALTERNATIVE DESIGN FROM AMONG A SET OF ALTERNATIVES, FOR DOCUMENTING HOW THIS ALTERNATIVE WAS SELECTED, AND FOR PORTRAYING GRAPHICALLY THE CENTRAL IDEAS BEHIND THE SELECTION.

PORTFOLIO 7
TRADEOFF ANALYSIS METHOD (TAM)

A method for choosing one alternative design from among a set of alternatives, for documenting how this alternative was selected, and for portraying graphically the central ideas behind the selection. A method for documenting, in great detail, how a choice was made from a set of alternatives. The method is intended to provide for the public sector of government a way of developing a choice through the use of a prescribed set of techniques that allow for broad participation, while at the same time providing a way to reveal all of the steps and procedures that led to a final choice. This same approach also allows for iterative choice-making, since all of the steps can be retraced.

APPROPRIATE CONDITIONS FOR USE

A complex choice is to be made from a set of alternatives. This choice will be a major one, involving a substantial and often long-term commitment. Usually it will involve the interests of many people, and many of them will desire that the basis for the choice be made clear. Participation in the making of the decisions is desired. The set of alternatives is small, usually less than ten.

APPLICATION AREAS

Environmental decisions, involving forestry, grasslands, land-use decisions, wildlilfe decisions. Large investment decisions, where there are competing alternatives. Major construction decisions. Prototype design of expensive systems of large equipment.

RESULTS

A thoroughly documented and rather easily interpreted basis for the decisions that have been made. Graphical portrayals of major aspects of decision-making.

RESOURCES REQUIRED

Knowledge of options and alternatives. Large wall for display purposes. Special-purpose software to facilitate the use of the method and the generation of appropriate displays. Means for keeping records of all steps. A group of persons familiar with the issues or topics being investigated, who will contribute to the dialogs and discussions. Facilitator who is throughly familiar with the method.

RELATION TO OTHER METHODS

The Options Profile Method (OPM) can be used to generate alternatives to be explored with the TAM. The TAM is the most complex and detailed of the decision-making methods used in consensus methodologies, takes longer to apply than the other decision-making methods, and is most useful when the number of alternatives is few. For large numbers of alternatives, ISM can be used, augmented with additional documentation.

The TAM method is most useful when the number of alternatives is small, while a method such as ISM can be used to prioritize a large number of alternatives. The ISM method provides less documentation than the TAM method.

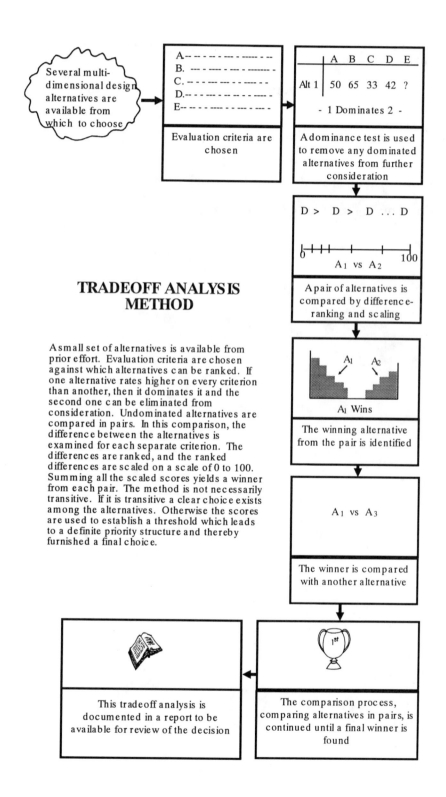

TRADEOFF ANALYSIS METHOD

A small set of alternatives is available from prior effort. Evaluation criteria are chosen against which alternatives can be ranked. If one alternative rates higher on every criterion than another, then it dominates it and the second one can be eliminated from consideration. Undominated alternatives are compared in pairs. In this comparison, the difference between the alternatives is examined for each separate criterion. The differences are ranked, and the ranked differences are scaled on a scale of 0 to 100. Summing all the scaled scores yields a winner from each pair. The method is not necessarily transitive. If it is transitive a clear choice exists among the alternatives. Otherwise the scores are used to establish a threshold which leads to a definite priority structure and thereby furnished a final choice.

Several multi-dimensional design alternatives are available from which to choose

Evaluation criteria are chosen

	A	B	C	D	E
Alt 1	50	65	33	42	?

- 1 Dominates 2 -

A dominance test is used to remove any dominated alternatives from further consideration

D > D > D ... D

0 ————————— 100
A₁ vs A₂

A pair of alternatives is compared by difference-ranking and scaling

A₁ Wins

The winning alternative from the pair is identified

A₁ vs A₃

The winner is compared with another alternative

This tradeoff analysis is documented in a report to be available for review of the decision

The comparison process, comparing alternatives in pairs, is continued until a final winner is found

QUESTIONS RELATED TO APPENDIX 3

1. How should one approach the question of comparing two methodologies to see if they are essentially the same?

2. Compare Ideawriting, Nominal Group Technique, and DELPHI to bring out their similarities and differences.

3. What historical features distinguish Interpretive Structural Modeling from other methodologies?

4. Describe an Options Field. How does it differ from an Options Profile?

5. What are the three main purposes of the Tradeoff Analysis Method?

APPENDIX 4

AUTOMATION OF DOCUMENTATION

One of the hazards in the use of many methodologies for design is that they do not incorporate provision for development of high-quality documentation (or any documentation) concurrently with the work. As a result, documentation is often deferred until later when memory is hazy, and the documentation may be done by someone who was not involved in the creative work. This often leads to mistakes which can propagate indefinitely into other documentation.

The Methodology from the Generic Design Science automatically produces documentation as it goes, for the tasks in the methodologies cannot be carried out without doing so.

The automatic production is partly manual and partly computer-implemented. Over time the percentage of documentation that is computer-produced will increase, as theory is already available to allow computer production of structural maps in ways that facilitate their reading. Such contributions make possible the automated production of deep/long logic in a form that is readily interpreted, and which is produced on a time scale compatible even with crisis-decision-making. A plotter will be needed to produce high-quality structural maps.

There is a gradation involved in the development of automated graphics that reveal the logic of a Design Situation. This gradation involves first the development of the fundamental information that is needed to represent the logic. This can be developed in any of several forms, but a form that has been especially useful as a beginning point is a "binary skeleton matrix" [1].

A second step in the gradation is to find a way to convert this binary skeleton matrix representation into a digraph representation. The question arises as to whether one should express this second step as a movement from the matrix to an optimally-laid out digraph, or just to a digraph. For present purposes we choose the latter. With this choice, existing methods readily permit such a representation.

The third step in the gradation is to discover a way of articulating what constitutes either an optimum or a good representation of a digraph, likely to be substantially superior to one that is arrived at without any such articulation. One of the principal concerns is to lay out the structure in such a way that the eye can readily follow the paths without being forced to deal with many line crossings that break up the visual continuity that is important in reading a logic structure.

If this third step is satisfied, then the fourth step becomes one of modifying the geometry of the digraph to allow its vertexes to be replaced by boxes that contain text, the sizing of the boxes being determined by the amount of text to be included, and the cognitive concerns of how it is entered in order to be most readily assimilated. This is to be done subject to the constraint that none of the benefits gained by laying out the digraph should be lost in making this transformation.

Another part of this consideration is the engineering problem of programming a machine to physically ink or otherwise construct the drawing in a form that is highly readable and can be duplicated by a duplicating machine.

Still another aspect is the importance of doing all of the foregoing in a way that anticipates the need for amendments which are readily facilitated, and which minimize the effort involved in moving from one product to the amended product.

In considering this matter, those who approach the topic with a background in the layout of electrical circuits, such as semiconductor circuits on chips, need to be aware that the problem of chip layout is not the same as the problem of construction of logic diagrams. This is because the latter involves the added constraints that the vertices are constrained to remain within levels, and the edges are constrained to be straight lines.

The mathematical theory that enters the picture can be referred to as a mix of "planarity theory" and "hierarchy mapping". The problem of automatic map construction has been studied by several researchers in the past two decades, and results are already sufficient to indicate that the problem is manageable and is close to being adequately solved.

In 1977, Warfield [2] studied the minimization of line crossings, and offered several algorithms for laying out digraphs. Figure A4.1 shows an initial structure and the result of applying the algorithms developed in [2].

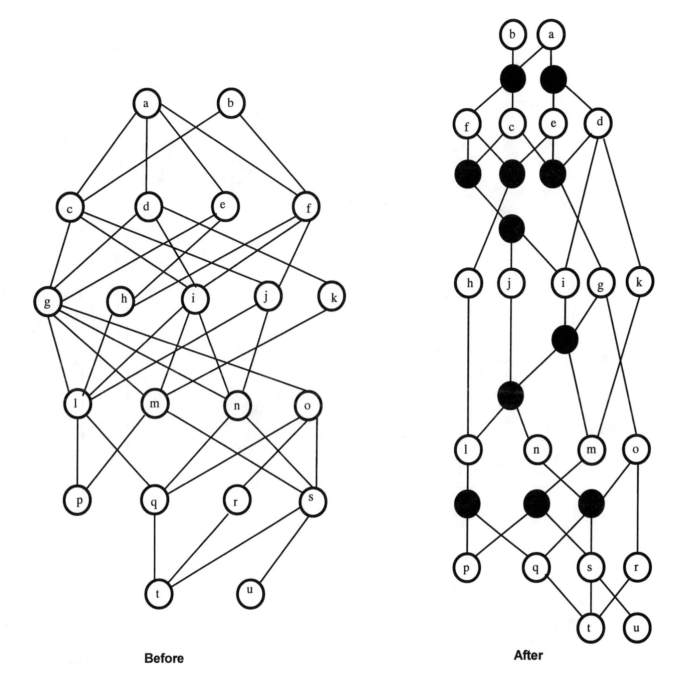

Before

After

Figure A4.1 Map of a structure before and after application of layout algorithms.
Copyright © 1977 IEEE.

Shortly thereafter, Sugiyama, Tagawa, and Toda, of the Fujitsu Research Laboratories, proposed algorithms for automating the construction of digraphs, and showed examples of the application of their algorithm to digraphs with over 100 vertices [3]. Figure A4.2 shows an initial structure and the result of applying the algorithms developed in [3].

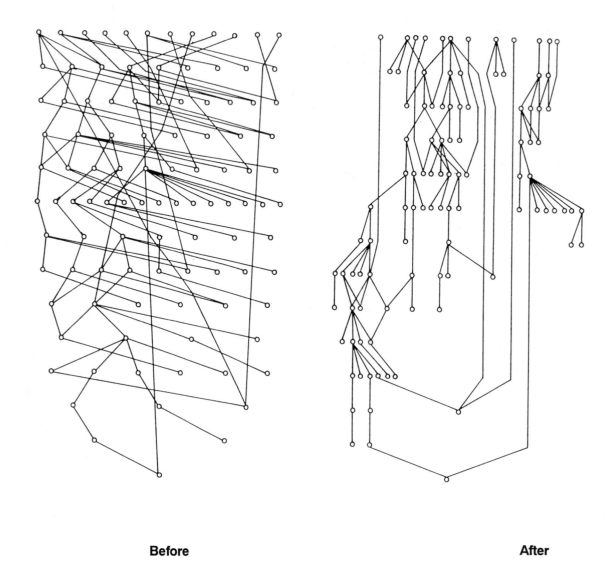

Before   **After**

Figure A4.2 Map of a structure before and after application of layout algorithms.
Copyright © 1981 IEEE.

A survey of the state of the art was presented by Tamassia, Batini, and Di Battista [4]. Further contributions to the understanding of the possibilities with algorithms were made by Batini, Nardelli, and Tamassia [5].

The rationale for continued studies in this area is hopefully clear. Because of the complexity of modern society, it is becoming mandatory to produce high-quality documentation that is clear, readable, authentic, defining, authoritative, and subject to ready modification to incorporate new knowledge and experience in a timely way. In no field is this capability more sorely needed than in the field of large system design.

Because the theory is rather extensive, it seems inappropriate to extend the length of this book by presenting it. However by calling attention to it, we indicate to the reader that the capacity to develop prototype systems is available, and that such systems can be made suitable for production purposes.

REFERENCES

1. J. N. Warfield, *Societal Systems: Planning, Policy, and Complexity*, New York: Wiley, 1976.

2. J. N. Warfield, "Crossing Theory and Hierarchy Mapping", *IEEE Transactions on Systems, Man, and Cybernetics*, SMC- 7(7), 1977, 502-523.

3. K. Sugiyama, S. Tagawa, and M. Toda, "Methods for Visual Understanding of Hierarchical Systems", *IEEE Transactions on Systems, Man, and Cybernetics*, SMC-11(2), 1981, 109-125.

4. R. Tamassia, C. Batini, and G. Di Battista, "Automatic Graph Drawing and Readability of Diagrams", report published by Universita degli Studi di Roma, Via Buonarroti 12, 00185, Rome, Italy, January, 1987.

5. C. Batini, E. Nardelli, and R. Tamassia, "A Layout Algorithm for Data-Flow Diagrams", *IEEE Transactions on Software Engineering*, SE-12(4), 1986, 538-546.

QUESTIONS RELATED TO APPENDIX 4

1. What documentation feature distinguishes the Methodology of the Generic Design Science from many other methodologies?

2. What is a good beginning point for development of an automated graphic?

3. What three steps follow in developing an automated graphic from a beginning with a skeleton matrix?

APPENDIX 5

DATA FROM APPLICATIONS

In this Appendix, data taken in numerous Interactive Management Workshops are presented. During the past few years, these and related data have been presented in various speaking situations before audiences comprised of university faculty, and corporate managers, scientists and engineers. Some of the conclusions drawn from these data seem to be of major significance insofar as they relate to expectations of various kinds of performance from groups. For example, it is very common in organizations that higher-level management will assign to working groups or task forces the obligation to consider a complex issue and formulate recommendations for management action, along with rationale for the chosen alternatives.

The author has been surprised repeatedly at the apparent lack of response to the information presented, especially among academics, but also among some corporate management personnel.

The reader will, perforce, make a personal determination as to the significance or lack thereof of the data and interpretations to be presented. But the author feels that it is important, before presenting the data and interpretations, to review the general basis for scientific discovery, and to consider the possibility that there are misconceptions guiding much of what goes on in the area of human behavior that may have significant and unwanted consequences.

Anyone who is proximate to survey research in social science areas knows that much of what is considered research in social science involves the statement of a hypothesis, the preparation of an "instrument" (questionnaire) for data-gathering, sending the instrument to hoped-for-respondents, the analysis of the returned data, usually using statistical methods, and the drawing of conclusions emanating from interpretation of the analysis.

It is virtually impossible to find a coherent statement of why this method of research has unassailable merit from any scientific perspective. Without doubt, the method has value in some settings, but the specific conditions that need to be satisfied for the method to have value seem to be lost. Justification for research methods in social science typically avoids discussion of the Universal Priors, even though one of them is the human being.

Suppose, for example, it turned out that almost all social science research done on small groups was defective. Suppose further that the results of such research have somehow become embedded in widespread current practice. Then one would expect something like the following: wherever groups are asked to work together, the results would be unproductive, unsatisfying, frustrating, and collectively could lead, over time, to the inability of an entire society to be competitive.

If the foregoing description resembles the reader's experience in some way, perhaps the explanation for the outcomes ties back directly to the assumptions involved in perpetuating the kinds of group behavior that seem to be so unproductive.

What assumptions appear to underpin group activity? First of all, it seems to be assumed that whenever a group meets to work together, there is not much need to prepare the group for the meeting. After all, people are working in a certain area. They should have the skills to contribute in a discussion group. But if this is true, why is it often so difficult for them to do so?

As is repeatedly emphasized in this book, complexity is a major villain in frustrating human endeavor. Couldn't it be the case that the ordinary group meeting in which people strive to work together is fundamentally an extremely complex situation (possibly because each individual human being is behaviorally complex, and when several are in juxtaposition to each other there is no any governing behavioral concept in place), doomed from the beginning to be ineffective? Well, certainly not all the time, because there are success experiences, but how many of those experiences relate to relatively simple items or situations, where the baleful influence of complexity has no opportunity to make its presence felt?

In recent years, there have been some highly-publicized events involving major public figures, in which extremely bad results have been obtained as outcomes of group efforts to advise high-level figures. The famous Bay of Pigs incident perpetrated by the administration of John F. Kennedy has been studied over and over, revealing the awesome dysfunctionality of the processes and guiding principles used by the persons involved in rendering advice in that situation. It is known that following that Bay of Pigs incident, when the time came in the Kennedy administration to consider what decision should be made concerning the Cuban Missile Crisis, major changes were made in the group process due to the experiential learning gained through the Bay of Pigs incident. Many of the same actors were involved in both incidents, and it is reasonable to believe that the more favorable outcome gained in the Cuban Missile Crisis was obtained because of the lessons learned from the Bay of Pigs incident.

But is it not amazing that persons in high leadership positions demonstrably knew so little about how to work together cooperatively on a complex issue, and had to use national crises as learning opportunities to find out things that one would hope would have been learned as students in educational institutions? Of course one could not expect teachers to run students through the Bay of Pigs incident years before it occurred, but one could expect that social scientists could convey something useful about human behavior in groups.

Why might it be the case that this has not occurred? First of all, one must keep in mind that members of the academic establishment literally cannot survive within that establishment unless they perform continuous research and publication; therefore if there is some accepted mode of behavior that can lead to such outcomes, it is unlikely to be significantly challenged. Thus it is possible to see dysfunctional behavior going on indefinitely within the academic environment, while at the same time bad information is being indiscriminately supplied to students who are in no position to criticize or make judgments about what they receive.

Much of the research on groups has been done with groups that have negligible stake in the outcome of the group activity. Is it possible that data taken on such groups is unlikely to be representative of data taken from groups that do have a significant stake in the outcome?

Much of the research on groups is done in settings that make little or no provision for the information-viewing and handling needs of the groups. When Harold Lasswell described his view of what a decision-seminar room ought to be like, he stressed repeatedly the importance of displays that presented information in readily viewable formats that was required for working on a complex issue.

To contrast the approaches that social scientists typically use with what was done to collect the data to be reported, please note that in not a single instance of data-taking to be reported in this chapter was there any suggestion that the participants were "subjects" to be studied. On the contrary, they were there to work together because they shared a common motivation, and the process to be used was not an "experiment", but rather it was a process designed to help them be very productive, carried out in a facility tailored to achieve that same goal. Whatever data accrued from the work were data that came naturally out of the products of the group activity. This means that the data are, pure and simple, the aggregate results of work done by very competent groups working on complex issues, motivated to achive, and generally pleased with the products that they created. This lends value to the data presented that goes far beyond what is normally obtained in social science research, at least insfoar as work on complex issues is concerned.

Before proceeding to identify the data, the essence of the findings will be discussed. This discussion incorporates new information obtained during the five-year period following the collection of the data presented in the Tables in this Appendix.

Guided by the data given in this Appendix and the interpretations of it to be presented, the four-year period from 1990 to 1994 has been used to test the conclusions drawn from the interpretation of the older data. As a result of this continuing evaluation, using data from new sets of Interactive Management Workshops carried out at numerous locations, working with different groups, dealing with different complex issues, it has been possible to gain an even stronger viewpoint of the correctness of what grew out of the prior interpretations.

It has now been established firmly that a phenomenon called "Spreadthink" will virtually always be found whenever and wherever a group of people begin to work on a complex issue. This phenomenon has primarily these three attributes:

- There is widespread variation in belief among the members of a group as to the relative importance of the various component problems involved in a complex situation

- It will be extremely rare that any component problem involved in a larger issue will be viewed by a majority of the group members as lying among a small group of the most important problems

- If, after discussion of the component problems and clarification of them, a recommendation for action is made by the group, there is a high probability that this recommendation will be the consequence of either (a) "Groupthink", (b) "Clanthink", or (c) a combination of Groupthink and Clanthink.

Groupthink is a well-known phenomenon, extensively analyzed in connection with the Bay of Pigs decision situation, where groups recommend a course of action that may not be thought well of by anyone in the group--and, in fact, misrepresents the views of individual members concerning the complex issue being considered, this coming about because of Clanthink: an incorrect view held by all or almost all members of the group about something other than the complex issue being considered, e.g., that time requires that they appear to support a decision along the lines they are being directed, without regard to whether that decision has merit in their eyes; or, as a second example of Clanthink: "the earth is flat".

The second major finding is that it is almost always possible to obtain a virtually opposite result to Spreadthink, by applying the Interpretive Structural Modeling (ISM) process in the group. After the Spreadthink finding is evident, the ISM process is applied, with these primary outcomes:

- The group produces a structural model containing a large number of relationships among the component problems involved in the issue, and portraying these relationships graphically on a structure such as a "problematique"

- Every single relationship (of which there are frequently more than a hundred) among the problems has been placed there because at least a majority of the participants have arrived at the view through discussion that the relationship holds

- The structure produced supplies consensus information for decisionmaking

The foregoing remarks can serve to alert the reader concerning what to look for in the following discussions. Data with similar results can be obtained by any serious investigator who wishes to reconstruct the conditions under which these data were gathered. A considerable amount of additional data are available in archived reports of Interactive Management sessions conducted at numerous locations by numerous individuals on a variety of topics extending over a period of several years. These individual reports and the data contained therein furnish additional verification of what has been concluded. What actions seems to be indicated by these data and the interpretations of the data? It is perhaps only a mild overstatement to say that any recommendation coming from any group that has used only ordinary dialog to discuss a complex issue should not be taken as a basis for a final decision on what to do about a complex issue. One could readily imagine that such recommendations could emerge from legislative bodies and from trial juries, both bodies suffering from Spreadthink, neither body having taken advantage of the availability of the ISM process to arrive collectively at a new and higher plane of understanding through the group dialog assisted by the process of organizing the logic of a complex issue. Perhaps a law is needed to require that "due process" be defined and applied to the issue of complex system design or complex alternatives design, and that a significant penalty should be attached to failure to take the responsibility for carrying out such a process.

The data presented here have been extracted from records of numerous group efforts in which several of the Consensus Methodologies described in Appendix 3 were used. These data, collected during the period 1983-1989 support the foregoing summary remarks. The data reveal certain common characteristics in the products of the work that are independent of the complex problem being investigated and independent of the group of people who were working on the complex problem. Specifically, these data validate the Law of Requisite Saliency, as they show that great diversity of belief exists in every group on the relative importance of factors involved in resolving the complexity.

The data also indicate the importance of extensive dialog in order to transform this diversity into a consensus approach to problem-solving and design. If the diversity of belief that is always present at the outset of problem solving and design involving complex issues is allowed to persist, these will be among the possible consequences:

- No agreement will be reached on the nature of the issue

- No agreement will be reached on the nature of the remedy

- No solution will be agreed upon (even if superficial agreement appears to surface)

- People may believe that agreement has been reached, and proceed with this false belief

- Teamwork in implementation will be guided by diversity of belief, which will produce incompatible results and make the problem-situation worse

The data also reveal clearly the appearance of protracted logic in every instance, validating the numerous references to the importance of this idea in designing complex systems.

A5.1 Data on the Nominal Group Technique.

Table A5.1 shows data on 43 sessions that were run by staff of the Center for Interactive Management, using the Nominal Group Technique.

The Case Number in Table A5.1 is simply a numerical key to a particular session. The Duration is the time consumed by the session, rounded to the nearest quarter hour.

In the Table, N_1 refers to the total number of ideas generated during the session. The number of ideas selected, N_2, refers to the number of ideas that received at least one vote from at least one participant as being among the five most important ideas generated during the session. As discussed in Chapter 7, the selection occurs after clarification of all ideas.

Diversity

The "Diversity", $N_2/5 - 1$, is a defined measure of the difference of opinion among the participants on the relative importance of the ideas generated to the issue being discussed. Please note that if the participants all agreed on which 5 of the ideas generated were the most important, the Diversity would be equal to 0. The more the participants differ on the relative importance of the ideas generated, the larger is the value of the Diversity.

Note that the average value of the Diversity is 5.6, found by averaging over all 43 sessions.

In 63% of the sessions, the number of ideas generated was equal to or greater than 5 times the number of participants. For these 27 sessions, the maximum possible disagreement could occur on relative importance, with each participant theoretically being able to choose, as the most important, 5 ideas that no other participant would include as among the 5 most important. For these sessions, if 11 participants are assumed, the maximum possible average value of the Diversity would have been 10. This means that the possible range of values for Diversity would be from 0 to 10, with 0 meaning perfect consensus and 10 meaning perfect disagreement.

Since the mean value of Diversity averaged over all sessions was 5.6, it is clear that on average, no matter what the issue, and no matter what the group, the Diversity was closer to perfect disagreement than to perfect consensus. This finding is believed to be very significant in terms of complex problem solving and complex system design, even though the number of samples is relatively small. It is easy to see from the Table that there is no sample for which the Diversity is less than 2.8.

Table A5.1
Data on Sessions Using the Nominal Group Technique

Case Number	Duration (hours)	Number of Ideas Generated (N_1)	Number of Ideas Selected (N_2)	Diversity ($N_2/5 - 1$)
1	2.5	56	26	4.2
2	3.0	67	35	6.0
3	2.0	68	36	6.2
4	2.0	42	20	3.0
5	2.0	48	31	5.2
6	3.0	79	36	6.2
7	5.0	54	26	4.2
8	2.5	59	46	8.2
9	3.0	64	40	7.0
10	4.0	101	43	7.6
11	2.0	50	28	4.6
12	3.0	84	55	10.0
13	3.0	92	67	12.4
14	2.5	58	29	4.8
15	2.0	36	24	3.8
16	2.0	47	31	5.2
17	3.0	49	29	4.8
18	4.0	43	21	3.2
19	3.0	96	44	7.8
20	2.0	64	48	8.6
21	3.0	71	48	8.6
22	2.0	52	35	6.0
23	2.0	57	30	5.0
24	2.0	37	19	2.8
25	3.0	56	35	6.0
26	3.0	74	45	8.0
27	4.0	80	44	7.8
28	3.0	45	22	3.4
29	5.0	127	34	5.8
30	4.0	51	26	4.2
31	2.75	58	40	7.0
32	3.5	93	34	5.8
33	5.0	82	35	6.0

Case Number	Duration (hours)	Number of Ideas Generated (N_1)	Number of Ideas Selected (N_2)	Diversity ($N_2/5 - 1$)
34	2.25	44	26	4.2
35	2.25	36	23	3.6
36	3.75	78	32	5.4
37	3.75	67	37	6.4
38	2.75	67	29	4.8
39	3.0	58	26	4.2
40	4.25	57	24	3.8
41	3.25	66	28	4.6
42	2.25	58	30	5.0
43	5.0	90	32	5.4
Mean	3.1 hours	64 ideas	33 ideas	5.6

Twenty-five of the cases (58%) show a Diversity that equals or exceeds 5.0, which would be half way between the minimum value of 0 and the maximum possible value of 10 (for those cases where sufficient ideas were generated to permit perfect disagreement).

It seems quite clear from these data that in order to reach any kind of reasonable consensus on a complex issue or design problem, significant changes in perspective will be required from members of the group in order to diminish substantially the Diversity that exists at the beginning of the attack on the problem. Such a view provides strong support for the Law of Requisite Saliency (Chap. 6). One must also believe that attempts to resolve the Diversity by fiat are ill-conceived.

Other data appear in the Table that are of value in planning NGT sessions. Specifically, one can estimate the average time needed for a session in which a complex issue is dealt with, and can get an estimate of the number of ideas that may be generated.

A5.2 Data on Interpretive Structural Modeling.

Table A5.2 presents data on cases in which Interpretive Structural Modeling was used. In every case but one in Table A5.2, there appears at least one cycle of length 2 or more, the mean value of the longest cycle being 7.1, which can be rounded to 7 for purposes of discussion. A cycle with 7 members exhibits protracted logic that stresses short-term memory.

Table A5.2
Data on Sessions Using Interpretive Structural Modeling

Case Number	Duration (Hours)	Number of Ideas Structured	Length of:		
			Condensed Hierarchy	Longest Cycle	Minimum Max. Walk
1	2.5	26	5	14	19
2	3.0	26	9	3	12
3	2.0	22	4	12	16
4	3.0	16	8	3	11
5	3.0	17	6	3	9
6	3.0	21	5	4	9
7	2.0	26	3	4	7
8	3.0	25	8	5	13
9	3.0	21	7	7	14
10	3.0	28	8	4	12
11	3.0	19	5	7	12
12	3.0	32	5	7	12
13	6.0	16	7	3	10
14	4.0	29	3	17	20
15	2.0	11	5	3	8
16	4.0	20	17	2	19
17	3.0	27	3	14	17
18	3.0	19	11	5	16
19	1.5	17	4	5	9
20	0.5	18	5	2	9
21	3.0	21	11	4	15
22	4.5	20	8	3	11
23	4.0	21	10	5	15
24	3.5	34	3	15	18
25	3.0	20	11	0	11
26	3.25	21	3	14	17
27	3.25	28	2	18	20
28	1.5	9	6	2	8
29	3.5	26	5	13	18
30	3.5	19	5	6	11
31	5.0	22	4	3	7
Mean	3.1 hours	22 ideas	6.3	7.1	13.4

A condensed hierarchy is a structure that is obtained from the original structure by replacing every cycle in the original structure with a single "proxy element" [1]. The length of the condensed hierarchy is one less than the number of levels in the hierarchy. It is seen from the Table that after rounding the mean length of the condensed hierarchy to 6, the average number of levels in this hierarchy is 7, represented protracted logic.

A graded approach to assessing the cognitive burden associated with the mean structure could take as the first stage of gradation just the length of the condensed hierarchy. A second stage in the gradation could substitute in the condensed hierarchy only the longest cycle (regardless of how many happened to be present in the original structure) to substitute for its proxy element. With this substitution made, the longest walk to be examined in the structure would be the sum of the length of the condensed hierarchy and the length of the longest cycle. This sum might be referred to as the length of the minimum "maximum walk", where the maximum walk is the longest walk on a given structure; in this case the structure found from the original structure by replacing every cycle except the longest cycle with a proxy element.

Still higher gradations would be found by replacing, one at a time, a proxy element with the full cycle that it represents.

If a single number were to be used to represent the cognitive burden associated with the original structure, the length of the minimum maximum walk would probably be the most representative one to use, although the specifics of any particular case could be used to explore the situation in detail.

Average Walk Length

Taking only this particular number, it is seen from Table A5.2 that the rounded length of 13 is the average value of walk length to be examined and interpreted, based on the 31 sessions for which data are presented. The number 13 is then a beginning measure of how protracted the logic is in assessing a complex issue or problem. Perhaps the most appropriate way to interpret the significance of this number is to note that it is highly unlikely that protracted logic of this type would be generated by individuals operating without cognitive assistance, at least in those situations where the protracted logic is a deep logic as opposed to a logic of time sequencing of events, for example. Even the development of the latter should not be taken lightly, although people clearly deal with temporal sequences constantly in their lives.

Changes in Perspective

Judge I. B. Kapelouzos has studied a sizeable subset of the cases to explore the correlations between the relationships perceived by members of the group immediately after the NGT work and the relationships developed by the group during the ISM work [2]. He concluded that there is virtually no correlation.

His work establishes that there is a significant change in perception of the issue, especially as indicated by the deep logic patterns developed, which he attributes to participation in the ISM process.

A5.3 Empirically-Suggested Laws.

The results of analysis of the data given in the foregoing sections suggests that three additional Laws of Design be articulated. Like any other empirically-derived generalizations, these three should be subjected to further study.

The Law of Inherent Conflict. The NGT data suggest the following Law, which may be called the Law of Inherent Conflict:

> **No matter what the complex issue, and no matter what the group involved in its study, there will be significant inherent conflict within the group stemming from different perceptions of the relative significance of the factors involved in the complex issue.**

The Law of Structural Underconceptualization. The ISM data strongly suggest the following Law, which may be called the Law of Structural Underconceptualization:

> **No matter what the complex issue, and no matter what the group involved in its study, the outcomes of ordinary group process (i.e., process in which computer support for developing the formal logical structure of the issue is lacking) will be structurally underconceptualized (as evidenced, for example, by the lack of delineation of the cycles and of any structural connections among them).**

The Law of Uncorrelated Extremes. The analysis of Judge Kapelouzos strongly suggests the following Law, which may be called the Law of Uncorrelated Extremes:

> **No matter what the complex issue, and no matter what the group involved in its study, the initial aggregate group opinion concerning the logical pattern of the factors involved in the issue and the final aggregate group-opinion concerning the logical pattern of the factors involved in the issue (i.e., the views at the two extremes of the application of the Generic Design Science, before and after), will be uncorrelated; showing that significant learning takes place through the application of the generic design processes.**

REFERENCES

1. J. N. Warfield, *Societal Systems: Planning, Policy, and Complexity*, New York: Wiley, 1976 (reprinted, Salinas, CA: Intersystems, 1989).

2. I. B. Kapelouzos, "The Impact of Structural Modeling on the Creation of New Perspectives in Problem Solving Situations", *Proceedings of the 1989 European Congress on Systems Science*, Lausanne: AFCET, October, 1989, 915-932.

QUESTIONS RELATED TO APPENDIX 5

1. What is the average time required for a NGT session?

2. What is the average number of ideas generated in a NGT session?

3. What percent of the average number of ideas generated in an NGT session is found in somebody's top five list?

4. Explain how the Diversity data support the Law of Requisite Saliency.

5. What is the average time required for an ISM session?

6. What is the average number of ideas structured in an ISM session?

7. What are the minimum, maximum, and average lengths of the condensed hierarchy found in the product of an ISM session?

8. What are the minimum, maximum, and average lengths of the longest cycle found in the product of an ISM session?

9. What are the minimum, maximum, and average lengths of the minimum maximum walk found in the product of an ISM session?

10. Discuss the meaning and significance of the Law of Inherent Conflict.

11. Discuss the meaning and significance of the Law of Structural Underconceptualization.

12. Discuss the meaning and significance of the Law of Uncorrelated Extremes.

13. Discuss the significance of the three Laws discussed in this Appendix for the workings of a large corporation and for the Congress of the United States.

APPENDIX 6

EXPERIENCE IN TEACHING
GENERIC DESIGN SCIENCE

The significant question arises: is it possible to teach design in higher education? More specifically, it is possible to teach the generic design science, and to incorporate into the teaching activities experiences of designing systems?

Another important question involves the issue of the contexts in which design should be taught. This has to do with the larger issue of who in society does design or should do design, and what kinds of systems should be designed.

Still another important question has to do with the extent to which higher education presents an environment, intellectual and physical, in which design can effectively be done within the rather tightly-drawn circumstances in which higher education allows learning to take place. It does not appear, for example, that design work can be done effectively, particularly in group settings, in formal classrooms where students sit for 50 minutes facing a professor, with relatively little space to do anything more than take notes.

This Appendix is intended to do two things: first to discuss questions of the foregoing type and, second to describe experience so far in teaching generic design science in universities. This Appendix is supplemented by Appendix 8, which describes a workshop held on the island of Chios, Greece, to explore questions related to the development of a design culture in higher education.

Possibilities of Teaching Generic Design.

The experience to be described in this Appendix seems to establish clearly that it is possible to teach generic design science in higher education. Or if it is not seen as clear, at least there is a strong indication that it can be done under appropriate conditions.

The argument is that if it is shown that one professor can do so, and if two sets of students at different institutions and in different stages of their studies can learn the subject and display evidence of that, it should be possible for others to do the same. The question then becomes one of appropriate conditions for doing so.

Contexts for Teaching Design.

Because teaching design is something that remains relatively novel for higher education, the contexts that might be involved bear discussion. It may even be appropriate to reinvent the university in order to make possible high-quality activities involving system design, given the number of large systems presently impacting life and the haphazard political design activity that goes on. With this in mind, a review was undertaken some years ago to explore the concept of the "great university", wherein learning design theory and carrying out designs would be an integral part of education.

The Great University was conceived as one based on the three fundamental objectives of higher education set forth by the late American Harvard University philosopher, Ralph Barton Perry. In his view, the three basic objectives could be separated on a time line. The one involving the past deals with "the inheritance", i.e., with what humanity can learn from the past, whether it be in literature, science, or other areas. The one involving the present deals with preparing people to perform effectively in today's society, for example in professional roles such as engineer, attorney, nurse, physician, economist, or faculty member. The third involves developing a capacity to contribute to the longer-range future of civilization. In our studies, it was argued that these three objectives could be matched one-to-one with three major divisions of higher education: (a) the **University College**, consisting largely of liberal arts and sciences, (b) the **Professional College**, combining medicine, engineering, law, and other professional studies under one ethics-linked leadership and, finally, (c) the **Horizons College**, in which future system designs to improve conditions in society became the central focus.

Managed interaction among these three would be required of the administration: a task for which they might not be prepared.

The Environment.

It appears that a new infrastructure is required to accomodate the Horizons College in higher education. Such an infrastructure would reflect the conditions more often found in the growing number of centers and institutes, which can accommodate laboratory environments within their organizations, normally paid for by outside sponsors. It is true that the U. S. Government has, in the past, been willing to pay for physical facilities in universities that become allied with special federal programs, such as the space program. On the other hand, governments are not generally excited about system design activities in universities, preferring so far to do political design as a means of filling their responsibilities; but in the absence of design science, this was the only avenue open to them.

The Conditions for Change.

Institutions of higher education are not prone to change except at the micro level of individual courses. Nonetheless it is true that all such institutions depend for their survival upon a healthy society. To the extent that unwillingness of institutions of higher education to make changes gradually destroys the base of their financial support, one might hope for motivated change to take place.

Realistically, however, one will most likely have to rely on modest incursions into the existing system. In this respect, it is encouraging to note that institutions of higher education have begun to play a role in advancing the capabilities of people to do system designs within university settings. Without exception, this has occurred only where there are individuals who are highly motivated to assist groups of people to work with complex systems. So far, the institutions who have taken leadership in their academic programs in this area include the University of São Paulo, Brazil; City University, London, England; and the Instituto Tecnológico y de Estudios Superiores de Monterrey, Nuevo Leon, Mexico. At least four well-known universities in the United States have uniformly chosen not even to explore possibilities.

A6.1 Four Offerings of Generic Design at Two Universities.

A 3-semester-credit-hour course in Generic Design has been offered at two universities on four different occasions by the author and his colleagues. The first two offerings were at the University of Virginia in 1982 and 1983 respectively. Both were offered to sections of fourth-semester honors students (Rodman Scholars) enrolled in various departments of the School of Engineering and Applied Science. The other two offerings were at George Mason University in 1985 and 1986. Both were offered as "University Courses", open to students from any part of the University. Almost all of these students who took the course were from non-engineering, liberal arts backgrounds.

On all four occasions, the specially-equipped Demosophia working environment was available along with the various forms of assistance to groups described in Chapter 8, and was used by the students enrolled in the course.

On all four occasions, there were individuals (graduate students or visiting scholars) who were receiving instruction in filling the role of facilitator (Pilotos), and who participated to fill that role with groups of students working on a common design project, as part of their own development in the role.

Each course can be described as consisting of a sequence of four Phases, which are labeled as (1) Frame-Breaking, (2) Remodeling, (3) Escalating, and (4) Exploiting. Table A6.1 provides a description of various facets of these course offerings as they relate to the four Phases just identified.

Table A6.1
Capsule Description of Four Course Offerings, By Phases

Duration	4 Weeks	2 Weeks	3 Weeks	5 Weeks
	Phase 1 Frame-breaking	Phase 2 Remodeling	Phase 3 Escalating	Phase 4 Exploiting
INSTRUCTIONAL MODE				
% of Time in Lecture	100%	100%	20%	0%
% of Time in Laboratory	0%	0%	80%	100%
ASSIGNMENTS				
Retrospective Design	Yes	Yes	No	No
1st Group Design Task	No	No	Yes	No
2nd Group Design Task	No	No	No	Yes
LEARNING SITUATION				
% Individual Work	100%	100%	20%	5%
% Group Work	0%	0%	80%	95%
OUTSIDER INVOLVEMENT				
Inventors Panel	No	Yes	No	No
Evaluators Panel	No	No	No	Yes
METHODOLOGIES USED				
Ideawriting	Yes	No	No	No
Nominal Group Technique	No	No	Yes	Yes
DELPHI	No	No	No	No
Inter. Struc. Mod.	No	No	Yes	Yes
Options Field Methodology	No	Yes	Yes	Yes
Options Profile Methodology	No	Yes	Yes	Yes
Tradeoff Analysis	No	No	No	Yes
PRODUCTS				
Individual Oral Report	No	Some	No	No
Shared Oral Reports	No	No	Yes	Yes
Individual Written Report	No	Yes	No	No
Shared Written Report	No	No	Yes	Yes

Following the presentation of this Table, a discussion of its contents is given. After that, some examples of the results of the student work are given, along with commentary about the work.

A6.2 Phase 1: Frame-Breaking.

The first Phase, Frame-Breaking, was intended to replace a student mind set that is accustomed to receiving knowledge and, to some extent, to analyzing it. It is intended to develop a new kind of mind set, oriented to creative thought and invention. But how is it possible to modify rapidly a mind set developed from years of receiving, in order to provide a mental basis for design in the latter part of a college course?

The approach taken is to get the student involved in "walking in the moccasins" of a previous designer, in relation to a Design Target that is relatively simple. The concept of "retrospective design" involves asking the student to attempt to recreate reasoning processes that might have been involved in the design of some common object, such as a thumb tack.

In order to provide a framework for organizing thoughts, and stimulating systematic accumulation of needed information, the Theory of Dimensionality is presented rapidly, and examples of its past use in describing Situations and Designs are presented. It is indicated that groups of people engaged with the Sigma-5 concept discussed in Chapter 8, are provided support in their design activity, and have consistently been productive. The class is held in the Demosophia environment, where examples of prior work can readily be displayed.

The students are told that initially they will not work in groups, but rather will select a simple object of interest to them which will become the basis for their retrospective design project. Every student has a different Target, and will turn in an individual report. A few of the reports will be selected for presentation.

To get the students started in thinking about what they might consider as the focus of their retrospective design project, the Ideawriting process is used with the class. A suitable trigger question is: "what relatively simple object might you be interested in re-designing?", which leads to a long list of possibilities from which students can choose that one Target of their work.

In their report, students are asked to identify the options, dimensions, and clusters (see Chapters 2 and 6), and to present an options field and one or more options profiles for possible designs, then to discuss their own design in the light of these structures.

A6.3 Phase 2: Remodeling.

Remodeling refers to what the student does personally during the retrospective design activity. Specifically, it refers to the changes that are experienced by the student en route to the development of the report that describes the retrospective design.

To help this process along, a panel of designers is invited to attend one class meeting. The panel is comprised of people who have been awarded one or more patents as a result of their inventive and design capabilities. Before the panel is held, students are shown a patent chosen to illustrate the importance of precise communication, highlighting the graphics parts of the patent. Also the variety of claims present in a typical patent is discussed, and the importance of exploring all the potential of an invention as part of the application is emphasized.

The panel of designers is chosen to reflect diversity. Experience with such panels has shown that people who receive patents can take very different routes to success, and can have very different approaches, while still having in common a creative bent and a desire to achieve. This experience not only shows students role models of successful designers, but also helps convince them that they do not have to fit into some particular mold to succeed. The enthusiasm of the panelists is also infectious, and helps further to interest the students to think about the potential joy of creating successful designs.

Three examples of student projects are described next that reflect the kind of outcomes achieved as the consequence of the relatively new behavioral mode developed in the process of carrying out the work.

Retrospective Design # 1: Portable Stereo System

The design study of the portable stereo system revealed that its development incorporated several innovations in product components. The headphone, especially, involved multiple demands: non-fatiguing to the jogger, efficient in order to play loudly from very small power input, and having capability for a bass response.

The interdependence of weight with the choice of magnet materials required that a new magnet material be devised. The desire for a good frequency response required that new techniques be devised to make a thin diaphragm, and diminution of stress on electrical connectors required novel attention to the mechanics of the conductors. An improved earpad material was needed to provide good sound without excess weight. Even a new conductor composition was needed to maximize performance, and a variety of user comfort factors were incorporated in the design.

Figure A6.1 shows the options profile developed for this system by the student.

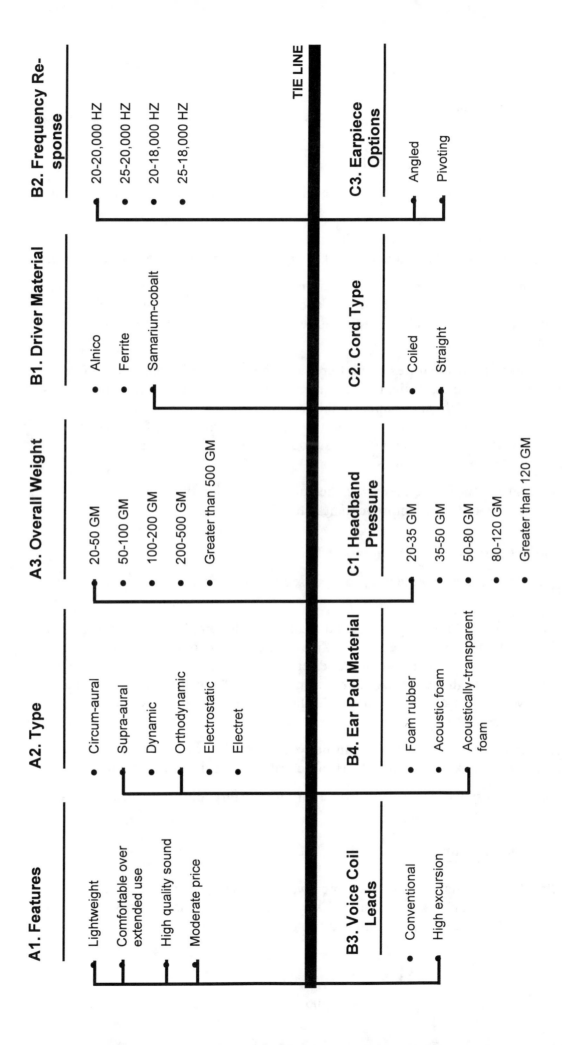

Figure A6.1 Student's retrospective options profile for portable stereo system.

A Science of Generic Design

Retrospective Design # 2: Steel Rail

Figure A6.2 shows an options field developed by the student for steel rail to be used in railroad travel.

This student used seven references for his study, including a book on railway transportation published in India, where long rail lines join cities that are far from each other.

In examining the history, he noted that in the evolution of rails, wooden beams with square cross-sections were used first, and they were followed by wooden beams with steel strapping. Later all-iron rail was developed including the T-rail which appeared in 1831.

Among the design features noted were: (a) the variation in weight with location, such as branch lines, straight runs, curves, switches, and steep grades; (b) the interdependence of weight and shape; (c) the relative independence of composition and shape; (d) the use of special treatment for crack prevention; (e) factors in selecting the length of sections; and (f) the ubiquitous nature of price and rail wear which impacts all of the design decisions.

From the study of the dimensions, the author concluded that the search for new alloys is the route to further improvement in the design of rails.

Retrospective Design # 3: Self-Threading Needle

The self-threading needle is a product used for people whose eyes make the use of ordinary needles difficult.

The student explored the details of the concept, with emphasis upon the geometry and its relation to user convenience. An early design failed because it did not provide enough asymmetry between the relative ease of getting the thread through and keeping it through the eye. A later design succeeded because the narrowed aperture allowed easy insertion, but made it difficult for the thread to escape once it had been inserted.

The price difference of only 9 cents between an ordinary needle and a self-threading needle makes the product very practical for consumer consideration.

Figure A6.3 shows the options profile for the self-threading needle, as developed by the student.

A6.4 Phase 3: Escalating.

After the students have successfully arrived at a retrospective design, they are now ready to enter a new kind of activity: working in groups. As discussed in Chapter 4, this involves escalation of complexity in a variety of ways.

506

A1. Weight (lbs./yard)

- 65
- 70
- 75
- 80
- 85
- 90
- 95
- 100

- 106
- 107
- 110
- 112
- 113
- 115
- 127
- 129

- 130
- 131
- 132
- 133
- 136
- 140
- 155

A2. Shape

- ARA-A
- ARA-B
- AREA
- ASCE
- CAN.PAC
- C & NW
- Interborough
- Lehigh Valley

- Dudley
- NY, NH, & C
- PENN
- R&P
- Misc.
- Head-free
- T.R.

TIE LINE

B. Composition

- Standard
- High-carbon
- High-manganese
- High-silicon
- High-chromium

- Chromium-molybdenum
- Chromium-vanadium
- Vanadium

C. Hardening

- Heat-treated heads
- Heat-treated ends

D. Special Processes

- Controlled cooling
- Bruno-rizing

E. Rail Length

- Standard
- CWR

Figure A6.2 Student's retrospective options field for steel rail.

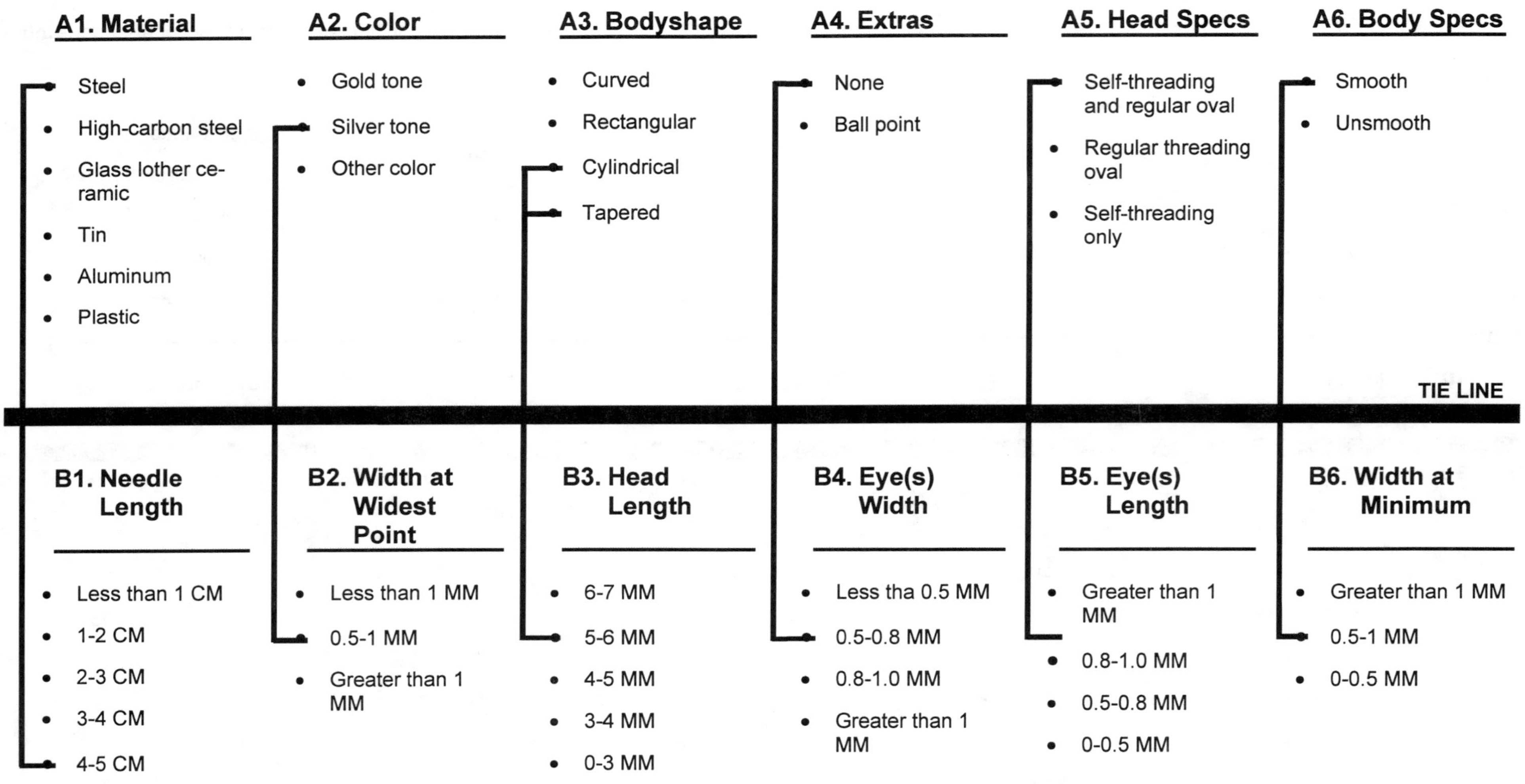

A1. Material

- Steel
- High-carbon steel
- Glass lother ce-ramic
- Tin
- Aluminum
- Plastic

A2. Color

- Gold tone
- Silver tone
- Other color

A3. Bodyshape

- Curved
- Rectangular
- Cylindrical
- Tapered

A4. Extras

- None
- Ball point

A5. Head Specs

- Self-threading and regular oval
- Regular threading oval
- Self-threading only

A6. Body Specs

- Smooth
- Unsmooth

TIE LINE

B1. Needle Length

- Less than 1 CM
- 1-2 CM
- 2-3 CM
- 3-4 CM
- 4-5 CM

B2. Width at Widest Point

- Less than 1 MM
- 0.5-1 MM
- Greater than 1 MM

B3. Head Length

- 6-7 MM
- 5-6 MM
- 4-5 MM
- 3-4 MM
- 0-3 MM

B4. Eye(s) Width

- Less tha 0.5 MM
- 0.5-0.8 MM
- 0.8-1.0 MM
- Greater than 1 MM

B5. Eye(s) Length

- Greater than 1 MM
- 0.8-1.0 MM
- 0.5-0.8 MM
- 0-0.5 MM

B6. Width at Minimum

- Greater than 1 MM
- 0.5-1 MM
- 0-0.5 MM

Figure A6.3 Student's retrospective options profile for self-threading needle.

The students are now split into groups of between 4 and 7 people, with one facilitator assigned to work with each group. The groups are given a very short list of group design projects by the instructor, and asked to choose which they will work on. These projects typically are chosen from Design Situations that are found in the campus environment. For example, projects were carried out on the School Mail Room, which was an inefficient and poorly managed environment, and on the design of a new student computer room to house a number of microprocessors to be shared by students in the beginning computer classes. By choosing such projects, groups have the opportunity to collect intelligence information, do analyses and, in general, carry out the various functions described in Section 1.7 as being inherent in design.

Once again the Options Field and Options Profile provide the organizing framework for the information, while other Consensus Methodologies are made available to the groups to help them define the problem better and to carry out other tasks associated with arriving at a design.

The primary emphasis during this project is to learn how to work in facilitated groups, and the quality of the group product is not given as much emphasis as will come in the final project.

Throughout this Phase, there are very few lectures, these coming only upon student demand, in order to free up the class for design meetings in small groups at times of their own choosing.

A6.5 Phase 4: Exploiting.

In the final Phase, which involves exploiting everything they have learned, new facets enter the picture. In this Phase the groups are asked to select their own design projects, but once again to choose projects that have the potential for application in their community, be it the academic community, or the surrounding community.

Moreover the groups are advised that a formal presentation of their design results will be required near the end of the term, at which time outside evaluators will be present to hear their presentations and to comment upon them.

The groups are told to take the position that they are trying to market their design concept through their group presentation and report, which thereby takes on the double status of both a report on a design and a marketing thrust to try to get support for continuing the work.

Throughout this activity the groups are provided with facilitative support, including the use of the Demosophia environment in which to carry out their group activity.

No lectures are held during this period. The groups meet at times that is convenient to their schedules and when the facilities are available for their use.

The next section describes one project carried out by several competing design groups. The purpose of this project was to design a late-night escort service primarily to serve students on a campus who needed to be out at night, but who desired to have escort services provided from where they were working to their residence.

A6.6 Design of a Late-Night Escort Service.

Three separate groups worked on the design of a Late-Night Escort Service to help students journey safely to their homes. The report of the Alpha group is identified in the References.

Initially, meeting as a whole, the class performed an Ideawriting exercise and identified eleven possible design topics. These were:

- Clemons Library Operations
- Government Document Room
- University Bus System
- U. S. Patent System
- Lottery for Basketball Tickets
- Safety at National Airport
- Election Process at University
- Housing Lottery System
- Rare Book Preservation System
- Student Escort Service
- Pre-Medical School Criteria

The ISM process was used with the entire class to prioritize these as possible topics for a design project. The selected project, the Student Escort Service, was chosen from this prioritization work.

The groups found that it was quite difficult to get any information on the existing system. Eventually they were able to find a person who knew most of its history. Data were available on incidents showing both the need for the service and the need for improvement of it. It was found that there were 50 volunteers, two co-chairs, four supervisors, people working in shifts 7 days a week, a dispatcher, one station wagon, funding of over $3,000 per year by the Student Council from a $250,000 budget, and very limited awareness and capacity in the system. It was also found that there was not much interest in trying to expand the services, and that there was a more-or-less permanent clientele.

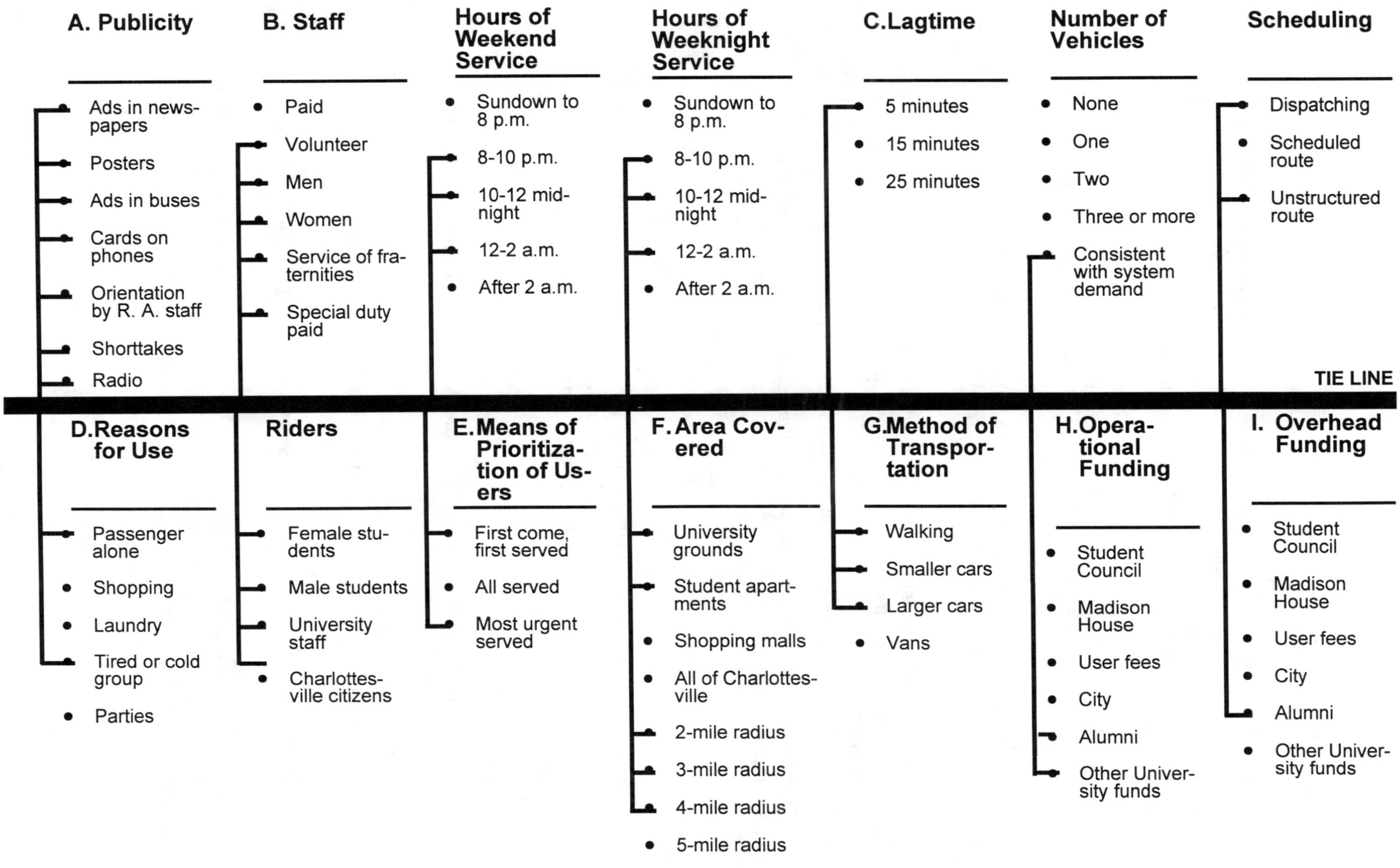

A. Publicity
- Ads in newspapers
- Posters
- Ads in buses
- Cards on phones
- Orientation by R. A. staff
- Shorttakes
- Radio

B. Staff
- Paid
- Volunteer
- Men
- Women
- Service of fraternities
- Special duty paid

Hours of Weekend Service
- Sundown to 8 p.m.
- 8-10 p.m.
- 10-12 midnight
- 12-2 a.m.
- After 2 a.m.

Hours of Weeknight Service
- Sundown to 8 p.m.
- 8-10 p.m.
- 10-12 midnight
- 12-2 a.m.
- After 2 a.m.

C. Lagtime
- 5 minutes
- 15 minutes
- 25 minutes

Number of Vehicles
- None
- One
- Two
- Three or more
- Consistent with system demand

Scheduling
- Dispatching
- Scheduled route
- Unstructured route

TIE LINE

D. Reasons for Use
- Passenger alone
- Shopping
- Laundry
- Tired or cold group
- Parties

Riders
- Female students
- Male students
- University staff
- Charlottesville citizens

E. Means of Prioritization of Users
- First come, first served
- All served
- Most urgent served

F. Area Covered
- University grounds
- Student apartments
- Shopping malls
- All of Charlottesville
- 2-mile radius
- 3-mile radius
- 4-mile radius
- 5-mile radius

G. Method of Transportation
- Walking
- Smaller cars
- Larger cars
- Vans

H. Operational Funding
- Student Council
- Madison House
- User fees
- City
- Alumni
- Other University funds

I. Overhead Funding
- Student Council
- Madison House
- User fees
- City
- Alumni
- Other University funds

Figure A6.4 Group's options profile for Student Escort Service.

A survey among students showed that there was an especially great need for late-night operation. The existing system stopped operating before the libraries closed. Also there was a lack of publicity. [As A. Downs has clearly explained in his *Inside Bureaucracy*, every agency that furnishes a low-cost service needs to find ways to limit its clientele.]

The Alpha Group decided that there was a clear need for an improved system design, and proceeded to establish goals based on their survey and the history of the system.

They then produced four options profiles representing four alternatives: (a) the current system, (b) a maximum-service system, (c) a minimum-cost system, and (d) a compromise system.

A tradeoff analysis was made using TAM, which produced a design having a 50% greater capacity, 8.5 more service hours per week at the most greatly needed times, greater publicity about the system, and an annual cost of $3,000 more than the existing system, which would be about 1% of the Student Council budget.

Recommendations were made for soliciting alumni support to purchase a second station wagon.

Figure A6.4 shows the options profile for the compromise design, which is the one that proved to be superior in terms of the application of the Tradeoff Analysis Methodology.

The work of all three groups in providing examples of the use of the Generic Design Science in carrying out and documenting a system design is appreciated, and has been used to help succeeding students gain quicker insight into the Science and its use in design work.

REFERENCES

A6.1 Michael Kennedy Osborn, "The Sony MDR-3: A Retrospective Design", Class Report, ENGR 250, March 3, 1983.

A6.2 Chapman Dilworth, "Retrospective Design Report: The Selection of Steel Rail Using the Options Field Method", Class Report, ENGR 250, March 3, 1983.

A6.3 Barbara Jean Muncy, "Design of a Self-Threading Needle: Retrospective Design Project", ENGR 250, March 3, 1983.

A6.4 Alpha Group (Michael Osborn, Karen Hardwick, Thomas Schuler, Patricia Gould, and Chapman Dilworth), "The University of Virginia Escort Service: An Improved Design Through Consensus Methodologies", ENGR 250, March 30, 1983.

QUESTIONS RELATED TO APPENDIX 6

1. List the four phases in teaching Generic Design Science.

2. How many weeks are spent in each of the four phases?

3. What is the purpose of each phase?

4. How many clusters appear in the Options Profile for the <u>portable stereo system</u>?

5. How many clusters appear in the Options Profile for the <u>steel rail</u>?

6. How many clusters appear in the Options Profile for the <u>self-threading needle</u>?

APPENDIX 7

TRIGGERING QUESTIONS, RELATIONSHIPS, AND GENERIC QUESTIONS

Control over group activity in applying the science of generic design is maintained by keeping a question before the group at all times when they are working participatively to accomplish a desired outcome. The questions are either triggering questions or generic questions. The former typically accompany work to generate ideas, and the latter typically accompany work to structure ideas. The constant presence of a question for the group makes the group a Socratic learning system, structuring, stimulating, and organizing the dialog whereby the group members learn from one another.

A7.1 Triggering Questions.

Both the Ideawriting process and the Nominal Group Technique are initiated with the display of a triggering question to the participants in these processes.

The success of these processes depends upon the careful design of the triggering question to which the participants respond.

Numerous examples of triggering questions that were successfully used appear in Chapter 10 of this book. However experience has shown that while it is helpful to see examples of successfully-applied triggering questions, it is also helpful to consider some underlying logic in designing such questions.

Successful triggering questions typically satisfy these criteria:

(1) Only a <u>single focus</u> is given to trigger the response; do not ask for more than one kind of concept in a given situation. If several different kinds of response are required, a separate question (and a separate process) should be used for each.

(2) It is <u>feasible</u> both to understand and to respond to the request; the question does not ask for something that is ambiguous, nor does it ask for something that one cannot reasonably expect the participants to provide.

(3) The word(s) used to provide the focus for the request is neither so general that the responses are unlikely to be to the point, nor so specific that the answers are likely to be overly restricted in utility. The focus should be <u>neither too general nor too specific</u> to be useful.

515

(4) The triggering question is <u>responsive to the pre-determined context</u> in which the work is embedded.

Questions that meet these four criteria can generally be expected to be satisfactory. One should always pre-test a question with a few associates before presenting it to a group as the basis for their activity, to help uncover any difficulties that it may present.

Triggering questions should be developed in conjunction with the Broker (see Chap. 8) especially to help assure that they meet Criterion 4 above.

These criteria and suggestions apply equally well to the design of triggering questions for both Ideawriting and the Nominal Group Technique.

A7.2 <u>Relationships.</u>

The choice of relationships for use with the Interpretive Structural Modeling (ISM) process is critical to its wise and effective use.

Numerous examples of relationships appear in this book, along with examples of their use and associations of specific relationships with particular Application Structural Types. People who are using ISM for the first time are advised to examine these Application Structural Types to see whether one or a combination of these will be suitable for their purpose. Experience has shown that, in most design applications, one or more of them will be suitable. If such is determined to be true in a particular context, the user can forego a detailed study of the criteria for choosing relationships.

Nevertheless it may be helpful to offer some criteria for choosing relationships, as these have been found to be either essential or very helpful in past applications.

Criteria for the choice of relationships include the following:

(1) Use a written description of the context to which the ISM work is to apply as a guide to the choice of relationship(s)

(2) The elements to which a relationship is to be applied should be of a single type (e.g., objectives, issues, problems, options)

(3) In the light of the chosen type of element, the relationship selected should be chosen to assure transitivity

(4) The type of relationship should be chosen first, and the type will almost always come from the list of types given in Table 2.7

516

(5) The relationship should be assessed as to whether it is hierarchical, cyclic, or hybrid; and the results of this assessment should be compatible with what one should anticipate as possible in light of the type of element chosen; e.g., if the elements are to be prioritized, one must choose a relationship that allows elements to have equal priorities, but one must not choose a relationship that permits leaving open the priority between any two elements in the set

(6) The use of an adjective as a modifier to the focus of the relationship may be helpful, especially if it is chosen in the light of how broad or how narrow the elements to be related are; e.g., one may use such variants as "may be a partial cause of", "has some influence upon", or "causes" in choosing a relationship from the influence type, in the light of the precise nature of the elements to be related. Note that relationships are subject to the Law of Gradation, and that by taking advantage of the use of modifiers that strengthen or weaken the tone of a relationship, one is able to achieve considerable gradation in expressing a relationship

(7) A relationship should have only a single focus, except that if the situation calls for the possibility of a hybrid structure, the relationship should be "equivocal" such as "less than or equal to"

(8) The relationship should lend itself to the design of a generic question (see below) for which the responses can be expected to be feasible

A7.3 Generic Questions.

In conducting an ISM session, the session will be driven by a generic question that is applicable to the entire set of elements that are to be related. Numerous examples of these kinds of questions appear in Chapter 10.

It has been found helpful to present a generic question by means of a computer-driven display in which the question appears on a wall.

The format of this display can be chosen to highlight selected parts of the generic question. It is helpful to think of such a question as having these parts:

(1) An identifier of the context to which the question applies

(2) An interrogative part

(3) An identifier of one of the two elements

(4) A phrase involving the relationship

(5) An identifier of the other element

(6) A concluding part terminated by a question mark

It will be helpful to keep each part confined to a particular line or lines, so that the context portion need not be read constantly, and so that the viewer can become accustomed to a repetitive format for quick reading.

It is suggested that the reader practice using some of the generic questions in Chapter 10, sorting out the six parts listed above. At times the concluding part will only be a question mark, no text being necessary.

It will be helpful to test a generic question with a small subset of the elements, in order to make sure that the responses are feasible, and that the chosen relationship has the right level of generality. Moreover the description of the context as well as the generic question should always be chosen in cooperation with and tested by the Broker.

QUESTIONS RELATED TO APPENDIX 7

1. What are four criteria that a good triggering question will satisfy?

2. Find three triggering questions in Chapter 10, and discuss them in terms of their responsiveness to the four criteria.

3. What are eight criteria that can be applied in choosing a relationship to apply in ISM?

4. What is meant by an "equivocal" relationship?

5. Under what conditions should an equivocal relationship be used?

6. What are the six parts of a generic question?

7. Discuss how the generic question should appear before a group, and the reasons for the format of the question.

8. Find three generic questions in Chapter 10, and assess them in the light of their responsiveness to the criteria.

9. Find three generic questions in Chapter 10, and identify the six parts of each.

10. What is the role of the Broker in developing triggering questions and generic questions?

APPENDIX 8

DEVELOPING A DESIGN CULTURE
IN HIGHER EDUCATION

M ajor changes for the better in design practice would presumably be a consequence of developing a design culture in higher education. With this in mind, a workshop was held in Chios, Greece, in August of 1988, to explore issues related to developing such a culture. The workshop was organized by the University of the Aegean, in cooperation with George Mason University. The nineteen participants in the workshop came from six countries: England, Greece, Hungary, India, Poland, and the United States of America.

The group applied the methods of the Generic Design Science to explore the issue. They identified 73 inhibitors that have prevented the development of such a culture. These were grouped into 9 Inhibitor Categories to facilitate analysis. The group then identified 48 options for helping to overcome the inhibitors. The options were grouped into four Action (Response) Categories. The Inhibitor Categories were organized into a hypothesized problematique. Then the Action Categories were matched with the Inhibitor Categories, to suggest ways in which the responses might overcome the inhibitors.

A8.1 The Inhibitors.

Table A8.1 shows the Inhibitor Categories, and the inhibitors within each category.

A8.2 The Problematique.

Figure A8.1 shows a hypothesized problematique that relates the Inhibitor Categories to one another.

A8.3 The Action Options.

Table A8.2 shows the Action Categories and the options within each.

A8.4 Responses to the Inhibitors.

Figure A8.2 shows the association of the Action Categories with the Inhibitor Categories.

Table A8.1
Categories of Inhibitors to Development of Design Culture

A. **UNACCEPTING ATTITUDES** (17 inhibitors)

Disciplinary emphasis, prevalence of analytic theories, entrenched barriers, stereotype of design, bounded cultures, lack of trust and understanding, inertia of existing system, lack of interest in commonality, restrictive view of science, journals hostile to design, academic preference for analysis instead of action, prejudice, design not seen as useful, curricular rigidity, self-sealing existing design groups, simplistic social theories, and rhetoric preferred to action

B. **DIFFUSE SUBJECT MATTER** (16 inhibitors)

No common understanding of design, no accepted theory, no methodological tools, need for varied methods, sparse literature, conceptual confusion, little consensus on the definition of global systems, poor definition in general, still informing stage, lack of standards, poor knowledge, lack of agreement about science/culture, negative byproducts from design, designer panic, no shared design philosophy, and no metaphysics underlying systems theory

C. **HARD TO ORGANIZE FOR ACTION** (13 inhibitors)

Levels of abstraction, complexity and variety, bounded specific design cultures, shortage of experts, no understanding of needed infrastructure, lack of knowledge of how to organize for teaching, variety of inputs, novel physical facilities needed, hard to validate, no support from general education, unclear role system, not enough cooperation, requires collectivity in a system that stresses individuality

D. **POLITICALLY DIFFICULT** (7 inhibitors)

Lack of political will, contrary to incrementalism, sensitive to choice of pilots, fluid political environment, may be fatal for some existing environments, may go against strong existing interests, and fear of technocrats

E. **INADEQUATE PROMOTION** (5 inhibitors)

Not enough lobbying, few success stories to use in promotion, marketability problems, past failures in similar situations, history of overstating benefits from innovation

F. **HARD TO TEACH** (5 inhibitors)

Hard to teach design, ideas cannot transcend experience, students lack relevant experience, lack of good language, lack of knowledge and experience for teaching transdisciplinary subject matter and synthesizing methods

G. **INDIFFERENCE TO SOCIETY'S FUTURE** (4 inhibitors)

Unarticulated vision of the benefits of design, academic disinterest in the future, lack of future images, lack of futures consciousness

H. **ECONOMIC PROBLEMS** (4 inhibitors)

Multiple demands on the education system, need money to support, conflicting interests in academia, insensitivity to limited resources in design practice

I. **INHERENT PROBLEMS** (3 inhibitors)

Human love of spontaneity, time is a constraint, little wisdom

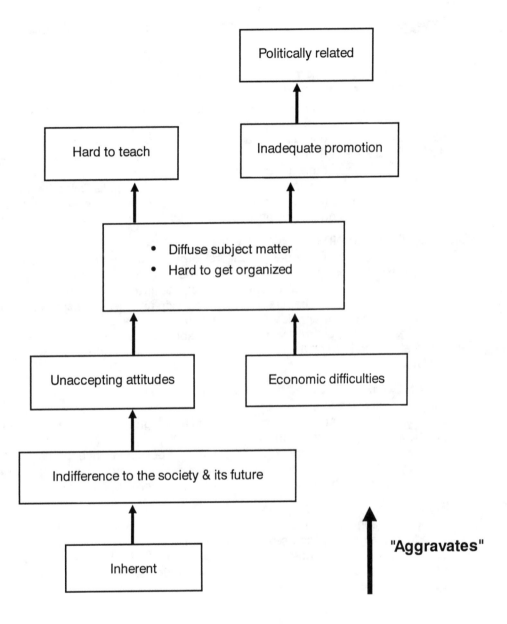

Figure A8.1 Hypothesized problematique.

Table A8.2
Categories of Action Options for Creating a Design Culture

I. **CREATE AN ORGANIZATION THAT WILL CARRY OUT ACTIONS TO DEVELOP THE DESIGN CULTURE IN HIGHER EDUCATION** (16 options)

Develop a devoted leadership group, introduce multidisciplinary research groups, speed up professionalization of the design community, establish an annual forum to build consensus, continue coordination among researchers, develop a model of an operating design culture, develop a lead group within the university, work with goal-setting organizations, establish centers to support an international network, work with traditional scientists, leadership group mentioned above must be multidisciplinary, expand the role of open universities, create teams of specialists to work on generic design, accelerate dissemination, engage with the philosophers, lead group must have eclectic composition.

II. **BUILD AWARENESS AND PROMOTE DESIGN** (14 options)

Academics must promote design culture, organize discussions with various publics, present generic design as a marketable product, increase awareness in academia by starting courses in various disciplines, get mass media to promote the design culture, get journals to publish more papers on design, develop and distribute computer games that introduce people to design, identify proximity disciplines and get them involved, facilitate social learning, popularize systems methodology and disseminate it, develop a Chios Declaration, start an international design competition for students, avoid overselling of design culture

III. **BUILD THE DOMAIN OF DESIGN SCIENCE** (11 options)

Develop glossary and consensus of design, develop common understanding of terms and connect to other relevant theories, design an integrated language, prove out ideas in practice, round out systems thinking and base design theory in it, allocate resources to allies who will help, demonstrate competence of design science, prepare multi-lingual glossary, reevaluate and strengthen existing design approaches, create an ethics of design, connect with specialists and show them the value of design in their spheres

IV. **EXPERIMENT IN THE CURRICULUM** (7 options)

Introduce teaching of design in areas where there seems to be some initial demand, introduce postgraduate courses, introduce some "soft subjects" in curricula of engineers and scientists, develop design as a core curriculum subject in systems science Ph. D. programs, introduce retrospective design by students, use more high technology, run pre-university courses in generic design

---

Where an arrow runs from an Action Category to a Inhibitor Category, it signifies the belief that the Action Category will help overcome the Inhibitor Category.

A8.5 Response Sequence.

Figure A8.3 shows a support structure among the Action Categories which suggests an appropriate sequencing of activity to overcome the inhibitors.

Inhibitor categories.

Response categories

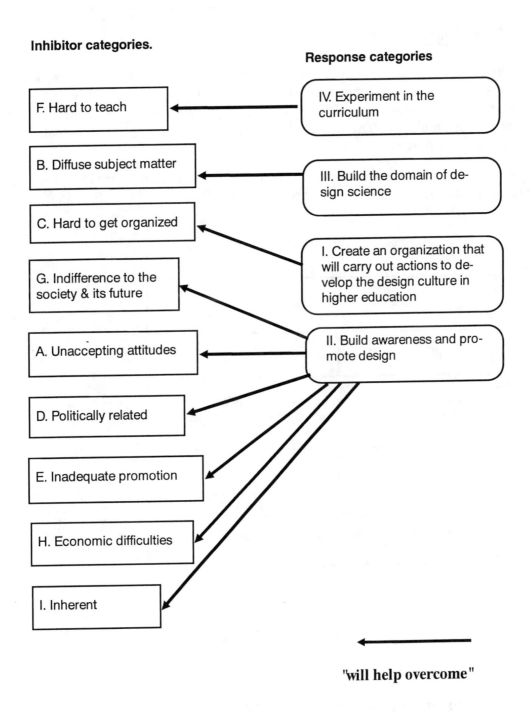

Figure A8.2 Responses to the inhibitors.

A8.6 Elaboration of the Workshop.

This Appendix has presented a much-abbreviated description of the workshop. A full 41-page report on the workshop was prepared to document it fully. Those who wish to see this elaboration may wish to contact one of the participating organizations to request a copy. The title of the report is "Developing a Design Culture in Higher Education: A Workshop".

Additional followup workshops in Greece to expand on the previous work are expected. A second followup workshop was held in Rhodes in the fall of 1989.

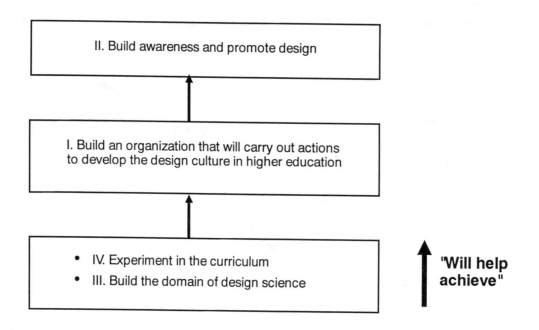

Figure A8.3 Support structure for responding to inhibitors.

QUESTIONS RELATED TO APPENDIX 8

1. In the Chios Workshop to examine the possibility of developing a design culture in higher education, how many of each of the following were found: (a) inhibitors, (b) inhibitor categories, (c) options for overcoming inhibitors, (d) action (response) categories?

2. What are the nine inhibitor categories that seem to prevent the development of a design culture in higher education?

3. What are the four action (response) categories that seem to hold the key to overcoming the inhibitors to development of a design culture in higher education?

POSTSCRIPT

ISSUES AND RESPONSES

"Our whole attitude toward nature, our violation of nature with the help of machines
and the heedless ingenuity of technicians and engineers, is hubris...".
--F. Nietzsche
"Philosophy's central concern is to be a general theory of representation, a theory which will divide
culture up into the areas which represent reality well, those which represent it less well,
and those which do not represent it at all (despite their pretense of doing so)." ...
"Uncovering the presuppositions of those who think they have none is one of the principal means
by which philosophers find new issues to debate".
--R. Rorty

I have served as editor of two journals for a cumulative period of about 13 years. During this time I have seen many manuscripts, and read many referee reports. An author must respond to suggestions and criticisms raised in the referee reports. To deny such a response undermines the refereeing system. The precise way in which the author responds should be the choice of the author, who has the responsibility to respond in the way that seems most likely to be effective in communicating.

Several referees read part of the manuscript for this book and offered many suggestions and criticisms. Many of these suggestions became the basis for changes in the manuscript. The remaining suggestions were aggregated to furnish a set of topics for this Postscript. Many of the referee comments dealt with here would never have occurred to me. By presenting them as issues, and responding to them, still a different approach becomes available to me for amplifying the Generic Design Science.

I have organized the various issues raised by one or more referees into eight categories. Within each category, I have assigned a code that can be used to identify individual sub-issues. The exact language used to present an issue is not generally that used by the referee. There are two reasons for this. First, some of the issues were raised by more than one referee, and in the interests of saving space I produced a composite phrasing. Second, I was able to slant the issue in a way that enabled me to give the most direct response to it. Some might say that this is a biased approach, and I won't deny it. But one must remember that the referees can continue to fire away at this work to the extent that they wish, as can any other reader.

Some of the sub-issues appear in more than one category. This deliberate redundancy recognizes that readers often read selectively, and may look at a particular issue rather than the whole set. Also some of the sub-issues properly belong under more than one category.

527

Table P.1 lists the issues in the sequence in which they are presented. Following the discussion of the issues, the table in Section P.9 correlates the issues with the responses that are given in Sections P.10, P.11, and P.12.

Table P.1
Issues Raised by Referees of the Manuscript

1. Origins of design science
2. Values and value systems
3. Definitions
4. Emphasis
5. Design Science Limitations
6. Context
7. Omissions
8. Misinterpretations

P.1 Issue 1: Origins of Design Science.

The treatment of the origins of design science is faulty. Much of design science has originated in systems engineering or industrial design. The manuscript's discussion relating to origins in philosophy or science is not very compatible with reality. The following specific criticisms elaborate on these general remarks.

Origins in Philosophy (1A)

To the extent that philosophy is relevant, pragmatism, as reflected in Peirce's philosophy is just one of many possible bases. Others in the pragmatism school were equally important, such as William James, John Dewey, and E. A. Singer. Pragmatism has no values such as truth, morality, ethics, freedom, etc. Moreover there is a heavy dose of subjectivity involved in the philosophy that is invoked here.

Origins in Science (1B)

The manuscript perpetuates the fiction that science is the best basis for belief -- a common fallacy made by all engineers and physical scientists. Moreover, there is already a field that lies between science and the humanities: systems engineering. Design is close to and part of application, but real science seeks knowledge for its own sake. Practitioners are major contributors, and have been slighted in this manuscript.

528

Origins in Systems Engineering and Industrial Design (1C)

There is a legacy from systems-oriented designers, including the industrial design community. No practitioners or systems engineers are cited in this manuscript for their contributions. Instead people who are cited are often, at best, peripheral or confused. The manuscript ignores the fact that most advances in technology are made by practitioners. These practitioners will not want to adjust to the criteria stemming from the foundations and theory of Generic Design Science, since practitioners do the advances and scientists explain their results later.

Origins from Secondary Sources (1D)

Frequently the original work of people is not cited (e.g., Peirce), but instead secondary sources are used, which is only hearsay. Original sources should be cited.

P.2 Issue 2: Values and Value Systems.

This work seems to ignore value system design altogether, even though it is the core of system design, while assigning high significance to pragmatism which lacks values. Also the work ignores the issue of science versus ethics as a basis for making choices.

Ignoring Value System Design (2A)

The work does not address the very core of design which is values, value theory and value systems. Design must proceed with a designed value system (objectives) to guide the search. There ought to be a rule that says "if you wait until you have discovered an alternative before searching for objectives, pay $50". As an example, new criteria are introduced at intermediate points during the development of the movie example in Chapter 7, which shows initial underconceptualization of the value system.

Pragmatism Lacks Values (2B)

The pragmatic philosophy incorporates a heavy load of subjectivity. Also pragmatism has no values such as truth, morality, ethics, freedom, etc.

Science versus Ethics (2C)

Fixing belief through the method of science is not consistent with the view expressed in Figure 1.8 that ethics must be used.

529

P.3 Issue 3: Definitions.

This work lacks some key definitions. Consequently, there are significant ambiguities. Also the work presents some bad definitions that are not consistent with accepted practice, and uses some terms that are better replaced with other terms.

Ambiguities (3A)

Design is not defined, and culture is not defined, even though these terms are heavily emphasized in the work. Different interpretations of "design" appear. One of your own references gave a definition of design that isn't consistent with this manuscript. There are too many terms from too many sources creating mixed signals about where you want to go. It seems like you think it (design) is an attempt at synthesis through sequential decision making. A clear definition is not to be found.

Poor Choice of Terminology (3B)

The terminology used in the Domain of Science Model is not consistent with widely accepted practice. Terms such as basic science and applied science will remain in the language long after your Domain of Science Model is forgotten, so why not ride with them? Pure science is pure because its objective is knowledge for its own sake, while applied science seeks utility for man. Your two-component, two-part, and three-component versions of the Domain of Science Model may all be straw men.

The use of the word "target" to represent the desired outcome of a design process is not consistent with the common practice of using the word "design" to represent both the process and the outcome of the process. The word "target" sounds like something that we would shoot at with bullets or arrows.

The Argyris' "governing variables" [1] are better described as objectives or, more generally, the value system. You would do better to use cybernetic models of the process instead of Argyris' double-loop model, which is a special case of many broader models given by systems engineers.

Your Principle of Cybernetic Embedding is a mouthful.

The DELTA chart has no features that qualify it as a "consensus methodology".

How can you call DELPHI a group process? There is no member-member and little leader-member interaction, these being suppressed by the structure. It is a variant of NGT.

P.4 Issue 4: Emphasis.

There are numerous instances of misplaced emphasis in this work.

Introduction of Superfluous Material (4A)

Your Law of Universal Priors is superfluous to make a point about the importance of management. Physical sciences don't recognize the importance of management, but design does.

Memory Divisions (4B)

Long term memory can deal with many more than 7 items. We have 3 tiers of memory in the brain. Linear programs can handle a thousand variables. The Span of Immediate Recall is not related to the question.

Simon didn't mean by "bounded rationality" what you say.

Set Theory (4C)

Emergent properties can't be represented as mathematical functions of component properties, which may be why set theory is not very useful at the system level.

Accuracy Versus Consensus (4D)

No amount of consensus will make false facts true. Accuracy is the important criterion -- not consensus. Look how long it took to get consensus on Darwin.

Leadership (4E)

If the individual who has the knowledge also is the best leader type, do you put him down? The Bennis leadership attributes fit Hitler, Mao, and many other notables who are not well-regarded. Many of the individuals who had these attributes were monsters. Shared leadership may be better in many cases.

Methodology is Far Ahead of Science (4F)

Stop using Argyris' reinvented wheel. Use models like Hall's models [2,3] and the GERT model. Existing methodology is so far ahead of the science in the Domain of Science Model that we couldn't solve real problems if we stayed with that.

Mistitled Manuscript (4G)

This manuscript could have been called *Science of Complex Systems*, which seems more appropriate than design science. Complexity is a characteristic of both living and non-living systems, so a deep study of complexity requires a foundation like science. The canvas is vast. Design is a minor part of such a vast study.

Group Pathologies (4H)

Group pathologies do exist. Experience shows that there are group pathologies, and that one should be able to diagnose them and evolve the skill to deal with them. However, an experienced group doesn't need a facilitator.

Groups Versus Individuals (4I)

The book says that there is only one formula for design -- to use a group -- and only one thing to do -- use morphological analysis -- and use a computer -- all of which are false. Why not allow that the group can be dispersed, and unified as needed by data network and/or video/audio teleconferencing? Then it need not stay in plenary session until it solves the problem. Groups are best for compiling lists. Did you ever see one design a single multifunctional circuit?

P.5 Issue 5: Design Science Limitations.

The manuscript seems to take the position that there are no limits to the sphere of design. But it seems clear that many system aspects cannot be designed, and many failures of systems cannot be attributed to system designers.

Emergence and Evolution Cannot be Designed (5A)

Can we consciously design a system? After a certain size and maturity, a society follows its own dynamics. Emergence and evolution are guided by that social self and cannot be designed. Human beings can only intervene to hasten the process. Management consists essentially of these catalytic interventions.

Misattribution of Causes of Failure (5B)

It may be true in some cases that failure of systems is due to under-conceptualization and oversight, but in most of them it is due to the new synergies that have entered into the original systems as they went on growing as open systems in changing environments. It could not have been possible to foresee all that later happened in the course of the original design.

P.6 Issue 6: Context.

You seem to be unaware of long-standing, high-quality architectural work to produce good research laboratories.

Design and Use of the Working Environment (6A)

People have done designs in the past for facilities, including designs by distinguished architects who knew a lot about laboratory design, including the Bell Telephone Murray Hill and Holmdel Laboratories, and the Cranbrook Academy. Such designs influenced laboratory designs elsewhere, all of which eclipsed and transcended the small work of Lasswell -- valid as he was.

P.7 Issue 7: Omissions.

Some important ideas have been left out, while others have not been adequately developed.

Need for Additional Laws of Design (7A)

Other laws of design could have been included. For example, the Law of Least Synthesis, the Law of Emergence, the Law of Bounded Concepts, the Law of Requisite Communication, the Law of Representation, and the Law of Imperfections or Approximations.

Other Methods of Fixing Belief (7B)

Judicial methods are more stringent ways of fixing belief than the methods of science.

Role of Systems Engineering (7C)

Systems engineering is relegated to a minor role. Important parts of designed processes have been omitted. Hall's Fig. 3-9(a) [3] reduces Argyris to a special case.

Hall came up with a "matching theorem" which is more general than Ashby -- in Hall's new book and in his old one too [2,3].

Methodology (7D)

The description of ISM is so brief that no one could use the method from what is given.

A reference to DELPHI should be provided.

If it were also required that convergence be attained, the DELPHI process would be like Hall's cornucopia model.

In developing design principles, it would be much better to rely on the work of Zeleny, Hall, and Beer than on the work of Argyris.

The section on the Options Profile Method is too short to convey how to use it.

Morphological Analysis (7E)

The work should credit Zwicky for initiating morphological analysis in reference to the Options Field Methodology and the Options Profile Methodology.

P.8. Issue 8: Misinterpretation and Errors.

Some work is misinterpreted, while other items are erroneous.

Poor Interpretation of Diversity (8A)

What the data on NGT show in your Appendix 5 is that NGT is not a consensus methodology (as you claim). After all diversity does not equal consensus.

Misrepresentation of the Work of Others (8B)

The work of C. P. Snow is not well-interpreted. Snow was using literature in lieu of a more careful definition of what constitutes the humanities.

Simon's meaning of bounded rationality is not that which you present.

You should believe that if a thing works it's good (pragmatism), since you believe in Peirce.

Structuring Errors (8C)

What does "steering" mean in connection with your Domain of Science Model? The arrows in this model should be two-way since there can be a flow from applications to methodology.

Unallowable Methods (8D)

In connection with the Tradeoff Analysis Methodology (which is misnamed), averaging is not a permissible operation on order scales. Also rank differences cannot be scaled (a double fallacy, scaling the unscalable). Also addition of items on a rank order scale is not allowed.

P.9 Correlating Issues and Responses.

Table P.2 correlates the foregoing issues to the responses to follow.

Table P.2
Correlation of the Issues with the Responses

Subsection(s) that Contain Response(s) to the Issue

ISSUE	Section P.10	Section P.11	Section P.12
1A		Pragmatism	
1B	Time Horizon	Means of Fixing Belief	
1C	System Scale	Design Legacy	
1D			Secondary Sources
2A			Value System Design
2B	Universal Priors and the Peircian Triad		
2C		Means of Fixing Belief	
3A		Culture	Miscellaneous Comments
3B	The Peircian Triad		Miscellaneous Comments
4A	The Peircian Triad		
4B			Memory Divisions, Bounded Relationality
4C		Set Theory and Classification	
4D	Time Horizon		
4E			Leadership
4F	Time Horizon		Hazard Gap
4G	Design and the Academic Mind		
4H			Group Pathologies
4I	System Scale		Groups Versus Individuals
5A	Design and the Academic Mind		System Failures
5B			System Failures
6A			Working Environments
7A	Design and the Academic Mind		
7B		Means of Fixing Belief	
7C	System Scale		
7D	Omissions I and Omissions II		Miscellaneous Comments
7E			Credit to Zwicky
8A			Interpretation of Diversity
8B		Pragmatism, Culture	

| 8C | | Structuring Errors |
| 8D | | Unallowable Methods |

P.10 Some Overview Responses.

Responses to the foregoing issues are organized as follows. First there are some "overview responses", which have a bearing on the circumstances surrounding these issues, and which may have some relevance to all of them. These will be given first, in this section. Then there are some responses that are found in the work of other authors that I think are so well-stated and so directly relevant to the issues that they form, in my opinion, the best responses to certain issues. I do not replicate the work of these authors, but indicate in P.11 its general nature and where it may be found. Responses that do not lie within these two categories are found in a final section (P.12) that I have labeled "Additional Responses". These are mainly specialized responses to particular sub-issues.

As mentioned earlier, referees did not have access to all of this manuscript when making the comments given in this Appendix. However they did have access to a large percentage of the manuscript. Their comments caused me to revise the Preface completely. Hopefully I have done a better job in the present Preface of dealing with some of the issues that they raised. But I chose, in this Appendix, to retain some of the issues that I tried to deal with in the Preface, to allow me to elaborate still more, and to give these issues more prominence.

System Scale

Many of the issues raised seem to me to be misdirected for the following reason. **This book is aimed at systems that are quite large in scale.** The word "large" is a relative term, of course. Virtually everything that is said about Generic Design Science in this book is intended to apply to very large-scale systems. I think it is axiomatic that if a person has a very thorough understanding of how to approach the design of very large systems, that person is in possession of the information needed to make choices as to how to approach the design or redesign of smaller systems, or even of components. In the conceptual stage, it is always possible that people will not know ahead of time whether the target of design will be a large system or not. A designer or manager or administrator may choose a conservative posture initially, and treat the target as a large system. Then as learning occurs, it may be possible to back away from this designation and revert to less ambitious or less encompassing approaches that cost less, involve less people, and do not produce significantly greater risk. This point of view is completely consistent with the concept of gradation, described in Chapter 6 and used frequently in assessing the state and evolution of design science.

Time Horizon

The ideas given about science in this book are largely intended to apply **over very long time periods**. Some of the issues raised seem to be viewing the development of science in the short run such as a decade or a few decades. The philosophy of Peirce, often alluded to in this book, reflects very long term considerations.

The Peircian Triad

I have little tolerance for the reification of science, technology, systems engineering, or any other non-living phenomenon. Science does not have a narrow attitude, although scientists may. Systems engineering does not carry out applications, although systems engineers may. In his extremely thoughtful 1989 Jefferson Lecture, sponsored by the National Endowment for the Humanities, the American author, Dr. Walker Percy, chose as his theme the Peircian distinction between the dyad and the triad and its relation to science and language. In this lecture, he pointed out that most science involves dyadic relations between object and name. The real cow and the word "cow" are in a dyadic relationship. But the act of association of the word with the real cow involves the human being, and it is the triadic relationship involved in this association, multiplied many times over in speech and other forms of representation, that constitutes human communication. Science refers to an organized body of knowledge, organized through relationships. **Human beings not only develop these relationships, but they are an integral part of them.**

The intimate connection between the human being, language, and all forms of science and other organized knowledge has been noted in many ways. The Lavoisier quotation quoted at the beginning of Chapter 2 is a representative example. Vickers [4] point of view gives significant insights, especially as it involves the relationships between people and technology. In my own paper [5], which was given the award as the best paper in the design symposium in the 1988 European Meeting on Cybernetics and Systems Research, I tried to emphasize that the language of system design itself should be thoughtfully designed.

Universal Priors and the Peircian Triad

The concept of Universal Priors to all science [6] reflects the Peircian triadic reality. The methodologies developed as part of the Generic Design Science can be viewed as a means of formally recognizing it. While the ISM process, for example, may appear superficially as a methodology for the developing of dyadic relationships, it is not such a methodology. On the contrary, it is a means for facilitating the evolutionary triadic events that provide relationships which can then take part in subsequent triadic events. It is through such events that human values enter and pervade design activity; rather than through articulating them in such a way that they become divorced from the human actors; or by having surrogates take the documented value systems as part of their own analytical apparatus. Such a step replaces one set of triadic events with another that, in the process, substitutes the origins of the values with surrogate origins that may be only weakly correlated with the original origins.

Whatever else distinguishes the Generic Design Science from other proposed systems for supporting design activity, key aspects are the insistence on dealing in one and the same context with the large, complex system; and with the anthropological, formal logical, and technological aspects of system design as an integrated conceptualization; and the implications that these concepts have for the way in which language is disciplined and its use is facilitated, to serve human purposes.

Omissions I

This book is not intended to be self-contained. It would not be possible, in my judgment, to put in one reasonably-sized book the full detail that is available to support what is in this book. To take one instance as representative, consider the Interpretive Structural Modeling process. I estimate that I have written at least 500 pages of text on this process alone in the past 15 years. In *Societal Systems: Planning, Policy, and Complexity* [7] I gave most of the theory of this process, along with much of the methodology. Later I reconstructed the theory to eliminate matrices completely so that it might be accessible to a set of readers who were not familiar with Boolean matrices [8]. In a number of articles given in the Bibliography, I dealt with special aspects of this process. In 1980, I published an annotated bibliography on the process [9] that included citations of publications of a number of other authors about ISM.

While people often think that all they need to have to use the ISM process is a suitable set of software, the fact is that this process should be very thoroughly studied by anyone who hopes to get maximum benefit from its use. It incorporates anthropological, formal logical, and technological aspects. All of these need to be well-understood. People also tend to perceive it as another methodology that is parallel to the many that are proposed for working with systems. But the ISM process instruments the formal logic that evolved over more than two millennia in a way that uses only natural language in the human-machine interface. Because its major components are "elements and relations", most other methodologies that involve relating elements can ultimately be reduced to the foundational components of the ISM process.

As a second example, the Nominal Group Technique is viewed by many as a simple process design cluttered with unnecessary manual operations, which can be eliminated by introducing technology. The fact is that the behavioral aspects of this process design are outstanding. The introduction of technology to replace behavioral features may well undo the outstanding results that this process has repeatedly demonstrated to its users.

Design and the Academic Mind

There is a widespread consensus, both within and without the academic community, that emphasis in academia on analysis is much heavier than emphasis on design. It is possible that academics might even find the word "design" frightening. Perhaps there are some deep incentives to try to continue to use language that is descriptive in nature, rather than language that seems to imply responsibility for the performance of systems.

It could be, then, that if a person feels that it is very important to work to counter these inherent incentives, that person would go out of his or her way to choose a title for a work that will be sufficiently action-oriented to attract the attention of that (small?) part of the academic community that takes a dim view of such incentives. It might even occur that the laws of design that are offered are those that provide prescriptive guidance to the conduct of design. One might deliberately downplay or even omit those descriptive laws that simply say, in effect, "people aren't very good at design", but don't say what to do to try to counteract that weakness.

Omissions II

The frequent references to the works of others are not given as window-dressing. A person who really wants to understand thoroughly what is given in this book should plan to read a good many of the references. In making this statement, I remember very well opening the book *The Fourier Integral* by Norbert Wiener. There I was confronted with theorem after theorem, most of which were unproved. Finally I encountered a statement in the text which said something like this: "naturally, only the extremely indolent will be willing to take these theorems on faith". I believe that my caution to the reader to be ready to do considerable additional reading is considerably less stringent than that of Norbert Wiener.

Of course I wish I could have had the ability to make this work self-contained. The reason I have not done so is that it is beyond my powers.

P.11 Responses in References.

Pragmatism

The view that Peirce is a part of a larger school of pragmatism has been amply refuted by Peirce himself, as Apel has clearly indicated [10] in his excellent biography of Peirce. The decision by Peirce to choose the term "pragmaticism" in lieu of pragmatism reflected his own dismay at the confusion of his work with that of later philosophers, including William James. While Rukeyser quotes James as saying "I owe everything to him [Peirce]" [11], Peirce took pains to make the relevant distinctions in a series of lectures arranged by James in Peirce's final return to Harvard

University. Peirce's Pragmatic Maxim to the effect that the meaning of a thing lies in its consequences, offers guidance to how to unravel the meaning of events and terms. The more familiar statement, often cited as the core of pragmatism, that a thing is "good if it works" is a judgment of what is valuable, but this point of view does not come from Peirce. (The concept of "Design Situation", as emphasized in this book, has a philosophical basis in works of John Dewey and Geoffrey Vickers.)

Design Legacy

The legacy from systems-oriented designers, such as systems engineers and industrial designers, is clearly relevant to design. Just as clearly, its relevance to large-system design lies in its contributions to what I have called "specific design sciences". By combining their contributions with the Generic Design Science, it will be possible ultimately to develop General Design Science. That will not be possible until the Generic Design Science is adequately articulated. In my 1976 book (reprinted in 1989) [7], I have alluded frequently and favorably to contributions from systems engineers and to methods for constructing value systems. It is not my intent, in the present book, to repeat what was in that work. It is also not my intent to give any kind of blanket endorsement to systems engineering methodology, because it is clearly not the ultimate or even near to the ultimate in regard to the design of sociotechnical systems.

A balanced overview of the history of design has been offered by Gasparski and his colleagues [12]. His Polish school has exhibited a conscientious approach to the amalgamation of the lessons of history with the nature of science and the nature of design. They have also undertook to rethink science in their study of the "science of science". This scholarly approach is supplemented by the thoughts of the British philosopher Glynn [13] who has shown that scientific work itself can be viewed as design. This point of view is one that I agree with. This view has not been widely recognized or debated. It does suggest that a narrow definition of design is not appropriate, and that a broad definition remains to be accepted.

Means of Fixing Belief

I take it that belief is the state of mind which, according to C. S. Peirce, is the origin of rules of action, which themselves underlie habits. The thought that there may be more ways of fixing belief than those four stated by Peirce depends, in my view, upon whether additional candidates can or cannot be properly subsumed under his four categories. Some of the other ways that have been proposed are: casuistry [3], transcendentalism, and esthetics. Casuistry is the determination of right and wrong in questions of conduct or conscience by the application of general principles of ethics. Transcendentalism is the belief that knowledge of reality is derived from intuitive sources rather than from objective (sensory) experience. Esthetics is the application of the singular criterion of sensory appeal to decisionmaking.

The term "subsumption" has been given some prominence in this book. It refers to the act of integrating a set of concepts within the umbrella of a larger, encompassing concept. The contrary term "supersumption" was not familiar to me, but I perceived the need for it. As I have defined this term [14]; it means to assign to a concept a significance, meaning, or context that substantially exceeds its proper scope; thereby preempting an appropriate subsumption of that concept, and propagating underconceptualized contexts.

To take another route to my ultimate conclusion about methods of fixing belief, I want to invoke some language from the field of mining. In gold prospecting, a very much admired condition is reflected in the language that "the vein is open at depth". This means that what is sought has not been limited by the initial image. Our design language should be "open at scale". **It should be amenable to continued subsumption.**

Philosophy and science are both open at scale. The description of science given by Peirce mandates that the human components constantly remember their fallibility, and that the findings and the knowledge be continually under review, even while being applied in good faith in the short run. Casuistry, transcendentalism, and esthetics all seem to me to be meritorious, but they should not be enshrined as supersumptions. There is no doubt in my mind that there is room in both philosophy and science for casuistry, transcendentalism, and esthetics; but to take any one of these latter three as a basis is to settle on a supersumption instead of a subsumption. Never mind that some argue that science is free of ethics, hostile to unproved intuition, or immune to sensory appeal. The reifying argument does not make it so. Both philosophy and science are inherently subsumptive, and the Peirce triadic relationship illuminated by Walker Percy reveals the means for subsumption to occur.

Culture

Kroeber and Kluckhohn several decades ago uncovered several hundred definitions of "culture" and finally settled on one that appeared to be the best, most subsumptive definition of the term [15]. In keeping with the tenor of the times, authors affiliated with professional schools frequently do not refer to this seminal research. Still it reflects extended thought about the meaning of the term on the part of numerous scholars who examined it in the traditional spirit of scientific exploration.

Set Theory and Classification

I doubt if it is possible to improve much on the remarks of Professor Atkin [16] in indicating the significance of set theory for all kinds of scientific investigation and representation. His highly creative application of it, augmented by the particular language of the Theory of Relations, to describe mathematically the "landscape" and "traffic" of the University of Essex seems to remain largely unfamiliar to most systems practitioners.

P.12 Additional Responses.

In this section, I respond briefly to a number of the more specialized issues raised by the referees, and also append a few additional remarks about some of the more general issues.

Secondary Sources

It is my experience that original sources are often much better than secondary sources, so as a rule I agree with the referee remark. However I think that philosophy is an area where secondary sources are often superior to original sources, in terms of providing overviews and emphasis. Philosophers often work for decades in the same general area. They may offer contradictory views of individual matters. As they grow older, their views may become more rounded, and they may discover that some of their earlier views have been changed. Their biographers, sensitive to the importance of assessing the total work of the source of their own study, and able to see the works of the person being studied in a larger and later perspective, can often provide the best treatment for the reader. Not all biographers are so capable, of course. Several have taken Peirce as the subject of their study, and I feel that Goudge and Apel have done excellent jobs of presenting Peirce's views. Apel has indicated that the passage of a decade since his own work was published [10] has caused him to rethink some of his own material. This should come as no surprise, since philosophy is a very old subject of study, and after over 2,000 years of study, there remains much to ponder.

Value System Design

I have committed to the idea that values are part of human beings and are not readily analyzable. In the design of large systems, the use of a formal value system to guide design may even be somewhat counterproductive. The large amount of documentation that is inherent in a well-designed large system will be most valuable if it is internally consistent. If designers are forced constantly to try to make large structures of alternatives and large structures of action consistent with large structures of values, the cognitive challenge may be too great. One of the reasons for this is that it is very hard, if not impossible, to construct a kind of canonical set of values such that the set is both exhaustive and mutually exclusive. As if this were not enough, agreement that may be reached on values may not be transferable to interpretations of how values relate to specific actions.

What I am saying is again a matter of gradation.

In his excellent article in the *Washington Post*, Broome [17] discussed pretty thoroughly the substantial dilemma faced by engineers in dealing with large system design, and how this dilemma was compounded by the variety of roles that influence what goes on in system design and implementation.

It is easy enough to say that the dilemma can be corrected by value system design. But when real organizations are involved, and organizational cultures dominate the value systems, even well-meaning and ostensibly supported efforts may come to naught, as Bushe [18] has demonstrated in his study of attempts to install statistical quality control in an American manufacturing organization.

The question of how to teach people to design has also been recognized as fraught with (relatively hidden) controversy that has close connections to philosophical bases, as Le Moigne has very thoughtfully argued [19]. What is involved here is again an embedded culture in professional schools that values Comte-like philosophy over Da Vinci-like approaches to design.

Value system design may be much more relevant to the issue of restructuring organizational cultures than it is to providing guidance for how particular design questions are handled within such organizations, at least at the present time. In the meantime, the design of value systems to steer the development of designs is not without its own problems.

Early in the work of the Center for Interactive Management (CIM), considerable emphasis was placed on value system design. Given the fact that time is always limited in developing initial versions of large system designs, experience has taught that there are better ways to use the time. One of the better ways to use the time is in developing a thorough understanding of the Design Situation. Without this, value system designs may simply serve to prolong the issue being studied.

Memory Divisions

There seems to be reasonably good evidence that the memory does have divisions, and that these divisions operate on different time scales. To say that human beings or mathematical algorithms can deal with hundreds or thousands of variables does not really come to grips with the fundamental issue of how they deal with them.

There seems to be no doubt that the mind, at any one time, really cannot deal with more than about seven items. So the question arises as to whether there is some way the mind can deal with large numbers of items in an integrative way by distributing activity over time. Even if the answer to this question is "yes", this does not mean that it is easy or that nothing needs to be done to make this more effective and less error-prone. In the final analysis, **it is the performance of large systems that must be used to gauge the ability of the mind to design them properly**. As long as so many design problems continue to surface as has been happening in our large systems, arguments that the mind can deal with these systems very well have to be taken with a grain of salt. Moreover, even with very small designs, we are constantly seeing severe design oversights. When the time comes that our systems, large and small, demonstrate extremely capable and inoffensive performance, we may then be-

543

gin to say that the mind really can work well with large numbers of items. Until that time comes, we can hardly be much impressed with the thought that the ability of linear programs to handle large numbers of variables is relevant in our context.

Bounded Rationality

In my 1976 book [7], on page 50, I made the following comments: "The concept of bounded rationality of the human has been studied and rather widely diffused. Specific discussions are found in the works of Miller, von Mises, March and Simon, Braybrooke and Lindblom, Alexander, Moynihan, Thompson, Hammond, Whitehead, and Simon, representing backgrounds in psychology, economics, sociology, business administration, political science, architecture, and philosophy. While the generic term "bounded rationality" is not always used in these works, the central idea that the human cannot handle logistically all of the knowledge available in working with complex issues is present in each. Variations in capacity to work with information are generally considered to be correlated with variations in ability to arrange and structure knowledge. (References were cited for each of the persons mentioned in [7]).

"To alleviate difficulties stemming from bounded rationality, it is appropriate to consider carefully ways of reducing the total behavioral load that the individual must carry in working with complex systems and issues. One example of a setting where such reallocation is needed is the debate, for in this setting the requirements for effective dialectic concerning complex systems and issues are most stringent."

Since writing the foregoing, I have become better educated in this area by learning of Peirce's writings having to do with "unshakeable cognitive burden", and how his ideas related to the older philosophical thought about how to approach a problem. Other authors have been added to the list of those who have recognized the widespread impact of "information overload".

To understand the concept of bounded rationality, one can benefit from a subsumptive approach, integrating the views of all scholars who have examined it. Naturally, no one scholar may have originated the subsumptive version of the concept, but that is not as important as the idea that this should be the goal in relation to assessing the concept for purposes of gaining insight into system design.

Leadership

I find it hard to agree with the referee that certain infamous leaders satisfied the four criteria for outstanding leadership set forth by Bennis [20]. It seems to me that many infamous individuals have been able to manage attention and meaning, but that they have not done very well at managing trust and self.

I have noted, however, that many systems engineers in particular do not want to discuss their own style of leadership. They are quick to criticize the use of criteria for judging leadership, but they are not prone to explaining what truly constitutes outstanding leadership. They are not interested in explaining why empirical research results <u>should not</u> be discussed at length, or in trying **to show why research procedures that produced results not compatible with their presuppositions were flawed**. This point of view extends further into large realms of social science research, which typically are written off as being pale shadows of thought coming from systems engineering. Furthermore this point of view is not expressed in measured and polite terms, but usually in heated and pejorative outbursts. Perhaps what is being seen here is symptomatic of something as basic as self-image or territoriality.

The idea of specifically-stated criteria for assessing the leadership potential of individuals is not too far removed from the question of establishing a modest value system for use in screening leaders. Yet these two issues seem to be kept at arms length in referee arguments.

Of course systems engineers do not deserve to be specially singled out for lack of interest in applying criteria to leadership assessment. The whole political realm seems to be averse to such matters. If the Pragmatic Maxim is applied here, to the effect that the meaning of a lack of interest in leadership assessment lies in its consequences, we can only say that there is great meaning attached to such a lack of interest, because the consequences of it are very great in many nations, many organizations, and in the world as a whole.

Concerning the issue of what to do when the leader is also the one who is most knowledgeable about the issue, and whether one should "put him down", the answer is straightforward. The leader should be a participant, not a facilitator of the group process, at least in using the design processes in their highest grade. The behavioral part of the design, in this situation, far outweighs the technical. One must also question the assumption as to whether the leader is the one who is most knowledgeable about the issue. **Leaders may be prone to make this assumption much more frequently than circumstances warrant**.

The Hazard Gap

This book shows a clear acceptance of the idea of a time gap between technology (as reflected in methodology and the technological artifacts produced by methodology) and science. That is not an issue.

This time gap can be given a name. I suppose it would be appropriate historically to call it the "curiosity gap". When people see an outstanding performance from some technology, it is probably reasonable to imagine that they would be curious about the origins of this performance and, through scientific study, eventually illuminate it.

In the light of large system performance in the past few decades, it may be important now to rename this gap. I propose to call it now the "**hazard gap**": the (unknown) period of time (which may be months, years, decades, or even centuries) between (a) the introduction of a potentially hazardous new system that involves new technologies and (b) the adequate development of the science that underlies and explains those technologies. I have also proposed to limit the use of this name to what can be called "**invasive systems**". These are systems that have these properties: (a) may affect many people who rendered no approval of its influence on their lives, (b) large in scale, (c) expensive, (d) costs are borne by people who did not accede to introducing them, and (e) have the potential for causing significant disasters [14].

In effect, this introduces a gradation into the type of time gap; conditioned by the size and impact of the system being discussed, along with its technologies and the methodologies that are applied in designing systems that contain such technologies.

Group Pathologies

That group pathologies exist is not an issue with me. One of the most troublesome, groupthink [21], has been described in this book.

The question of the extent to which such pathologies influence what goes on in groups, **as a function of the process being used**, is one that is researchable. Our own research has involved dozens of groups working on dozens of complex issues. What we find is that virtually all of the so-called pathologies that are associated with group work are simply not demonstrated in the group work founded in the Generic Design Science. No amount of pontification about group pathologies can dominate the observed performance of groups and the testimony of participants who have taken part in this work over the past fifteen years.

Groups Versus Individuals

The literature that discusses what goes on in groups (and their larger manifestation, organizations) is extremely large. Much of this literature illustrates what is bad about such work, including the stultifying effects of organizational or professional cultures [e.g., 1, 4, 18, 19, 21-24]. If one assumes that nothing can be done to overcome these effects, it is easy to reach the conclusion that everything should be done by rugged individualists.

Our own research convinces us that such an assumption is unwarranted, and especially it is unwarranted in instances involving complexity. Examples that illustrate why groups are needed and what they can produce have been given in Chapter 10, but two of the most notable examples are not discussed there [25, 26].

For contrast with what is done in [25] and [26], one may look at [27] and [28] which reflect more standard, less-selective, non-science-based approaches.

System Failures

Comprehensive studies of the causes of systems failures, addressed to large sets of instances of such failures, are in short supply. Opinion as to causes is the less valuable, the more it reflects the following: (a) absence of study of specific cases, (b) absence of cross-case studies to show common elements, (c) self-interest in the continuation of current practices, (d) territorial violation, (e) failure to comment on those relatively few comprehensive studies that have been made in the past few years.

It is true, of course, that the future cannot be entirely foreseen in designing systems. But this truth is largely irrelevant to correcting much of what goes on now in design practice that leads to system failures. Wherever designer ego stands in the way of broad inquiry and participation in trying to envisage the future, bad systems are designed, and preventable failures occur. It is better to approach a system design with the philosophy that diligent efforts to unveil future possibilities by the involvement of many players is likely to make the design better than if one approaches it with the view that it is not possible to foretell the future. Design omissions shown in many cases reveal that it is the readily foreseeable that is often not foreseen, leading to the most bizarre, yet preventable outcomes.

Working Environments

The fact that architects have created large complexes of buildings and large buildings within which research is done is largely irrelevant to what is being discussed in this book. I do believe that such designs can have significant impact on what is done, especially in what I have called specific design sciences, but to have significant impact on cross-disciplinary work or on large system design, one must deal with the immediate working environment, and that involves a much smaller scale than a large building or a large complex of buildings. What is important is to get people together in a congenial working space that is tailored to enhance their joint productivity.

Having spent eight years trying to find a design of such a working environment, before finally designing such a space, I am glad to be able to say that the Demosophia concept is demonstrably successful, as dozens of cases reveal, in enhancing the joint productivity of groups working on complex issues.

Credit to Zwicky

In some of my earlier writings, including [7], I have credited F. Zwicky for his contributions to creative ways to approach issues. It is true that Zwicky's morphological box was one of the stimuli to the development of the Options Field Method and the Options Profile Method. Other stimuli included the "field-relaxation method", usually associated with the Stanford Research Institute, and the often-referenced views of Harold Lasswell [23], as well as the views of Atkin [14]. The primary ideas relating to Zwicky's work were the obvious shortcomings of the "morphological box". These included: its limitations to three dimensions (failure to be open at scale), the absence of any tested methodology for developing the components, the awkwardness of trying to visualize individual cells or even designate them on a graphic, the absence of any way to display incremental progress toward the choice of an alternative, and the absence of any way to show composite selections (as opposed to single choices from particular edges of the box).

Interpretation of Diversity

I introduced the term "consensus methodologies" in an unpublished article that was rather widely distributed in 1982, and which became the basis for a revised version that was published [29]. Both of these articles gave very extensive definition of the criteria represented by the term. Certainly a consensus methodology is not a methodology that guarantees agreement on every aspect of an issue. There is no way that anyone or anything can assure this outcome. The following quotation is from the unpublished article:

"We introduce seven methodologies that we describe as 'consensus methodologies'. These seven methodologies should not be perceived only as individuals, but rather as a set of methodologies from which an appropriate subset can be taken for use in working with a given problem of management or planning.

"How do we know when we have a set of consensus methodologies? The set must meet certain requirements in order to have this name. Here are requirements that are met by this set of seven methodologies.

- There must be at least one (and preferable several) methodology that permits efficient generation of ideas by groups (such as sets of goals, objectives, activities, program titles, and project titles)

- There must be at least one (and preferably several) methodology that allows for efficient structuring of ideas by individuals or groups (to produce such things as intent structures, activity sequence diagrams, priority structures, and DELTA charts)

- There must be at least one (and preferably several) methodology that offers a complete process for individuals or groups to use in designing alternatives, and which recognizes certain laws of design

- The division of labor between the people and the computer should be explicitly appropriate to assure that people do what they do best and the computer does what it does best, thereby maximizing the contribution of the group and saving their time

- The methodologies should exhibit both a sound behavioral design and a sound technical design, both being clearly explainable, with the two components of methodological design being mutually compatible and reinforcing wherever possible

- The methodologies should have histories of successful application which are available in the open literature

- The methodologies should themselves be described in the open literature, in which their connection to the corpus of scientific knowledge is exhibited

- To be admitted to the set of consensus methodologies, it must be clear that an admitted methodology either (a) is not a special case of one that is already in the set, or (b) that there is some unique benefit by giving membership to that special case

- Except in the case of some clear advantage, membership in a set of consensus methodologies shall favor non-proprietary methodologies over proprietary methodologies

- The methodologies should be transferable from the source organization to the client organization with a reasonable amount of training and software modification

- Other things being equal, methodologies that have undergone rigorous peer review in refereed publications are preferred to those that have not been so tested

- The methodologies must be participative, i.e., they must be specifically amenable to contributions from all who are involved in their use

- The methodologies must involve specific activities that help to assure good communication, especially clarification of the individual component topics that are dealt with when working with an issue

- There must be provision for open dialog, and for equal decision-making powers for all participants, in order to stimulate consensus

- Process roles must be clearly defined for these methodologies (Generally speaking, participants in the processes will be distinguished from facilitators, with the latter playing only process roles and not substantive roles involving issues under discussion.)

- There must be provision for possible iteration in the use of the consensus methodologies, to allow for the introduction of new knowledge that was not readily available at the time of [initial] use

- There must be provision for full documentation of what is done, should it be required

- The methodologies must be very efficient in the use of the time of the participants

- The graphics used in the methodologies shall be translatable, rather than intuitive (This means that the graphics must be uniquely translatable into prose. While this does not absolutely assure good communication, it does assure that the graphics do not introduce new ambiguity. Also it allows us to take advantage of the compactness of graphic expression, while retaining the explanatory power of prose expression.)

- The graphics that accompany the methodologies shall, in the choice of symbols, anticipate the rapidly-approaching time when the graphics can be organized and printed automatically (While the benefit in time saving and clarity of presentation will be appealing, it is even more important that the graphics encourage and stimulate revision, so that the graphics can be kept up to date and reflect new knowledge that is gained.)"

Notably, nothing in the above requires that any individual methodology should produce consensus on anything or everything.

The Nominal Group Technique, as seen many times in applications carried out by the Center for Interactive Management and others, produces consensus on the content of one or more sets of elements that should be part of the exploration of an issue. It also produces consensus on moving ahead to do the exploration. This provides a base from which the relationships among the members of those sets can be explored by the group.

It is fortunate that the NGT does not produce a consensus on the relative importance of individual elements. If it did so before any systematic exploration of relationships were carried out, one or more of the following conditions almost certainly would apply: (a) the issue is not really complex and does not require the use of consensus methodologies, (b) the cultural phenomenon called "groupthink" has been at work in the group, (c) the group does not understand the scope of the issue, or (d) new members must be added to try to help the group "unlearn" what they have committed to in the absence of an adequate understanding.

Judge John Kapelouzos, a member of the Council of State of Greece, explored the correlation between the views of group members at two different points in their studies of complex issues: at the completion of their use of NGT, and at the completion of their use of ISM in which elements were related that were taken from the NGT [30]. The groups involved and the issues studied were taken from the same population as those that yielded the data given in Appendix 5.

In the concluding section of his research paper, Judge Kapelouzos stated:

"In maintaining that the conceptualization of new perspectives on the problem situation...is due to the ISM method, the following matter needs to be clarified: In each of the 23 cases, both the group of participants and the issue under study were different. What these cases share in common is the method employed. Since the compared data show a discontinuity in most cases of participants' initial perception (represented by NGT data) with their final perception of the problem situation (represented by ISM data), it is highly improbable for these findings to be attributed to other factors.

"The primary benefit from Interactive Management lies in that it promotes learning by the participant group. ISM provides the major vehicle towards this learning. There is no way to estimate by the use of statistical evidence the quality of learning that occurs during the process. Yet, the span of inference in the structures produced with the application of Interactive Management indicates that the groups reach wide perspectives on the problem situation. Furthermore the data offered in this paper support the assumption that these perspectives are largely due to the ISM process."

Structuring Errors

The arrows that appear in the Domain of Science Model represent a "steering" relationship. This means, e.g., that the concepts expressed in the Foundations must have a strong impact on the content of the Theory. This impact takes the form of influencing the choice of topics with which the Theory deals, the way in which those topics are related, the kinds of laws that are sought in the Theory, and the impact that the Theory should have upon Methodology.

The components of the Domain of Science Model are structurally related in what is called a "cycle", as discussed at length in this book. The steering relationship is transitive. Consequently it propagates throughout the Model.

As explained earlier in this book, cycles can be represented in at least three ways. The least convenient, and most difficult to interpret, is that form where all the members of cycle have arrows to and from all other members. In the "outer cycle" representation, the elements that are cyclically related are shown in the "box-bullet" form, to avoid having to show all the arrows. This promotes readability and makes readability independent of the size of the cycle to the extent possible. The alternative form is the "inner cycle". With this form only direct relationships are shown. These are shown by arrows, except that there may be a subcycle of the cycle such that a box-bullet form is needed even to show that part of the direct relationship that is involved in an outer cycle.

Unallowable Methods

As I mentioned in my 1976 book [7], some authors start a long chain of analysis of decisionmaking with the assumption that, whatever the issue, people have a built-in mental ordering of preferences over the entire set of choices open to them. This basic assumption, if accepted, relieves methodologists of the task of finding a way to "compare apples and oranges" that is consistent with their view of methodological elegance or validity.

In general, people not only do not have built-in preference orderings, but are not aware individually of the range of choices open to them. Since they are forced by situations to make choices among sets of things that are quite different (even apples and oranges tend to be have some similarity of shape), they need methodological help in making such choices. The seemingly essential aspect of such help is to help steer the individual through the thought processes that are involved in comparing unlike things, even if all that is done is to produce an intuitive preference that can be applied to help reach a final decision.

It is true that methodology should not be allowed to violate scientific knowledge of the type that is pinned down by the eternal referents, the primary standards. But for those areas where no such standards exist, arbitrary judgments about what can or cannot be done in methodology must be strongly supported if they are to cope with the necessary conditions of effective living.

The processes used in the Tradeoff Analysis Methodology do incorporate features that most methodology lacks -- including the capacity to deal with qualitative and quantitative factors in the same decision-making situation. The process steers the participants through a detailed and extended sequence of thinking that cannot help but improve the basis upon which their choices are made. The final judgment about processes is to be found in the consequences of their use, rather than in arbitrary rules about what can and cannot be done.

Miscellaneous Comments

To the statement that design is not defined, I would respond that the dictionaries that we use embody a certain fiction: that every concept can be defined adequately in a few lines of prose. As I see it, a definition of design is distributed throughout this manuscript. In the future, this definition will be upgraded.

To the statement that the DELTA chart is not a Consensus Methodology, I can only agree. To the best of my knowledge, no one has ever said that the DELTA chart is a Consensus Methodology. In my view it is a form of representation of a kind of relationship, and to this extent it can be developed as an outcome of the use of the Consensus Methodologies.

To the suggestion that DELPHI is not a group process, one can say that it depends on what is meant by "group process". In my view, a process is a group process whenever ideas generated by two or more individuals enter into the same arena of interaction under a common aegis. To the argument that it is not a group process because the individuals are not interacting in a face to face mode, I would suggest reading my comments on "Admissions of Extremes" made in respect to ways of thinking about systems in general [31].

To the statement that a reference to DELPHI should be included, I note that the Delbecq, Van De Ven, and Gustafson reference [32] which serves as the best source of understanding of the Nominal Group Technique, also incorporates a good discussion of DELPHI.

REFERENCES

1. Chris Argyris, *Reasoning, Learning, and Action*, San Francisco: Jossey-Bass, 1982.

2. Arthur D. Hall III, *A Methodology for Systems Engineering*, New York: Litton Educational Publishing, 1962.

3. Arthur D. Hall III, *Metasystems Methodology*, Oxford: Pergamon Press, 1989.

4. G. Vickers, *Human Systems are Different*, London: Harper and Row, 1983.

5. J. N. Warfield, "On the Design of Language for System Design", in *Cybernetics and Systems '88, Proc. 9th European Meeting on Cybernetics and Systems Research* (R. Trappl, Ed.), Dordrecht: Kluwer Academic, 1988, 133-140.

6. J. N. Warfield, "Underconceptualization", *Proceedings of the Conference on Support, Society, and Culture: Mutual Uses of Cybernetics and Science*, (G. De Zeeuw and R. Glanville, Eds.), Univ. of Amsterdam, March, 1989, 15-39.

7. J. N. Warfield, *Societal Systems: Planning, Policy, and Complexity*, New York: Wiley, 1976 (reprinted, Salinas, CA: Intersystems, 1989).

8. J. N. Warfield, "Interpretive Structural Modeling", Chapter 5 in *Group Planning and Problem-Solving Methods in Engineering*, S. A. Olsen (Ed.), New York: Wiley, 1982, 155- 201.

9. J. N. Warfield, *"Interpretive Structural Modeling and Related Work (an annotated bibliography)"*, Fairfax, VA: IASIS, May, 1990 (available through Interlibrary Loan from Fenwick Library, George Mason University, Fairfax, Virginia, 22030-4444).

10. Karl-Otto Apel, *Charles S. Peirce: From Pragmatism to Pragmaticism*, Amherst: Univ. of Massachusetts Press, 1981.

11. Muriel Rukeyser, *Willard Gibbs*, Woodbridge, Conn.: Ox Bow, 1988 (reprint of the 1942 book published by Doubleday, Doran).

12. Wojceich W. Gasparski, S. A. Gregory, R. Foque, and A. Strzalecki, "Contemporary History of Design Science", *Praxiology Yearbook* 3, 1983, 147-156.

13. S. Glynn, "Science and Perception as Design", *Design Studies* 6(3), July, 1985, 122-126.

14. J. N. Warfield, "Artificial Philosophy and the Decline of Technology", *TI & Sociedade/IT and Society*, 1989 Simposio Internacional de Lisboa/Lisbon 1989 International Symposium, Lisbon: APDC & SDF, 1992, 484-510.

15. A. L. Kroeber and C. Kluckhohn, "Culture: A Critical Review of Concepts and Definitions", *Papers of the Peabody Museum of American Archaeology and Ethnology*, 47(1), Cambridge: Harvard University Press, 1952.

16. R. H. Atkin, *Mathematical Structure in Human Affairs*, New York: Crane, Russak, 1974.

17. Taft H. Broome, Jr., "The Slippery Ethics of Engineering", *The Washington Post* (Outposts Section), December 28, 1986.

18. G. R. Bushe, "Cultural Contradictions of Statistical Process Control in American Manufacturing Organizations", *Journal of Management* 14(1), 1988, 19-31.

19. J. L. LeMoigne, "The Paradoxes of the Contemporary Engineer", *European Journal of Engineering Education* 6, 1981, 105-115.

20. Warren Bennis, "The Four Competencies of Leadership", *Training and Development Journal* 38(8), Aug. 1984, 15-19.

21. I. L. Janis, *Stress, Attitudes, and Decisions*, New York: Praeger, 1982.

22. John Kemeny, "Saving American Democracy: The Lessons of Three-Mile Island", *Technol. Rev.* 83(7), 67-75, 1980.

23. Harold Lasswell, *A Pre-View of the Policy Sciences*, New York: American Elsevier, 1971.

24. Anthony Downs, *Inside Bureaucracy*, Boston: Little, Brown, 1967.

25. Alexander Christakis, "High-Technology Participative Design: The Space-Based Laser", *Proc. Society for General Systems Research*, Vol. 2, 1985, 925-933.

26. E. Zamierowski, D. Hornbach, and R. Fitz, "Ecological Components of Climax Agriculture: An Example of Structuring Complex Feedback Systems", *Proc. International Conference on Cybernetics and Society*, New York: IEEE, 1976, 667-673.

27. Gerald A. Nadler, *Planning and Design Approaches*, New York, Wiley, 1981.

28. James Martin and Carma McClure, *Diagramming Techniques for Analysts and Programmers*, Englewood Cliffs: Prentice-Hall, 1985.

29. J. N. Warfield, "Selecting Participation Methodologies for Systems Design", *Proc. 1984 IEEE Conference on Cybernetics and Society*, New York: IEEE, January, 1984, 762-764.

30. I. B. Kapelouzos, "The Impact of Structural Modeling on the Creation of New Perspectives in Problem Solving Situations", *Proceedings of the 1989 European Congress on Systems Science*, Lausanne: AFCET, October, 1989, 915-932.

31. J. N. Warfield, "Thinking About Systems", *Systems Research* 4(4), 1987, 227-234.

32. A. L. Delbecq, A. H. Van De Ven and D. H. Gustafson, *Group Techniques for Program Planning: A Guide to Nominal Group and DELPHI Processes*, Glenview, IL: Scott, Foresman, 1975.

QUESTIONS RELATED TO THE POSTSCRIPT

1. What is "one of the principal means by which philosophers find new issues to debate"?

2. According to Rorty, what is the central concern of philosophy?

3. What must be understood in order to understand the possibility and nature of knowledge?

4. Elaborate on the concept of "heedless ingenuity"?

5. What are the eight issues raised by referees of this book manuscript?

6. What basis is there for declaring that the American philosophers Peirce, James, Dewey, and Singer belong in a "pragmatism school"?

7. Discuss the possibility that there is a better basis for belief than science.

8. Who constitutes the "industrial design community" and how is it organized and managed?

9. What publications are products of the industrial design community?

10. Discuss the validity of the statement that "pragmatism...lacks values"?

11. Discuss the idea that science and ethics are distinctive, without overlap.

12. Discuss the positive and negative aspects of reification.

13. Discuss the possibility that Hitler and Mao satisfied the Bennis leadership criteria.

14. A referee who read the manuscript for this book asserted that "it could not have been possible to foresee all that later happened in the course of the original design". Examine five cases that illustrate design failures, and test each of them against this referee statement to see whether the specific causes that were identified might have been foreseen, and what action could have helped them to be foreseen.

15. Study Lasswell's papers on decision rooms and try to determine whether his proposed design features have been incorporated by architects in the design of research laboratories (see page 535).

16. Study and compare Hall's "Matching Theorem" with Ashby's "Law of Requisite Variety".

17. Discuss the criticism that "the arrows in the model should be two-way since there can be a flow from applications to methodology" (page 536).

18. Elaborate on the comment that the ISM process is "a means for facilitating the evolutionary triadic events that provide relationships which can then take part in subsequent triadic events" (page 539).

19. Discuss specific options for making the NGT process more mechanical, and compare what might be gained and what might be lost if these changes were introduced.

20. What is the Pragmatic Maxim?

21. What arguments does Glynn present to the effect that science can be viewed as design (page 542)?

22. What is the meaning of "casuistry"?

23. What is the meaning of "transcendentalism"?

24. What is the meaning of "esthetics"?

25. What is the meaning of "ethics"?

26. Name two fields of study that are open at scale.

27. Compare the <u>views</u> of Comte and Da Vinci.

28. Compare the <u>products</u> of Comte and Da Vinci.

29. If a person wants to establish self-qualification for leadership, and especially if a leader wants to establish self-superiority in terms of knowledge of an issue, what approaches might demonstrably be effective in doing so?

30. What is meant by hazard gap?

31. What is meant by invasive systems?

32. Discuss the relationship between group <u>pathologies</u>, group <u>processes</u>, group <u>facilitation</u>, and group <u>leadership</u>.

33. Describe the morphological box invented by Zwicky.

34. Twenty criteria are given that relate <u>not</u> to whether a given methodology can be admitted to a set of consensus methodologies, but rather to conditions that must be satisfied <u>by the set</u>. Given that a set of seven has been proposed, construct a DELTA chart that provides guidance in testing whether a new candidate could be admitted to the set and, if so, whether an existing member should then be eliminated.

35. What are the three ways of representing a cycle, and under what conditions is one likely to be superior to the other two?

BIBLIOGRAPHY

[NOTE: This Bibliography contains the references listed at the ends of the book chapters. In addition, it includes other citations that are not referenced in the book chapters, but which have significance to design scholars. This latter group of citations is included for the convenience of the reader.]

Alexander, *Notes on the Synthesis of Form*, Cambridge, MA: Harvard University Press, 1964.

W. L. Alpert, "A $230 Million Turkey: The Sad Saga of Trilogy", *Barrons*, New York: Dow-Jones, 1984, Aug. 27.

Karl-Otto Apel, *Charles S. Peirce: From Pragmatism to Pragmaticism*, Amherst: Univ. of Massachusetts Press, 1981.

L. B. Archer, "Systematic Method for Designer", *Design*, 1965.

Chris Argyris, *Reasoning, Learning, and Action*, San Francisco: Jossey-Bass, 1982.

Ross Ashby, "Requisite Variety and Its Implications for the Control of Complex Systems", *Cybernetica*, 1(2), 1958, 1- 17.

M. Asimow, *Introduction to Design*, Englewood Cliffs: Prentice-Hall, 1962.

R. H. Atkin, *Mathematical Structure in Human Affairs*, New York: Crane, Russak, 1974.

R. H. Atkin, *Combinatorial Connectivities in Social Systems*, Basel: Birkhauser, 1977.

R. F. Bales, *Interaction Process Analysis*, Addison-Wesley, Cambridge, 1951.

Bela Banathy, Editor, *Design Inquiry, Vol. I*, San Francisco: International Systems Institute and International Society for General Systems Research, 1987.

C. Batini, E. Nardelli, and R. Tamassia, "A Layout Algorithm for Data-Flow Diagrams", *IEEE Transactions on Software Engineering*, SE- 12(4), 1986, 538-546.

Warren Bennis, "The Four Competencies of Leadership", *Training and Development Journal* 38(8), Aug. 1984, 15-19.

I. M. Bochenski, *A History of Formal Logic*, New York: Chelsea, 1970.

Kenneth Boulding, *The Impact of the Social Sciences*, New Brunswick: Rutgers University Press, 1966.

F. Brooks, (Chair), *Report of the Defense Science Board on Military Software, Office of the Under Secretary of Defense for Acquisition*, Washington, D. C. 20301, September, 1987.

B. J. Broome and A. N. Christakis, "A Culturally-Sensitive Approach to Tribal Governance Issue Management", *International Journal of Intercultural Relations* 12, 1988, 107-123.

Taft H. Broome, Jr., "The Slippery Ethics of Engineering", *The Washington Post* (Outposts Section), December 28, 1986, page D3.

G. R. Bushe, "Cultural Contradictions of Statistical Process Control in American Manufacturing Organizations", *Journal of Management* 14(1), 1988, 19-31.

G. R. Bushe and A. B. Shani, "Parallel Learning Structure Interventions in Bureaucratic Organizations", to appear in R. W. Woodman and W. A. Passmore (Eds.), *Research in Organizational Change and Development,* Vol. 4, Greenwich, CT: JAI Press, 1990.

Peter Checkland, *Systems Thinking, Systems Practice,* New York: Wiley, 1981.

Alexander Christakis, "The National Forum on Nonindustrial Private Forest Lands", *Systems Research* 2(3), 1985, 189- 199.

Alexander Christakis, "High-Technology Participative Design: The Space-Based Laser", *Proceedings of the Society for General Systems Research,* Vol. 2, 1985, 925-933.

A. N. Christakis and Y. Prabhu, "A New Role for Systems Scientists,", *Proceedings of the 30th Annual Meeting of the Society for General Systems Research,* Salinas: Intersystems, 1986, A48-A62.

Patricia S. Churchland, *Neurophilosophy: Toward a Unified Science of the Mind-Brain,* Cambridge: The MIT Press, 1986.

C. West Churchman, *Thought and Wisdom,* Seaside, CA: Intersystems, 1982.

J. G. Coke and C. M. Moore, *Toward a Balanced Budget: Making the Tough Decisions,* Washington, D. C.: National Association of Counties, 1980.

J. G. Coke and C. M. Moore, Chapter 6 in *Managing Fiscal Retrenchment in Cities* (H. J. Bryce, Ed.), Columbus: Academy for Contemporary Problems, 1980.

J. G. Coke and C. M. Moore, "Coping with a Budgetary Crisis: Helping a City Council Decide Where Expenditure Cuts Should be Made", Chapter 5 in *Building City Council Leadership Skills: A Casebook of Models and Methods* (S. W. Burks and J. F. Wolf, Editors), Washington, D. C.: National League of Cities, February, 1981.

J. B. Conant, *Two Modes of Thought,* New York: Trident, 1964.

Karen O. Crim, "Use of ISM in Environmental Studies at the Senior High Level", Univ. of Dayton Report, Grant No. G-007700611, UDR- TR-79-27, April, 1979.

I. L. Cromer and V. D. Feeg, "Forum on the Future of Pediatric Nursing", *Pediatric Nursing* 14(5), 393-396.

A. Cross, "Design and General Education", *Design Studies* 1(4), 1980, 202-206.

N. Cross, "Design Education for Laypeople", *Studies in Design Education, Craft and Technology* 11(2), 1979, 68-72.

N. Cross (Ed.), *Developments in Design Methodology,* New York: Wiley, 1984.

A. L. Delbecq, A. H. Van De Ven and D. H. Gustafson, *Group Techniques for Program Planning: A Guide to Nominal Group and DELPHI Processes,* Glenview, IL: Scott, Foresman, 1975.

J. R. Dixon, *Design Engineering--Inventiveness, Analysis, and Decision-Making,* New York: McGraw-Hill, 1966.

Anthony Downs, *Inside Bureaucracy,* Boston: Little, Brown, 1967.

H. Ernst Eder, "Design Science--A Survey of Some Approaches", *1987 American Society for Engineering Education Annual Conference Proceedings,* Vol. II, Washington, D. C.: American Society for Engineering Education, 1987, 668-674.

A. M. El Mokadem, J. N. Warfield, D. M. Pollick, and K. Kawamura, "Modularization of Large Econometric Models: An Application of Structural Modeling", *Proceedings of the 1974 Institute of Electrical and Electronics Engineers Conference on Decision & Control,* New York, Institute of Electrical and Electronics Engineers, 1974, 683-692.

Amatai Etzioni, "Societal Overload: Sources, Components, and Corrections", *Political Science Quarterly* 92(4), 1977-78, 607-631.

P. Fitzhorn, "A Computational Theory of Design", *Design Computing* 3(1), 1988.

E. Fontela and M. Gilli, "Analysis of the Causal Structure of Economic Models", *Proceedings of the 1978 Institute of Electrical and Electronics Engineers International Conference on Cybernetics & Society,* New York: Institute of Electrical and Electronics Engineers, 1978, 516-519.

A. Gabus and E. Fontela, "Perceptions of the World Problematique", *DE-MATEL Report # 3,* Geneva: Battelle Geneva Laboratories Research Report, 1975.

Wojceich W. Gasparski, *Understanding Design: The Praxiological-Systemic Perspective,* Seaside, CA:Intersystems, 1984.

Wojceich W. Gasparski, "Praxiological-Systemic Approach to Design Studies", *Design Studies* 1(2), 1979, 101-106.

Wojceich W. Gasparski, S. A. Gregory, R. Foque, and A. Strzalecki, "Contemporary History of Design Science", *Praxiology Yearbook* 3, 1983, 147-156.

J. E. Gibson, *Introduction to Engineering Design*, New York: Holt, Rinehart and Winston, 1968.

G. L. Glegg, *The Design of Design*, Cambridge: Cambridge University Press, 1969.

S. Glynn, "Science and Perception as Design", *Design Studies* 6(3), July, 1985, 122-126.

T. A. Goudge, *The Thought of C. S. Peirce*, New York: Dover, 1969.

Paul Gray, "Group Decision Support Systems", *Decision Support Systems* 3, 1987, 233-242.

S. Gregory (Ed.), *The Design Method*, London: Butterworths, 1966.

V. Gupta and P. N. Murthy, *An Introduction to Engineering Design Method*, New Delhi: Tata McGraw-Hill, 1980.

Arthur D. Hall III, *A Methodology for Systems Engineering*, New York: Litton Educational Publishing, 1962.

Arthur D. Hall III, *Metasystems Methodology*, Oxford: Pergamon Press, 1989.

F. Harary, R. F. Norman, and D. Cartwright, *Structural Models: An Introduction to the Theory of Directed Graphs*, New York: Wiley, 1965.

J. Hartmanis and R. E. Stearns, *Algebraic Structure Theory of Sequential Machines*, Englewood Cliffs: Prentice-Hall, 1966.

B. L. T. Hedberg, P. C. Nystrom, and W. H. Starbuck, "Camping on Seesaws: Prescriptions for a Self-Designing Organization," *Administrative Science Quarterly* 21, March, 1976, 41-65.

P. H. Hill, *The Science of Engineering Design*, New York: Holt, Rinehart, and Winston, 1968.

R. W. House, "Application of ISM in Brazil's Alcohol Fuel Program", *Proceedings of the 1978 Institute of Electrical and Electronics Engineers International Conference on Cybernetics & Society*, New York: Institute of Electrical and Electronics Engineers, 1978, 1008-1012.

T. Inagaki and E. M. Himmelblau, "Hierarchical Determination of Precedence Order and Representation of Digraphs", *Institute of Electrical and Electronics Engineers Transactions on Systems, Man, and Cybernetics*, 13(3), May/June, 1983, 406-413.

F. R. Janes, "Interpretive Structural Modelling: A Methodology for Structuring Complex Issues", *Transactions of the Institute of Measurement and Control,* 10(3), August, 1988, 145-154.

F. R. Janes and R. Jowitt, "Applications of Interactive Management in Planning for a University Department" in *Systems Prospects (Proc. of the International Conference of the U. K. Systems Society),* Hull, U. K., July, 1988; R. L. Flood, M. C. Jackson and P. Keys (Eds.), New York: Plenum, 1989.

I. L. Janis, *Stress, Attitudes, and Decisions,* New York: Praeger, 1982.

A. Jedlicka and R. Meyer, "Interpretive Structural Modeling: Cross-Cultural Uses," *Institute of Electrical and Electronics Engineers, Transactions on Systems, Man, and Cybernetics,* Jan. 1980, 49-51.

J. C. Jones, *Design Methods--Seeds of Human Future,* New York: Wiley, 1970.

I. B. Kapelouzos, "The Impact of Structural Modeling on the Creation of New Perspectives in Problem Solving Situations", *Proceedings of the 1989 European Congress on Systems Science,* Lausanne: AFCET, October, 1989, 915-932.

A. Kaplan, *The Conduct of Inquiry,* San Francisco: Chandler, 1964.

K. Kawamura and D. W. Malone, "Structuring Objectives in a Systematic Decision-Making Methodology", *Proc. 1975 Pittsburgh Conference on Modeling and Simulation,* Pittsburgh: Instrument Society of America, 1975, 779-784.

D. B. Keever, "Design for Improving University/Industry Cooperative Research Projects", *Proceedings of the 1985 Annual Meeting of the Society for General Systems Research,* Seaside, CA: Intersystems, 1985, 934-943.

D. B. Keever and A. N. Christakis, "Interactive Management for Organizational Redesign", *Proceedings of the Conference on Planning and Design in the Management of Business and Organizations,* New York: American Society of Mechanical Engineers, 83-90.

John Kemeny, "Saving American Democracy: The Lessons of Three-Mile Island", *Technology Review* 83(7), 1980, 67-65.

A. L. Kroeber and C. Kluckhohn, "Culture: A Critical Review of Concepts and Definitions", *Papers of the Peabody Museum of American Archaeology and Ethnology* 47(1), Cambridge: Harvard University Press, 1952.

R. M. Lala, *The Creation of Wealth: The Tata Story,* Bombay: IBH Publishing Company, 1981.

Harold Lasswell, *A Pre-View of the Policy Sciences,* New York: American Elsevier, 1971.

B. R. Lawson, *How Designers Think,* London: Architectural Press, 1970.

D. J. Leech, *Management of Engineering Design,* New York: Wiley, 1972.

J. L. LeMoigne, "The Paradoxes of the Contemporary Engineer", *European Journal of Engineering Education* 6, 1981, 105-115.

Charles I. Lewis and Cooper H. Langford, *Symbolic Logic,* New York: Dover, 1959.

Sidney F. Love, *Planning and Creating Successful Engineered Designs,* New York: Van Nostrand Reinhold, 1980.

Lionel March, *The Architecture of Form,* Cambridge: Cambridge University Press, 1976.

James Martin and Carma McClure, *Diagramming Techniques for Analysts and Programmers,* Englewood Cliffs: Prentice-Hall, 1985.

G. A. Miller, "The Magical Number Seven, Plus or Minus Two: Some Limits on Our Capacity for Processing Information", *Psychology Review* 63(2), 81-97.

Harlan D. Mills, R. C. Linger, and A. R. Hevner, *Principles of Information Systems Analysis and Design,* Orlando: Academic Press, 1986.

Carl M. Moore, *Group Techniques for Idea Building,* Newbury Park: Sage, 1987.

Gerald A. Nadler, *Planning and Design Approaches,* New York, Wiley, 1981.

Gerald A. Nadler, "Systems Methodology and Design", *Proceedings of the International Conference of the IEEE Systems, Man, and Cybernetics Society,* New York: Institute of Electrical and Electronics Engineers, 1984, 427-437.

F. S. C. Northrup, *Science and First Principles,* Cambridge: The University Press, 1931.

F. S. C. Northrup, *The Logic of the Sciences and the Humanities,* Westport: Greenwood Press (reprint of the 1947 Macmillan book), 1979.

A. Ohuchi, M. Kurihara and K. Kaji, "An Efficient Procedure for Transitive Coupling in ISM", *Institute of Electrical and Electronics Engineers Transactions of the Systems, Man, and Cybernetics Society,* SMC-15(3), May/June, 1985, 426-431.

A. Ohuchi, I. Kaji, and J. N. Warfield, "Structural Analysis and a Complexity Metric for High-Level Software Languages", *Proceedings of the Conference of the Japan Information Processing Society* (in Japanese), 1988, 646-647.

S. Olsen (Ed.), *Group Planning and Problem-Solving Methods in Engineering Management,* New York: Wiley, 1982.

G. Pahl and W. Beitz, *Engineering Design (edited by K. Wallace)*, London: The Design Council, 1984 (original German edition published in Berlin: Springer-Verlag, 1977).

Charles Perrow, *Normal Accidents: Living With High-Risk Technologies*, New York: Basic Books, 1984.

T. R. Renckly and G. Orwig, "Curriculum Viewed as Binary System: An Approach to the Determination of Sequence--a Project Report", presented at the Third Interservice/Industry Training and Equipment Conference, Nov. 30-Dec. 2, 1981, Orlando, Florida

Fenton Robb, "Towards a 'Better' Scientific Theory of Human Organizations", *Journal of the Operational Research Society*, 36(6), 1985, 463-466.

Muriel Rukeyser, *Willard Gibbs*, Woodbridge, Conn.: Ox Bow, 1988 (reprint of the 1942 book published by Doubleday, Doran).

Jonas Salk, *Anatomy of Reality: Merging of Intuition and Reason*, New York: Praeger, 1985 (originally published by Columbia University Press)

T. Sato, "Determination of Hierarchical Networks of Instructional Units Using the ISM Method", *Education Technology Research* 3, 67-75, 1979.

T. Sato, M. Takeya, M. Kurata, Y. Morimoto, and H. Chimura, "An Instructional Data Analysis Machine with a Microprocessor-- SPEEDY", *Nippon Electric Company Research and Development*, No. 61, April, 1981, 55-63.

Y. Sawaragi and K. Kawamura, *Participatory Systems Approach: Methods and Applications*, Tokyo: Daily Industrial Newspaper Company, 1982 (in Japanese).

N. F. Schneidewind, "Software Metrics for Aiding Program Development and Debugging", *Proceedings of the National Computer Conference*, 1979, 989-994.

H. A. Simon, *The Sciences of the Artificial*, Cambridge, MA: MIT Press, 1967.

H. A. Simon, "How Big is a Chunk?", *Science* 183, Feb. 8, 1974, 482-488.

K. Sugiyama, S. Tagawa, and M. Toda, "Methods for Visual Understanding of Hierarchical System Structures", *Institute of Electrical and Electronics Engineers Transactions on Systems, Man, and Cybernetics*, 11(2), 109-125, 1981.

Patrick Suppes, *Axiomatic Set Theory*, New York: Dover, 1960.

M. Szyperski and M. Eul-Bischoff, *Interpretative Strukturmodellierung (ISM)*, Braunschweig: Vieweg, 1983 (in German).

R. Tamassia, C. Batini, and G. Di Battista, "Automatic Graph Drawing and Readability of Diagrams", report published by Universita degli Studi di Roma, Via Buonarroti 12, 00185, Rome, Italy, January, 1987.

Myron Tribus, *Rational Descriptions, Decisions, and Designs*, New York: Pergamon, 1969.

B. W. Tuckman, "Developmental Sequences in Small Groups", *Psychology Bulletin,* 63(6), 1965, 384-399.

G. Vickers, *The Art of Judgment: A Study of Policy Making,* London: Harper and Row, 1983 (originally published by Chapman and Hall, 1965.)

G. Vickers, *Human Systems are Different,* London: Harper and Row, 1983.

G. Vickers, *Responsibility--Its Sources and Limits,* Seaside: Intersystems, 1980.

R. J. Waller, "Comparing and Combining Structural Models of Complex Systems", *Institute of Electrical and Electronics Engineers Transactions on Systems, Man, and Cybernetics,* September, 1979, 580-586.

R. J. Waller, "Contextual Relations and Mathematical Relations in Interpretive Structural Modeling", *Institute of Electrical and Electronics Engineers Transactions on Systems, Man, and Cybernetics,* March, 1980, 143-145.

J. N. Warfield, *Structuring Complex Systems,* Columbus: Battelle, 1974.

J. N. Warfield, *Societal Systems: Planning, Policy, and Complexity,* New York: Wiley, 1976 (reprinted, Salinas, CA: Intersystems, 1989).

J. N. Warfield, "Crossing Theory and Hierarchy Mapping", *Institute of Electrical and Electronics Engineers Transactions on Systems, Man, and Cybernetics,* SMC7(7), July, 1977, 505- 523.

J. N. Warfield, "Some Principles of Knowledge Organization", *Institute of Electrical and Electronics Engineers Transactions on Systems, Man, and Cybernetics,* June, 1979, 317-325.

J. N. Warfield, "You Create a Design", Report No. UVA/522032/EE79/125, August, 1979, report submitted to the Office of Environmental Education.

J. N. Warfield, "Science and Systems Science: A Technology Perspective", *Proceedings of the Society for General Systems Research Annual Meeting,* January, 1980, 212-218.

J. N. Warfield, "Complementary Relations and Map Reading", *Institute of Electrical and Electronics Engineers Transactions on Systems, Man, and Cybernetics,* June, 1980, 285-291.

J. N. Warfield, *Annotated Bibliography: ISM and Related Work*, Department of Electrical Engineering, University of Virginia, June, 1980 (106 pp.), available through Interlibrary Loan from George Mason University, Fenwick Library, Reserve Desk, Fairfax, Virginia, 22030.

J. N. Warfield, "Priority Structures", *Institute for Electrical and Electronics Engineers Transactions on Systems, Man, and Cybernetics,* SMC-10(10), Oct., 1980, 642-645.

J. N. Warfield, "Organizations and Systems Learning", *General Systems,* Vol. 27, 1982, 5-74.

J. N. Warfield, "Interpretive Structural Modeling", Chapter 5 in *Group Planning and Problem-Solving Methods in Engineering,* S. A. Olsen (Ed.), New York: Wiley, 1982, 155-201.

J. N. Warfield, "Principles of Interactive Management", *Proceedings of the International Conference on Cybernetics & Society,* New York: Institute of Electrical and Electronics Engineers, January, 1984, 746-750.

J. N. Warfield, "Selecting Participation Methodologies for Systems Design", *Proceedings of the International Conference on Cybernetics and Society,* New York: Institute of Electrical and Electronics Engineers, January, 1984, 762-764.

J. N. Warfield, "Structural Analysis of a Computer Language", *Proc. 17th Southeastern Symposium of System Theory,* New York: Institute of Electrical and Electronics Engineers, 1985, 229-234.

J. N. Warfield, "Education in Generic Design", *Proceedings of the Society for General Systems Research International Conference,* Salinas, CA: Intersystems, 1986, H22-H33.

J. N. Warfield, "The Domain of Science Model: Evolution and Design", *Proceedings of the Society for General Systems Research,* Salinas, CA: Intersystems, 1986, H46-H59.

J. N. Warfield, "Dimensionality", *Proceedings of the International Conference on Systems, Man, and Cybernetics,* New York: Institute of Electrical and Electronics Engineers, Vol. II, 1986, 1118-1121.

J. N. Warfield, "Micromathematics and Macromathematics", *Proceedings of the International Conference on Systems, Man, and Cybernetics,* New York: Institute of Electrical and Electronics Engineers, Vol. II, 1986, 1127-1131.

J. N. Warfield, "Developing a Design Culture in Higher Education", *General Systems,* Vol. XXX, 1987, 63-67.

J. N. Warfield, "Implications of Scale for Systems Design", *Proceedings of the Society for General Systems Research International Conference,* Budapest, 1987, 1205-1211.

J. N. Warfield, "What Disciplines Large-Scale System Design?", *Proceedings of the 1987 Conf. on Planning and Design in the Management of Business and Organizations* (P. C. Nutt, Editor), New York: American Society of Mechanical Engineers, 1987, 1-8.

J. N. Warfield, "A Complexity Metric for High-Level Software Languages", *Proceedings of the International Conference on Systems, Man, and Cybernetics,* New York: Institute for Electrical and Electronics Engineers, October, 1987, 438-442.

J. N. Warfield, "Thinking About Systems", *Systems Research,* 4(4), 1987, 227-234.

J. N. Warfield, *Annotated Bibliography of Publications,* IASIS, George Mason University, May, 1988 (67 pages), available through Interlibrary Loan from George Mason University, Fenwick Library, Reserve Desk, Fairfax, Virginia 22030.

J. N. Warfield, "Simple System Models Based on Sophisticated Assumptions", prepared for American Association for the Advancement of Science Annual Meeting, Boston, 1988.

J. N. Warfield, "On the Design of Language for System Design", in *Cybernetics and Systems '88, Proceedings of the 9th European Meeting on Cybernetics and Systems Research* (R. Trappl, Ed.), Dordrecht: Kluwer Academic, 1988, 133-140.

J. N. Warfield, "Criteria for a Science of Design", *Proceedings of the 19th Annual Pittsburgh Conference on Modeling and Simulation,* Research Triangle Park, NC: Instrument Society of America, 1988, 643-646.

J. N. Warfield, "Implicit Aspects of Much Systems Thinking", *Systems Research* 5(4), 1988, 333-342.

J. N. Warfield, "The Magical Number Three--Plus or Minus Zero", *Cybernetics and Systems* 19, 1988, 339-358. (First presented at the 1987 annual conference of the International Society for General Systems Research, Budapest.)

J. N. Warfield, "Underconceptualization", *Proceedings of the Conference on Support, Society, and Culture: Mutual Uses of Cybernetics and Science,* (G. De Zeeuw and R. Glanville, Eds.), Univ. of Amsterdam, March, 1989, 15-39.

J. N. Warfield, "Artificial Philosophy and the Decline of Technology", *Proceedings of the 1989 Lisbon Conference on Philosophy versus Information Technology,* Lisbon: September, 1989.

J. N. Warfield and A. N. Christakis, "Dimensionality", *Systems Research* 4(2), June, 1987, 127-137.

J. N. Warfield and J. D. Hill, "The DELTA Chart", *Institute of Electrical and Electronics Engineers Transactions on Engineering Management,* EM-18(4), November, 1971, 132-139.

J. N. Warfield and J. D. Hill, *A Unified Systems Engineering Concept,* Columbus: Battelle, 1972.

A. N. Whitehead, *An Introduction to Mathematics,* New York: Oxford Univ. Press, 1958 (first published in 1911).

A. N. Whitehead, *Adventures of Ideas,* New York: Macmillan, 1952.

N. Wiener, "A Simplification of the Logic of Relations", *Proceedings of the Cambridge Philosophical Society,* 17, 1914, 387-390.

T. Winograd and F. Flores, *Understanding Computers and Cognition,* Norwood, NJ: Ablex, 1986.

D. Yeoman, "Monitoring the Design Process", in B. Evans et al (Eds.), *Changing Design,* New York: Wiley, 1982.

E. Zamierowski, D. Hornbach, and R. Fitz, "Ecological Components of Climax Agriculture: An Example of Structuring Complex Feedback Systems", *Proceedings of the International Conference on Cybernetics and Society,* New York: Institute of Electrical and Electronics Engineers, 1976, 667-673.

Index to Topics

Index to Names

A

Abelard, Peter 63, 404, 405
Ackoff, Russell 117
Alberts, H. xxxvii, 295, 373, 379, 381
Alexander, C. 544, 559
Alpert, W. L. 102, 559
Apel, Karl-Otto 10, 32, 539, 542, 553, 559
Argyris, Chris xvi, 136, 150, 155, 261, 530, 553, 559
Aristotle 73, 403, 419
Ashby, Ross 180, 190, 533, 559
Atkin, R. H. 541, 547, 554, 559

B

Backus, J. 432
Bales, R. F. xxxvii, 38, 103, 559
Banathy, B. xxxvii, 559
Barrett, I. xxix, 357
Batini, C. 487, 559, 565
Batra, S. K. xxix, xxxvii, 24, 263, 294, 331
Beer, S. 533
Beitz, W. 565
Bennis, Warren 18, 33, 148, 264, 531, 542, 554, 559
Bochenski, I. M. xxxv, 37, 49, 103, 559
Boileau, D. 296
Boole, George 46, 50, 403
Boulding, Kenneth 559
Braybrooke, D. 544
Brooks, Frederic 435, 560
Broome, Benjamin J. xxxvii, 295, 397, 560
Broome, Taft H., Jr. 28, 33, 542, 554, 560
Brown, Brack xxxvii
Brown, Lester R. xxi
Bryce, H. J. 290, 560
Burks, S. W. 290, 560
Bushe, G. R. 104, 543, 554, 560

C

Cárdenas, R. xxxviii, 294
Cartwright, D. 434, 562
Chandy, G. S. xxix
Chaplin, R. xxxvii
Checkland, Peter 560
Chimura, H. 290, 565
Christakis, Alexander xxix, xxxvii, 190, 264, 272, 285, 398, 554, 560, 563, 568
Churchland, Patricia S. 56, 96, 103, 293, 560
Churchman, C. West 138, 155, 560
Clark, Robert xxxvii
Coke, James xxviii, 285, 290, 560
Comte, A. 543
Conant, James Bryant 28, 33, 277, 560
Connelly, Moira xxxvii
Crim, Karen O. 286, 291, 561
Crognale, S. 295
Cromer, I. xxxvii, 296, 346, 355, 398, 561
Cross, A. 561
Cross, Nigel 561

D

Da Vinci, Leonardo 543
Darrow, Karl K. 159
De Morgan, Augustus 46, 50, 56, 58, 403
De Zeeuw, G. xxxvi, 553, 568
Delbecq, A. L. 253, 553, 561
Descartes, Rene 272
Dewey, John 528
Di Battista, G. 485, 561
Dierolf, D. xxxvii
Dilworth, Chapman 512
Dixon, John R. 561
Downs, Anthony xxxi, 512, 554, 561
Duhem, P. M. M. 56

E

Eder, H. Ernst 561
Einstein, Albert 1, 37, 171, 293
Ellis, K. xxxviii, 294
El-Mokadem, A. M. 286, 291, 561
Etzioni, Amatai 561
Eul-Bischoff, Margot 254, 565
Evans, B. 569

F

Feeg, V. xxxvii, 337, 344, 540
Fields, Craig 367
Fiore, M. xxxvii, 398
Fitz, Raymond xxviii, xxxvi, 104, 554, 569
Fitzhorn, P. 561
Flood, R. L. xxxvi, 563
Flores, F. 569
Fontela, Emilio 271, 273, 290, 561
Foque, R. 552, 562
Frege, G. 46, 403

G

Gabus, André 271, 290, 561
Galilei, Galileo 94, 171
Gasparski, Wojceich W. 540, 554, 561
Gibbs, J. Willard xxxi, 28, 46, 131, 171, 554
Gibson, J. E. 562
Gilli, Manfred 290, 561
Glanville, R. 553, 570
Glegg, G. L. 562
Glynn, S. 540, 554, 562
Gödel, K. 46, 52
Gorbachev, Mikhail 148
Gordon, Gerald W. 25
Gordon, William 357
Goudge, T. A. 33, 104, 542, 562
Gould, Patricia 512
Gray, Paul 272, 562
Gregory, S. A. 554, 562
Gupta, V. 562
Gustafson, D. H. 253, 553, 561

Index to Organizations

585

Index to Divisions